Improve Your Grade!

Access included with any new book.

Get help with exam prep! REGISTER NOW!

Registration will let you:

– Prepare for exams by taking online quizzes.

– Understand the key topics using *GEODe: Earth Science*.

– Grasp difficult concepts with interactive animations.

– Access and annotate your text online 24/7 using your Pearson eText.

www.mygeoscienceplace.com

TO REGISTER

1. Go to www.mygeoscienceplace.com

2. Click "Register."

3. Follow the on-screen instructions to create your login name and password.

Your Access Code is:

USWLF6-JIDDA-SALIC-PAEAN-GIGOT-WIPES

TO LOG IN

1. Go to www.mygeoscienceplace.com

2. Click "Log In."

3. Pick your book cover.

4. Enter your login name and password.

Hint:
Remember to bookmark the site after you log in.

Technical Support:
http://247pearsoned.custhelp.com

PEARSON   ALWAYS LEARNING

Frederick K. Lutgens • Edward J. Tarbuck • Dennis Tasa

Foundations of Earth Science

A Custom Edition

Taken from:
Foundations of Earth Science, Sixth Edition
by Frederick K. Lutgens and Edward J. Tarbuck
illustrated by Dennis Tasa

Cover Art: Courtesy of PhotoDisc and Getty images.

Taken from:

Foundations of Earth Science, Sixth Edition
by Frederick K. Lutgens, Edward J. Tarbuck, and Dennis Tasa
Copyright © 2011, 2008, 2005 by Pearson Education, Inc.
Published by Prentice Hall
Upper Saddle River, New Jersey 07548

This special edition published in cooperation with Pearson Learning Solutions.

Pearson Learning Solutions, 501 Boylston Street, Suite 900, Boston, MA 02116
A Pearson Education Company
www.pearsoned.com

Printed in the United States of America

10 V011 18 17 16 15

000200010271769513

CW

ISBN 10: 1-269-30894-7
ISBN 13: 978-1-269-30894-6

BRIEF TABLE OF CONTENTS

Introduction to Earth Science   2

UNIT I EARTH MATERIALS   20

1 Minerals: Building Blocks of Rocks   20
2 Rocks: Materials of the Solid Earth   42

UNIT II SCULPTURING EARTH'S SURFACE   72

3 Landscapes Fashioned by Water   72
4 Glacial and Arid Landscapes   110

UNIT III FORCES WITHIN   140

5 Plate Tectonics: A Scientific Theory Unfolds   140
6 Restless Earth: Earthquakes, Geologic Structures, and Mountain Building   170
7 Fires Within: Igneous Activity   206

UNIT IV DECIPHERING EARTH'S HISTORY   236

8 Geologic Time   236

UNIT V THE GLOBAL OCEAN   258

9 Oceans: The Last Frontier   258
10 The Restless Ocean   280

UNIT VI EARTH'S DYNAMIC ATMOSPHERE   308

11 Heating the Atmosphere   308
12 Moisture, Clouds, and Precipitation   340
13 The Atmosphere in Motion   370
14 Weather Patterns and Severe Weather   390

UNIT VII EARTH'S PLACE IN THE UNIVERSE   418

15 The Nature of the Solar System   418
16 Beyond Our Solar System   456

APPENDIX A

Metric and English Units Compared   481

APPENDIX B

Mineral Identification Key   482

APPENDIX C

Relative Humidity and Dew Point Tables   484

APPENDIX D

Earth's Grid System   486

GLOSSARY   489

INDEX   499

GEODe: EARTH SCIENCE v.3

GEODe: Earth Science v. 3 can be accessed from your book's Companion Website **www.mygeoscienceplace.com.** This easy to use learning aid reinforces key concepts by using tutorials, animations, and interactive exercises.

UNIT I EARTH MATERIALS

A. Minerals
1. Introduction to Minerals
2. Mineral Groups
3. Physical Properties of Minerals
4. Quiz: Minerals

B. Rock Cycle

C. Igneous Rocks
1. Introduction to Igneous Rocks
2. Igneous Textures
3. Igneous Compositions
4. Naming Igneous Rocks
5. Quiz: Igneous Rocks

D. Sedimentary Rocks
1. Introduction to Sedimentary Rocks
2. Types of Sedimentary Rocks
3. Sedimentary Environments
4. Quiz: Sedimentary Rocks

E. Metamorphic Rocks
1. Introduction to Metamorphic Rocks
2. Agents of Metamorphism
3. Textural and Mineralogical Changes
4. Common Metamorphic Rocks
5. Quiz: Metamorphic Rocks

UNIT II SCULPTURING EARTH'S SURFACE

A. Weathering and Soil *ALL NEW*
1. Earth's External Processes
2. Types of Weathering
3. Mechanical Weathering
4. Chemical Weathering
5. Rates of Weathering
6. Quiz: Weathering and Soil

B. Mass Wasting: The Works of Gravity *ALL NEW*
1. Controls and Triggers of Mass Wasting
2. Mass-Wasting Processes
3. Quiz: Mass Wasting

C. Running Water
1. Hydrologic Cycle
2. Stream Characteristics
3. Reviewing Valleys and Stream-Related Features *NEW SECTION*
4. Quiz: Running Water

D. Groundwater
1. Importance and Distribution
2. Springs and Wells
3. Quiz: Groundwater

E. Glaciers and Glaciation
1. Introduction
2. Budget of a Glacier
3. Reviewing Glacial Features *NEW SECTION*
4. Quiz: Glaciers and Glaciation

F. Deserts and Winds
1. Distribution and Causes of Dry Lands
2. Common Misconceptions about Deserts
3. Reviewing Landforms and Landscapes *NEW SECTION*
4. Quiz: Deserts and Winds

UNIT III FORCES WITHIN

A. Plate Tectonics *EXPANDED AND REVISED*
1. Introduction to Plate Tectonics
2. Divergent Boundaries
3. Convergent Boundaries
4. Transform Fault Boundaries
5. Formation and Breakup of Pangaea
6. Quiz: Plate Tectonics

B. Earthquakes
1. What is an Earthquake?
2. Seismology
3. Locating the Source of an Earthquake
4. Earthquakes at Plate Boundaries
5. Quiz: Earthquakes

C. Earth's Interior *ALL NEW*
1. Earth's Layered Structure
2. Quiz: Earth's Interior

D. Volcanoes and Other Igneous Activity
1. The Nature of Volcanic Eruptions
2. Materials Extruded During an Eruption
3. Volcanic Structures and Eruptive Styles
4. Quiz: Volcanoes

E. Mountain Building *ALL NEW*
1. Deformation
2. Folds
3. Faults and Fractures
4. Continental Collisions
5. Crustal Fragments and Mountain Building
6. Quiz: Mountain Building

v

UNIT IV DECIPHERING EARTH'S HISTORY

A. Geologic Time Scale

B. Relative Dating—Key Principles

C. Dating With Radioactivity

D. Quiz: Geologic Time

UNIT V THE GLOBAL OCEAN

A. Floor of the Ocean
1. Mapping the Ocean Floor
2. Features of the Ocean Floor
3. Quiz: Ocean Floor

B. Coastal Processes
1. Waves and Beaches
2. Wave Erosion
3. Quiz: Coastal Processes

UNIT VI EARTH'S DYNAMIC ATMOSPHERE

A. Introduction to the Atmosphere *ALL NEW*
1. The Importance of Weather
2. Weather and Climate
3. Composition of the Atmosphere
4. Extent of the Atmosphere
5. Temperature Structure of the Atmosphere
6. Quiz: Introduction to the Atmosphere
7. In the Lab: Reading Weather Maps

B. Heating Earth's Surface and Atmosphere
1. Understanding Seasons, Part 1 *NEW SECTION*
2. Understanding Seasons, Part 2 *NEW SECTION*
3. Solar Radiation
4. What Happens to Incoming Solar Radiation
5. The Greenhouse Effect
6. Quiz: Heating Earth's Surface and Atmosphere
7. In the Lab: The Influence of Color on Albedo *NEW SECTION*

C. Temperature Data and the Controls of Temperature
1. Basic Temperature Data
2. Controls of Temperature
3. Quiz: Temperature Data and Controls

D. Moisture and Cloud Formation
1. Water's Changes of State
2. Humidity: Water Vapor in the Air
3. The Basics of Cloud Formation: Adiabatic Cooling
4. Processes That Lift Air *NEW SECTION*
5. The Critical Weathermaker: Atmospheric Stability *NEW SECTION*
6. Quiz: Moisture and Cloud Formation
7. In the Lab: Atmopsheric Stability

E. Forms of Condensation and Precipitation
1. Classifying Clouds
2. Types of Fog
3. How Precipitation Forms
4. Forms of Precipitation
5. Quiz: Forms of Condensation and Precipitation

F. Air Pressure and Wind
1. Measuring Air Pressure
2. Factors Affecting Wind
3. Highs and Lows
4. Quiz: Air Pressure and Wind

G. Basic Weather Patterns
1. Air Masses
2. Fronts
3. Introducing Middle-Latitude Cyclones
4. In The Lab: Examining a Middle-Latitude Cyclone
5. Quiz: Basic Weather Patterns

UNIT VII EARTH'S PLACE IN THE UNIVERSE

A. The Planets: An Overview

B. Calculating Your Age and Weight on Other Planets

C. Earth's Moon

D. A Brief Tour of the Planets

E. Quiz: Solar System

This GEODe: Earth Science icon appears throughout the book wherever a text discussion has a corresponding module on the CD-ROM.

CONTENTS

Preface   xv

INTRODUCTION TO EARTH SCIENCE   2
   FOCUS ON LEARNING   2
   What Is Earth Science?   4
   Earth's Spheres   5
      Hydrosphere   6
      Atmosphere   7
      Geosphere   7
      Biosphere   8
   Earth as a System   9
   Scales of Space and Time in Earth Science   11
   Resources and Environmental Issues   11
      Resources   13
      Environmental Problems   14
   The Nature of Scientific Inquiry   14
      Hypothesis   15
      Theory   16
      Scientific Methods   16
   Studying Earth Science   17
   THE CHAPTER IN REVIEW   17
   KEY TERMS   18
   QUESTIONS FOR REVIEW   19
   COMPANION WEBSITE   19

UNIT I EARTH MATERIALS   20

1 MINERALS: BUILDING BLOCKS OF ROCKS   20
   FOCUS ON LEARNING   20
   Minerals: The Building Block of Rocks   22
   Atoms: The Building Block of Minerals   24
      Properties of Protons, Neutrons, and Electrons   24
      Elements: Defined by Their Number of Protons   24
   Why Atoms Bond   26
      Ionic Bonds: Electrons Transferred   26
      Covalent Bonds: Electrons Shared   27
      Metallic Bonds: Electrons Free to Move   27
   Isotopes and Radioactive Decay   28
   Physical Properties of Minerals   28
      Optical Properties   28
      Crystal Shape or Habit   30
      Mineral Strength   30
      Density and Specific Gravity   33
      Other Properties of Minerals   33
   Mineral Groups   34
      Silicate Minerals   34
      Important Nonsilicate Minerals   37
   Mineral Resources   38
   THE CHAPTER IN REVIEW   38
   KEY TERMS   39
   QUESTIONS FOR REVIEW   39
   COMPANION WEBSITE   40

2 ROCKS: MATERIALS OF THE SOLID EARTH   42
   FOCUS ON LEARNING   42
   Earth as a System: The Rock Cycle   44
      The Basic Cycle   44
      Alternative Paths   46
   Igneous Rocks: "Formed by Fire"   46
      From Magma to Crystalline Rock   46
      What Can Igneous Textures Tell Us?   48
      Igneous Compositions   49
      Classifying Igneous Rocks   50
      How Different Igneous Rocks Form   51
   Weathering of Rocks to Form Sediment   54
      Mechanical Weathering of Rocks   54
      Chemical Weathering of Rocks   56
   Sedimentary Rocks: Compacted and Cemented
      Sediment   57
      Classifying Sedimentary Rocks   57
      Lithification of Sediment   62
      Features of Sedimentary Rocks   63
   Metamorphic Rocks: New Rock from Old   63
      What Drives Metamorphism?   65
      Metamorphic Textures   66
      Common Metamorphic Rocks   67
   THE CHAPTER IN REVIEW   70
   KEY TERMS   70
   QUESTIONS FOR REVIEW   71
   COMPANION WEBSITE   71

UNIT II SCULPTURING EARTH'S
SURFACE   72

3 LANDSCAPES FASHIONED BY WATER   72
   FOCUS ON LEARNING   72
   Earth's External Processes   74
   Mass Wasting: The Work of Gravity   74
      Mass Wasting and Landform Development   75
      Controls and Triggers of Mass Wasting   75
   The Hydrologic Cycle   78
   Running Water   79
      Drainage Basins   79
      River Systems   80

Streamflow 80
  Gradient and Channel Characteristics 80
  Discharge 81
  Changes from Upstream to Downstream 82
The Work of Running Water 82
  Erosion 82
  Transportation 83
  Deposition 84
Stream Channels 84
  Bedrock Channels 84
  Alluvial Channels 85
Base Level and Stream Erosion 86
Shaping Stream Valleys 87
  Valley Deepening 88
  Valley Widening 88
  Changing Base Level and Incised Meanders 89
Depositional Landforms 89
  Deltas 89
  Natural Levees 91
Drainage Patterns 91
Floods and Flood Control 92
  Causes of Floods 92
  Flood Control 93
Groundwater: Water Beneath the Surface 94
  The Importance of Groundwater 94
  Groundwater's Geologic Roles 94
Distribution and Movement of Groundwater 95
  Distribution 95
  Factors Influencing the Storage and Movement of Groundwater 96
  Groundwater Movement 96
Springs 97
  Hot Springs 97
  Geysers 97
Wells 98
Artesian Wells 98
Environmental Problems of Groundwater 100
  Treating Groundwater as a Nonrenewable Resource 100
  Land Subsidence Caused by Groundwater Withdrawal 100
  Groundwater Contamination 101
The Geologic Work of Groundwater 102
  Caverns 102
  Karst Topography 104
THE CHAPTER IN REVIEW 106
KEY TERMS 107
QUESTIONS FOR REVIEW 107
COMPANION WEBSITE 109

4 GLACIAL AND ARID LANDSCAPES 110
FOCUS ON LEARNING 110
Glaciers: A Part of Two Basic Cycles 112
  Valley (Alpine) Glaciers 112
  Ice Sheets 112
  Other Types of Glaciers 113

How Glaciers Move 114
  Observing and Measuring Movement 115
  Budget of a Glacier: Accumulation versus Wastage 115
Glacial Erosion 117
  How Glaciers Erode 117
  Landforms Created by Glacial Erosion 119
Glacial Deposits 121
  Types of Glacial Drift 121
  Moraines, Outwash Plains, and Kettles 122
  Drumline, Eskers, and Kames 124
Other Effects of Ice Age Glaciers 124
Glaciers of the Ice Age 126
Deserts 126
  Distribution and Causes of Dry Lands 127
  The Role of Water in Arid Climates 128
Basin and Range: The Evolution of a Mountainous Desert Landscape 130
Wind Erosion 131
  Deflation, Blowouts, and Desert Pavement 132
  Wind Abrasion 133
Wind Deposits 134
  Loess 134
  Sand Dunes 135
THE CHAPTER IN REVIEW 136
KEY TERMS 137
QUESTIONS FOR REVIEW 138
COMPANION WEBSITE 139

UNIT III FORCES WITHIN 140

5 PLATE TECTONICS: A SCIENTIFIC THEORY UNFOLDS 140
FOCUS ON LEARNING 140
Continental Drift: An Idea Before Its Time 143
  Evidence: The Continental Jigsaw Puzzle 143
  Evidence: Fossils Match across the Seas 143
  Evidence: Rock Types and Geologic Features 145
  Evidence: Ancient Climates 146
The Great Debate 147
  Rejection of the Continental Drift Hypothesis 147
Plate Tectonics 147
  Earth's Major Plates 150
  Plate Boundaries 150

Divergent Boundaries 151
   Oceanic Ridges and Seafloor Spreading 151
   Continental Rifting 151
Convergent Boundaries 152
   Oceanic–Continental Convergence 153
   Oceanic–Oceanic Convergence 155
   Continental–Continental Convergence 155
Transform Fault Boundaries 156
How Do Plates and Plate Boundaries Change? 158
Testing The Plate Tectonics Model 158
   Evidence from Ocean Drilling 159
   Hot Spots and Mantle Plumes 159
   Evidence: Paleomagnetism 160
   Apparent Polar Wandering 161
The Breakup of Pangaea 163
What Drives Plate Motions? 164
   Plate-Mantle Convection 164
   Forces that Drive Plate Motion 166
   Models of Plate-Mantle Convection 166
THE CHAPTER IN REVIEW 167
KEY TERMS 168
QUESTIONS FOR REVIEW 168
COMPANION WEBSITE 169

6 RESTLESS EARTH: EARTHQUAKES,
   GEOLOGIC STRUCTURES,
   AND MOUNTAIN BUILDING 170
FOCUS ON LEARNING 170
What Is an Earthquake? 172
   Discovering the Causes of Earthquakes 172
   Aftershocks and Foreshocks 174
   Earthquakes and Faults 175
Seismology: The Study of Earthquake
   Waves 176
Locating an Earthquake 178
Measuring the Size of Earthquakes 179
   Intensity Scales 179
   Magnitude Scales 180
Earthquake Belts and Plate Boundaries 183
Earthquake Destruction 183
   Destruction from Seismic Vibrations 183
   Landslides and Ground Subsidence 185
   Fire 185
   What Is a Tsunami? 186
Probing Earth's Interior: "Seeing" Seismic Waves 188
   Formation of Earth's Layered Structure 189
   Earth's Internal Structure 189
Geologic Structures 191
   Rock Deformation 191
   Folds 192
   Faults 192
   Dip-Slip Faults 193
Mountain Building 196
   Convergence and Subducting Plates 197
   Collisional Mountain Belts 199

THE CHAPTER IN REVIEW 203
KEY TERMS 204
QUESTIONS FOR REVIEW 204
COMPANION WEBSITE 205

7 FIRES WITHIN: IGNEOUS ACTIVITY 206
FOCUS ON LEARNING 206
The Nature of Volcanic Eruptions 209
   Factors Affecting Viscosity 209
   Why Do Volcanoes Erupt? 210
Materials Extruded During an Eruption 211
   Lava Flows 211
   Gases 213
   Pyroclastic Materials 213
Volcanic Structures and Eruptive Styles 214
   Anatomy of a Volcano 214
   Shield Volcanoes 215
   Cinder Cones 216
   Composite Cones 218
Living in the Shadow of a Composite
   Cone 218
   Nuée Ardente: A Deadly Pyroclastic Flow 218
   *Lahars: Mudflows on Active and
     Inactive Cones* 220
Other Volcanic Landforms 221
   Calderas 221
   Fissure Eruptions and Basalt Plateaus 222
   Volcanic Pipes and Necks 223
Intrusive Igneous Activity 224
   Nature of Intrusive Bodies 224
   Tabular Intrusive Bodies: Dikes and Sills 224
   *Massive Intrusive Bodies: Batholiths, Stocks,
     and Laccoliths* 226
Plate Tectonics and Igneous Activity 227
   Volcanism at Convergent Plate Boundaries 228
   Volcanism at Divergent Plate Boundaries 229
   Intraplate Volcanism 229
Living with Volcanoes 229
   Volcanic Hazards 232
   Monitoring Volcanic Activity 233
THE CHAPTER IN REVIEW 233
KEY TERMS 234
QUESTIONS FOR REVIEW 234
COMPANION WEBSITE 235

UNIT IV DECIPERING EARTH'S HISTORY 236

8 GEOLOGIC TIME 236
FOCUS ON LEARNING 236

Geology Needs a Time Scale 238
Some Historical Notes about Geology 239
  Catastrophism 239
  The Birth of Modern Geology 239
  Geology Today 239
Relative Dating—Key Principles 240
  Law of Superposition 240
  Principle of Original Horizontality 241
  Principle of Cross-Cutting Relationships 241
  Inclusions 241
  Unconformities 242
  Applying Relative Dating Principles 243
Correlation of Rock Layers 244
Fossils: Evidence of Past Life 245
  Types of Fossils 247
  Conditions Favoring Preservation 248
  Fossils and Correlation 248
Dating with Radioactivity 249
  Reviewing Basic Atomic Structure 249
  Radioactivity 249
  Half-Life 250
  Radiometric Dating 251
  Dating with Carbon-14 251
  Importance of Radiometric Dating 252
The Geologic Time Scale 252
  Structure of the Time Scale 252
  Terminology and the Geologic Time Scale 254
  Precambrian Time 254
Difficulties in Dating the Geologic Time Scale 255
THE CHAPTER IN REVIEW 255
KEY TERMS 256
QUESTIONS FOR REVIEW 256
COMPANION WEBSITE 257

UNIT V THE GLOBAL OCEAN 258

9 OCEANS: THE LAST FRONTIER 258
FOCUS ON LEARNING 258

The Vast World Ocean 260
  Geography of the Oceans 260
  Comparing the Oceans to the Continents 261
Composition of Seawater 261
  Salinity 261
  Sources of Sea Salts 262
  Processes Affecting Seawater Salinity 263
Ocean Temperature Variations with Depth 263
Ocean Density Variation 264
  Factors Affecting Seawater Density 264
  Density Variation with Depth 264
  Ocean Layering 264

An Emerging Picture of the Ocean Floor 265
  Mapping the Seafloor 265
  Viewing the Ocean Floor from Space 267
  Provinces of the Ocean Floor 267
Continental Margins 267
  Passive Continental Margins 268
  Active Continental Margins 272
Deep-Ocean Basin 272
  Deep-Ocean Trenches 272
  Abyssal Plains 273
  Seamounts, Guyots, and Oceanic Plateaus 273
The Oceanic Ridge 273
  Anatomy of the Oceanic Ridge 273
  Why Is the Oceanic Ridge Elevated? 274
Seafloor Sediments 275
  Types of Seafloor Sediments 275
  Seafloor Sediment—A Storehouse of Climate Data 276
THE CHAPTER IN REVIEW 277
KEY TERMS 278
QUESTIONS FOR REVIEW 278
COMPANION WEBSITE 279

10 THE RESTLESS OCEAN 280
FOCUS ON LEARNING 280

The Ocean's Surface Circulation 282
  The Pattern of Ocean Currents 282
  Ocean Currents Influence Climate 284
  Upwelling 285
Deep-Ocean Circulation 285
The Shoreline: A Dynamic Interface 286
Waves 287
  Wave Characteristics 287
  Circular Orbital Motion 289
  Waves in the Surf Zone 289
Beaches and Shoreline Processes 289
  Wave Erosion 290
  Sand Movement on the Beach 291
Shoreline Features 293
  Erosional Features 293
  Depositional Features 294
  The Evolving Shore 295

Stabilizing the Shore **295**
   Hard Stabilization **295**
   Alternatives to Hard Stabilization **298**
   Erosion Problems along U.S. Coasts **299**
Coastal Classification **300**
   Emergent Coasts **300**
   Submergent Coasts **300**
Tides **301**
   Causes of Tides **301**
   Monthly Tidal Cycle **302**
   Tidal Patterns **302**
   Tidal Currents **303**
THE CHAPTER IN REVIEW **304**
KEY TERMS **305**
QUESTIONS FOR REVIEW **306**
COMPANION WEBSITE **307**

UNIT VI EARTH'S DYNAMIC ATMOSPHERE **308**

11 HEATING THE ATMOSPHERE **308**
FOCUS ON LEARNING **308**
Weather and Climate **310**
Composition of the Atmosphere **311**
   Major Components **312**
   Variable Component **313**
   Ozone Depletion—A Global Issue **314**
Vertical Structure of the Atmosphere **315**
   Pressure Changes **315**
   Temperature Changes **315**
Earth–Sun Relationships **316**
   Earth's Motions **317**
   Seasons **317**
   Earth's Orientation **318**
   Solstices and Equinoxes **318**
Energy, Heat, and Temperature **321**
Mechanisms of Heat Transfer **321**
   Conduction **322**
   Convection **322**
   Radiation **322**
The Fate of Incoming Solar Radiation **323**
   Reflection and Scattering **324**
   Absorption **325**
Heating the Atmosphere: The Greenhouse Effect **325**
Human Impact on Global Climate **325**
   CO_2 Levels Are Rising **326**
   The Atmosphere's Response **326**
   Some Possible Consequences **328**
For the Record: Air Temperature Data **328**
Why Temperatures Vary: The Controls of Temperature **330**
   Land and Water **332**
   Altitude **333**
   Geographic Position **333**
   Cloud Cover and Albedo **333**

World Distribution of Temperature **335**
THE CHAPTER IN REVIEW **336**
KEY TERMS **337**
QUESTIONS FOR REVIEW **338**
COMPANION WEBSITE **339**

12 MOISTURE, CLOUDS, AND PRECIPITATION **340**
FOCUS ON LEARNING **340**
Water's Changes of State **342**
   Ice, Liquid Water, and Water Vapor **342**
   Latent Heat **342**
Humidity: Water Vapor in the Air **344**
   Saturation **344**
   Mixing Ratio **344**
   Relative Humidity **344**
   Dew-Point Temperature **346**
   Measuring Humidity **347**
The Basis of Cloud Formation: Adiabatic Cooling **348**
   Fog and Dew versus Cloud Formation **348**
   Adiabatic Temperature Changes **348**
   Adiabatic Cooling and Condensation **348**
Processes that Lift Air **349**
   Orographic Lifting **349**
   Frontal Wedging **350**
   Convergence **350**
   Localized Convective Lifting **351**
The Weathermaker: Atmospheric Stability **351**
   Types of Stability **352**
   Stability and Daily Weather **354**
Condensation and Cloud Formation **355**
   Types of Clouds **355**
Fog **359**
   Fogs Caused by Cooling **359**
   Evaporation Fogs **360**
Precipitation **361**
   How Precipitation Forms **361**
   Forms of Precipitation **362**
   Measuring Precipitation **364**
THE CHAPTER IN REVIEW **366**
KEY TERMS **367**
QUESTIONS FOR REVIEW **368**
COMPANION WEBSITE **369**

13 THE ATMOSPHERE IN MOTION **370**
FOCUS ON LEARNING **370**
Understanding Air Pressure **372**
Measuring Air Pressure **373**
Factors Affecting Wind **374**
   Pressure-Gradient Force **374**
   Coriolis Effect **375**
   Friction with Earth's Surface **376**
Highs and Lows **378**
   Cyclonic and Anticyclonic Winds **378**
   Weather Generalizations about High and Lows **378**

General Circulation of the Atmosphere   381
  Circulation on a Nonrotating Earth   381
  Idealized Global Circulation   381
  Influence of Continents   382
The Westerlies   382
Local Winds   382
  Land and Sea Breezes   382
  Mountain and Valley Breezes   384
  Chinook and Santa Ana Winds   384
How Wind Is Measured   385
THE CHAPTER IN REVIEW   387
KEY TERMS   388
QUESTIONS FOR REVIEW   388
COMPANION WEBSITE   389

14 WEATHER PATTERNS AND SEVERE
    WEATHER   390
FOCUS ON LEARNING   390
Air Masses   392
  What Is an Air Mass?   392
  Source Regions   393
  Weather Associated with Air Masses   393
Fronts   395
  Warm Fronts   395
  Cold Fronts   396
  Stationary Fronts and Occluded Fronts   397
The Middle-Latitude Cyclone   397
  Idealized Weather of a Middle-Latitude Cyclone   397
  The Role of Airflow Aloft   399
What's in a Name?   400
Thunderstorms   401
  Thunderstorm Occurrence   401
  Stages of Thunderstorm Development   402
Tornadoes   403
  Tornado Occurrence and Development   404
  Tornado Destruction   406
  Tornado Forecasting   407
Hurricanes   408
  Profile of a Hurricane   409
  Hurricane Formation and Decay   410
  Hurricane Destruction   411
  Tracking Hurricanes   413

THE CHAPTER IN REVIEW   414
KEY TERMS   415
QUESTIONS FOR REVIEW   415
COMPANION WEBSITE   416

UNIT VII EARTH'S PLACE IN THE UNIVERSE   418

15 THE NATURE OF THE SOLAR
    SYSTEM   418
FOCUS ON LEARNING   418
Ancient Astronomy   420
  The Golden Age of Astronomy   420
  Ptolemy's Model   421
The Birth of Modern Astronomy   422
  Nicolaus Copernicus   423
  Tycho Brahe   423
  Johannes Kepler   424
  Galileo Galilei   425
  Sir Isaac Newton   427
Our Solar System: An Overview   428
  *Nebular Theory: Formation of the Solar
    System*   429
  *The Planets: Internal Structures and
    Atmospheres*   430
  Planetary Impacts   433
Earth's Moon: A Chip Off the Old
  Block   434
  How Did the Moon Form?   434
Planets and Moons   436
  Mercury: The Innermost Planet   436
  Venus: The Veiled Planet   437
  Mars: The Red Planet   438
  Jupiter: The Lord of the Heavens   440
  Saturn: The Elegant Planet   442
  Uranus and Neptune: Twins   444
Minor Members of the Solar System   446
  Asteroids: Leftover Planetesimals   446
  Comets: Dirty Snowballs   447
  Meteoroids: Visitors to Earth   449
  Dwarf Planets   451
THE CHAPTER IN REVIEW   452
KEY TERMS   453
QUESTIONS FOR REVIEW   453
COMPANION WEBSITE   454

16 BEYOND OUR SOLAR SYSTEM   456
FOCUS ON LEARNING   456
Stars Like the Sun   458
  Measuring Distances to the Closest Stars   458
  Stellar Brightness   459
  Stellar Color and Temperature   460
  Binary Stars and Stellar Mass   461

Variable Stars   461
Hertzsprung-Russell Diagram   462
Interstellar Matter   464
Stellar Evolution   465
  Stellar Birth   465
  Protostar Stage   465
  Main-Sequence Stage   466
  Red Giant Stage   466
  Burnout and Death   467
  H-R Diagrams and Stellar Evolution   469
Stellar Remnants   469
  White Dwarfs   469
  Neutron Stars   470
  Black Holes   471
The Milky Way Galaxy   472
Normal Galaxies   473
  Types of Galaxies   473
  Galactic Clusters   475
The Big Bang and the Fate of the
  Universe   475
  The Expanding Universe   475
  The Origin of the Universe   475
  The End of the Universe   477
THE CHAPTER IN REVIEW   477
KEY TERMS   478
QUESTIONS FOR REVIEW   479
COMPANION WEBSITE   480

APPENDIX A
Metric and English Units Compared   481

APPENDIX B
Mineral Identification key   482

APPENDIX C
Relative Humidity and Dew-Point Tables   484

APPENDIX D
Earth's Grid System   486

GLOSSARY   489

INDEX   499

PREFACE

Foundations of Earth Science, Sixth Edition, like its predecessors, is a college-level text designed for an introductory course in Earth science. It consists of seven units that emphasize broad and up-to-date coverage of basic topics and principles in geology, oceanography, meteorology, and astronomy. The book is intended to be a meaningful, nontechnical survey for undergraduate students with little background in science. Usually these students are taking an Earth science class to meet a portion of their college's or university's general requirements.

In addition to being informative and up-to-date, *Foundations of Earth Science* strives to meet the need of beginning students for a readable and user-friendly text, a book that is a highly usable "tool" for learning basic Earth science principles and concepts.

The sixth edition of *Foundations of Earth Science* represents a thorough revision. Every part of the book was examined carefully with the dual goals of keeping topics current and improving the clarity of text discussions. People familiar with the preceding edition will see much that is new in the sixth edition.

DISTINGUISHING FEATURES

Readability

The language of this book is straightforward and *written to be understood.* Clear, readable discussions with a minimum of technical language are the rule. The frequent headings and subheadings also help students follow discussions and identify the important ideas presented in each chapter. In the sixth edition, improved readability was achieved by examining chapter organization and flow and by writing in a more personal style. Many sections were substantially rewritten in an effort to make the material more understandable.

Focus on Basic Principles and Instructor Flexibility

The main focus of the sixth edition remains the same as in the first five—to develop student understanding of basic Earth science principles. With this in mind, we have attempted to provide the reader with a sense of the observational techniques and reasoning processes that characterize the Earth sciences.

Whereas student use of the text is a primary concern, the book's adaptability to the needs and desires of the instructor is equally important. Realizing the broad diversity of Earth science courses in both content and approach, we have continued to use a relatively nonintegrated format to allow maximum flexibility for the instructor. Each of the major units stands alone; hence, they can be taught in any order. A unit can be omitted entirely without appreciable loss of continuity, and portions of some chapters may be interchanged or excluded at the instructor's discretion.

The Art Program

Earth science is highly visual, so the art program plays a critical role in an introductory book. As in the five previous editions, Dennis Tasa, a gifted artist and respected Earth science illustrator, has again worked closely with the authors to plan and produce the diagrams, maps, graphs, and sketches that are so basic to student understanding. Dozens of figures are new or redrawn.

FOCUS ON LEARNING

Foundations of Earth Science, Sixth Edition, consists of two products—a traditional college textbook and an interactive Companion Website featuring Pearson eText. Both contain helpful student learning aids.

End-of-Chapter Review

When a chapter has been completed, four useful devices help students review. First, the *Chapter in Review* recaps all the major points. Next is the checklist of *Key Terms* with page references. Learning the language of Earth science helps students learn the material. This is followed by the *Questions for Review* section, which helps students examine their knowledge of significant facts and ideas.

Next is a reminder to visit the Website for *Foundations of Earth Science,* Sixth Edition (www.mygeoscienceplace.com). It contains many excellent opportunities for review and exploration. Finally, many chapters close with a note about *GEODe* to remind students about this unique and effective learning aid.

Companion Website with *GEODe: Earth Science*

Included with every copy of *Foundations of Earth Science* is access to the interactive Companion Website containing quizzes for review, the Pearson eText, animations, and *GEODe: Earth Science.* Prepared by the authors in conjunction with Dennis Tasa, *GEODe: Earth Science* is a dynamic program that provides broad coverage of basic principles and reinforces key concepts by using tutorials, interactive exercises, animations, and "In the Lab" activities. A table of contents appears in the front matter for easy reference, and a special icon appears throughout the book wherever a text discussion has a corresponding *GEODe: Earth Science* activity.

NEW TO THIS EDITION

- Several basic discussions in the chapters that focus on geology have been improved and updated. For example, portions of Chapter 1 on minerals were rewritten to make a sometimes difficult (chemistry-oriented) topic easier for the beginning student to understand. In addition, discussions of plate tectonics (Chapter 5), earthquakes

(Chapter 6), and volcanic activity (Chapter 7) received special attention.

- Unit V, The Global Ocean, has been thoroughly updated. Changes include revised discussions and line art dealing with ocean circulation, the influence of ocean currents on climate, temperature and density variations, ocean-floor topography, and seafloor sediments.

- Unit VI, Earth's Dynamic Atmosphere, includes a completely revised discussion of the human impact on global climate and many new graphs and diagrams. There is also updated and expanded coverage of hurricanes, including a new section on hurricane forecasts.

- The two chapters comprising Unit VII, Earth's Place in the Universe, have been revised and updated to reflect the most recent research. This is the *most complete* revision of this unit ever. The subject matter is better organized, more readable, and more up-to-date. Discussions progress in a manner that is easier to follow for the beginning student. The chapters are filled with many new images.

- New *GEODe: Earth Science*, version 3. The text includes access to the *new* version of this highly praised, student-tested, student-friendly learning tool. This dynamic, easy-to-use program has *significantly broader coverage* than previous versions.

- The strongest art program. Dozens of figures are new or redrawn. The result is art that is clearer and easier to understand. Numerous diagrams and maps are paired with photographs for greater effectiveness. Many new and revised art pieces also have additional labels that "narrate" the process being illustrated and/or "guide" readers as they examine the figure.

- More than 100 *new*, high-quality photos and satellite images. Geologist's sketches accompany some images and numerous labels were added to many other images. Our aim is to get *maximum effectiveness* from the visual component of the book.

THE TEACHING AND LEARNING PACKAGE

For the Instructor

Instructor Manual and Test Bank

The Instructor Manual contains learning objectives, chapter outlines, and answers to review questions. It also gives professors over 1,200 text-specific true/false, multiple choice, fill-in, and short-answer questions to gauge student's knowledge.

Instructor Resource Center (IRC) on DVD

The IRC puts all of your lecture resources in one easy-to-reach place:

- *All* of the line art, tables, and photos from the text in.jpg files
- *Images of Earth* photo gallery
- PowerPoint presentations

- *Instructor's Manual* and Test Bank in Microsoft Word
- TestGen test generation and management software
- Electronic transparency acetates

Animations The Prentice Hall Geoscience Animation Library includes over 100 animations illuminating many difficult-to-visualize topics. Created through a unique collaboration among five of Prentice Hall's leading geoscience authors, these animations represent a most significant leap forward in lecture presentation aids. They are provided both as Flash files and, for your convenience, loaded into PowerPoint slides.

PowerPoint Presentations Found on the IRC are three PowerPoint files for each chapter. Cut down on your preparation time, no matter what your lecture needs:

1. *Exclusively Art*—All of the photos, art, and tables from the text, in order, loaded into PowerPoint slides.
2. *Lecture Outline*—This set averages 35 slides per chapter and includes customizable lecture outlines with supporting art.
3. *Classroom Response System (CRS) Questions*—Authored for use in conjunction with classroom response systems, these PowerPoint slides allow you to electronically poll your class for responses to questions, pop quizzes, attendance, and more.

Transparency Acetates Provided electronically, every table and most of Dennis Tasa's illustrations in *Foundations of Earth Science,* Sixth Edition, are available to be printed out as full-color, projection-enhanced transparencies.

TestGen

Use this electronic version of the Text Bank to customize and manage your tests. Create multiple versions, add or edit questions, add illustrations—your customization needs are easily addressed by this powerful software.

For the Student

Companion Website with *GEODe: Earth Science*

Included with every copy of *Foundations of Earth Science* is access to the interactive Companion Website containing quizzes for review, the Pearson eText, animations, and *GEODe: Earth Science*. Prepared by the authors in conjunction with Dennis Tasa, *GEODe: Earth Science* is a dynamic program that provides broad coverage of basic principles and reinforces key concepts by using tutorials, interactive exercises, animations, and "In the Lab" activities. A table of contents appears in the front matter for easy reference, and a special icon appears throughout the book wherever a text discussion has a corresponding *GEODe: Earth Science* activity.

Applications and Investigations in Earth Science,
Sixth Edition 0-13-600007-X

This versatile and adaptable collection of introductory-level laboratory experiences goes beyond traditional offerings to examine the basic principles and concepts of the Earth sciences. Widely praised for its concise coverage and dynamic illustrations by Dennis Tasa, the text contains 23 step-by-step exercises that reinforce major topics in geology, oceanography, meteorology, and astronomy.

ACKNOWLEDGEMENTS

Writing a college textbook requires the talents and cooperation of many people. We value the excellent work of Mark Watry and Teresa Tarbuck of Spring Hill College whose talents helped us improve Chapter 2, Minerals: Building Blocks of Rocks, and Chapters 15 and 16 that comprise Unit VII, Earth's Place in the Universe. They helped make these chapters more readable, engaging, and up-to-date.

Working with Dennis Tasa, who is responsible for all of the text's outstanding illustrations and much of the developmental work on *GEODe: Earth Science,* is always special for us. We not only value his outstanding artistic talents and imagination but his friendship as well.

Great thanks also go to those colleagues who prepared in-depth reviews. Their critical comments and thoughtful input helped guide our work and clearly strengthened the text. Special thanks to:

Patricia Crews, Florida Community College of Jacksonville; Adam Davis, Vincennes University; Doug Fischer, CSU Northridge; Richard Kroll, Kean University; Carrie Manfrino, Kean University; Gustavo Morales, Valencia Community College; William Parker, Florida State University; Patrick Seward, Rogers State University; Krista Syrup, Moraine Valley Community College; Courtney R. Voehl, Indian River State College; and Lisa Yon, Palomar College.

As always, we want to acknowledge the team of professionals at Pearson Prentice Hall. We sincerely appreciate the company's continuing strong support for excellence and innovation. All are committed to producing the best textbooks possible. Special thanks to our new geology editor, Andy Dunaway, and to our conscientious project manager, Crissy Dudonis, for a job well done. The production team led by Maureen Pancza at Pearson and Kelly Keeler at GGS Higher Education Resources did an outstanding job. All are true professionals with whom we are very fortunate to be associated.

Fred Lutgens
Ed Tarbuck

FOUNDATIONS OF
EARTH SCIENCE

INTRODUCTION
TO EARTH SCIENCE

To assist you in learning the concepts in the Introduction, you will find it helpful to focus on the following questions:

1. What are the sciences that collectively make up Earth science?

2. What are the four "spheres" that comprise Earth's natural environment?

3. What are the principal divisions of the solid Earth?

4. Why should Earth be thought of as a system?

5. What are the sources of energy that power the Earth system?

6. What are some of Earth's important environmental issues?

7. How is a scientific hypothesis different from a scientific theory?

Volcanic eruption of Italy's Mt. Etna in late 2006. The volcano towers above the city of Catania. (Photo by Marco Fulle)

The spectacular eruption of a volcano, the magnificent scenery of a rocky coast, and the destruction created by a hurricane are all subjects for the Earth scientist. The study of Earth science deals with many fascinating and practical questions about our environment. What forces produce mountains? Why is our daily weather so variable? Is climate really changing? How old is Earth and how is it related to the other planets in the solar system? What causes ocean tides? What was the Ice Age like? Will there be another? Can a successful well be located at this site?

The subject of this text is *Earth science*. To understand Earth is not an easy task, because our planet is not a static and unchanging mass. Rather, it is a dynamic body with many interacting parts and a long and complex history.

WHAT IS EARTH SCIENCE?

Earth science is the name for all the sciences that collectively seek to understand Earth and its neighbors in space. It includes geology, oceanography, meteorology, and astronomy.

In this book, Units 1 through 4 focus on the science of **geology,** a word that literally means "study of Earth." Geology is traditionally divided into two broad areas—physical and historical.

Physical geology examines the materials comprising Earth and seeks to understand the many processes that operate beneath and upon its surface. Earth is a dynamic, ever-changing planet. Internal forces create earthquakes, build mountains, and produce volcanic structures. At the surface, external processes break rock apart and sculpture a broad array of landforms. The erosional effects of water, wind, and ice result in a great diversity of landscapes. Because rocks and minerals form in response to Earth's internal and external processes, the study of Earth materials is basic to an understanding of our planet.

In contrast to physical geology, the aim of *historical geology* is to understand the origin of Earth and the development of the planet through its 4.6-billion-year history. It strives to establish an orderly chronological arrangement of the multitude of physical and biological changes that have occurred in the geologic past (**FIGURE I.1A**). The study of physical geology

FIGURE I.1   A. This hiker is resting atop the Kaibab Formation, the uppermost layer in the Grand Canyon. Hundreds of millions of years of Earth history is contained in the strata that lay beneath him. This is a view of Cape Royal on the Grand Canyon's North Rim. (Photo by Michael Collier) **B.** The *Chikyu* (meaning "Earth" in Japanese), the world's most advanced scientific drilling vessel. It can drill as deep as 7000 meters (nearly 23,000 feet) below the seabed in water as deep as 2500 meters (8200 feet). It is part of the Integrated Ocean Drilling Program (IODP). (AP Photo/Itsuo Inouye)

logically precedes the study of Earth's history because we must first understand how Earth works before we attempt to unravel its past.

Unit 5, *The Global Ocean,* is devoted to **oceanography.** Oceanography is actually not a separate and distinct science. Rather, it involves the application of all sciences in a comprehensive and interrelated study of the oceans in all their aspects and relationships. Oceanography integrates chemistry, physics, geology, and biology. It includes the study of the composition and movements of seawater, as well as coastal processes, seafloor topography, and marine life (**FIGURE I-1B**).

Unit 6, *Earth's Dynamic Atmosphere,* examines the mixture of gases that is held to the planet by gravity and thins rapidly with altitude. Acted on by the combined effects of Earth's motions and energy from the Sun, the formless and invisible atmosphere reacts by producing an infinite variety of weather, which in turn creates the basic pattern of global climates. **Meteorology** is the study of the atmosphere and the processes that produce weather and climate. Like oceanography, meteorology involves the application of other sciences in an integrated study of the thin layer of air that surrounds Earth.

Unit 7, *Earth's Place in the Universe,* demonstrates that an understanding of Earth requires that we relate our planet to the larger universe. Because Earth is related to all of the other objects in space, the science of **astronomy**—the study of the universe—is very useful in probing the origins of our own environment. As we are so closely acquainted with the planet on which we live, it is easy to forget that Earth is just a tiny object in a vast universe. Indeed, Earth is subject to the same physical laws that govern the many other objects populating the great expanses of space. Thus, to understand explanations of our planet's origin, it is useful to learn something about the other members of our solar system. Moreover, it is helpful to view the solar system as a part of the great assemblage of stars that comprise our galaxy, which in turn is but one of many galaxies.

To understand Earth science is challenging because our planet is a dynamic body with many interacting parts and a complex history. Throughout its long existence, Earth has been changing. In fact, it is changing as you read this page and will continue to do so into the foreseeable future. Sometimes the changes are rapid and violent, as when severe storms, landslides, or volcanic eruptions occur. Just as often, change takes place so gradually that it goes unnoticed during a lifetime. Scales of size and space also vary greatly among the phenomena studied in Earth science.

Earth science is often perceived as science that is done in the out-of-doors, and rightly so. A great deal of what Earth scientists study is based on observations and experiments performed in the field. But Earth science is also conducted in the laboratory, where, for example, the study of various Earth materials provides insights into many basic processes, and the creation of complex computer models allows for the simulation of our planet's complicated climate system. Frequently, Earth scientists require an understanding and application of knowledge and principles from physics, chemistry, and biology. Geology, oceanography, meteorology, and astronomy are sciences that seek to expand our knowledge of the natural world and our place in it.

EARTH'S SPHERES

A view such as the one in **FIGURE I.2A** provided the *Apollo 8* astronauts as well as the rest of humanity with a unique perspective of our home. Seen from space, Earth is breathtaking in its beauty and startling in its solitude. Such an image reminds us that our home is, after all, a planet—small, self-contained, and in some ways even fragile.

A.

B.

FIGURE I.2 **A.** View that greeted the *Apollo 8* astronauts as their spacecraft emerged from behind the Moon. **B.** Africa and Arabia are prominent in this classic image of Earth taken from *Apollo 17.* The tan cloud-free zones over the land coincide with major desert regions. The band of clouds across central Africa is associated with a much wetter climate that sustains tropical rain forests. The dark blue of the oceans and the swirling cloud patterns remind us of the importance of the oceans and the atmosphere. Antarctica, a continent covered by glacial ice, is visible at the South Pole. (Both photos courtesy of NASA)

As we look closely at our planet from space, it becomes clear that Earth is much more than rock and soil. In fact, the most conspicuous features in Figure I.2A are not continents, but swirling clouds suspended above the surface and the vast global ocean. These features emphasize the importance of air and water to our planet.

The closer view of Earth from space, shown in Figure I.2B, helps us appreciate why the physical environment is traditionally divided into three major parts: the water portion of our planet, the hydrosphere; Earth's gaseous envelope, the atmosphere; and, of course, the solid Earth, or geosphere.

It should be emphasized that our environment is highly integrated and not dominated by water, air, or rock

alone. Rather, it is characterized by continuous interactions as air comes in contact with rock, rock with water, and water with air. Moreover, the biosphere, the totality of life forms on our planet, extends into each of the three physical realms and is an equally integral part of the planet. Thus, Earth can be thought of as consisting of four major spheres: the hydrosphere, atmosphere, geosphere, and biosphere.

The interactions among Earth's four spheres are incalculable. **FIGURE I.3** provides an easy-to-visualize example. The shoreline is an obvious meeting place for rock, water, and air. In this scene, ocean waves that were created by the drag of air moving across the water are breaking against the rocky shore. The force of the water can be powerful, and the erosional work that is accomplished can be great.

Hydrosphere

Earth is sometimes called the *blue planet*. Water, more than anything else, makes Earth unique. The **hydrosphere** is a dynamic mass of water that is continually on the move, evaporating from the oceans to the atmosphere, precipitating to the land, and flowing back to the ocean. The global ocean is certainly the most prominent feature of the hydrosphere, blanketing nearly 71 percent of Earth's surface to an average depth of about 3800 meters (12,500 feet). It accounts for about 97 percent of Earth's water (**FIGURE I.4**). However, the hydrosphere also includes the freshwater found underground and in streams, lakes, and glaciers. Moreover, water is an important component of all living things.

Although these latter sources constitute just a tiny fraction of the total, they are much more important than their meager percentage indicates. In addition to providing the freshwater that is so vital to life on the continents, streams, glaciers, and groundwater are responsible for sculpturing and creating many of our planet's varied landforms.

FIGURE I.3 The shoreline is one obvious example of an *interface*—a common boundary where different parts of a system interact. In this scene, along the coast of Oahu, ocean waves *(hydrosphere)* that were created by the force of moving air *(atmosphere)* break against the rocky shore *(geosphere)*. The force of the water can be powerful, and the erosional work that is accomplished can be great. (Photo by Douglas Peebles/Corbis)

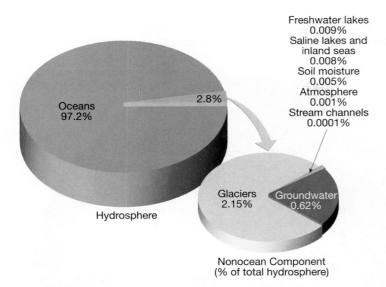

Freshwater lakes
0.009%
Saline lakes and
inland seas
0.008%
Soil moisture
0.005%
Atmosphere
0.001%
Stream channels
0.0001%

Oceans
97.2%

2.8%

Hydrosphere

Glaciers
2.15%

Groundwater
0.62%

Nonocean Component
(% of total hydrosphere)

FIGURE I.4 Distribution of Earth's water. The oceans clearly dominate. When we consider only the nonocean component, ice sheets and glaciers represent nearly 85 percent of Earth's fresh water. Groundwater accounts for just over 14 percent. When only *liquid* freshwater is considered, the significance of groundwater is obvious.

Atmosphere

Earth is surrounded by a life-giving gaseous envelope called the **atmosphere** (**FIGURE I.5**). When we watch a high-flying jet plane cross the sky, it seems that the atmosphere extends upward for a great distance. However, when compared to the thickness (radius) of the solid Earth (about 6400 kilometers or 4000 miles), the atmosphere is a very shallow layer. One-half lies below an altitude of 5.6 kilometers (3.5 miles), and 90 percent occurs within just 16 kilometers (10 miles) of Earth's surface. This thin blanket of air is nevertheless an integral part of the planet. It not only provides the air that we breathe, but it also acts to protect us from the dangerous radiation emitted by the Sun. The energy exchanges that continually occur between the atmosphere and Earth's surface and between the atmosphere and space produce the effects we call *weather* and *climate*.

If, like the Moon, Earth had no atmosphere, our planet would be lifeless because many of the processes and interactions that make Earth's surface such a dynamic place could not operate. Without weathering and erosion, the face of our planet might more closely resemble the surface of the Moon, which has not changed appreciably in nearly 3 billion years.

Geosphere

Lying beneath the atmosphere and the ocean is the solid Earth or **geosphere.** The geosphere extends from the surface to the center of the planet, a depth of nearly 6400 kilometers (4000 miles), making it by far the largest of Earth's spheres. Much of our study of the solid Earth focuses on the more accessible surface and near-surface features, but it is worth noting that many of these features are linked to the dynamic behavior of Earth's interior. **FIGURE I.6** provides a diagrammatic view of Earth's interior. As you can see, it is not uniform but is divided into various layers. Based on compositional differences, three principal layers are identified: a dense inner sphere called the **core;** the less dense **mantle;** and the **crust,** which is the light and very thin outer skin of Earth. The crust is not a layer of uniform thickness. It is thinnest beneath the oceans and thickest where continents exist. Although the crust may seem insignificant when compared with the other layers of the geosphere, which are much thicker, it was created by the same general processes that formed Earth's present structure. Thus, the crust is important in understanding the history and nature of our planet.

The solid Earth is also divided based on how materials behave when various forces and stresses are applied. The term **lithosphere** refers to the rigid outer layer that includes the

160 —
140 —
120 —
100 —
80 —
60 —
40 —
20 —
0 —

Altitude in kilometers (km)

Noctilucent clouds

Top of troposphere

Earth's surface

FIGURE I.5 This unique image of Earth's atmosphere merging with the emptiness of space resembles an abstract painting. It was taken over western China in June 2007 by a Space Shuttle crew member. The thin silvery streaks (called noctilucent clouds) high in the blue area are at a height of about 80 kilometers (50 miles). The atmosphere at this altitude is *very* thin. Air pressure here is less than a thousandth that at sea level. The thin reddish zone in the lower portion of the image is the densest part of the atmosphere. It is here, in a layer called the *troposphere*, that practically all weather and cloud formation occur. Ninety percent of Earth's atmosphere occurs within just 16 kilometers (10 miles) of the surface. (NASA)

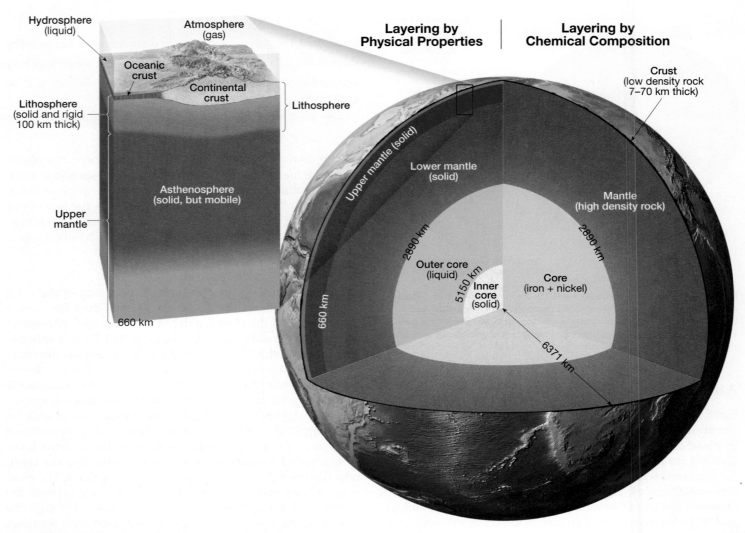

FIGURE I.6 The right side of the globe shows that Earth's interior is divided into three layers based on compositional differences—the crust, mantle, and core. The left side of the globe shows the five main layers of Earth's interior based on physical properties and mechanical strength—the lithosphere, asthenosphere, lower mantle, outer core, and inner core. The block diagram shows an enlarged view of the upper portion of Earth's interior.

crust and uppermost mantle. Beneath the rigid rocks that compose the lithosphere, the rocks of the **asthenosphere** are weak and are able to slowly flow in response to the uneven distribution of heat deep within Earth.

The two principal divisions of Earth's surface are the continents and the ocean basins. The most obvious difference between these two diverse provinces is their relative levels. The average elevation of the continents above sea level is about 840 meters (2750 feet), whereas the average depth of the oceans is about 3800 meters (12,500 feet). Thus, the continents stand on the average 4640 meters (about 4.6 kilometers or nearly 3 miles) above the level of the ocean floor.

DID YOU KNOW?

We have never sampled the mantle or core directly. The structure of Earth's interior is determined by analyzing seismic waves from earthquakes. As these waves of energy penetrate Earth's interior, they change speed and are bent and reflected as they move through zones having different properties. Monitoring stations around the world detect and record this energy.

Biosphere

The fourth "sphere," the **biosphere,** includes all life on Earth. Ocean life is concentrated in the sunlit waters of the sea (**FIGURE I.7**). Most life on land is also concentrated near the surface, with tree roots and burrowing animals reaching a few meters underground and flying insects and birds reaching a kilometer or so above the surface. A surprising variety of life forms are also adapted to extreme environments. For example, on the deep ocean floor where pressures

FIGURE I.7 The hydrosphere contains a significant portion of Earth's biosphere. Modern coral reefs are unique and complex examples and are home to about 25 percent of all marine species. Because of this diversity, they are sometimes referred to as the ocean equivalent of rain forests. (Photo by Darryl Leniuk/age fotostock)

are extreme and no light penetrates, there are places where vents spew hot, mineral-rich fluids that support communities of exotic life forms. On land, some bacteria thrive in rocks as deep as 4 kilometers (2.5 miles) and in boiling hot springs. Moreover, air currents can carry microorganisms many kilometers into the atmosphere. But even when we consider these extremes, life still must be thought of as being confined to a narrow band very near Earth's surface.

Plants and animals depend on the physical environment for the basics of life. However, organisms do more than just respond to this environment. Through countless interactions, life forms help maintain and alter their physical environment. Without life, the makeup and nature of the geosphere, hydrosphere, and atmosphere would be very different.

EARTH AS A SYSTEM

Anyone who studies Earth soon learns that our planet is a dynamic body with many separate but interacting parts or spheres. The hydrosphere, atmosphere, biosphere, and geosphere and all of their components can be studied separately. However, the parts are not isolated. Each is related in many ways to the others to produce a complex and continuously interacting whole that we call the **Earth system.**

A simple example of the interactions among different parts of the Earth system occurs every winter as moisture evaporates from the Pacific Ocean and subsequently falls as rain in the hills of southern California, triggering destructive landslides (**FIGURE I.8**). The processes that move water from the hydrosphere to the atmosphere and then to the geosphere have a profound impact on the physical landscape and on the

FIGURE I.8 This image provides an example of interactions among different parts of the Earth system. On January 10, 2005, extraordinary rains triggered this debris flow (popularly called a *mudslide*) in the coastal community of La Conchita, California. (AP Wideworld Photo)

plants and animals (including humans) that inhabit the affected regions.

Scientists have recognized that in order to more fully understand our planet, they must learn how its individual components (land, water, air, and life forms) are interconnected. This endeavor, called *Earth system science,* aims to study Earth as a *system* composed of numerous interacting parts, or *subsystems.* Using an interdisciplinary approach, those who practice Earth system science attempt to achieve the level of understanding necessary to comprehend and solve many of our global environmental problems.

A **system** is a group of interacting, or interdependent, parts that form a complex whole. Most of us hear and use the term frequently. We may service our car's cooling *system,* make use of the city's transportation *system,* and participate in the political *system. A* news report might inform us of an approaching weather *system.* Further, we know that Earth is just a small part of a large system known as the *solar system,* which, in turn, is a subsystem of an even larger system called the Milky Way galaxy.

The parts of the Earth system are linked so that a change in one part can produce changes in any or all of the other parts. For example, when a volcano erupts, lava from Earth's interior may flow out at the surface and block a nearby valley. This new obstruction influences the region's drainage system by creating a lake or causing streams to change course. The large quantities of volcanic ash and gases that can be emitted during an eruption might be blown high into the atmosphere and influence the amount of solar energy that can reach Earth's surface. The result could be a drop in air temperatures over the entire hemisphere.

Where the surface is covered by lava flows or a thick layer of volcanic ash, existing soils are buried. This causes the soil-forming processes to begin anew to transform the new surface material into soil (**FIGURE I.9**). The soil that eventually forms will reflect the interactions among many parts of the Earth system—the volcanic parent material, the type and rate of weathering, and the impact of biological activity. Of course, there would also be significant changes in the biosphere. Some organisms and their habitats would be eliminated by the lava and ash, whereas new settings for life, such as the lake, would be created. The potential climate change could also affect sensitive life forms.

The Earth system is characterized by processes that vary on spatial scales from fractions of millimeters to thousands of kilometers. Time scales for Earth's processes range from milliseconds to billions of years. As we learn about Earth, it becomes increasingly clear that despite significant separations in distance or time, many processes are connected and that a change in one component can influence the entire system.

The Earth system is powered by energy from two sources. The Sun drives external processes that occur in the atmosphere, hydrosphere, and at Earth's surface. Weather and climate, ocean circulation, and erosional processes are driven by energy from the Sun. Earth's interior is the second source of energy. Heat remaining from when our planet formed and heat that is continuously generated by radioactive decay power the internal processes that produce volcanoes, earthquakes, and mountains.

Humans are *part of* the Earth system, a system in which the living and nonliving components are entwined and interconnected. Therefore, our actions produce changes in all of the other parts. When we burn gasoline and coal, build seawalls along the shoreline, dispose of our wastes, and clear the land, we cause other parts of the system to respond, often in unforeseen ways. Throughout this book, you will learn about many of Earth's subsystems: the hydrologic system, the tectonic (mountain-building) system, and the climate system, to name a few. Remember that these components *and we humans* are all part of the complex interacting whole we call the Earth system.

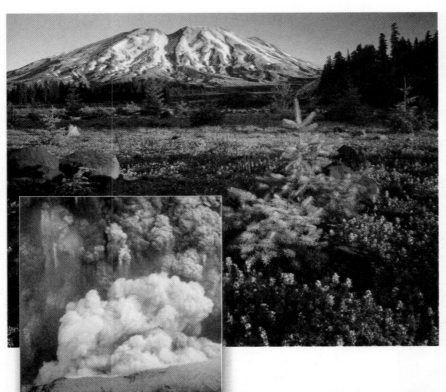

SCALES OF SPACE AND TIME IN EARTH SCIENCE

When we study Earth, we must contend with a broad array of space and time scales (**FIGURE 1.10**). Some phenomena are relatively easy for us to imagine, such as the size and duration of an afternoon thunderstorm or the dimensions of a sand dune. Other phenomena are so vast or so small that they are difficult to imagine. The number of stars and distances in our galaxy (and beyond!) or the internal arrangement of atoms in a mineral crystal are examples of such phenomena.

Some of the events we study occur in fractions of a second. Lightning is an example. Other processes extend over spans of tens or hundreds of millions of years. The lofty Himalaya Mountains began forming nearly 50 million years ago, and they continue to develop today.

The concept of geologic time is new to many nonscientists. People are accustomed to dealing with increments of time that are measured in hours, days, weeks, and years. Our history books often examine events over spans of centuries, but even a century is difficult to appreciate fully. For most of us, someone or something that is 90 years old is *very old*, and a 1000-year-old artifact is *ancient*.

By contrast, those who study Earth science must routinely deal with vast time periods—millions or billions (thousands of millions) of years. When viewed in the context of Earth's nearly 4.6-billion-year history, an event that occurred 100 million years ago may be characterized as "recent" by a geologist, and a rock sample that has been dated at 10 million years may be called "young."

An appreciation for the magnitude of geologic time is important in the study of our planet because many processes are so gradual that vast spans of time are needed before significant changes occur.

How long is 4.6 billion years? If you were to begin counting at the rate of one number per second and continued 24 hours a day, seven days a week and never stopped, it would take about two lifetimes (150 years) to reach 4.6 billion!

Over the past 200 years or so, Earth scientists have developed the **geologic time scale** of Earth history. It subdivides the 4.6-billion-year history of Earth into many different units and provides a meaningful time frame within which the events of the geologic past are arranged (**FIGURE 1.11**). The principles used to develop the geologic time scale are examined at some length in Chapter 8.

RESOURCES AND ENVIRONMENTAL ISSUES

Environment refers to everything that surrounds and influences an organism. Some of these things are biological and social, but others are nonliving. The factors in this latter category are collectively called our physical environment. The **physical environment** encompasses water, air, soil, and rock, as well as conditions such as temperature, humidity, and sunlight. The phenomena and processes studied by the Earth sciences are basic to an understanding of the physical environment. In this sense, most of Earth science may be characterized as environmental science.

However, when the term *environmental* is applied to Earth science today, it usually means relationships between

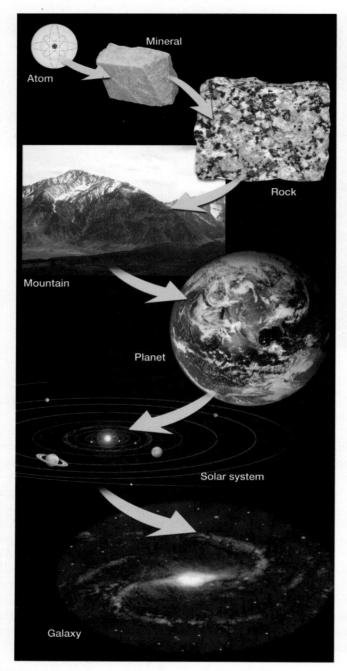

FIGURE 1.10   Earth science involves investigations of phenomena that range in size from atoms to galaxies and beyond.

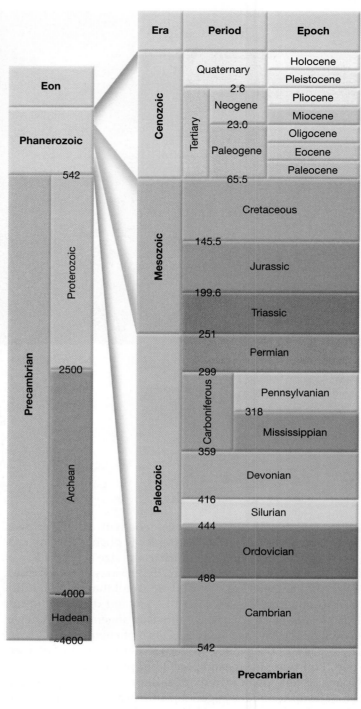

FIGURE 1.11   The geologic time scale divides the vast 4.6-billion-year history of Earth into eons, eras, periods, and epochs. We presently live in the Holocene epoch of the Quaternary period. This period is part of the Cenozoic era, which is the latest era of the Phanerozoic eon. There is much more about geologic time in Chapter 8.

people and the physical environment. Application of the Earth sciences is necessary to understand and solve problems that arise from these interactions.

We can dramatically influence natural processes. For example, river flooding is natural, but the magnitude and frequency of flooding can be changed significantly by human activities such as clearing forests, building cities, and constructing dams. Unfortunately, natural systems do not always adjust to artificial changes in ways we can anticipate. Thus, an alteration to the environment that was intended to benefit society may have the opposite effect.

Resources

Resources are an important focus of the Earth sciences that is of great value to people. Resources include water and soil, a great variety of metallic and nonmetallic minerals, and energy. Together, they form the very foundation of modern civilization (**FIGURE 1.12**). The Earth sciences deal not only with

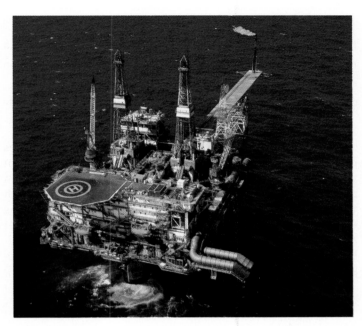

FIGURE 1.12 Petroleum accounts for nearly 40 percent of U.S. energy use. This modern offshore drilling operation is in the North Sea. (Photo by Peter Bowater/ Photo Researchers, Inc.)

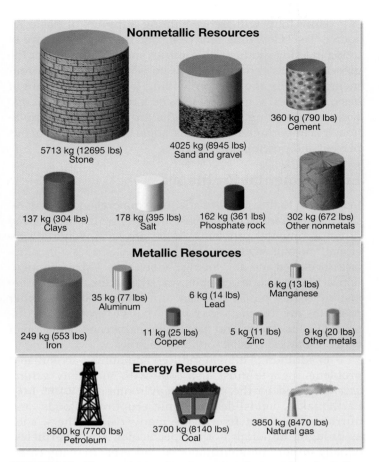

FIGURE 1.13 The annual per capita consumption of nonmetallic and metallic mineral resources for the United States is about 11,000 kilograms (12 tons)! About 97 percent of the materials are nonmetallic. The per capita use of coal, oil, and natural gas exceeds 11,000 kilograms. (After U.S. Geological Survey)

the formation and occurrence of these vital resources but also with maintaining supplies and the environmental impact of their extraction and use.

Few people who live in highly industrialized nations realize the quantity of resources needed to maintain their present standard of living. **FIGURE 1.13** shows the annual per capita consumption of several important metallic and nonmetallic mineral resources for the United States. This is each person's prorated share of the materials required by industry to provide the vast array of products modern society demands. Figures for other highly industrialized countries are comparable.

Resources are commonly divided into two broad categories. Some are classified as **renewable,** which means that they can be replenished over relatively short time spans. Common examples are plants and animals for food, natural fibers for clothing, and forest products for lumber and paper. Energy from flowing water, wind, and the Sun is also considered renewable (**FIGURE 1.14**).

By contrast, many other basic resources are classified as **nonrenewable.** Important metals such as iron, aluminum, and copper fall into this category, as do our most important fuels: oil, natural gas, and coal. Although these and other resources continue to form, the processes that create them are so slow that significant deposits take millions of years to accumulate. In essence, Earth contains *fixed* quantities of these substances. When the present supplies are mined or pumped from the ground, there will be no more. Although some nonrenewable resources, such as aluminum, can be used over and over again, others, such as oil, cannot be recycled.

FIGURE 1.14 Wind energy is considered to be a *renewable* resource. The use of wind turbines for generating electricity is growing rapidly. These wind turbines are operating near Palm Springs, California. (Photo by John Mead/Science Photo Library/Photo Researchers, Inc.)

How long will the remaining supplies of basic resources last? How long can we sustain the rising standard of living in today's industrial countries and still provide for the growing needs of developing regions? How much environmental deterioration are we willing to accept in pursuit of basic resources? Can alternatives be found? If we are to cope with an increasing demand and a growing world population, it is important that we have some understanding of our present and potential resources.

Environmental Problems

In addition to the quest for adequate mineral and energy resources, the Earth sciences must also deal with a broad array of environmental problems. Some are local, some are regional, and still others are global in extent. Serious difficulties face developed and developing nations alike. Urban air pollution, acid rain, ozone depletion, and global climate change are just a few that pose significant threats (**FIGURE 1.15**). Other problems involve the loss of fertile soils to erosion, the disposal of toxic wastes, and the contamination and depletion of water resources. The list continues to grow.

In addition to human-induced and human-accentuated problems, people must also cope with the many *natural hazards* posed by the physical environment (**FIGURE 1.16**). Earthquakes, landslides, volcanic eruptions, floods, and hurricanes are just five of the many risks. Others, such as drought, although not as spectacular, are nevertheless equally important environmental concerns. In many cases, the threat of natural hazards is aggravated by increases in population as more people crowd into places where an impending danger exists or attempt to cultivate marginal lands that should not be farmed.

As world population continues to grow, pressures on the environment will increase as well. Therefore, an understanding of Earth is essential not only for the location and recovery of basic resources, but also for dealing with the human impact on the environment and minimizing the effects of natural hazards. Knowledge about our planet and how it works is necessary to our survival and well-being. Earth is the only suitable habitat we have, and its resources are limited.

THE NATURE OF SCIENTIFIC INQUIRY

As members of a modern society, we are constantly reminded of the benefits derived from science. But what exactly is the nature of scientific inquiry? Developing an understanding of how science is done and how scientists work is an important theme in this book. You will explore the difficulties in gathering data and some of the ingenious methods that have been developed to overcome these difficulties. You will also see examples of how hypotheses are formulated and tested, as well as learn about the evolution and development of some major scientific theories.

FIGURE 1.15 A severe air pollution episode at Beijing, China, on March 18, 2008. Fuel combustion by motor vehicles and power plants provides a high proportion of the pollutants. Meteorological factors determine whether pollutants remain "trapped" in the city or are dispersed. (Photo by Ng Han Guan/Associated Press)

A.

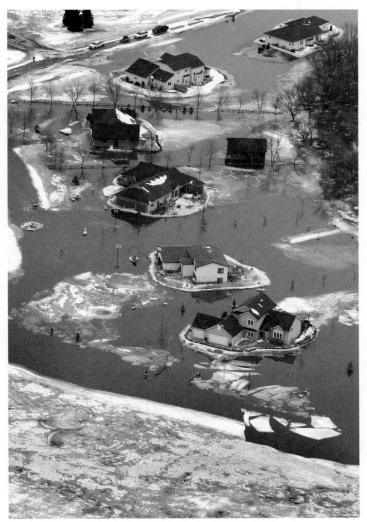

B.

FIGURE I.16 Natural hazards are a part of living on Earth. **A.** Aerial view of earthquake destruction at Muzaffarabad, Pakistan, January 31, 2006. (Photo by Danny Kemp/AFP/Getty Images. Inc.) **B.** Record-setting floods along the Red River of the North in late March 2009 in the Fargo, North Dakota/Moorhead, Minnesota area. (Photo by Scott Olson/Getty Images)

All science is based on the assumption that the *natural world behaves in a consistent and predictable manner.* The overall goal of science is to discover the underlying patterns in the natural world and then to use this knowledge to predict what will or will not happen, given certain facts or circumstances.

The development of new scientific knowledge involves some basic logical processes that are universally accepted. To determine what is occurring in the natural world, scientists collect *facts* through observation and measurement (**FIGURE I.17**). Because some error is inevitable, the accuracy of a particular measurement or observation is always open to question. Nevertheless, these data are essential to science and serve as the springboard for the development of scientific theories.

Hypothesis

Once facts have been gathered and principles have been formulated to describe a natural phenomenon, investigators try to explain how or why things happen in the manner observed. They can do this by constructing a preliminary, untested explanation, which we call a scientific **hypothesis.** It is best if an investigator can formulate more than one hypothesis to explain a given set of observations. If an individual scientist is unable to devise multiple hypotheses, others in the scientific community will almost always develop alternative explanations. A spirited debate frequently occurs. As a result, extensive research is conducted by proponents of opposing hypotheses, and the results are made available to the wider scientific community in scientific journals.

FIGURE I.17 Laboratory work is an important part of what many Earth scientists do. These scientists are working with a sediment core recovered from the ocean floor. Such cores often contain useful data about the geologic past and Earth's climate history. (Photo by Science Source/Photo Researchers, Inc.)

Before a hypothesis can become an accepted part of scientific knowledge, it must pass objective testing and analysis. (If a hypothesis cannot be tested, it is not scientifically useful, no matter how interesting it might seem.) The verification process requires that *predictions* be made based on the hypothesis being considered and that the predictions be tested by comparing them against objective observations of nature. Put another way, hypotheses must fit observations other than those used to formulate them in the first place. Those hypotheses that fail rigorous testing are ultimately discarded. The history of science is littered with discarded hypotheses. One of the best known is the Earth-centered model of the universe—a proposal that was supported by the apparent daily motion of the Sun, Moon, and stars around Earth. As the mathematician Jacob Bronowski so ably stated, "Science is a great many things, but in the end they all return to this: Science is the acceptance of what works and the rejection of what does not."

Theory

When a hypothesis has survived extensive scrutiny, and when competing hypotheses have been eliminated, a hypothesis may be elevated to the status of a scientific **theory**. In everyday language, we may say, "That's only a theory." But a scientific theory is a well-tested and widely accepted view that scientists agree best explains certain observable facts.

Some theories that are extensively documented and extremely well supported are comprehensive in scope. One well-known example is the theory of evolution, which explains the development of life on Earth. Another example is the theory of plate tectonics, which provides the framework for understanding the origin of mountains, earthquakes, and volcanic activity. In addition, plate tectonics explains the evolution of the continents and the ocean basins through time—a topic we will consider later in this book.

Scientific Methods

The process just described, in which scientists gather facts through observations and formulate scientific hypotheses that may eventually become theories, is termed the *scientific method*. Contrary to popular belief, the scientific method is not a standard recipe that scientists apply in a routine manner to unravel the secrets of our natural world. Rather, it is an endeavor that involves creativity and insight. Rutherford and Ahlgren put it this way: "Inventing hypotheses or theories to imagine how the world works and then figuring out how they can be put to the test of reality is as creative as writing poetry, composing music, or designing skyscrapers."*

*F. James Rutherford and Andrew Ahlgren, *Science for All Americans* (New York: Oxford University Press, 1990), p. 7.

DID YOU KNOW?

A scientific *law* is a basic principle that describes a particular behavior of nature that is generally narrow in scope and can be stated briefly—often as a simple mathematical equation.

There is no fixed path that scientists always follow that leads unerringly to scientific knowledge. Nevertheless, many scientific investigations involve the following steps: (1) the collection of scientific facts through observation and measurement (**FIGURE 1.18**); (2) the formulation of questions that relate to the facts and the development of one or more working hypotheses that may answer these questions; (3) development of observations and experiments to test each hypothesis; and (4) the acceptance, modification, or rejection of the hypothesis based on extensive testing.

Other scientific discoveries represent purely theoretical ideas, which stand up to extensive examination. Some researchers use high-speed computers to simulate what is

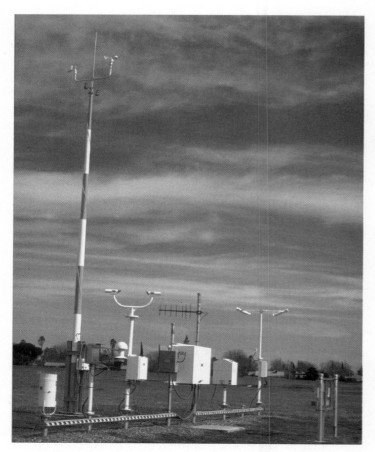

FIGURE 1.18 Gathering data is a basic part of the scientific method. This Automated Surface Observing System (ASOS) installation is one of nearly 900 in use for data gathering as part of the U.S. primary surface observing network. (Photo by Bobbe Christopherson)

happening in the "real" world. These models are useful when dealing with natural processes that occur on very long time scales or take place in extreme or inaccessible locations. Still other scientific advancements have been made when a totally unexpected happening occurred during an experiment. These serendipitous discoveries are more than pure luck, for as Louis Pasteur said, "In the field of observation, chance favors only the prepared mind."

Scientific knowledge is acquired through several avenues, so it might be best to describe the nature of scientific inquiry as the *methods* of science rather than the scientific method. In addition, it should always be remembered that even the most compelling scientific theories are still simplified explanations of the natural world.

STUDYING EARTH SCIENCE

In this book, you will discover the results of centuries of scientific work. You will see the end product of millions of observations, thousands of hypotheses, and hundreds of theories. We have distilled all of this to give you a "briefing" in Earth science.

But realize that our knowledge of Earth is changing daily, as thousands of scientists worldwide make satellite observations, analyze drill cores from the seafloor, study earthquake waves, develop computer models to predict climate, examine the genetic codes of organisms, and discover new facts about our planet's long history. This new knowledge often updates hypotheses and theories. Expect to see many new discoveries and changes in scientific thinking in your lifetime.

THE CHAPTER IN REVIEW

• Earth science is the name for all the sciences that collectively seek to understand Earth and its neighbors in space. It includes geology, oceanography, meteorology, and astronomy. Geology is traditionally divided into two broad areas—physical and historical.

• Earth's physical environment is traditionally divided into three major parts: the solid Earth, the geosphere; the water portion of our planet, the hydrosphere; and Earth's gaseous envelope, the atmosphere. In addition, the biosphere, the totality of life on Earth, interacts with each of the three physical realms and is an equally integral part of Earth.

• Although each of Earth's four spheres can be studied separately, they are all related in a complex and continuously interacting whole that we call the Earth system. Earth system science uses an interdisciplinary approach to integrate the knowledge of several academic fields in the study of our planet and its global environmental problems.

• The two sources of energy that power the Earth system are (1) the Sun, which drives the external processes that occur in the atmosphere, hydrosphere, and at Earth's surface, and (2) heat from the Earth's interior that powers the internal processes that produce volcanoes, earthquakes, and mountains.

• Environment refers to everything that surrounds and influences an organism. These influences can be biological, social, or physical. When applied to Earth science today, the term

environmental is usually reserved for those aspects that focus on the relationships between people and the natural environment.

• Resources are an important environmental concern. The two broad categories of resources are (1) renewable, which means that they can be replenished over relatively short time spans, and (2) nonrenewable. As population grows, the demand for resources expands as well.

• Environmental problems can be local, regional, or global. Human-induced problems include urban air pollution, acid rain, ozone depletion, and global climate change. Natural hazards include earthquakes, landslides, floods, and hurricanes. As world population grows, pressures on the environment also increase.

• All science is based on the assumption that the natural world behaves in a consistent and predictable manner. The process by which scientists gather facts through observation and careful measurement and formulate scientific hypotheses and theories is called the scientific method. To determine what is occurring in the natural world, scientists often (1) collect facts, (2) pose questions and develop one or more working hypotheses that address these questions, (3) construct experiments to validate each hypothesis, and (4) accept, modify, or reject the hypothesis on the basis of extensive testing. Other discoveries represent purely theoretical ideas that have stood up to extensive examination. Still other scientific advancements have been made when a totally unexpected happening occurred during an experiment.

KEY TERMS

asthenosphere (p. 8)

atmosphere (p. 7)

astronomy (p. 5)

biosphere (p. 8)

core (p. 7)

crust (p. 7)

Earth science (p. 4)

Earth system (p. 9)

geologic time scale (p. 11)

geology (p. 4)

geosphere (p. 7)

hydrosphere (p. 6)

hypothesis (p. 15)

lithosphere (p. 7)

mantle (p. 7)

meteorology (p. 5)

nonrenewable
  resource (p. 13)

oceanography (p. 5)

physical environment
  (p. 11)

renewable resource (p. 13)

system (p. 10)

theory (p. 16)

QUESTIONS FOR REVIEW

1. Name the specific Earth science described by each of the following statements:

   a. This science deals with the dynamics of the oceans.

   b. This word literally means "the study of Earth."

   c. An understanding of the atmosphere is the primary focus of this science.

   d. This science helps us understand Earth's place in the universe.

2. List and briefly define the four "spheres" that constitute our environment.

3. Name the three principal divisions of the solid Earth based on compositional differences. Which one is thinnest?

4. The oceans cover nearly _____ percent of Earth's surface and contain about _____ percent of the planet's total water supply.

5. What are the two sources of energy for the Earth system?

6. Contrast renewable and nonrenewable resources. Give one or more examples of each.

COMPANION WEBSITE

The *Foundations of Earth Science* Website uses the resources and flexibility of the Internet to aid in your study of the topics in this chapter. Written and developed by the authors and other Earth science instructors, this site will help improve your understanding of Earth science. Visit **www.mygeoscienceplace.com** in order to:

• **Review** key chapter concepts.

• **Read** with links to the ebook and to chapter-specific web resources.

• **Visualize** and comprehend challenging topics using learning activities in *GEODe: Earth Science*.

• **Test** yourself with online quizzes.

MINERALS
BUILDING BLOCKS OF ROCKS

FOCUS ON LEARNING

To assist you in learning the important concepts in this chapter, you will find it helpful to focus on the following questions:

1. What are minerals, and how are they different from rocks?

2. What are the smallest particles of matter? How do atoms bond?

3. How do isotopes of the same element vary, and why are some isotopes radioactive?

4. What are some of the physical and chemical properties of minerals? How can these properties be used to distinguish one mineral from another?

5. What are the eight elements that make up most of Earth's continental crust?

6. What is the most abundant mineral group? What do all minerals within this group have in common?

7. When is the term *ore* used with reference to a mineral? What are the common ores of iron and lead?

Crystal shape or habit is a basic mineral property. (Photo by Jeffry Scovil)

Earth's crust and oceans are the source of a wide variety of useful and essential minerals. Most people are familiar with the common uses of many basic metals, including aluminum in beverage cans, copper in electrical wiring, and gold and silver in jewelry. But some people are not aware that pencil lead contains the greasy-feeling mineral graphite and that bath powders and many cosmetics contain the mineral talc. Moreover, many do not know that drill bits impregnated with diamonds are employed by dentists to drill through tooth enamel, or that the common mineral quartz is the source of silicon for computer chips. In fact, practically every manufactured product contains materials obtained from minerals. As the mineral requirements of modern society increase, the task of locating new sources of useful minerals becomes more challenging.

In addition to the economic uses of rocks and minerals, all of the processes studied by geologists are in some way dependent on the properties of these basic Earth materials. Events such as volcanic eruptions, mountain building, weathering and erosion, and even earthquakes involve rocks and minerals. Consequently, a basic knowledge of rocks and minerals is essential to the understanding of all geologic phenomena.

MINERALS: BUILDING BLOCKS OF ROCKS

Earth Materials
▼ Minerals

We begin our discussion of Earth materials with an overview of **mineralogy** (*mineral* = mineral, *ology* = the study of), because minerals are the building blocks of rocks. In addition, minerals have been employed by humans for both useful and decorative purposes for thousands of years (**FIGURE 1.1**). The first minerals mined were flint and chert, which people fashioned into weapons and cutting tools. As early as 3700 B.C., Egyptians began mining gold, silver, and copper; and by 2200 B.C. humans discovered how to combine copper with tin to make bronze, a strong, hard alloy. Later, humans developed a process to extract iron from minerals such as hematite—a discovery that marked the decline of the Bronze Age. By about 800 B.C., iron-working technology had advanced to the point that weapons and many everyday objects were made of iron rather than copper, bronze, or wood. During the Middle Ages, mining of a variety of minerals was common throughout Europe and the impetus for the formal study of minerals was in place.

The term *mineral* is used in several different ways. For example, those concerned with health and fitness extol the benefits of vitamins and minerals. The mining industry typically uses the word when referring to anything taken out of the ground, such as coal, iron ore, or sand and gravel. The guessing game known as *Twenty Questions* usually begins with the question, *Is it animal, vegetable, or mineral?* What criteria do geologists use to determine whether something is a mineral?

Geologists define **minerals** as *any naturally occurring inorganic solid that possesses an orderly crystalline structure and a well-defined chemical composition.* Thus, those Earth materials that are classified as minerals exhibit the following characteristics:

1. **Naturally occurring.** Minerals form by natural, geologic processes. Synthetic materials, meaning those produced in a laboratory or by human intervention, are not considered minerals.

2. **Solid substance.** Minerals are solids within the temperature ranges normally experienced at Earth's surface. For example, ice (frozen water) is considered a mineral, whereas liquid water and water vapor are not.

3. **Orderly crystalline structure.** Minerals are crystalline substances, which means their atoms are arranged in an orderly, repetitive manner (**FIGURE 1.2**). This orderly packing of atoms is reflected in the regularly shaped objects we call crystals. Some naturally occurring solids, such as volcanic glass (obsidian), lack a repetitive atomic structure and are not considered minerals.

4. **Well-defined chemical composition.** Most minerals are chemical compounds having compositions expressed by chemical formulas. In nature, however, it is not uncommon for some atoms within a crystal structure to be replaced by others of similar size without changing the internal structure or properties

FIGURE 1.1 Collection of well-developed quartz crystals found near Hot Springs, Arkansas. (Photo by Jeff Scovil)

A. Sodium and chlorine ions.

B. Basic building block of the mineral halite.

C. Collection of basic building blocks (crystal).

D. Intergrown crystals of the mineral halite.

FIGURE 1.2 Illustration of the orderly arrangement of sodium and chloride atoms (ions) in the mineral halite. The arrangement of atoms into basic building blocks having a cubic shape results in regularly shaped cubic crystals. (Photo by Dennis Tasa)

crystalline solid like salt but which comes from sugarcane or sugar beets, is a common example of such an organic compound. However, many marine animals secrete inorganic compounds, such as calcium carbonate (calcite), in the form of shells and coral reefs. If these materials are buried and become part of the rock record, they are considered minerals by geologists.

In contrast to minerals, rocks are more loosely defined. Simply, a **rock** is any solid mass of mineral, or mineral-like, matter that occurs naturally as part of our planet. Some rocks are composed almost entirely of one mineral. A common example is the sedimentary rock *limestone,* which consists of impure masses of the mineral calcite. However, most rocks, like the common rock granite shown in **FIGURE 1.3**, occur as aggregates of several different minerals. The term *aggregate* implies that the minerals are joined in such a way that their individual properties are retained. Note that the mineral constituents of granite can be easily identified (Figure 1.3).

Some rocks are composed of nonmineral matter. These include the volcanic rocks *obsidian* and *pumice,* which are noncrystalline glassy substances, and *coal,* which consists of solid organic debris.

Although this chapter deals primarily with the nature of minerals, keep in mind that most rocks are simply aggregates of minerals. Because the properties of rocks are determined largely by the chemical composition and crystalline structure of the minerals contained within

of that mineral. Therefore, the chemical compositions of minerals may vary, but they do so *within specific, well-defined limits.*

5. **Generally inorganic.** Inorganic crystalline solids, such as ordinary table salt (halite), that are found naturally in the ground are considered minerals. Organic compounds, on the other hand, are generally not. Sugar, a

FIGURE 1.3 Most rocks are aggregates of one or more minerals. Shown here is a hand sample of the igneous rock granite and three of its major constituent minerals. (Photos courtesy E. J. Tarbuck)

Granite (Rock)

Quartz (Mineral)

Hornblende (Mineral)

Feldspar (Mineral)

them, we will first consider these Earth materials. Then, in Chapter 2, we will take a closer look at Earth's major rock groups.

ATOMS: BUILDING BLOCKS OF MINERALS

When minerals are carefully examined, even under optical microscopes, the innumerable tiny particles of their internal structures are not discernable. Nevertheless, all matter, including minerals, is composed of minute building blocks called **atoms**—the smallest particles that cannot be chemically split. Atoms, in turn contain even smaller particles—*protons* and *neutrons* located in a central **nucleus** that is surrounded by *electrons* (**FIGURE 1.4**).

Properties of Protons, Neutrons, and Electrons

Protons and **neutrons** are very dense particles with almost identical masses. By contrast, **electrons** have a negligible mass, about 1/2000th that of a proton. For comparison, if a proton or a neutron had the mass of a baseball, an electron would have the mass of a single grain of rice.

Both protons and electrons share a fundamental property called *electrical charge*. Protons have an electrical charge of +1 and electrons have a charge of −1. Neutrons, as the name suggests, have no charge. The charge of protons and electrons are equal in magnitude, but opposite in polarity, so when these two particles are paired, the charges cancel each other. Since matter typically contains equal numbers of positively charged protons and negatively charged electrons, most substances are electrically neutral.

In illustrations, electrons are sometimes shown orbiting the nucleus in a manner that resembles the planets of our solar system orbiting the Sun (**FIGURE 1.4A**). However, electrons do not actually behave this way. A more realistic depiction shows electrons as a cloud of negative charges surrounding the nucleus (**FIGURE 1.4B**). Studies of the arrangements of electrons show that they move about the nucleus in regions called *principal shells*, each with an associated energy level. In addition, each shell can hold a specific number of electrons, with the outermost shell

FIGURE 1.4   Two models of the atom. **A.** This simplified view of an atom has a central nucleus, consisting of protons and neutrons, encircled by high-speed electrons. **B.** Another model of an atom showing spherically shaped electron clouds (principal shells). Note that these models are not drawn to scale. Electrons are minuscule in size compared to protons and neutrons, and the relative space between the nucleus and electron shells is much greater than illustrated.

containing **valence electrons** that interact with other atoms to form chemical bonds.

Most of the atoms in the universe (except hydrogen and helium) were created inside massive stars by nuclear fusion and released into interstellar space during hot, fiery supernova explosions. As this ejected material cooled, the newly formed nuclei attracted electrons to complete their atomic structure. At the temperatures found at Earth's surface, all free atoms (not bonded to other atoms) have a full complement of electrons—one for each proton in the nucleus.

Elements: Defined by Their Number of Protons

The simplest atoms have only one proton in their nuclei whereas others have more than 100. The number of protons in the nucleus of an atom, called the **atomic number**, determines

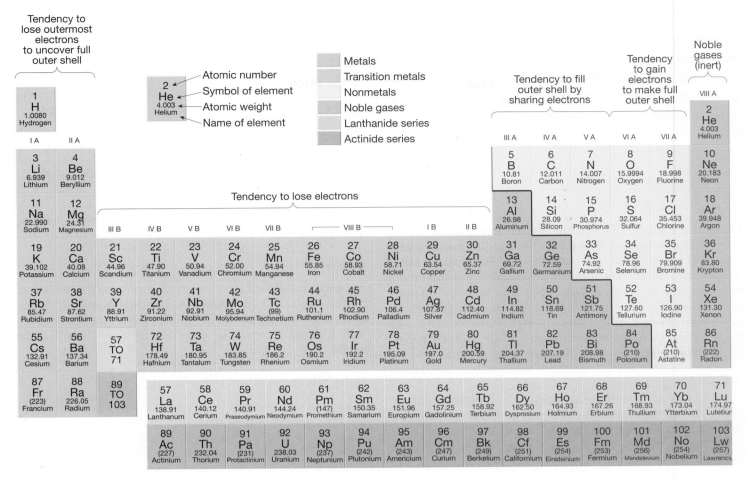

FIGURE 1.5   Periodic table of the elements.

its chemical nature. All atoms with the same number of protons have the same chemical and physical properties. Together, a group of the same kind of atoms is called an **element**. There are about 90 naturally occurring elements and 23 that have been synthesized.

You are probably familiar with the names of many elements including copper, iron, oxygen, and carbon. Since the number of protons identifies an element, all carbon atoms have 6 protons and 6 electrons. Likewise, any atom that contains 8 protons is an oxygen atom.

Elements are organized so that those with similar properties line up in columns. This arrangement, called the **periodic table**, is shown in **FIGURE 1.5**. Each element has been assigned a one- or two-letter symbol. The atomic numbers and masses are also included for each element.

Atoms of the naturally occurring elements are the basic building blocks of Earth's minerals. A few minerals, such as native copper, diamonds, and gold, are made entirely of atoms of only one element (**FIGURE 1.6**). However, most elements tend to join with atoms of other elements to form **chemical compounds**. Most minerals are chemical compounds composed of atoms of two or more elements.

FIGURE 1.6   Gold mixed with quartz. Gold, silver, copper, and diamonds are naturally occurring minerals composed entirely of atoms of a single element.

DID YOU KNOW?

Although wood pulp is the main ingredient for making newsprint, many higher grades of paper contain large quantities of clay minerals. In fact, each page of this textbook consists of about 25 percent clay (the mineral kaolinite). If rolled into a ball, this much clay would be roughly the size of a tennis ball.

WHY ATOMS BOND

Except for a group of elements known as the noble gases, atoms bond to one another under the conditions (temperatures and pressures) that occur on Earth.* Some atoms bond to form *ionic compounds*, some form *molecules*, and still others form *metallic substances*. Why does this happen? Experiments show that electrical forces hold atoms together and bond them to each other. These electrical attractions lower the total energy of the bonded atoms, which, in turn, generally makes them more stable. Consequently, atoms that are bonded in compounds tend to be more stable than atoms that are free (not bonded).

As was noted earlier, valence (outer shell) electrons are generally involved in chemical bonding. **FIGURE 1.7** shows a shorthand way of representing the number of valence electrons. Notice that the elements in Group I have one valence electron, those in Group II have two valence electrons, and so on up to eight valence electrons in Group VIII.

Octet Rule

The noble gases (except helium) have very stable electron arrangements with eight valence electrons and, therefore, tend to lack chemical reactivity. Many other atoms gain, lose, or share electrons during chemical reactions to end up with electron arrangements of the noble gases. This observation led to a chemical guideline known as the **octet rule:** *Atoms tend to gain, lose, or share electrons until they are surrounded by eight valence electrons.* Although there are exceptions to the octet rule, it is a useful *rule of thumb* for understanding chemical bonding.

When an atom's outer shell does not contain eight electrons, it is likely to chemically bond to other atoms to fill its shell. A **chemical bond** is the transfer or sharing of electrons that allows each atom to attain a full valence shell of electrons. Some atoms do this by transferring all of their valence electrons to other atoms so that an inner shell becomes the full valence shell.

When the valence electrons are transferred between the elements to form ions, the bond is an *ionic bond*. When the electrons are shared between the atoms, the bond is a

*Examples of noble gases are helium, neon, and argon. In each case, their outer shell of valence electrons is considered to be full and therefore they have little tendency to participate in chemical reactions.

FIGURE 1.7 Dot diagrams for some representative elements. Each dot represents a valence electron found in the outermost principal shell.

covalent bond. When the valence electrons are shared among all the atoms in a substance, the bonding is *metallic*. In any case, the bonding atoms get stable electron configurations, which usually consist of eight electrons in their outmost shells.

Ionic Bonds: Electrons Transferred

Perhaps the easiest type of bond to visualize is the *ionic bond* in which one atom gives up one or more of its valence electrons to another atom to form **ions**—*positively and negatively charged atoms.* The atom that loses electrons becomes a positive ion, and the atom that gains electrons becomes a negative ion. Oppositely charged ions are strongly attracted to one another and join to form ionic compounds.

Consider the ionic bonding that occurs between sodium (Na) and chlorine (Cl) to produce sodium chloride, the mineral halite—common table salt. Notice in **FIGURE 1.8A** that sodium gives up its single valence electron to chlorine. As a result, sodium now has a stable configuration with eight electrons in its outermost shell. By acquiring the electron the sodium loses, chlorine—which has seven valence electrons—gains the eighth electron needed to complete its outermost shell. Thus, through the transfer of a single electron, both the sodium and chlorine atoms have acquired a stable electron configuration.

After electron transfer takes place, the atoms are no longer electrically neutral. By giving up one electron, a neutral sodium atom becomes positively charged (with 11 protons and 10 electrons). Similarly, by acquiring one electron, a neutral chlorine atom becomes negatively charged (with 17 protons and 18 electrons). We know that ions with like charges repel, and those with unlike charges attract. Thus, an **ionic bond** is the attraction of oppositely charged ions to one another, producing an electrically neutral compound.

FIGURE 1.8B illustrates the arrangement of sodium and chlorine ions in ordinary table salt. Notice that salt consists of alternating sodium and chlorine ions, positioned in such a manner that each positive ion is attracted to and sur-

FIGURE 1.8 Chemical bonding of sodium chloride (table salt). **A.** Through the transfer of one electron in the outer shell of a sodium atom to the outer shell of a chlorine atom, the sodium becomes a positive ion and chlorine a negative ion. **B.** Diagram illustrating the arrangement of sodium and chlorine ions in table salt.

rounded on all sides by negative ions, and vice versa. This arrangement maximizes the attraction between ions with opposite charges while minimizing the repulsion between ions with identical charges. Thus, ionic compounds consist of an orderly arrangement of oppositely charged ions assembled in a definite ratio that provides overall electrical neutrality.

The properties of a chemical compound are dramatically different from the properties of the elements comprising it. For example, sodium is a soft silvery metal that is extremely reactive and poisonous. If you were to consume even a small amount of elemental sodium, you would need immediate medical attention. Chlorine, a green poisonous gas, is so toxic it was used as a chemical weapon during World War I. Together, however, these elements produce sodium chloride, a harmless flavor enhancer that we call table salt. When elements combine to form compounds, their properties change significantly.

Covalent Bonds: Electrons Shared

Sometimes the forces that hold atoms together cannot be understood on the basis of the attraction of oppositely charged ions. One example is the hydrogen molecule (H_2), in which the two hydrogen atoms are held together tightly and no ions are present. The strong attractive force that holds two hydrogen atoms together results from a **covalent bond**, *a chemical bond formed by the sharing of a pair of electrons between atoms.*

Imagine two hydrogen atoms (each with one proton and one electron) approaching one another so that their orbitals overlap (**FIGURE 1.9**). Once they meet, the electron configuration will change so that both electrons will mainly occupy the space between the atoms. In other words, the two electrons are shared by both hydrogen atoms and attracted simultaneously by the positive charge of the proton in the nucleus of each atom (Figure 1.9). The attraction between the electrons and both nuclei holds these atoms together. Although ions do not exist in hydrogen molecules, the force that holds these atoms together arises from the attraction of oppositely charged particles—protons in the nuclei and electrons shared by the atoms.

Metallic Bonds: Electrons Free to Move

In **metallic bonds**, the valence electrons are free to move from one atom to another so that all atoms share the available valence electrons. This type of bonding is found in metals such as copper, gold, aluminum, and silver, and in alloys such as brass and bronze. Metallic bonding accounts for the high electrical conductivity of metals, the ease with which metals are shaped, and numerous other special properties.

$$H \cdot + H \cdot \longrightarrow H:H$$

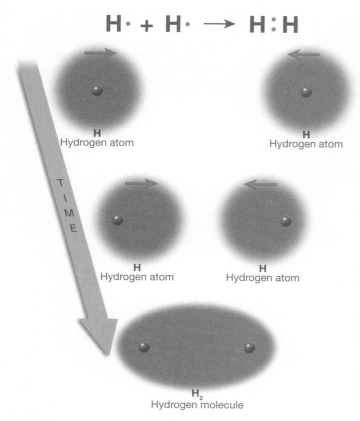

FIGURE 1.9 Formation of a covalent bond between two hydrogen atoms (H) to form a hydrogen molecule (H_2). When hydrogen atoms bond, the electrons are shared by both hydrogen atoms and attracted simultaneously by the positive charge of the protons in the nucleus of each atom. The attraction between electrons and both nuclei holds (bonds) these atoms together.

DID YOU KNOW?

The purity of gold is expressed by the number of *karats*. Twenty-four karats is pure gold. Gold less than 24 karats is an alloy (mixture) of gold and another metal, usually copper or silver. For example, 14-karat gold contains 14 parts gold (by weight) mixed with 10 parts of other metals.

ISOTOPES AND RADIOACTIVE DECAY

The **mass number** of an atom is simply the total number of its protons and neutrons. All atoms of a particular element have the same number of protons, but may have varying numbers of neutrons. Atoms with the same number of protons, but different numbers of neutrons are **isotopes** of that element. Isotopes of the same element are labeled by placing the mass number after the element's name or symbol. For example, carbon has three well-known isotopes. One has a mass number of 12 (carbon-12), another has a mass number of 13 (carbon-13), and the third, carbon-14, has a mass number of 14. Since all atoms of the same element have the same number of protons, and carbon has six, carbon-12 also has

six neutrons to give it a mass number of 12. Carbon-14, on the other hand, has six protons plus eight neutrons to give it a mass number of 14.

In chemical behavior, all isotopes of the same element are nearly identical. To distinguish among them is like trying to differentiate identical twins, with one weighing slightly more than the other. Because isotopes of an element behave the same chemically, different isotopes often become parts of the same mineral. For example, when the mineral calcite forms from calcium, carbon, and oxygen, some of its carbon atoms are carbon-12 and some are carbon-14.

The nuclei of most atoms are stable. However, many elements do have isotopes in which the nuclei are unstable—carbon-14 is one example of an unstable isotope. In this context, *unstable* means that the nuclei change through a random process called **radioactive decay**. During radioactive decay, unstable isotopes radiate energy and emit particles. The rates at which unstable isotopes decay are measurable. Therefore, certain radioactive atoms are used to determine the ages of fossils, rocks, and minerals. A discussion of radioactive decay and its applications in dating past geologic events appears in Chapter 8.

DID YOU KNOW?

One of the world's heaviest cut and polished gemstones is z 22,892.5-carat golden-yellow topaz. Currently housed in the Smithsonian Institution, this roughly 10-pound gem is about the size of an automobile headlight and could hardly be used as a piece of jewelry, except perhaps by an elephant.

PHYSICAL PROPERTIES OF MINERALS

Earth Materials
▼ Minerals

Each mineral has a definite crystalline structure and chemical composition that give it a unique set of physical and chemical properties shared by all samples of that mineral. For example, all specimens of halite have the same hardness, the same density, and break in a similar manner. Because a mineral's internal structure and chemical composition are difficult to determine without the aid of sophisticated tests and equipment, the more easily recognized physical properties are frequently used in identification.

Optical Properties

Of the many optical properties of minerals—luster, the ability to transmit light, color, and streak—are most frequently used for mineral identification.

FIGURE 1.10 The freshly broken sample of galena (right) displays a metallic luster, whereas the sample on the left is tarnished and has a submetallic luster. (Photo courtesy of E. J. Tarbuck)

Luster

The appearance or quality of light reflected from the surface of a mineral is known as **luster**. Minerals that have the appearance of metals, regardless of color, are said to have a *metallic luster* (**FIGURE 1.10**). Some metallic minerals, such as native copper and galena, develop a dull coating or tarnish when exposed to the atmosphere. Because they are not as shiny as samples with freshly broken surfaces, these samples are often said to exhibit a *submetallic luster.*

Most minerals have a *nonmetallic luster* and are described using various adjectives such as *vitreous* or *glassy*. Other nonmetallic minerals are described as having a *dull* or *earthy luster* (a dull appearance like soil), or a *pearly luster* (such as a pearl, or the inside of a clamshell). Still others exhibit a *silky luster* (like satin cloth), or a *greasy luster* (as though coated in oil).

The Ability to Transmit Light

Another optical property used in the identification of minerals is the ability to transmit light. When no light is transmitted, the mineral is described as *opaque*; when light, but not an image, is transmitted through a mineral it is said to be *translucent*. When both light and an image are visible through the sample, the mineral is described as *transparent*.

Color

Although **color** is generally the most conspicuous characteristic of any mineral, it is considered a diagnostic property of only a few minerals. Slight impurities in the common mineral quartz, for example, give it a variety of tints including pink, purple, yellow, white, gray, and even black (**FIGURE 1.11**). Other minerals, such as tourmaline, also exhibit a variety of hues, with multiple colors sometimes occurring in the same sample. Thus, the use of color as a means of identification is often ambiguous or even misleading.

Streak

The color of the powdered mineral, called **streak,** is often useful in identification. A mineral's streak is obtained by rubbing it across a *streak plate* (a piece of unglazed porcelain) and observing the color of the mark it leaves (**FIGURE 1.12**).

FIGURE 1.11 Quartz. Some minerals, such as quartz, occur in a variety of colors. These samples include crystal quartz (colorless), amethyst (purple quartz), citrine (yellow quartz), and smoky quartz (gray to black). (Photo by E.J. Tarbuck)

FIGURE 1.12 Although the color of a mineral is not always helpful in identification, the streak, which is the color of the powdered mineral, can be very useful. (Photo by Dennis Tasa)

FIGURE 1.13 Although most minerals exhibit only one common crystal shape, some such as pyrite have two or more characteristic habits. (Photos by Dennis Tasa)

Although the color of a mineral may vary from sample to sample, its streak usually does not.

Streak can also help distinguish between minerals with metallic luster or nonmetallic luster. Metallic minerals generally have a dense, dark streak, whereas minerals with non-metallic luster typically have a light-colored streak.

It should be noted that not all minerals produce a streak when using a streak plate. For example, if the mineral is harder than the streak plate, no streak is observed.

Crystal Shape or Habit

Mineralogists use the term **crystal shape** or **habit** to refer to the common or characteristic shape of a crystal or aggregate of crystals. A few minerals exhibit somewhat regular polygons that are helpful in their identification. For example, magnetite crystals sometimes occur as octahedrons, garnets often form dodecahedrons, and halite and fluorite crystals tend to grow as cubes or near cubes. While most minerals have only one common habit, a few have two or more characteristic crystal shapes such as the pyrite sample shown in **FIGURE 1.13**.

By contrast, some minerals rarely develop perfect geometric forms. Many, however, develop a characteristic shape useful for identification. Some minerals tend to grow equally in all three dimensions, whereas others tend to be elongated in one direction, or flattened if growth in one dimension is

suppressed. Commonly used terms to describe these and other crystal habits include *equant* (equidimensional), *bladed, fibrous, tabular, prismatic, platy, blocky*, and *botryoidal* (**FIGURE 1.14**).

Mineral Strength

How easily minerals break or deform under stress is determined by the type and strength of the chemical bonds that hold the crystals together. Mineralogists use terms including *tenacity, hardness, cleavage*, and *fracture* to describe mineral strength and how minerals break when stress is applied.

A. Bladed

B. Prismatic

C. Banded

D. Botryoidal

FIGURE 1.14 Some common crystal habits. **A.** *Bladed.* Elongated crystals that are flattened in one direction. **B.** *Prismatic.* Elongated crystals with faces that are parallel to a common direction. **C.** *Banded.* Minerals that have stripes or bands of color or texture. **D.** *Botryoidal.* Groups of intergrown crystals resembling a bunch of grapes.

Tenacity

The term **tenacity** describes a mineral's toughness, or its resistance to breaking or deforming. Minerals that are ionically bonded, such as fluorite and halite, tend to be *brittle* and shatter into small pieces when struck. By contrast, minerals with metallic bonds, such as native copper, are *malleable*, or easily hammered into different shapes. Minerals, including gypsum and talc, that can be cut into thin shavings are described as *sectile*. Still others, notably the micas, are *elastic* and will bend and snap back to their original shape after the stress is released.

Hardness

One of the most useful diagnostic properties is **hardness**, a measure of the resistance of a mineral to abrasion or scratching. This property is determined by rubbing a mineral of unknown hardness against one of known hardness, or vice versa. A numerical value of hardness can by obtained by using the **Mohs scale** of hardness, which consists of 10 minerals arranged in order from 1 (softest) to 10 (hardest), as shown in **FIGURE 1.15A**. The Mohs scale is a relative ranking, and it does not imply that mineral number 2, gypsum, is twice as hard as mineral 1, talc. In fact, gypsum is only slightly harder than talc, as **FIGURE 1.15B** indicates.

In the laboratory, other common objects can be used to determine the hardness of a mineral. These include a human fingernail, which has a hardness of about 2.5, a copper penny (3.5), and a piece of glass (5.5). The mineral gypsum, which has a hardness of 2, can be easily scratched with a fingernail. On the other hand, the mineral calcite, which has a hardness of 3, will scratch a fingernail but will not scratch glass. Quartz, one of the hardest common minerals, will easily scratch glass. Diamonds, hardest of all, scratch anything, including other diamonds.

Cleavage

In the crystal structure of many minerals, some atomic bonds are weaker than others. It is along these weak bonds that minerals tend to break when they are stressed. **Cleavage** (*Kleiben* = carve) is the tendency of a mineral to break (cleave) along planes of weak bonding. Not all minerals have cleavage, but those that do can be identified by the relatively smooth, flat surfaces that are produced when the mineral is broken.

The simplest type of cleavage is exhibited by the micas (**FIGURE 1.16**). Because these minerals have very weak bonds in one direction, they cleave to form thin, flat sheets. Some minerals have excellent cleavage in one, two, three, or more directions, whereas others exhibit fair or poor cleavage, and still others have no cleavage at all. When minerals break evenly in more than one direction, cleavage is described by

FIGURE 1.15 Hardness scales. **A.** Mohs scale of hardness, with the hardness of some common objects. **B.** Relationship between Mohs relative hardness scale and an absolute hardness scale.

FIGURE 1.16 The thin sheets shown here were produced by splitting a mica (muscovite) crystal parallel to its perfect cleavage. (Photo by Breck P. Kent)

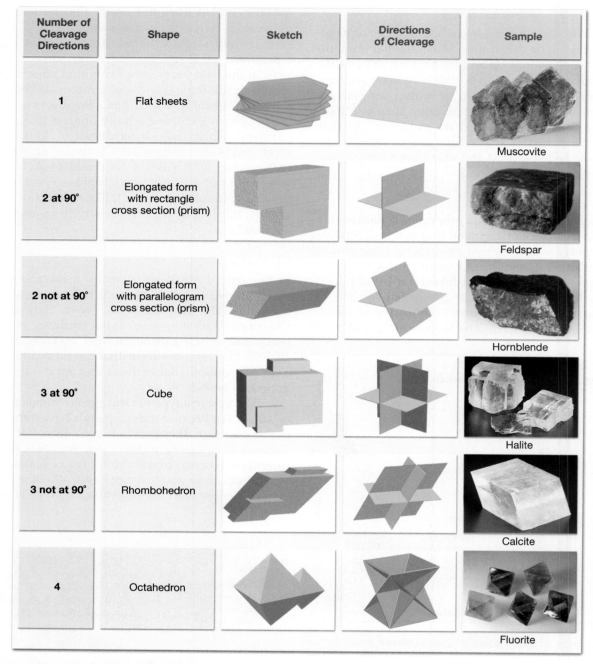

Number of Cleavage Directions	Shape	Sketch	Directions of Cleavage	Sample
1	Flat sheets			Muscovite
2 at 90°	Elongated form with rectangle cross section (prism)			Feldspar
2 not at 90°	Elongated form with parallelogram cross section (prism)			Hornblende
3 at 90°	Cube			Halite
3 not at 90°	Rhombohedron			Calcite
4	Octahedron			Fluorite

FIGURE 1.17   Common cleavage directions exhibited by minerals. (Photos by E. J. Tarbuck and Dennis Tasa)

the number of cleavage directions and the angle(s) at which they meet (**FIGURE 1.17**).

Each cleavage surface that has a different orientation is counted as a different direction of cleavage. For example, some minerals cleave to form six-sided cubes. Because cubes are defined by three different sets of parallel planes that intersect at 90-degree angles, cleavage is described as *three directions of cleavage that meet at 90 degrees.*

Do not confuse cleavage with crystal shape. When a mineral exhibits cleavage, it will break into pieces that all have the same geometry. By contrast, the smooth-sided quartz crystals shown in Figure 1.1 (p. 22) do not have cleavage. If broken, they fracture into shapes that do not resemble one another or the original crystals.

Fracture

Minerals having chemical bonds that are equally, or nearly equally, strong in all directions exhibit a property called **fracture**. When minerals fracture, most produce uneven surfaces and are described as exhibiting *irregular fracture.* However, some minerals, such as quartz, break into smooth, curved surfaces resembling broken glass. Such breaks are called *conchoidal fractures* (**FIGURE 1.18**). Still other minerals exhibit fractures that produce splinters or

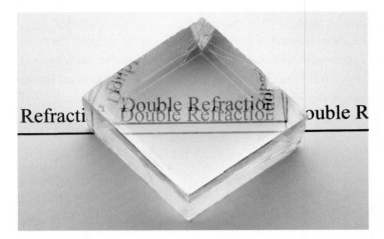

FIGURE 1.19   Double refraction illustrated by the mineral calcite. (Photo by Chip Clark)

FIGURE 1.18   Conchoidal fracture. The smooth, curved surfaces result when minerals break in a glasslike manner. (Photo by E. J. Tarbuck)

fibers that are referred to as *splintery* and *fibrous fracture*, respectively.

Density and Specific Gravity

Density, an important property of matter, is defined as mass per unit volume. Mineralogists often use a related measure called **specific gravity** to describe the density of minerals. Specific gravity is a unitless number representing the ratio of a mineral's weight to the weight of an equal volume of water.

Most common rock-forming minerals have a specific gravity of between 2 and 3. For example, quartz has a specific gravity of 2.65. By contrast, some metallic minerals such as pyrite, native copper, and magnetite are more than twice as dense as quartz. Galena, an ore of lead, has a specific gravity of roughly 7.5, whereas the specific gravity of 24-karat gold is approximately 20.

With a little practice, you can estimate the specific gravity of a mineral by hefting it in your hand. Ask yourself, does this mineral feel about as "heavy" as similar sized rocks you have handled? If the answer is "yes," the specific gravity of the sample will likely be between 2.5 and 3.

Other Properties of Minerals

In addition to the properties already discussed, some minerals can be recognized by other distinctive properties. For example, halite is ordinary salt, so it can be quickly identified through taste. Talc and graphite both have distinctive feels; talc feels soapy, and graphite feels greasy. Further, the streak of many sulfur-bearing minerals smells like rotten eggs. A few minerals, such as magnetite, have a high iron content and can be picked up with a magnet, while some

DID YOU KNOW?

Clay minerals are sometimes used as an additive to thicken milkshakes in fast-food restaurants.

varieties (lodestone) are natural magnets and will pick up small iron-based objects such as pins and paper clips (see Figure 1.25, p. 37).

Moreover, some minerals exhibit special optical properties. For example, when a transparent piece of calcite is placed over printed text, the letters appear twice. This optical property is known as *double refraction* (**FIGURE 1.19**).

One very simple chemical test involves placing a drop of dilute hydrochloric acid from a dropper bottle onto a freshly broken mineral surface. Certain minerals, called carbonates, will effervesce (fizz) as carbon dioxide gas is released (**FIGURE 1.20**). This test is especially useful in identifying the common carbonate mineral calcite.

FIGURE 1.20   Calcite reacting with a weak acid. (Photo by Chip Clark)

MINERAL GROUPS

Earth Materials
▼ Minerals

Nearly 4000 minerals have been named, and several new ones are identified each year. Fortunately, for students who are beginning to study minerals, no more than a few dozen are abundant! Collectively, these few make up most of the rocks of Earth's crust and, as such, are often referred to as the **rock-forming minerals**.

Although less abundant, many other minerals are used extensively in the manufacture of products and are called *economic minerals*. Rock-forming minerals and economic minerals are not mutually exclusive groups. When found in large deposits, some rock-forming minerals are economically significant. One example is the mineral calcite, which is the primary component of the sedimentary rock limestone and has many uses including the production of cement.

It is worth noting that *only eight elements* make up the bulk of the rock-forming minerals and represent more than 98 percent (by weight) of the continental crust (**FIGURE 1.21**). These elements, in order of abundance, are oxygen (O), silicon (Si), aluminum (Al), iron (Fe), calcium (Ca), sodium (Na), potassium (K), and magnesium (Mg). As shown in Figure 1.21, silicon and oxygen are by far the most common elements in Earth's crust. Furthermore, these two elements readily combine to form the basic "building block" for the

most common mineral group, the **silicates**. More than 800 silicate minerals are known and they account for more than 90 percent of Earth's crust.

Because other mineral groups are far less abundant in Earth's crust than the silicates, they are often grouped together under the heading **nonsilicates.** Although not as common as silicates, some nonsilicate minerals are very important economically. They provide us with iron and aluminum to build our automobiles, gypsum for plaster and drywall for home construction, and copper wire that carries electricity and connects us to the Internet. Some common nonsilicate mineral groups include the carbonates, sulfates, and halides. In addition to their economic importance, these mineral groups include members that are major constituents in sediments and sedimentary rocks.

We first discuss the most common mineral group, the silicates, and then consider some of the prominent nonsilicate mineral groups.

Silicate Minerals

Every silicate mineral contains oxygen and silicon atoms. Except for a few minerals, such as quartz, most silicate minerals also contain one or more additional elements that join to produce an electrically neutral compound. These elements give rise to the great variety of silicate minerals and their varied properties.

All silicates have the same fundamental building block, the **silicon-oxygen tetrahedron.** This structure consists of four oxygen atoms surrounding a much smaller silicon atom, as shown in **FIGURE 1.22**. Thus, a typical hand-size silicate mineral specimen contains millions of these silicon-oxygen tetrahedra, joined together in a variety of ways.

In some minerals, the tetrahedra are joined into chains, sheets, or three-dimensional networks by sharing oxygen atoms (**FIGURE 1.23**). These larger silicate structures

FIGURE 1.21   Relative abundance of the eight most common elements in the continental crust.

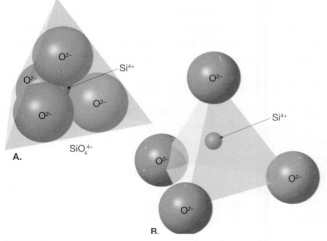

FIGURE 1.22   Two representations of the silicon-oxygen tetrahedron. **A.** The four large red spheres represent oxygen atoms, and the blue sphere represents a silicon atom. The spheres are drawn in proportion to the radii of the atoms. **B.** An expanded view of the tetrahedron that has an oxygen atom at each of the four corners.

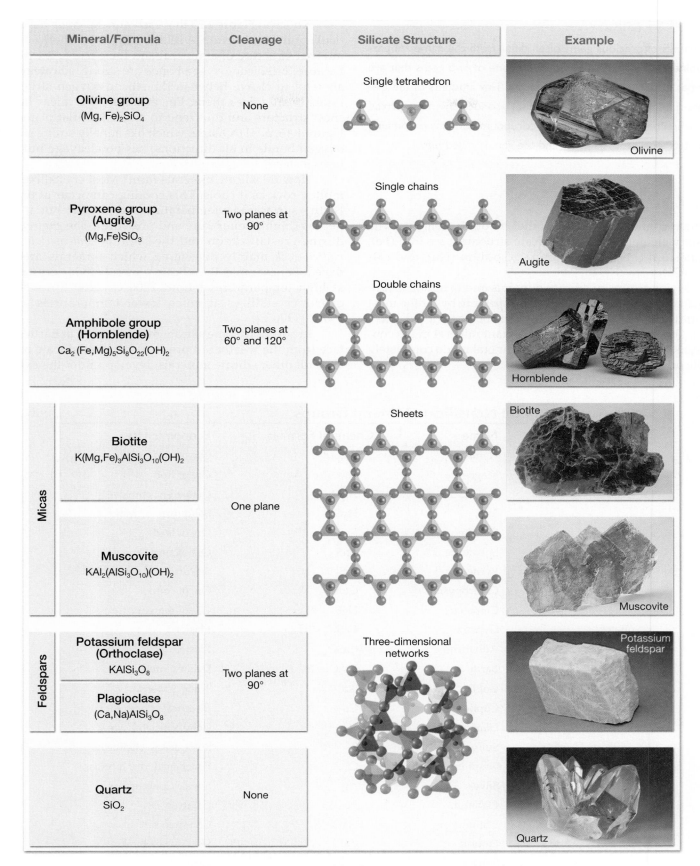

Mineral/Formula	Cleavage	Silicate Structure	Example
Olivine group $(Mg, Fe)_2SiO_4$	None	Single tetrahedron	Olivine
Pyroxene group (Augite) $(Mg,Fe)SiO_3$	Two planes at 90°	Single chains	Augite
Amphibole group (Hornblende) $Ca_2(Fe,Mg)_5Si_8O_{22}(OH)_2$	Two planes at 60° and 120°	Double chains	Hornblende
Micas — **Biotite** $K(Mg,Fe)_3AlSi_3O_{10}(OH)_2$	One plane	Sheets	Biotite
Micas — **Muscovite** $KAl_2(AlSi_3O_{10})(OH)_2$	One plane	Sheets	Muscovite
Feldspars — **Potassium feldspar (Orthoclase)** $KAlSi_3O_8$	Two planes at 90°	Three-dimensional networks	Potassium feldspar
Feldspars — **Plagioclase** $(Ca,Na)AlSi_3O_8$	Two planes at 90°	Three-dimensional networks	
Quartz SiO_2	None	Three-dimensional networks	Quartz

FIGURE 1.23 Common silicate minerals. Note that the complexity of the silicate structure increases down the chart.

DID YOU KNOW?

The names of precious gems often differ from the names of parent minerals. For example, *sapphire* is one of two gems that are varieties of the same mineral, *corundum*. Tiny amounts of the elements titanium and iron in corundum produce the most prized blue sapphires. When the mineral corundum contains chromium, it exhibits a brilliant red color and the gem is called *ruby*.

are then connected to one another by other elements. The primary elements that join silicate structures are iron (Fe), magnesium (Mg), potassium (K), sodium (Na), and calcium (Ca).

Major groups of silicate minerals and common examples are given in Figure 1.23. The *feldspars* are by far the most plentiful group, comprising more than 50 percent of Earth's crust. *Quartz,* the second most abundant mineral in the continental crust, is the only common mineral made completely of silicon and oxygen.

Notice in Figure 1.23 that each mineral *group* has a particular silicate *structure.* A relationship exists between this internal structure of a mineral and the *cleavage* it exhibits. Because the silicon-oxygen bonds are strong, silicate minerals tend to cleave between the silicon-oxygen structures rather than across them. For example, the micas have a sheet structure and thus tend to cleave into flat plates (see Figure 1.16, p. 31). Quartz, which has equally strong silicon-oxygen bonds in all directions, has no cleavage but fractures instead.

How do silicate minerals form? Most crystallize from molten rock as it cools. This cooling can occur at or near Earth's surface (low temperature and pressure) or at great depths (high temperature and pressure). The *environment* during crystallization and the *chemical composition of the molten rock* mainly determine which minerals are produced. For example, the silicate mineral olivine crystallizes at high temperatures (about 1200°C [2200°F]), whereas quartz crystallizes at much lower temperatures (about 700°C [1300°F]).

In addition, some silicate minerals form at Earth's surface from the weathered products of other silicate minerals. Still other silicate minerals develop under the extreme

Table 1.1   Common Nonsilicate Mineral Groups

Mineral Group	Name	Chemical Formula	Economic Use
Oxides	Hematite	Fe_2O_3	Ore of iron, pigment
	Magnetite	Fe_3O_4	Ore of iron
	Corundum	Al_2O_3	Gemstone, abrasive
	Ice	H_2O	Solid form of water
Sulfides	Galena	PbS	Ore of lead
	Sphalerite	ZnS	Ore of zinc
	Pyrite	FeS_2	Sulfuric acid production
	Chalcopyrite	$CuFeS_2$	Ore of copper
	Cinnabar	HgS	Ore of mercury
Sulfates	Gypsum	$CaSO_4 \cdot 2H_2O$	Plaster
	Anhydrite	$CaSO_4$	Plaster
	Barite	$BaSO_4$	Drilling mud
Native elements	Gold	Au	Trade, jewelry
	Copper	Cu	Electrical conductor
	Diamond	C	Gemstone, abrasive
	Sulfur	S	Sulfa drugs, chemicals
	Graphite	C	Pencil lead, dry lubricant
	Silver	Ag	Jewelry, photography
	Platinum	Pt	Catalyst
Halides	Halite	NaCl	Common salt
	Fluorite	CaF_2	Used in steelmaking
	Sylvite	KCl	Fertilizer
Carbonates	Calcite	$CaCO_3$	Portland cement, lime
	Dolomite	$CaMg(CO_3)_2$	Portland cement, lime

pressures associated with mountain building. Each silicate mineral, therefore, has a structure and a chemical composition that *indicate the conditions under which it formed.* Thus, by carefully examining the mineral makeup of rocks, geologists can often determine the circumstances under which they formed.

Important Nonsilicate Minerals

Although nonsilicates make up only about 8 percent of Earth's crust, some minerals, such as gypsum, calcite, and halite, are major constituents in sedimentary rocks. Furthermore, many others are important economically. Table 1.1 lists some of the nonsilicate mineral classes and a few examples of each. Some of the most common nonsilicate minerals belong to one of three classes of minerals—the carbonates (CO_3^{2-}), the sulfates (SO_4^{2-}), and the halides (Cl^{1-}, F^{1-}, B^{1-}).

The carbonate minerals are much simpler structurally than the silicates. This mineral group is composed of the carbonate ion (CO_3^{2-}) and one or more kinds of positive ions. The most common carbonate mineral is *calcite*, $CaCO_3$ (calcium carbonate). This mineral is the major constituent in two well-known rocks: limestone and marble. Limestone has many uses, including road aggregate, building stone, and the main ingredient in portland cement. Marble is primarily used decoratively in homes, businesses, and places of worship.

Two other nonsilicate minerals frequently found in sedimentary rocks are *halite* and *gypsum*. Both minerals are commonly found in thick layers that are the last vestiges of ancient seas that have long since evaporated (**FIGURE 1.24**).

FIGURE 1.24   Thick bed of halite (salt) at an underground mine in Grand Saline, Texas. (Photo by Tom Bochsler)

Like limestone, both are important nonmetallic resources. Halite is the mineral name for common table salt (NaCl). Gypsum ($CaSO_4 \cdot 2H_2O$), which is calcium sulfate with water bound into the structure, is the mineral of which plaster and other similar building materials are composed.

Most nonsilicate mineral classes contain members that are prized for their economic value. This includes the oxides, whose members hematite and magnetite are important ores of iron (**FIGURE 1.25**). Also significant are the sulfides, which are basically compounds of sulfur (S) and one or more metals. Examples of important sulfide minerals include galena (lead), sphalerite (zinc), and chalcopyrite (copper). In addition, native elements, including gold, silver, and carbon (diamonds), plus a host of other nonsilicate minerals—fluorite (flux in making steel), corundum (gemstone, abrasive), and uraninite (a uranium source)—are important economically.

FIGURE 1.25   Two important ores of iron. **A.** Magnetite. **B.** Hematite. (Photos by E. J. Tarbuck)

A. Magnetite

B. Hematite

MINERAL RESOURCES

Mineral resources are Earth's storehouse of useful minerals that can be recovered for use. Resources include already identified deposits from which minerals can be extracted profitably, called **reserves,** as well as known deposits that are not yet recoverable under present economic conditions or technology. Deposits assumed to exist based on geologic evidence are also considered mineral resources.

The term **ore** denotes useful metallic minerals that can be mined for profit. In common usage, the term is also applied to some nonmetallic minerals, such as fluorite and sulfur. However, materials used for such purposes as building stone, road paving, abrasives, ceramics, and fertilizers are not usually called ores; rather, they are classified as *industrial rocks and minerals.*

Recall that more than 98 percent of Earth's crust is composed of only eight elements. Except for oxygen and silicon, all other elements make up a relatively small fraction of common crustal rocks (see Figure 1.21, p. 34). Indeed, the natural concentrations of most elements in crustal rocks are exceedingly small. A rock containing the average crustal percentage of a valuable element such as gold has no economic value, because the cost of extracting it greatly exceeds the value of the gold that could be recovered.

To have economic value, an element must be concentrated above the level of its average crustal abundance. For example, copper makes up about 0.0135 percent of the crust. For a deposit to be considered an ore of copper, it must contain a concentration that is about 100 times this amount. Aluminum, on the other hand, represents 8.13 percent of the crust and can be extracted profitably when found in concentrations only about four times its average crustal percentage.

It is important to realize that economic changes affect whether or not a deposit is profitable to extract. If demand for a metal increases and its price rises sufficiently, the status of a previously unprofitable deposit changes. Unprofitable deposits may also become profitable if improved mining techniques allow the material to be extracted at a lower cost. This situation was illustrated at the copper-mining operation located at Bingham Canyon, Utah, one of the largest open-pit mines on Earth (**FIGURE 1.26**). Mining was halted there in 1985 because obsolete equipment had driven the cost of extracting the copper beyond the selling price. The owners responded by replacing an antiquated 1000-car railroad with conveyor belts and pipelines for transporting the ore and waste. These devices achieved a cost reduction of nearly 30 percent and returned this mining operation to profitability.

THE CHAPTER IN REVIEW

• A *mineral* is a naturally occurring inorganic solid that possesses an orderly crystalline structure and a definite chemical composition. Most *rocks* are aggregates composed of two or more minerals.

• The building blocks of minerals are *elements*. An *atom* is the smallest particle of matter that still retains the characteristics of an element. Each atom has a *nucleus,* which contains *protons* and *neutrons*. Orbiting the nucleus of an atom are *electrons*. The number of protons in an atom's nucleus determines its *atomic number* and the name of the element. Atoms bond together to form a *compound* by either gaining, losing, or sharing electrons with another atom.

• *Isotopes* are variants of the same element but with a different *mass number* (the total number of neutrons plus protons found in an atom's nucleus). Some isotopes are unstable and disintegrate naturally through a process called *radioactive decay.*

• The properties of minerals include *crystal shape (habit), luster, color, streak, hardness, cleavage, fracture,* and *density* or *specific gravity.* In addition, a number of special physical and chemical properties (*taste, smell, elasticity, feel, magnetism, double refraction,* and *chemical reaction to hydrochloric acid*) are useful in identifying certain minerals. Each mineral has a unique set of properties that can be used for identification.

• Of the nearly 4000 minerals, no more than a few dozen make up most of the rocks of Earth's crust and, as such, are classified as rock-forming minerals. Eight elements (oxygen, silicon, aluminum, iron, calcium, sodium, potassium, and magnesium) make up the bulk of these minerals and represent more than 98 percent (by weight) of Earth's continental crust.

• The most common mineral group is the *silicates*. All silicate minerals have the *silicon-oxygen tetrahedron* as their fundamental building block. In some silicate minerals, the tetrahedra are joined in chains; in others, the tetrahedra are arranged into sheets or three-dimensional networks. Each silicate mineral has a structure and a chemical

FIGURE 1.26 Aerial view of Bingham Canyon copper mine near Salt Lake City, Utah. This huge open-pit mine is about 4 kilometers (2.5 miles) across and 900 meters (nearly 3000 feet) deep. Although the amount of copper in the rock is less than 1 percent, the huge volumes of material removed and processed each day (about 200,000 tons) yield significant quantities of metal. (Photo by Michael Collier)

composition that indicates the conditions under which it formed. The *nonsilicate* mineral groups include the *oxides* (e.g., magnetite, mined for iron), *sulfides* (e.g., sphalerite, mined for zinc), *sulfates* (e.g., gypsum, used in plaster and frequently found in sedimentary rocks), *native elements* (e.g., graphite, a dry lubricant), *halides* (e.g., halite, common salt, and frequently found in sedimentary rocks), and *carbonates* (e.g., calcite, used in portland cement and a major constituent in two well-known rocks: limestone and marble).

• The term *ore* is used to denote useful metallic minerals, such as hematite (mined for iron) and galena (mined for lead), that can be mined at a profit, as well as some nonmetallic minerals, such as fluorite and sulfur, that contain useful substances.

KEY TERMS

atom (p. 24)

atomic number (p. 24)

chemical bond (p. 26)

chemical compound (p. 25)

cleavage (p. 31)

color (p. 29)

covalent bond (p. 27)

crystal shape (p. 30)

density (p. 33)

electron (p. 24)

element (p. 25)

fracture (p. 32)

habit (p. 30)

hardness (p. 31)

ionic bond (p. 26)

ions (p. 26)

isotope (p. 28)

luster (p. 29)

mass number (p. 28)

metallic bonds (p. 27)

mineral (p. 22)

mineralogy (p. 22)

mineral resource (p. 38)

Mohs scale (p. 31)

neutron (p. 24)

nonsilicate (p. 34)

nucleus (p. 24)

octet rule (p. 26)

ore (p. 38)

periodic table (p. 25)

proton (p. 24)

radioactive decay (p. 28)

reserve (p. 38)

rock (p. 23)

rock-forming minerals (p. 34)

silicates (p. 24)

silicon-oxygen tetrahedron
  (p. 34)

specific gravity (p. 33)

streak (p. 29)

tenacity (p. 31)

valence electrons (p. 24)

QUESTIONS FOR REVIEW

1. Briefly describe the five characteristics an Earth material should have in order to be considered a mineral.

2. Define the term *rock*.

3. List the three main particles of an atom and explain how they differ from one another.

4. If the number of electrons in an atom is 35 and its mass number is 80, calculate the following:
   a. the number of protons
   b. the atomic number
   c. the number of neutrons

5. What occurs in an atom to produce an ion?

6. What is an isotope?

7. Although all minerals have an orderly internal arrangement of atoms (crystalline structure), most mineral samples do not visibly demonstrate their crystal form. Why?

8. Why might it be difficult to identify a mineral by its color?

9. If you found a glassy-appearing mineral while rock hunting and had hopes that it was a diamond, what simple test might help you make a determination?

10. Table 1.1 (p. 36) lists a use for corundum as an abrasive. Explain why it makes a good abrasive in terms of the Mohs hardness scale.

11. Gold has a specific gravity of almost 20. If a five-gallon pail of water weighs about 40 pounds, how much would a five-gallon pail of gold weigh?

12. What are the two most common elements in Earth's crust?

13. What is the term used to describe the basic building block of all silicate minerals?

14. What are the two most common silicate minerals in Earth's crust?

15. List three nonsilicate minerals that are commonly found in rocks.

16. Contrast a mineral *resource* and a mineral *reserve*.

17. What might cause a mineral deposit that had not been considered an ore to become reclassified as an ore?

COMPANION WEBSITE

The *Foundations of Earth Science* Website uses the resources and flexibility of the Internet to aid in your study of the topics in this chapter. Written and developed by the authors and other Earth science instructors, this site will help improve your understanding of Earth science. Visit **www.mygeoscienceplace.com** in order to:

• **Review** key chapter concepts.

• **Read** with links to the ebook and to chapter-specific web resources.

• **Visualize** and comprehend challenging topics using learning activities in *GEODe: Earth Science*.

• **Test** yourself with online quizzes.

GEODe: EARTH SCIENCE

GEODe: Earth Science is a valuable and easy to use learning aid that can be accessed from your book's Companion Website **www.mygeoscienceplace.com.** It is a dynamic instructional tool that promotes understanding and reinforces important concepts by using tutorials, animations, and exercises that actively engage the student.

ROCKS
MATERIALS OF
THE SOLID EARTH

To assist you in learning the important concepts in this chapter, you will find it helpful to focus on the following questions:

1. What is the rock cycle and why is it important?

2. What are the three groups of rocks and the geologic processes involved in the formation of each?

3. What two criteria are used to classify igneous rocks?

4. What are the two major types of weathering and the processes associated with each?

5. What are the names and environments of formation for some common detrital and chemical sedimentary rocks?

6. What are the names, textures, and environments of formation for some common metamorphic rocks?

The mass of igneous rock challenging this climber originated deep beneath Earth's surface. (Photo by Cliff Leigh/Aurora Photos)

CHAPTER

2

Why study rocks? You have already learned that some rocks and minerals have great economic value. In addition, all Earth processes depend in some way on the properties of these basic Earth materials. Events such as volcanic eruptions, mountain building, weathering, erosion, and even earthquakes involve rocks and minerals. Consequently, a basic knowledge of Earth materials is essential to understanding most geologic phenomena.

Every rock contains clues about the environment in which it formed. For example, some rocks are composed entirely of small shell fragments. This tells Earth scientists that the rock originated in a shallow marine environment. Other rocks contain clues that indicate they formed from a volcanic eruption or deep in the Earth during mountain building (**FIGURE 2.1**). Thus, rocks contain a wealth of information about events that have occurred over Earth's long history.

We classify rocks into three groups—*igneous*, *sedimentary*, and *metamorphic*—based on the processes that created them. Before examining each group, we will view the *rock cycle*, which depicts the interrelationships among them.

EARTH AS A SYSTEM: THE ROCK CYCLE

Earth Materials
▼ The Rock Cycle

Earth as a system is illustrated most vividly when we examine the rock cycle. The **rock cycle** allows us to see many of the interactions among the many components and processes of the Earth system (**FIGURE 2.2**). It helps us understand the origin of igneous, sedimentary, and metamorphic rocks and how they are connected. In addition, the rock cycle demonstrates that any rock type, under the right circumstances, can be transformed into any other type.

The Basic Cycle

We begin our discussion of the rock cycle with molten rock, called *magma*, which forms by melting that occurs primarily within Earth's crust and upper mantle. Once formed, a magma body often rises toward the surface because it is less dense than the surrounding rock. Occasionally magma

FIGURE 2.1   Rocks contain information about the processes that produce them. This large exposure of igneous rocks located in the Sierra Nevada of California, was once a molten mass found deep within Earth. (Photo by Brian Bailey/Getty Images)

2. Igneous rock

3. Sediments

Weathering breaks down rock

Crystalization at depth produces igneous rock

Crystalization

Crystalization at surface produces igneous rock

Weathering/transport

Lava

Streams transport sediment

4. Sedimentary rock

Lithification

Sediment

Heating produces metamorphic rock

Compaction and cementation turns sediment into sedimentary rock

Melting

Metamorphism

Melting

Heat and pressure trigger metamorphism

1. Molten rock

5. Metamorphic rock

FIGURE 2.2   The rock cycle. Viewed over long spans, rocks are constantly forming, changing, and reforming. The rock cycle helps us understand the origin of the three basic rock groups. Arrows represent processes that link each group to the others.

reaches Earth's surface where it erupts as *lava*. Eventually, molten rock cools and solidifies, a process called *crystallization* or *solidification*. Molten rock may solidify either beneath the surface or, following a volcanic eruption, at the surface. In either situation, the resulting rocks are called *igneous rocks*.

If igneous rocks are exposed at the surface, they undergo *weathering*, in which the daily influences of the atmosphere slowly disintegrate and decompose rocks. The loose materials that result are often moved downslope by gravity, and then picked up and transported by one or more erosional agents—running water, glaciers, wind, or waves. Eventually, these particles and dissolved substances, called *sediment*, are deposited. Although most sediment ultimately comes to rest in the ocean, other sites of deposition include river floodplains, desert basins, swamps, and sand dunes.

Next, the sediments undergo *lithification*, a term meaning "conversion into rock." Sediment is usually lithified into *sedimentary rock* when compacted by the weight of overlying materials or when cemented as percolating groundwater fills the pores with mineral matter.

If the resulting sedimentary rock becomes deeply buried or is involved in the dynamics of mountain building, it will be subjected to great pressures and intense heat. The sedimentary rock may react to the changing environment by turning into the third rock type, *metamorphic rock*. If metamorphic rock is subjected to still higher temperatures, it may melt, creating magma, and the cycle begins again.

Although rocks may appear to be stable, unchanging masses, the rock cycle shows they are not. The changes, however, take time—sometimes millions or even billions of years. In addition, the rock cycle operates continuously around the globe, but in different stages depending on the location. Today, new magma is forming under the island of Hawaii, whereas the rocks that comprise the Colorado Rockies are slowly being worn down by weathering and erosion. Some of this weathered debris will eventually be carried to the Gulf of Mexico, where it will add to the already substantial mass of sediment that has accumulated there.

Alternative Paths

Rocks do not necessarily go through the cycle in the order that was just described. Other paths are also possible. For example, igneous rocks, rather than being exposed to weathering and erosion at Earth's surface, may remain deeply buried. Eventually, these masses may be subjected to the strong compressional forces and high temperature associated with mountain building. When this occurs, they are transformed directly into metamorphic rocks.

Metamorphic and sedimentary rocks, as well as sediment, do not always remain buried. Rather, overlying layers may be eroded away, exposing the once buried rock. When this happens, the material is attacked by weathering processes and turned into new raw materials for sedimentary rocks.

In a similar manner, igneous rocks that formed at depth can be uplifted, weathered, and turned into sedimentary rocks. Alternatively, igneous rocks may remain at depth where the high temperatures and forces associated with mountain building may metamorphose or even melt them. Over time, rocks may be transformed into any other rock type, or even into a different form of its original type. There are many paths that rocks may take through the rock cycle.

What drives the rock cycle? Earth's internal heat is responsible for the processes that form igneous and metamorphic rocks. Weathering and the transport of weathered material are external processes, powered by energy from the Sun. External processes produce sedimentary rocks.

IGNEOUS ROCKS: "FORMED BY FIRE"

Earth Materials
▼ Igneous Rocks

In the discussion of the rock cycle, we pointed out that **igneous rocks** form as *magma* cools and crystallizes. But what is magma and what is its source? **Magma** is molten rock generated by partial melting of rocks in Earth's mantle and in the lower crust in smaller amounts. This molten material consists mainly of the elements found in silicate minerals. Silicon and oxygen are the main constituents in magma, with lesser amounts of aluminum, iron, calcium, sodium, potassium, magnesium, and others. Magma also contains some gases, particularly water vapor, which are confined within the magma body by the weight (pressure) of the overlying rocks.

Once formed, a magma body buoyantly rises toward the surface because it is less dense than the surrounding rocks. Occasionally molten rock reaches the surface, where it is called **lava** (FIGURE 2.3). Sometimes, lava is emitted as fountains produced when escaping gases propel molten rock skyward. On other occasions, magma is explosively ejected from vents, producing a spectacular eruption such as the 1980 eruption of Mount St. Helens. However, most eruptions are not violent; rather, volcanoes more often emit quiet outpourings of lava.

Igneous rocks that form when molten rock solidifies *at the surface* are classified as **extrusive** or **volcanic** (after the Roman fire god Vulcan). Extrusive igneous rocks are abundant in western portions of the Americas, including the volcanic cones of the Cascade Range and the extensive lava flows of the Columbia Plateau. In addition, many oceanic islands, including the Hawaiian Islands, are composed almost entirely of volcanic igneous rocks.

Most magma, however, loses its mobility before reaching the surface and eventually crystallizes deep below the surface. Igneous rocks that *form at depth* are termed **intrusive** or **plutonic** (after Pluto, the god of the lower world in classical mythology). Intrusive igneous rocks remain at depth unless portions of the crust are uplifted and the overlying rocks stripped away by erosion. Exposures of intrusive igneous rocks occur in many places, including Mount Washington, New Hampshire; Stone Mountain, Georgia; the Black Hills of South Dakota; and Yosemite National Park, California (FIGURE 2.4).

From Magma to Crystalline Rock

Magma is a very hot, thick fluid, that contains solids (mineral crystals) and gases. The liquid portion of a magma body is composed of atoms that move about freely. As magma cools, random movements slow, and atoms begin to arrange themselves into orderly patterns—a process called *crystallization*. As cooling continues, numerous small crystals develop and atoms are systematically added to these centers of crystal growth. When the crystals grow large enough for their edges to meet, their growth ceases for lack of space. Eventually, all of the liquid is transformed into a solid mass of interlocking crystals.

The rate of cooling strongly influences crystal size. If a magma cools very slowly, it allows atoms to migrate over

DID YOU KNOW?

During the catastrophic eruption of Mount Vesuvius in A.D. 79, the entire city of Pompeii (near Naples, Italy) was completely buried by several meters of pumice and volcanic ash. Centuries passed, and new towns developed around Vesuvius. It was not until 1595, during a construction project, that the remains of Pompeii were discovered. Yearly, thousands of tourists stroll around the excavated remains of ancient Pompeii's shops, taverns, and villas.

FIGURE 2.3 Fluid basaltic lava emitted from Hawaii's Kilauea Volcano. (Photo by Photo Resource Hawaii/www.DanitaDelimont.com)

FIGURE 2.4 Mount Rushmore National Memorial, located in the Black Hills of South Dakota, is carved from the intrusive igneous rock granite. This massive igneous body cooled very slowly at depth and has since been uplifted and the overlying rocks stripped away by erosion. (Photo by Barbara A. Harvey/Shutterstock)

great distances. Consequently, *slow cooling results in the formation of large crystals.* On the other hand, if cooling occurs rapidly, the atoms lose their motion and quickly combine. This results in a large number of tiny crystals that all compete for the available atoms. Therefore, *rapid cooling results in the formation of a solid mass of small intergrown crystals.*

If a geologist encounters igneous rock containing crystals large enough to be seen with the unaided eye, it means it formed from molten rock, which cooled slowly at depth. But if the crystals can be seen clearly only with a microscope, the geologist knows that the magma cooled quickly, at or near Earth's surface.

If the molten material is quenched almost instantly, there is insufficient time for the atoms to arrange themselves into a crystalline network. Solids produced in this manner consist of randomly distributed atoms. Such rocks are called *glass* and are quite similar to ordinary manufactured glass. "Instant" quenching sometimes occurs during violent volcanic eruptions that produce tiny shards of glass called *volcanic ash.*

In addition to the rate of cooling, the composition of a magma and the amount of dissolved gases influence crystallization. Because magmas differ in each of these aspects, the physical appearance and mineral composition of igneous rocks vary widely. Nevertheless, it is possible to classify igneous rocks based on their *texture* and *mineral composition.*

What Can Igneous Textures Tell Us?

Texture describes the overall appearance of an igneous rock, based on the *size* and *arrangement* of its interlocking crystals. Texture is an important property because it allows geologists to make inferences about a rock's origin based on careful observations of crystal size and other characteristics. You learned that rapid cooling produces small crystals, whereas very slow cooling produces much larger crystals. As you might expect, the rate of cooling is slow in magma chambers lying deep within the crust, whereas a thin layer of lava extruded upon Earth's surface may chill to form solid rock in a matter of hours. Small molten blobs ejected from a volcano during a violent eruption can solidify in mid-air.

Igneous rocks that form rapidly at the surface or as small masses within the upper crust have a **fine-grained texture**, with the individual crystals too small to be seen with the unaided eye (**FIGURE 2.5B**). Common in many fine-grained igneous rocks are voids, called *vesicles,* left by gas bubbles that formed as the lava solidified (**FIGURE 2.6**). Rocks containing these voids are said to display a **vesicular texture**.

When large masses of magma solidify far below the surface, they form igneous rocks that exhibit a **coarse-grained texture**. These coarse-grained rocks have the appearance of a mass of intergrown crystals, roughly equal in size and large enough that individual minerals can be identified with the unaided eye. Granite is a classic example (**FIGURE 2.5D**).

A large mass of magma located at depth may require tens of thousands, even millions, of years to solidify. Because materials crystallize under different environmental conditions (temperature, pressure), it is possible for crystals of one mineral to become quite large before others even start to form. Should molten rock containing some large crystals move to a different environment—for example, by erupting at the surface—the remaining molten portion of the lava would cool more quickly. The resulting rock, which will have large crystals embedded in a matrix of smaller crystals, is said to have a **porphyritic texture** (**FIGURE 2.5C**).

Extrusive igneous activity

Intrusive igneous activity

A. **Glassy texture** produced by very rapid cooling. (Pumice, a frothy, glassy mass.)

B. **Fine-grained texture** produced when lava cooled quickly on Earth's surface

C. **Porphyritic texture** produced by slow then rapid cooling

D. **Coarse-grained texture** produced when magma cools slowly at depth

FIGURE 2.5   Igneous rock textures. **A.** During a volcanic eruption in which silica-rich lava is ejected into the atmosphere, a frothy glass called pumice may form. **B.** Igneous rocks that form at or near Earth's surface cool quickly and often exhibit a fine-grained texture. **C.** A porphyritic texture results when magma that already contains some large crystals migrates to a new location where the rate of cooling increases. The resulting rock consists of large crystals embedded within a matrix of smaller crystals. **D.** Coarse-grained igneous rocks form when magma slowly crystallizes at depth. (Photos courtesy of E. J. Tarbuck)

FIGURE 2.6   Scoria is a volcanic rock that is vesicular. Vesicles form as gas bubbles escape near the top of a lava flow. (Photo courtesy of E. J. Tarbuck)

FIGURE 2.8   Pumice, a glassy rock, is very lightweight because it contains numerous vesicles. (Photo by E. J. Tarbuck; inset photo by Chip Clark)

During some volcanic eruptions, molten rock is ejected into the atmosphere, where it is quenched quickly. Rapid cooling may generate rock having a **glassy texture** (**FIGURE 2.5A**). Glass results when unordered atoms are "frozen in place" before they are able to unite into an orderly crystalline structure. In addition, magmas containing large amounts of silica (SiO_2) are more likely to form rocks that exhibit a glassy texture than those with a low silica content.

Obsidian, a common type of natural glass, is similar in appearance to a dark chunk of manufactured glass (**FIGURE 2.7**). Another volcanic rock that usually exhibits a glassy texture is *pumice.* Often found with obsidian, pumice forms when large amounts of gas escape from molten rock to generate a gray, frothy mass (**FIGURE 2.8**). In some samples, the vesicles

are quite noticeable, whereas in others, the pumice resembles fine shards of intertwined glass. Because of the large volume of air-filled voids, many samples of pumice will float in water (Figure 2.8).

Igneous Compositions

Igneous rocks are composed mainly of silicate minerals. Chemical analysis shows that silicon and oxygen—usually expressed as the silica (SiO_2) content of a magma—are by far the most abundant constituents of igneous rocks. These two elements, plus ions of aluminum (Al), calcium (Ca), sodium (Na), potassium (K), magnesium (Mg), and iron (Fe), make up roughly 98 percent by weight of most magmas. In addition, magma contains small amounts of many other elements, including titanium and manganese, and trace amounts of much rarer elements such as gold, silver, and uranium.

As magma cools and solidifies, these elements combine to form two major groups of silicate minerals. The *dark silicates* are rich in iron and/or magnesium and are relatively low in silica (SiO_2). *Olivine, pyroxene, amphibole,* and *biotite mica* are the common dark silicate minerals of Earth's crust. By contrast, the *light silicates* contain greater amounts of

FIGURE 2.7   Obsidian, a natural glass, was used by Native Americans for making arrowheads and cutting tools. (Photo by E. J. Tarbuck; inset photo by Jeffrey Scovil)

DID YOU KNOW?

Quartz watches actually contain a quartz crystal to keep time. Before quartz watches, timepieces used some sort of oscillating mass or tuning fork. Cogs and wheels converted this mechanical movement to the movement of the hand. It turns out that if voltage is applied to a quartz crystal, it will oscillate with a consistency that is hundreds of times better for timing than a tuning fork. Because of this property, and modern integrated-circuit technology, quartz watches are now built so inexpensively that when they stop working, they are typically replaced rather than repaired. Modern watches that employ mechanical movements are very expensive indeed.

potassium, sodium, and calcium and are richer in silica than dark silicates. Light silicates include *quartz, muscovite mica,* and the most abundant mineral group, the *feldspars.* Feldspars make up at least 40 percent of most igneous rocks. Thus, in addition to feldspar, igneous rocks contain some combination of the other light and/or dark silicates listed earlier.

Classifying Igneous Rocks

Igneous rocks are classified by their texture and mineral composition. The texture of an igneous rock is mainly a result of its cooling history, whereas its mineral composition is largely a consequence of the chemical makeup of the parent magma and the environment of crystallization.

Despite their great compositional diversity, igneous rocks can be divided into broad groups according to their proportions of light and dark minerals. A general classification scheme based on texture and mineral composition is provided in **FIGURE 2.9**.

Granitic (Felsic) Rocks

Near one end of the continuum are rocks composed almost entirely of light-colored silicates—quartz and potassium feldspar. Igneous rocks in which these are the dominant minerals have a **granitic composition**. Geologists also refer to granitic rocks as being **felsic**, a term derived from *f*eldspar and *si*lica (quartz). In addition to quartz and feldspar, most granitic rocks contain about 10 percent dark silicate minerals,

usually biotite mica and amphibole. Granitic rocks are rich in silica (about 70 percent) and are major constituents of the continental crust.

Granite is a coarse-grained igneous rock that forms where large masses of magma slowly solidify at depth. During episodes of mountain building, granite and related crystalline rocks may be uplifted, where the processes of weathering and erosion strip away the overlying crust. Areas where large quantities of granite are exposed at the surface include Pikes Peak in the Rockies, Mount Rushmore in the Black Hills, Stone Mountain in Georgia, and Yosemite National Park in the Sierra Nevada (see Figure 2.4).

Granite is perhaps the best-known igneous rock (**FIGURE 2.10**), in part, because of its natural beauty, which is enhanced when polished, and partly because of its abundance. Slabs of polished granite are commonly used for tombstones, monuments, and countertops.

Rhyolite is the extrusive equivalent of granite and, likewise, is composed essentially of light-colored silicates (Figure 2.10). This fact accounts for its color, which is usually buff to pink or light gray. Rhyolite is fine-grained and frequently contains glass fragments and voids, indicating rapid cooling in a surface environment. In contrast to granite, which is widely distributed as large intrusive masses, rhyolite deposits are less common and generally less voluminous. Yellowstone Park is one well-known exception where extensive lava flows and thick ash deposits of rhyolitic composition are found.

Chemical Composition		**Granitic** (Felsic)	**Andesitic** (Intermediate)	**Basaltic** (Mafic)	**Ultramafic**
Dominant Minerals		Quartz Potassium feldspar Sodium-rich plagioclase feldspar	Amphibole Sodium- and calcium-rich plagioclase feldspar	Pyroxene Calcium-rich plagioclase feldspar	Olivine Pyroxene
TEXTURE	Coarse-grained	**Granite**	**Diorite**	**Gabbro**	**Peridotite**
	Fine-grained	**Rhyolite**	**Andesite**	**Basalt**	**Komatiite** (rare)
	Porphyritic	"Porphyritic" precedes any of the above names whenever there are appreciable phenocrysts			Uncommon
	Glassy	**Obsidian** (compact glass) **Pumice** (frothy glass)			
Rock Color (based on % of dark minerals)		0% to 25%	25% to 45%	45% to 85%	85% to 100%

FIGURE 2.9 Classification of the major groups of igneous rocks based on their mineral composition and texture. Coarse-grained rocks are plutonic, solidifying deep underground. Fine-grained rocks are volcanic, or solidify as shallow, thin plutons. Ultramafic rocks are dark, dense rocks, composed almost entirely of minerals containing iron and magnesium. Although relatively rare on Earth's surface, these rocks are believed to be major constituents of the upper mantle.

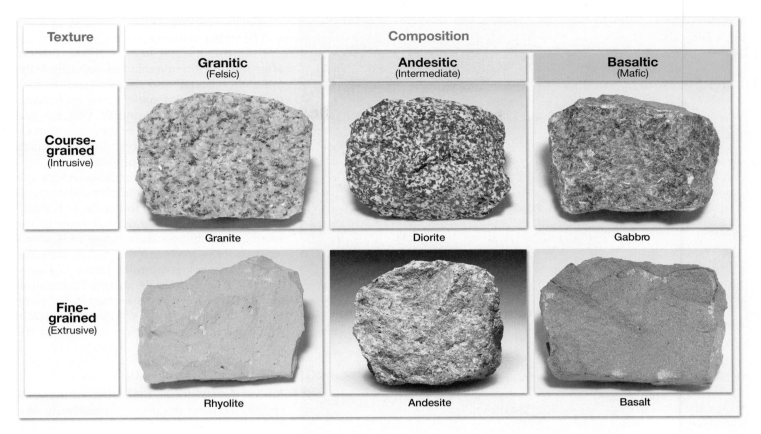

Texture	Composition		
	Granitic (Felsic)	**Andesitic** (Intermediate)	**Basaltic** (Mafic)
Course-grained (Intrusive)	Granite	Diorite	Gabbro
Fine-grained (Extrusive)	Rhyolite	Andesite	Basalt

FIGURE 2.10   Common igneous rocks. (Photos by E. J. Tarbuck)

Basaltic (Mafic) Rocks

Rocks that contain substantial dark silicate minerals and calcium-rich plagioclase feldspar (but no quartz) are said to have a **basaltic composition** (Figure 2.10). Basaltic rocks contain a high percentage of dark silicate minerals, so geologists also refer to them as **mafic** (from *ma*gnesium and *ferrum*, the Latin name for iron). Because of their iron content, basaltic rocks are typically darker and denser than granitic rocks.

Basalt, the most common extrusive igneous rock, is a very dark green to black, fine-grained volcanic rock composed primarily of pyroxene, olivine, and plagioclase feldspar. Many volcanic islands, such as the Hawaiian Islands and Iceland, are composed mainly of basalt (**FIGURE 2.11**). Further, the upper layers of the oceanic crust consist of basalt. In the United States, large portions of central Oregon and Washington were the sites of extensive basaltic outpourings.

The coarse-grained, intrusive equivalent of basalt is *gabbro* (Figure 2.10). Although gabbro is not commonly exposed at the surface, it makes up a significant percentage of the oceanic crust.

Andesitic (Intermediate) Rocks

As you can see in Figure 2.10, rocks with a composition between granitic and basaltic rocks are said to have an **andesitic** or **intermediate composition** after the common volcanic rock *andesite*. Andesitic rocks contain a mixture of both light- and dark-colored minerals, mainly amphibole and plagioclase feldspar. This important category of igneous rocks is associated with volcanic activity typically confined to continental margins. When magma of intermediate composition crystallizes at depth, it forms the coarse-grained rock called *diorite* (Figure 2.10).

Ultramafic Rocks

Another important igneous rock, *peridotite,* contains mostly the dark-colored minerals olivine and pyroxene and thus, falls on the opposite side of the compositional spectrum from granitic rocks (Figure 2.10). Because peridotite is composed almost entirely of dark silicate minerals, its chemical composition is referred to as **ultramafic**. Although ultramafic rocks are rare at Earth's surface, peridotite is believed to be the main constituent of the upper mantle.

How Different Igneous Rocks Form

Because a large variety of igneous rocks exist, it is logical to assume that an equally large variety of magmas also exist. However, geologists have observed that a single volcano may extrude lavas exhibiting quite different compositions. Data of this type led them to examine the possibility that magma might change (evolve) and thus, become the parent to a variety of igneous rocks. To explore this idea, a pioneering investigation into the crystallization of magma was carried out by N. L. Bowen in the first quarter of the 20th century.

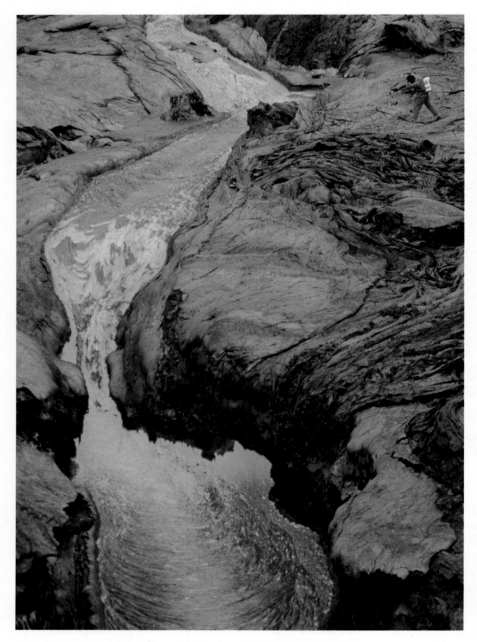

FIGURE 2.11 Basaltic lava flowing from Kilauea volcano, Hawaii. (Photo by Roger Ressmeyer/CORBIS)

Bowen's Reaction Series

In a laboratory setting, Bowen demonstrated that magma with its diverse chemistry crystallizes over a temperature range of at least 200°C unlike simple compounds (such as water), which solidify at specific temperatures. As magma cools, certain minerals crystallize first, at relatively high temperatures (top of **FIGURE 2.12**). At successively lower temperatures, other minerals begin to crystallize. This arrangement of minerals, shown in Figure 2.12, became known as **Bowen's reaction series**.

Bowen discovered that the first mineral to crystallize from a body of magma is *olivine*. Further cooling results in the formation of *pyroxene*, as well as *plagioclase feldspar*. At inter-

mediate temperatures the minerals *amphibole* and *biotite* begin to crystallize.

During the last stage of crystallization, after most of the magma has solidified, the minerals *muscovite* and *potassium feldspar* may form (Figure 2.12). Finally, *quartz* crystallizes from any remaining liquid. Olivine and quartz are seldom found in the same igneous rock, because quartz crystallizes at much lower temperatures than olivine.

Analysis of igneous rocks provides evidence that this crystallization model approximates what can happen in nature. In particular, we find that minerals that form in the same general temperature range on Bowen's reaction series are found together in the same igneous rocks. For example, notice in Figure 2.12 that the minerals quartz, potassium feldspar, and muscovite, located in the same region of Bowen's diagram, are typically found together as major constituents of the igneous rock *granite*.

Magmatic Differentiation

Bowen demonstrated that different minerals crystallize from magma systematically. But how do Bowen's findings account for the great diversity of igneous rocks? During the crystallization process, the composition of magma continually changes. This occurs because as crystals form, they selectively remove certain elements from the magma, which leaves the remaining liquid portion depleted in these elements. Occasionally, separation of the solid and liquid components of magma occurs during crystallization, which creates different mineral assemblages. One such scenario, called **crystal settling**, occurs when the earlier formed minerals are denser (heavier) than the liquid portion and sink toward the bottom of the magma chamber, as shown in **FIGURE 2.13**. When the remaining molten material solidifies—either in place or in another location if it migrates into fractures in the surrounding rocks—it will form a rock with a chemical composition much different from the parent magma (Figure 2.13). The formation of one or more secondary magmas from a single parent magma is called **magmatic differentiation.**

At any stage in the evolution of a magma, the solid and liquid components can separate into two chemically distinct units. Further, magmatic differentiation within the secondary magma can generate other chemically distinct masses of molten rock. Consequently, magmatic differentiation and separation of the solid and liquid components at various stages of crystallization can produce several chemically diverse magmas and, ultimately, a variety of igneous rocks.

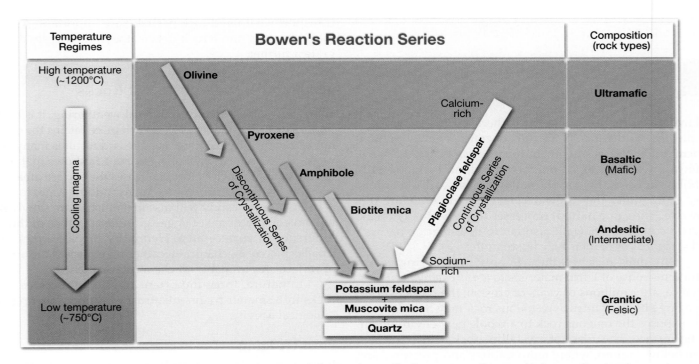

FIGURE 2.12 Bowen's reaction series shows the sequence in which minerals crystallize from a magma. Compare this figure to the mineral composition of the rock groups in Figure 2.9. Note that each rock group consists of minerals that crystallize in the same temperature range.

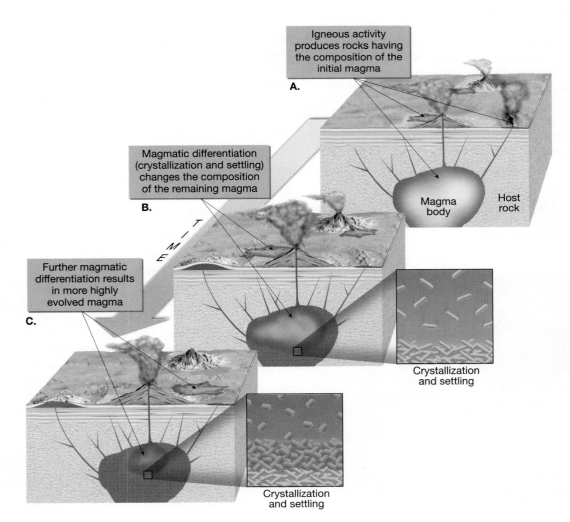

Crystallization and settling

Crystallization and settling

FIGURE 2.13 Illustration of how a magma evolves as the earlier formed minerals (those richer in iron, magnesium, and calcium) crystallize and settle to the bottom of the magma chamber, leaving the remaining melt richer in sodium, potassium, and silica (SiO_2). **A.** Emplacement of a magma body and associated igneous activity generates rocks having a composition similar to that of the initial magma. **B.** After a period of time, crystallization and settling change the composition of the melt, while generating rocks having a composition quite different from the original magma. **C.** Further magmatic differentiation results in another more highly evolved melt with its associated rock types.

WEATHERING OF ROCKS TO FORM SEDIMENT

Sculpturing Earth's Surface
▼ Weathering and Soils

All materials are susceptible to weathering. Consider, for example, the synthetic rock we call concrete. A newly poured concrete sidewalk is smooth, but many years later, the same sidewalk will appear chipped, cracked, and rough, with pebbles exposed at the surface. If a tree is nearby, its roots may grow under the sidewalk, heaving and buckling the concrete. The same natural processes that eventually break apart a concrete sidewalk also act to disintegrate natural rocks, regardless of their type or strength.

Why does rock weather? Simply, **weathering** is the natural response of Earth materials to a *new environment*. For instance, after millions of years of erosion, the rocks overlying a large body of intrusive igneous rock may be removed. This exposes the igneous rock to a whole new environment at the surface. This mass of crystalline rock, which formed deep below ground, where temperatures and pressures are high, is now subjected to very different and comparatively hostile surface conditions. In response, this rock mass will gradually change until it is once again in equilibrium, or balance, with its new environment. Such transformation of rock is what we call *weathering*.

In the following sections, we will discuss the two basic categories of weathering—mechanical and chemical. Mechanical weathering is the physical breaking up of rocks. Chemical weathering actually alters what a rock is, changing it into different substances. Although we will consider these two processes separately, keep in mind that they usually work simultaneously in nature. Furthermore, the activities of erosional agents—wind, water, and glaciers—that transport weathered rock particles are important. As these mobile agents move rock debris, they relentlessly disintegrate it further.

Mechanical Weathering of Rocks

When a rock undergoes **mechanical weathering**, it is broken into smaller and smaller pieces. Each piece retains the characteristics of the original material. The end result is many small pieces from a single large one. **FIGURE 2.14** shows that breaking a rock into smaller pieces increases the surface area available for chemical attack. An example is adding sugar to water. A chunk of rock candy will dissolve much more slowly than will an equal volume of sugar granules because of the vast difference in surface area. Hence, by breaking rocks into smaller pieces, mechanical weathering increases the amount of surface area available for chemical weathering.

In nature, three important physical processes break rocks into smaller fragments: frost wedging, sheeting, and biological activity.

Frost Wedging

If you leave a glass bottle full of water in a freezer too long, you will find the bottle fractured. The bottle breaks because liquid water has the unique property of expanding about 9 percent upon freezing. This is also the reason that poorly insulated or exposed water pipes rupture during frigid weather. You might also expect this process to fracture rocks in nature. After water works its way into cracks in the rock, it freezes, expands, and enlarges the openings (**FIGURE 2.15**). After many freeze-thaw cycles, the rock is broken into pieces.

This process is appropriately called **frost wedging** (Figure 2.15). Frost wedging is most pronounced in mountainous regions in the middle latitudes where a daily freeze-thaw cycle often exists. Here, sections of rock are wedged loose and may tumble into large piles called *talus* or *talus slopes* that often form at the base of steep rock outcrops (Figure 2.15).

Sheeting

When large masses of intrusive igneous rock are exposed by erosion, entire slabs begin to break loose, like the layers of an onion. This process, called **sheeting**, is thought to occur because of the great reduction in pressure that accompanies the removal of the overlaying rock (**FIGURE 2.16**). The outer layers expand more than the rock below and thus separate from the rock body. Granite is particularly prone to sheeting.

Continued weathering eventually causes the slabs to separate and spall off, creating

FIGURE 2.14 Chemical weathering can occur only to those portions of a rock that are exposed to the elements. Mechanical weathering breaks rock into smaller and smaller pieces, thereby increasing the surface area available for chemical attack.

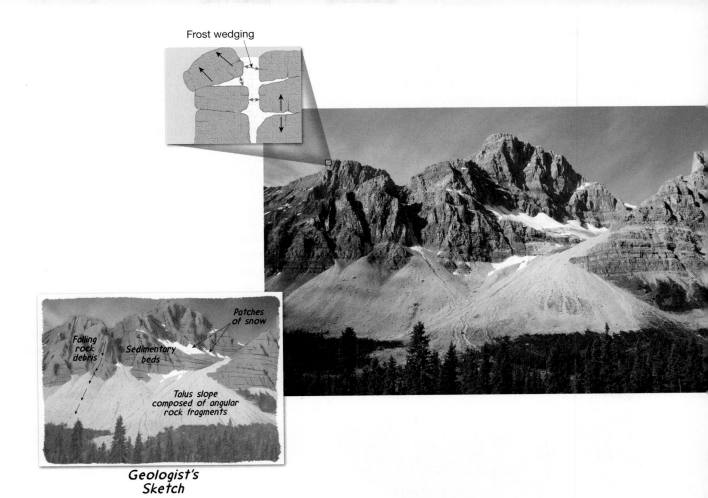

Frost wedging

Geologist's
Sketch

Falling
rock
debris

Sedimentary
beds

Patches
of snow

Talus slope
composed of angular
rock fragments

FIGURE 2.15 Frost wedging. As water freezes, it expands, exerting a force great enough to break rock. When frost wedging occurs in a setting such as this, the broken rock fragments fall to the base of the cliff and create a cone-shaped accumulation known as talus. (Photo by Marli Miller)

Confining
pressure

Deep
pluton

**A. Deeply buried
igneous pluton**

Joints

Expansion
and
sheeting

Uplift

**B. Uplift and erosion
of overlying rock**

C. Exfoliation dome

FIGURE 2.16 Sheeting is caused by the expansion of crystalline rock as erosion removes the overlying material. When the deeply buried pluton (**A**) is exposed at the surface following uplift and erosion (**B**), the igneous mass fractures into thin slabs. The photo (**C**) is of the summit of Half Dome in Yosemite National Park, California. It is an exfoliation dome and illustrates the onionlike layers created by sheeting. (Photo by (Gary Moon/agefotostock) *exfoliation domes.* Excellent examples of exfoliation domes include Stone Mountain, Georgia, and Half Dome in Yosemite National Park (Figure 2.16).

Biological Activity

Weathering is also accomplished by the activities of organisms, including plants, burrowing animals, and humans. Plant roots in search of water grow into fractures, and as the roots grow, they wedge the rock apart (**FIGURE 2.17**). Burrowing animals further break down the rock by moving fresh material to the surface, where physical and chemical processes can more effectively attack it.

Chemical Weathering of Rocks

Chemical weathering alters the internal structure of minerals by removing and/or adding elements. During this transformation, the original rock is altered into substances that are stable in the surface environment.

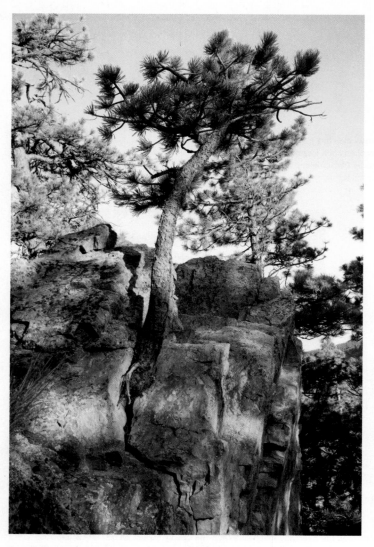

FIGURE 2.17 Root wedging widens fractures in rocks and aids the process of mechanical weathering. (Photo by Kristin Piljay)

Water is the most important agent of chemical weathering. Oxygen dissolved in water will *oxidize* some materials. For example, when an iron nail is found in the soil, it will have a coating of rust (iron oxide), and if the time of exposure has been long, the nail will be so weak that it can be broken as easily as a toothpick. When rocks containing iron-rich minerals (such as hornblende) oxidize, a yellow to reddish-brown rust will appear on the surface.

Carbon dioxide (CO_2) dissolved in water (H_2O) forms carbonic acid (H_2CO_3). This is the same weak acid produced when soft drinks are carbonated. Rain dissolves some carbon dioxide as it falls through the atmosphere, so normal rainwater is mildly acidic. Water in the soil also dissolves carbon dioxide released by decaying organic matter. The result is that acidic water is everywhere on Earth's surface.

How does rock decompose when attacked by carbonic acid? Consider the weathering of the common igneous rock, granite. Recall that granite is composed mainly of quartz and potassium feldspar. As the weak acid slowly reacts with crystals of potassium feldspar, potassium ions are displaced. *This destroys the mineral's crystalline structure.*

The most abundant products of the chemical breakdown of feldspar are clay minerals. Because clay minerals are the end product of chemical weathering, they are very stable under surface conditions. Consequently, clay minerals make up a high percentage of the inorganic material in many soils.

In addition to the formation of clay minerals, some silica (SiO_2) is dissolved from the feldspar structure and is carried away by groundwater. The dissolved silica will eventually precipitate to produce a hard, dense sedimentary rock (chert), fill pore spaces between mineral grains, or be carried to the ocean, where microscopic animals will build silica shells from it.

Quartz, the other main component of granite, is very resistant to chemical weathering. Because it is durable, quartz remains substantially unaltered when attacked by weak acid. As granite weathers, the feldspar crystals become dull and slowly turn to clay, releasing the once interlocked quartz grains, which still retain their fresh, glassy appearance. Although some quartz remains in the soil, much is transported to the sea and other sites, where it becomes sandy beaches and sand dunes.

To summarize, *the chemical weathering of granite produces clay minerals along with potassium ions and silica, which enter into solution.* In addition, durable quartz grains are freed.

Table 2.1 lists the weathered products of some of the most common silicate minerals. Remember that silicate minerals make up most of Earth's crust and are composed primarily of just eight elements (see Figure 1.21, p. 34). When chemically weathered, the silicate minerals yield sodium, calcium, potassium, and magnesium ions. These may be used by plants or removed by groundwater. The element iron combines with oxygen to produce iron-oxide compounds that give soil a reddish-brown or yellowish color. The three remaining elements—aluminum, silicon, and oxygen—join with water to produce clay minerals that become an important part of the soil. Ultimately, the products of

Table 2.1   Products of weathering

Original Mineral	Weathers to Produce	Released into Solution
Quartz	Quartz grains	Silica (SiO_2)
Feldspar	Clay minerals	Silica (SiO_2)
		Ions of potassium, sodium, and calcium
Hornblende	Clay minerals	Silica (SiO_2)
	Iron minerals (limonite and hematite)	Ions of calcium and magnesium
Olivine	Iron minerals (limonite and hematite)	Silica (SiO_2)
		Ions of magnesium

weathering form the raw materials for building sedimentary rocks, which we consider next.

SEDIMENTARY ROCKS: COMPACTED AND CEMENTED SEDIMENT

Earth Materials
▼ Sedimentary Rocks

Recall the rock cycle, which shows the origin of **sedimentary rocks**. Weathering begins the process. Next, gravity and erosional agents (running water, wind, waves, and glacial ice) remove the products of weathering and carry them to a new location where they are deposited. Usually, the particles are broken down further during this transport phase. Following deposition, this **sediment** may become lithified, or "turned to rock." Commonly, *compaction* and *cementation* transform the sediment into solid sedimentary rock.

The word *sedimentary* indicates the nature of these rocks, for it is derived from the Latin *sedimentum,* which means "settling," a reference to a solid material settling out of a fluid. Most sediment is deposited in this fashion. Weathered debris is constantly being swept from bedrock and carried away by water, ice, or wind. Eventually, the material is deposited in lakes, river valleys, seas, and countless other places. The particles in a desert sand dune, the mud on the floor of a swamp, the gravels in a streambed, and even household dust are examples of sediment produced by this never-ending process.

The weathering of bedrock and the transport and deposition of the weathering products are continuous. Therefore, sediment is found almost everywhere. As piles of sediment accumulate, the materials near the bottom are compacted by the weight of the overlying layers. Over long periods, these sediments are cemented together by mineral matter deposited from water in the spaces between particles. This forms solid sedimentary rock.

Geologists estimate that sedimentary rocks account for only about 5 percent (by volume) of Earth's outer 16 kilometers (10 miles). However, the importance of this group of rocks is far greater than this percentage implies. If you sampled the rocks exposed at Earth's surface, you would find that the great majority are sedimentary (**FIGURE 2.18**). Indeed, about 75 percent of all rock outcrops on the continents are sedimentary. Therefore, we can think of sedimentary rocks as comprising a relatively thin and somewhat discontinuous layer in the uppermost portion of the crust. This makes sense because sediment accumulates at the surface.

It is from sedimentary rocks that geologists reconstruct many details of Earth's history. Because sediments are deposited in a variety of different settings at the surface, the rock layers that they eventually form hold many clues to past surface environments. They may also exhibit characteristics that allow geologists to decipher information about the method and distance of sediment transport. Furthermore, it is sedimentary rocks that contain fossils, which are vital evidence in the study of the geologic past.

Finally, many sedimentary rocks are important economically. Coal, which is burned to provide a significant portion of U.S. electrical energy, is classified as a sedimentary rock. Other major energy resources (petroleum and natural gas) occur in pores within sedimentary rocks. Other sedimentary rocks are major sources of iron, aluminum, manganese, and fertilizer, plus numerous materials essential to the construction industry.

Classifying Sedimentary Rocks

Materials accumulating as sediment have two principal sources. First, sediments may originate as solid particles from weathered rocks, such as the igneous rocks earlier described. These particles are called *detritus,* and the sedimentary rocks that they form are called **detrital sedimentary rocks (FIGURE 2.19)**.

The second major source of sediment is soluble material produced largely by chemical weathering. When these dissolved substances are precipitated back as solids, they are called *chemical sediment,* and they form **chemical sedimentary rocks**. We will now look at detrital and chemical sedimentary rocks (Figure 2.19).

Detrital Sedimentary Rocks

Though a wide variety of minerals and rock fragments may be found in detrital rocks, clay minerals and quartz dominate. As you learned earlier, clay minerals are the most abundant product of the chemical weathering of silicate minerals, especially the feldspars. Quartz, on the other hand, is abundant because it is extremely durable and very resistant to chemical weathering. Thus, when igneous rocks such as granite are weathered, individual quartz grains are set free.

Geologists use particle size to distinguish among detrital sedimentary rocks. Figure 2.19 presents the four size categories for particles making up detrital rocks. When gravel-size particles predominate, the rock is called *conglomerate* if the sediment is rounded (**FIGURE 2.20A**) and *breccia* if the pieces are angular (**FIGURE 2.20B**). Angular fragments indicate that the particles were not transported very far from their source prior to deposition and so have not had corners

FIGURE 2.18 Sedimentary rocks exposed at Capital Reef National Park, Utah. Sedimentary rocks are exposed at the surface more than igneous and metamorphic rocks. Because they contain fossils and other clues about the geologic past, sedimentary rocks are important in the study of Earth history. Vertical changes in rock types represent environmental changes through time. (Photo by Scott T. Smith/CORBIS)

and rough edges abraded. *Sandstone* is the name given rocks when sand-size grains prevail (**FIGURE 2.21**). *Shale,* the most common sedimentary rock, is made of very fine-grained sediment (**FIGURE 2.22**). *Siltstone,* another rather fine-grained rock, is sometimes difficult to differentiate from rocks such as shale, which are composed of even smaller clay-size sediment.

Particle size is not only a convenient method of dividing detrital rocks; the sizes of the component grains also provide useful information about the environment in which the sediment was deposited. Currents of water or air sort the particles by size. The stronger the current, the larger the particle size carried. Gravels, for example, are moved by swiftly

flowing rivers, rockslides, and glaciers. Less energy is required to transport sand; thus, it is common in windblown dunes, river deposits, and beaches. Because silts and clays settle very slowly, accumulations of these materials are generally associated with the quiet waters of a lake, lagoon, swamp, or marine environment.

Although detrital sedimentary rocks are classified by particle size, in certain cases the mineral composition is also part of naming a rock. For example, most sandstones are predominantly quartz-rich, and they are often referred to as quartz sandstone. In addition, rocks consisting of detrital sediments are rarely composed of grains of just one size. Consequently, a rock containing quantities of both sand and

Detrital Sedimentary Rocks		
ClasticTexture (particle size)	**Sediment Name**	**Rock Name**
Coarse (over 2 mm)	Gravel (Rounded particles)	Conglomerate
Coarse (over 2 mm)	Gravel (Angular particles)	Breccia
Medium (1/16 to 2 mm)	Sand (If abundant feldspar is present the rock is called **Arkose**)	Sandstone
Fine (1/16 to 1/256 mm)	Mud	Siltstone
Very fine (less than 1/256 mm)	Mud	Shale or Mudstone

Chemical and Organic Sedimentary Rocks			
Composition	**Texture**	**Rock Name**	
Calcite, $CaCO_3$	Nonclastic: Fine to coarse crystalline	Crystalline Limestone	
Calcite, $CaCO_3$	Nonclastic: Fine to coarse crystalline	Travertine	
Calcite, $CaCO_3$	Clastic: Visible shells and shell fragments loosely cemented	Coquina	Biochemical Limestone
Calcite, $CaCO_3$	Clastic: Various size shells and shell fragments cemented with calcite cement	Fossiliferous Limestone	Biochemical Limestone
Calcite, $CaCO_3$	Clastic: Microscopic shells and clay	Chalk	Biochemical Limestone
Quartz, SiO_2	Nonclastic: Very fine crystalline	Chert (light colored) Flint (dark colored)	
Gypsum $CaSO_4 \cdot 2H_2O$	Nonclastic: Fine to coarse crystalline	Rock Gypsum	
Halite, NaCl	Nonclastic: Fine to coarse crystalline	Rock Salt	
Altered plant fragments	Nonclastic: Fine-grained organic matter	Bituminous Coal	

FIGURE 2.19 Identification of sedimentary rocks. Sedimentary rocks are divided into two major groups, detrital and chemical, based on their source of sediment. The main criterion for naming detrital rocks is particle size, whereas the primary basis for distinguishing among chemical rocks is their mineral composition.

silt can be correctly classified as sandy siltstone or silty sandstone, depending on which particle size dominates.

Chemical Sedimentary Rocks

In contrast to detrital rocks, which form from the solid products of weathering, chemical sediments are derived from material that is carried in solution to lakes and seas. This material does not remain dissolved in the water indefinitely. When conditions are right, it precipitates to form chemical sediments. This precipitation may occur directly as the

DID YOU KNOW?

The most important and common material used for making glass is silica, which is usually obtained from the quartz in "clean," well-sorted sandstones.

A.

B.

FIGURE 2.20 Detrital rocks made up of gravel-sized particles. **A.** *Conglomerate* (rounded particles) **B.** *Breccia* (angular particles). (Photos by E. J. Tarbuck)

Close up

FIGURE 2.21   Quartz sandstone. After shale, sandstone is the most abundant sedimentary rock. (Photos by E. J. Tarbuck)

Close up

FIGURE 2.23   This rock, called *coquina*, consists of shell fragments; therefore, it has a biochemical origin. (Photos by E. J. Tarbuck)

result of physical processes, or indirectly through life processes of water-dwelling organisms. Sediment formed in this second way has a *biochemical* origin.

An example of a deposit resulting from physical processes is the salt left behind as a body of saltwater evaporates. In contrast, many water-dwelling animals and plants extract dissolved mineral matter to form shells and other hard parts. After the organisms die, their skeletons may accumulate on the floor of a lake or ocean.

Limestone is the most abundant chemical sedimentary rock. It is composed chiefly of the mineral calcite ($CaCO_3$). Ninety percent of limestone is biochemical sediment,

while the remaining amount chemically precipitates from seawater.

One easily identified biochemical limestone is *coquina*, a coarse rock composed of loosely cemented shells and shell fragments (**FIGURE 2.23**). Another less obvious but familiar example is *chalk*, a soft, porous rock made up almost entirely of the hard parts of microscopic organisms that are no larger than the head of a pin (**FIGURE 2.24**).

Inorganic limestone forms when chemical changes or high water temperatures increase the concentration of calcium carbonate to the point that it precipitates. *Travertine*, the type of limestone that decorates caverns, is one example. Groundwater is the source of travertine that is deposited in caves. As water drops reach the air in a cavern, some of the carbon dioxide dissolved in the water escapes, causing calcium carbonate to precipitate.

Dissolved silica (SiO_2) precipitates to form varieties of microcrystalline quartz (**FIGURE 2.25**). Sedimentary rocks composed of microcrystalline quartz include chert (light color), flint (dark), jasper (red), and agate (banded). These chemical sedimentary rocks may have either an inorganic or biochemical origin, but the mode of origin is usually difficult to determine.

Very often, evaporation causes minerals to precipitate from water. Such minerals include halite, the chief component of *rock salt,* and gypsum, the main ingredient of *rock gypsum.* Both materials have significant commercial importance. Halite is familiar to everyone as the common salt used in cooking and seasoning foods. Of course, it has many other uses and has been considered important enough that people have sought, traded, and fought over it for much of human history. Gypsum is the basic ingredient of plaster of Paris. This material is used most extensively in the construction industry for "drywall" and plaster.

FIGURE 2.22   Shale is a fine-grained detrital rock that is, by far, the most abundant of all sedimentary rocks. Dark shales containing plant remains are relatively common. (Photo courtesy of E. J. Tarbuck)

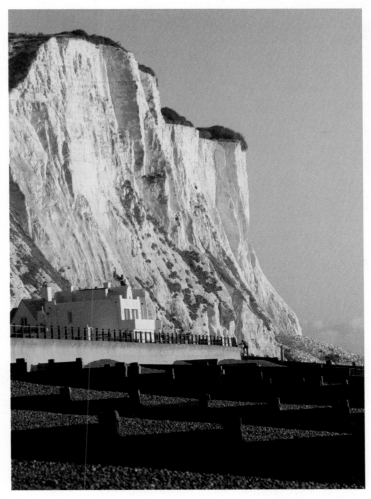

FIGURE 2.24   White Chalk Cliffs, East Sussex, England. (Photo by Prisma/ Superstock)

A. Agate

B. Flint   **C.** Jasper   **D.** Arrowhead

FIGURE 2.25   *Chert* is a name used for a number of dense, hard rocks made of microcrystalline quartz. Three examples are shown here. **A.** *Agate* is the banded variety. (Photo by Jeffrey A. Scovil) **B.** The dark color of *flint* results from organic matter. (Photo by E. J. Tarbuck) **C.** The red variety, called *jasper*, gets its color from iron oxide. (Photo by E. J. Tarbuck) **D.** Native Americans frequently made arrowheads and sharp tools from chert. (Photo by LA VENTA/CORBIS/SYGMA)

In the geologic past, many areas that are now dry land were covered by shallow arms of the sea that had only narrow connections to the open ocean. Under these conditions, water continually moved into the bay to replace water lost by evaporation. Eventually, the waters of the bay became saturated and salt deposition began. Today, these arms of the sea are gone, and the remaining deposits are called **evaporite deposits**.

On a smaller scale, evaporite deposits can be seen in such places as Death Valley, California. Here, following rains or periods of snowmelt in the mountains, streams flow from surrounding mountains into an enclosed basin. As the water evaporates, *salt flats* form from dissolved materials left behind as a white crust on the ground (**FIGURE 2.26**).

DID YOU KNOW?

Each year, about 30 percent of the world's supply of salt is extracted from seawater. The seawater is pumped into ponds and allowed to evaporate, leaving behind "artificial evaporites," which are harvested.

Coal is quite different from other chemical sedimentary rocks. Unlike other rocks in this category, which are calcite- or silica-rich, coal is made mostly of organic matter. Close examination of a piece of coal under a microscope or magnifying glass often reveals plant structures such as leaves, bark, and wood that have been chemically altered but are still identifiable. This supports the conclusion that coal is the end product of the burial of large amounts of plant material over extended periods (**FIGURE 2.27**).

The initial stage in coal formation is the accumulation of large quantities of plant remains. However, special conditions are required for such accumulations, because dead plants normally decompose when exposed to the atmosphere. An ideal environment that allows for the buildup of plant material is a swamp. Because stagnant swamp water is oxygen-deficient, complete decay (oxidation) of the plant material is not possible. At various times during Earth history, such environments have been common. Coal undergoes successive stages of formation. With each successive stage, higher temperatures and pressures drive off impurities and volatiles, as shown in Figure 2.27.

Lignite and bituminous coals are sedimentary rocks, but anthracite is a metamorphic rock. Anthracite forms

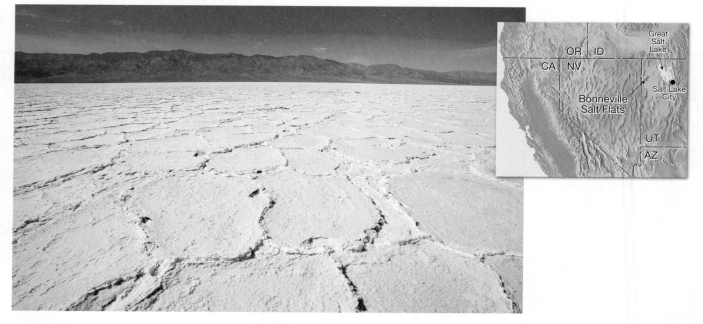

FIGURE 2.26 Bonneville Salt Flats, Utah. (Photo by Creates/Photolibrary)

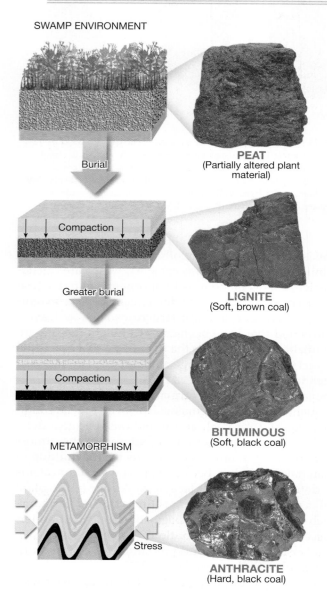

SWAMP ENVIRONMENT

Burial

PEAT
(Partially altered plant material)

Compaction

Greater burial

LIGNITE
(Soft, brown coal)

Compaction

METAMORPHISM

BITUMINOUS
(Soft, black coal)

Stress

ANTHRACITE
(Hard, black coal)

FIGURE 2.27 Successive stages in the formation of coal.

when sedimentary layers are subjected to the folding and deformation associated with mountain building.

In summary, we divide sedimentary rocks into two major groups: detrital and chemical. The main criterion for classifying detrital rocks is particle size, whereas chemical rocks are distinguished by their mineral composition. The categories presented here are more rigid than is the actual state of nature. Many detrital sedimentary rocks are a mixture of more than one particle size. Furthermore, many sedimentary rocks classified as chemical also contain at least small quantities of detrital sediment, and practically all detrital rocks are cemented with material that was originally dissolved in water.

Lithification of Sediment

Lithification refers to the processes by which sediments are transformed into solid sedimentary rocks. One of the most common processes is *compaction*. As sediments accumulate through time, the weight of overlying material compresses the deeper sediments. As the grains are pressed closer and closer, pore space is greatly reduced. For example, when clays are buried beneath several thousand meters of material, the volume of the clay may be reduced as much as 40 percent. Compaction is most significant in fine-grained sedimentary rocks such as shale, because sand and other coarse sediments compress little.

Cementation is another important means by which sediments are converted to sedimentary rock. The cementing materials are carried in solution by water percolating through the pore spaces between particles. Over time, the cement precipitates onto the sediment grains, fills the open spaces, and joins the particles. Calcite, silica, and iron oxide are the most common cements. Identification of the cementing material is simple. Calcite cement will effervesce (fizz) with dilute hydrochloric acid. Silica is the hardest cement and thus produces the hardest sedimentary rocks. When a sedimentary rock has an orange or red color, this usually means iron oxide is present.

A   B

FIGURE 2.28   Sedimentary environments. **A.** Ripple marks preserved in sedimentary rocks may indicate a beach or stream channel environment. (Photo by Marli Miller) **B.** Mud cracks form when wet mud or clay dries and shrinks, perhaps signifying a tidal flat or desert basin. (Photo by Gary Yeowell/Getty Images Inc.—Stone Allstock)

Features of Sedimentary Rocks

Sedimentary rocks are particularly important in the study of Earth history. These rocks form at Earth's surface, and as layer upon layer of sediment accumulates, each records the nature of the environment at the time the sediment was deposited. These layers, called **strata**, or **beds**, are the *single most characteristic feature of sedimentary rocks* (see Figure 2.18).

The thickness of beds ranges from microscopically thin to tens of meters thick. Separating the strata are *bedding planes*, flat surfaces along which rocks tend to separate or break. Generally, each bedding plane marks the end of one episode of sedimentation and the beginning of another.

Sedimentary rocks provide geologists with evidence for deciphering past environments. A conglomerate, for example, indicates a high-energy environment, such as a rushing stream, where only the coarse materials can settle out. By contrast, black shale and coal are associated with a low-energy, organic-rich environment, such as a swamp or lagoon. Other features found in some sedimentary rocks also give clues to past environments (**FIGURE 2.28**).

Fossils, the traces or remains of prehistoric life, are perhaps the most important inclusions found in some sedimentary rock. Knowing the nature of the life forms that existed at a particular time may help answer many questions about the environment. Was it land or ocean, lake or swamp? Was the climate hot or cold, rainy or dry? Was the ocean water shallow or deep, turbid or clear? Furthermore, fossils are important time indicators and play a key role in matching up rocks from different places that are the same

age. Fossils are important tools used in interpreting the geologic past and will be examined in some detail in Chapter 8.

METAMORPHIC ROCKS: NEW ROCK FROM OLD

 Earth Materials
▼ Metamorphic Rocks

Recall from the discussion of the rock cycle that metamorphism is the transformation of one rock type into another. **Metamorphic rocks** are produced from preexisting igneous, sedimentary, or even other metamorphic rocks. Thus, every metamorphic rock has a *parent rock*—the rock from which it was formed.

Metamorphism, which means to "change form," is a process that leads to changes in the mineralogy, texture (for example, grain size), and sometimes the chemical composition of rocks. Metamorphism takes place when preexisting rock is subjected to a physical or chemical environment that is significantly different from that in which it initially formed. In response to these new conditions the rock gradually changes until a state of equilibrium with the new environment is reached. Most metamorphic changes occur at the elevated temperatures and pressures that exist in the zone beginning a few kilometers below Earth's surface and extending into the upper mantle.

Metamorphism often progresses incrementally, from slight changes (*low-grade metamorphism*) to substantial changes *(high-grade metamorphism)*. For example, under low-grade metamorphism, the common sedimentary rock *shale* becomes the more compact metamorphic rock called *slate*. Hand samples of these rocks are sometimes difficult to distinguish, illustrating that the transition from sedimentary to metamorphic rock is often gradual and the changes can be subtle.

In more extreme environments, metamorphism causes a transformation so complete that the identity of the parent rock cannot be determined. In high-grade metamorphism, such features as bedding planes, fossils, and vesicles that may have existed in the parent rock are obliterated. Further, when rocks deep in the crust (where temperatures are high) are subjected to directed pressure, the entire mass may deform, producing large-scale structures, such as folds (**FIGURE 2.29**).

In the most extreme metamorphic environments, the temperatures approach those at which rocks melt. However, *during metamorphism the rock must remain essentially solid,* for if complete melting occurs, we have entered the realm of igneous activity.

Most metamorphism occurs in one of two settings:

1. When rock is intruded by magma, **contact** or **thermal metamorphism** may take place. In such a situation, change is caused by the rise in temperature within the host rock surrounding the mass of molten material.

2. During mountain building, great quantities of rock are subjected to directed pressures and high temperatures associated with large-scale deformation called **regional metamorphism**.

Extensive areas of metamorphic rocks are exposed on every continent. Metamorphic rocks are an important component of many mountain belts, where they make up a large portion of a mountain's crystalline core. Even the stable continental interiors, which are generally covered by sedimentary rocks, are underlain by metamorphic basement rocks. In all of these settings, the metamorphic rocks are usually highly deformed and intruded by igneous masses. Consequently, significant parts of Earth's continental crust are composed of metamorphic and associated igneous rocks.

DID YOU KNOW?

Some low-grade metamorphic rocks actually contain fossils. When fossils are present in metamorphic rocks, they provide useful clues for determining the original rock type and its depositional environment. In addition, fossils whose shapes have been distorted during metamorphism provide insight into the extent to which the rock has been deformed.

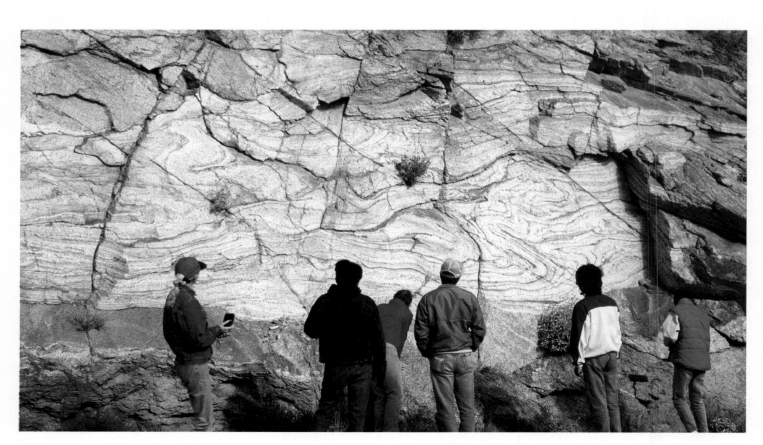

FIGURE 2.29   Folded and metamorphosed rocks in Anza Borrego Desert State Park, California. (Photo by A. P. Trujillo/APT Photos)

What Drives Metamorphism?

The agents of metamorphism include *heat, pressure (stress),* and *chemically active fluids.* During metamorphism, rocks are usually subjected to all three metamorphic agents simultaneously. However, the degree of metamorphism and the contribution of each agent vary greatly from one environment to another.

Heat as a Metamorphic Agent

Thermal energy (*heat*) is the most important factor driving metamorphism. It triggers chemical reactions that result in the recrystallization of existing minerals and the formation of new minerals. Thermal energy for metamorphism comes mainly from two sources. Rocks experience a rise in temperature when they are intruded by magma rising from below. This is called *contact* or *thermal metamorphism.* In this situation, the adjacent host rock is "baked" by the emplaced magma.

By contrast, rocks that formed at Earth's surface will experience a gradual increase in temperature as they are taken to greater depths. In the upper crust, this increase in temperature averages about 25°C per kilometer. When buried to a depth of about 8 kilometers (5 miles), where temperatures are between 150°C and 200°C, clay minerals tend to become unstable and begin to recrystallize into other minerals, such as chlorite and muscovite, that are stable in this environment. (Chlorite is a micalike mineral formed by the metamorphism of iron- and magnesian-rich silicates.) However, many silicate minerals, particularly those found in crystalline igneous rocks—quartz and feldspar, for example—remain stable at these temperatures. Thus, metamorphic changes in these minerals require much higher temperatures in order to recrystallize.

Confining Pressure and Differential Stress as Metamorphic Agents

Pressure, like temperature, also increases with depth as the thickness of the overlying rock increases. Buried rocks are subjected to *confining pressure*—similar to water pressure in that the forces are equally applied in all directions (**FIGURE 2.30 A**). The deeper you go in the ocean, the greater the confining pressure. The same is true for buried rock. Confining pressure causes the spaces between mineral grains to close, producing a more compact rock having greater density. Further, at great

FIGURE 2.30 Pressure (stress) as a metamorphic agent. **A.** In a depositional environment, as confining pressure increases, rocks deform by decreasing in volume. **B.** During mountain building, rocks subjected to differential stress are shortened in the direction that pressure is applied, and lengthened in the direction perpendicular to that force.

FIGURE 2.31 Deformed metamorphic rocks exposed in a road cut in the Eastern Highland of Connecticut. Imagine the tremendous force required to fold rock in this manner. (Photo by Phil Dombrowski)

depths, confining pressure may cause minerals to recrystallize into new minerals that display more compact crystalline forms.

During episodes of mountain building, large rock bodies become highly crumpled and metamorphosed (**FIGURE 2.30B**). The forces that generate mountains are unequal in different directions and are called *differential stress*. Unlike confining pressure, which "squeezes" rock equally in all directions, differential stresses are greater in one direction than in others. As shown in Figure 2.30B, rocks subjected to differential stress are shortened in the direction of greatest stress, and elongated, or lengthened, in the direction perpendicular to that stress. The deformation caused by differential stresses plays a major role in developing metamorphic textures.

In surface environments where temperatures are relatively low, rocks are *brittle* and tend to fracture when subjected to differential stress. Continued deformation grinds and pulverizes the mineral grains into small fragments. By contrast, in high-temperature environments, rocks are *ductile*. When rocks exhibit ductile behavior, their mineral grains tend to flatten and elongate when subjected to differential stress. This accounts for their ability to deform by flowing (rather than fracturing) to generate intricate folds (**FIGURE 2.31**).

Chemically Active Fluids

Fluids composed mainly of water and other volatiles (materials that readily change to gases at surface conditions), including carbon dioxide, are believed to play an important role in some types of metamorphism. Fluids that surround mineral grains act as catalysts to promote recrystallization by enhancing ion migration. In progressively hotter environments, these ion-rich fluids become correspondingly more reactive.

When two mineral grains are squeezed together, the parts of their crystalline structures that touch are the most highly stressed. Atoms at these sites are readily dissolved by the hot fluids and move to the voids between individual grains. Thus, hot fluids aid in the recrystallization of mineral grains by dissolving material from regions of high stress and then precipitating (depositing) this material in areas of low stress. As a result, *minerals tend to recrystallize and grow longer in a direction perpendicular to compressional stresses.*

When hot fluids circulate freely through rocks, ionic exchange may occur between adjacent rock layers, or ions may migrate great distances before they are finally deposited. The latter situation is particularly common when we consider hot fluids that escape during the crystallization of an intrusive mass of magma. If the rocks surrounding the magma differ markedly in composition from the invading fluids, there may be a substantial exchange of ions between the fluids and host rocks. When this occurs, the overall composition of the surrounding rock changes.

Metamorphic Textures

The degree of metamorphism is reflected in the rock's *texture* and *mineralogy*. (Recall that the term *texture* is used to describe the size, shape, and arrangement of grains within a rock.) When rocks are subjected to low-grade metamorphism, they become more compact and thus denser. A common example is the metamorphic rock slate, which forms when shale is subjected to temperatures and pressures only slightly greater than those associated with the compaction that lithifies sediment. In this case, differential stress causes the microscopic clay minerals in shale to align into the more compact arrangement found in slate.

Under more extreme conditions, stress causes certain minerals to recrystallize. In general, recrystallization encourages the growth of larger crystals. Consequently, many metamorphic rocks consist of visible crystals, much like coarse-grained igneous rocks.

Foliation

The term **foliation** refers to any planer (nearly flat) arrangement of mineral grains or structural features within a rock (**FIGURE 2.32**). Although foliation may occur in some sedimentary and even a few types of igneous rocks, it is a fundamental characteristic of regionally metamorphosed rocks—that is, rock units that have been strongly deformed, mainly by folding. In metamorphic environments, foliation is ultimately driven by compressional stresses that shorten rock units, causing mineral grains in preexisting rocks to develop parallel, or nearly parallel, alignments. Examples of foliation include the parallel alignment of platy minerals such as the micas; the parallel alignment of flattened pebbles; compositional banding in which dark and light minerals separate generating a layered appearance; and rock cleavage in which rocks can be easily split into tabular slabs.

A. Before metamorphism (Uniform stress)

B. After metamorphism (Differential stress)

METAMORPHISM

FIGURE 2.32 Under the pressures of metamorphism, some mineral grains become reoriented and aligned at right angles to the stress. The resulting orientation of mineral grains gives the rock a foliated (layered) texture. If the coarse-grained igneous rock (granite) on the left underwent intense metamorphism, it could end up closely resembling the metamorphic rock on the right (gneiss). (Photos by E. J. Tarbuck)

Nonfoliated Textures

Not all metamorphic rocks exhibit a foliated texture. Those that do not are referred to as **nonfoliated**, and typically develop in environments where deformation is minimal and the parent rocks are composed of minerals that exhibit equidimensional crystals, such as quartz or calcite. For example, when a fine-grained limestone (made of calcite) is metamorphosed by the intrusion of a hot magma body, the small calcite grains recrystallize to form larger interlocking crystals. The resulting rock, *marble*, exhibits large, equidimensional grains that are randomly oriented, similar to those in a coarse-grained igneous rock.

To review, metamorphic processes cause many changes in existing rocks, including increased density, growth of larger crystals, foliation (reorientation of the mineral grains into a layered or banded appearance), and the transformation of low-temperature minerals into high-temperature minerals (**FIGURE 2.33**). Further, the introduction of ions generates new minerals, some of which are economically important.

Common Metamorphic Rocks

Here is a brief overview of common rocks produced by metamorphic processes.

Rock Name			Texture	Grain Size	Comments	Original Parent Rock
Slate	Increasing	Metamorphism	Foliated	Very fine	Excellent rock cleavage, smooth dull surfaces	Shale, mudstone, or siltstone
Schist			Foliated	Medium to Coarse	Micaceous minerals dominate, scaly foliation	Shale, mudstone, or siltstone
Gneiss			Foliated	Medium to Coarse	Compositional banding due to segregation of minerals	Shale, granite, or volcanic rocks
Marble			Nonfoliated	Medium to coarse	Interlocking calcite or dolomite grains	Limestone, dolostone
Quartzite			Nonfoliated	Medium to coarse	Fused quartz grains, massive, very hard	Quartz sandstone
Anthracite			Nonfoliated	Fine	Shiny black rock that may exhibit conchoidal fracture	Bituminous coal

FIGURE 2.33 Classification of common metamorphic rocks.

Foliated Rocks

Slate is a very fine-grained foliated rock composed of minute mica flakes that are too small to be visible (**FIGURE 2.34**). A noteworthy characteristic of slate is its excellent rock cleavage, or tendency to break into flat slabs. This property has made slate a useful rock for roof and floor tile, and billiard tables (**FIGURE 2.35**). Slate is usually generated by the low-grade metamorphism of shale. Less frequently, it is produced when volcanic ash is metamorphosed. Slate's color is variable. Black slate contains organic material; red slate gets its color from iron oxide; and green slate is usually composed of chlorite, a greenish micalike mineral.

Schists are strongly foliated rocks formed by regional metamorphism (Figure 2.34). They are platy and can be readily split into thin flakes or slabs. Many schists, like slates, originate from shale parent rock. However, schist forms under more extreme metamorphic conditions. The term *schist* describes the *texture* of a rock regardless of composition. For example, schists composed primarily of muscovite and biotite are called *mica schists*.

Gneiss (pronounced "nice") is the term applied to banded metamorphic rocks in which elongated and granular (as opposed to platy) minerals predominate (Figure 2.34). The most common minerals in gneisses are quartz and feldspar, with lesser amounts of muscovite, biotite, and hornblende. Gneisses exhibit strong segregation of light and dark silicates, giving them a characteristic banded texture. While still deep below the surface where temperatures and pressures are great, banded gneisses can be deformed into intricate folds.

Nonfoliated Rocks

Marble is a coarse, crystalline rock whose parent rock is limestone. Marble is composed of large interlocking calcite crystals, which form from the recrystallization of smaller grains in the parent rock. Because of its color and relative softness (hardness of only 3 on the Mohs scale), marble is a popular building stone. White marble is particularly prized as a stone from which to carve monuments and statues, such as the Lincoln Memorial in Washington D.C. (**FIGURE 2.36**). The parent rocks from which various marbles form contain impurities that color the stone. Thus, marble can be pink, gray, green, or even black.

Quartzite is a very hard metamorphic rock most often formed from quartz sandstone. Under moderate- to

Foliated metamorphic rocks

Slate

Schist

Gneiss

Nonfoliated metamorphic rocks

Marble

Quartzite

FIGURE 2.34 Common metamorphic rocks. (Photos by E. J. Tarbuck)

high-grade metamorphism, the quartz grains in sandstone fuse. Pure quartzite is white, but iron oxide may produce reddish or pinkish stains, and dark minerals may impart a gray color.

FIGURE 2.35   Because slate breaks into flat slabs, it has many uses. The larger image shows crates full of slate ready to be shipped from a quarry in England. (Photo by Alamy). In the inset photo, slate is used to roof a house in Switzerland. (Photo by E. J. Tarbuck)

A.

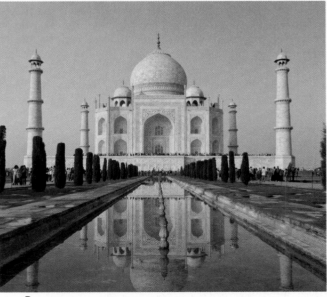

B.

FIGURE 2.36   Marble, because of its workability, is a widely used building stone. **A.** The white exterior of the Lincoln Memorial in Washington, D.C., is constructed mainly of marble that was quarried in Marble, Colorado. Inside, pink Tennessee marble was used for the floors, Alabama marble for the ceilings, and Georgia marble for Lincoln's statue. (Photo by Daniel Grill/iStockphoto) **B.** The exterior of India's Taj Mahal is constructed primarily of the metamorphic rock marble. (Holger Mette/Shutterstock)

THE CHAPTER IN REVIEW

• The three rock groups are igneous, sedimentary, and metamorphic. *Igneous rock* forms from *magma* that cools and solidifies in a process called *crystallization. Sedimentary rock* forms from the *lithification* of sediment. *Metamorphic rock* forms from rock that has been subjected to great pressure and heat in a process called *metamorphism.*

• Igneous rocks are classified by their *texture* and *mineral composition.*

• The rate of cooling of magma greatly influences the size of mineral crystals in igneous rock and thus its texture. The four basic igneous rock textures are (1) *fine-grained,* (2) *coarse-grained,* (3) *porphyritic,* and (4) *glassy.*

• Igneous rocks are divided into broad compositional groups based on the percentage of dark and light silicate minerals they contain. *Felsic rocks* (e.g., granite and rhyolite) are composed mostly of the light-colored silicate minerals potassium feldspar and quartz. Rocks of *intermediate* composition (e.g., andesite) contain plagioclase feldspar and amphibole. *Mafic rocks* (e.g., basalt) contain abundant pyroxene and calcium-rich plagioclase feldspar.

• The mineral makeup of an igneous rock is ultimately determined by the chemical composition of the magma from which it crystallized. N. L. Bowen showed that as magma cools, minerals crystallize in an orderly fashion at different temperatures. *Magmatic differentiation* changes the composition of magma and causes more than one rock type to form from a common parent magma.

• *Weathering* is the response of surface materials to a changing environment. *Mechanical weathering,* the physical disintegration of material into smaller fragments, is accomplished by *frost wedging,* sheeting, and *biological activity. Chemical weathering* involves processes by which the internal structures of minerals are altered by the removal and/or addition of elements. It occurs when materials are *oxidized* or *react with acid,* such as carbonic acid.

• *Detrital sediments* originate as solid particles derived from weathering and are transported. *Chemical sediments* are soluble materials produced largely by chemical weathering that are precipitated by either inorganic or biological processes. *Detrital sedimentary rocks,* which are classified by particle size, contain a variety of mineral and rock fragments, with clay minerals and quartz the chief constituents. *Chemical sedimentary rocks* often contain the products of biological processes or mineral crystals that form as water evaporates and minerals precipitate. *Lithification* refers to the processes by which sediments are transformed into solid sedimentary rocks.

• Common detrital sedimentary rocks include *shale* (the most common sedimentary rock), *sandstone,* and *conglomerate.* The most abundant chemical sedimentary rock is *limestone,* consisting chiefly of the mineral calcite. *Rock gypsum* and *rock salt* are chemical rocks that form as water evaporates.

• Some features of sedimentary rocks that are often used in the interpretation of Earth history and past environments include *strata* or *beds* (the single most characteristic feature), *bedding planes,* and *fossils.*

• Two types of metamorphism are (1) *regional metamorphism* and (2) *contact or thermal metamorphism.* The agents of metamorphism include *heat, pressure* (stress), and *chemically active fluids.* Heat is the most important because it provides the energy to drive the reactions that result in the *recrystallization* of minerals. Metamorphic processes cause many changes in rocks, including *increased density,* growth of *larger mineral crystals, reorientation of the mineral grains* into a layered or banded appearance known as *foliation,* and the formation of *new minerals.*

• Some common metamorphic rocks with a *foliated texture* include *slate, schist,* and *gneiss.* Metamorphic rocks with a *nonfoliated texture* include *marble* and *quartzite.*

KEY TERMS

andesitic (intermediate) composition (p. 51)

basaltic composition (p. 51)

Bowen's reaction series (p. 52)

chemical sedimentary rock (p. 56)

chemical weathering (p. 57)

coarse-grained texture (p. 48)

contact (thermal) metamorphism (p. 64)

crystal settling (p. 52)

detrital sedimentary rock (p. 57)

evaporite deposit (p. 61)

extrusive (volcanic) (p. 61)

felsic (p. 50)

fine-grained texture (p. 48)

foliation (p. 66)

fossil (p. 63)

frost wedging (p. 54)

glassy texture (p. 49)

granitic composition (p. 50)

igneous rock (p. 46)

intrusive (plutonic) (p. 46)

lava (p. 46)

lithification (p. 62)

mafic (p. 51)

magma (p. 46)

magmatic differentiation (p. 52)

mechanical weathering (p. 54)

metamorphic rock (p. 63)

metamorphism (p. 63)

nonfoliated texture (p. 67)

porphyritic texture (p. 48)

regional metamorphism (p. 64)

rock cycle (p. 44)

sediment (p. 57)

sedimentary rock (p. 57)

sheeting (p. 54)

strata (beds) (p. 63)

texture (p. 48)

ultramafic composition (p. 51)

vesicular texture (p. 48)

weathering (p. 54)

QUESTIONS FOR REVIEW

1. Explain the statement "One rock is the raw material for another" using the rock cycle.

2. If a lava flow at Earth's surface had a basaltic composition, what rock type would the flow likely be (see Figure 2.10)? What igneous rock would form from the same magma if it did not reach the surface but instead crystallized at great depth?

3. What does a porphyritic texture indicate about the history of an igneous rock?

4. How are granite and rhyolite different? The same? (See Figure 2.10.)

5. Relate the classification of igneous rocks to Bowen's reaction series.

6. If two identical rocks were weathered, one mechanically and the other chemically, how would the products of weathering for the two rocks differ?

7. How does mechanical weathering add to the effectiveness of chemical weathering?

8. How is carbonic acid formed in nature? What are the products when this acid reacts with potassium feldspar?

9. Which minerals are most common in detrital sedimentary rocks? Why are these minerals so abundant?

10. What is the primary basis for distinguishing among various detrital sedimentary rocks?

11. Distinguish between the two categories of chemical sedimentary rocks.

12. What are evaporite deposits? Name a rock that is an evaporite.

13. Compaction is an important lithification process with which sediment size?

14. What is probably the single most characteristic feature of sedimentary rocks?

15. What is metamorphism?

16. List the three agents of metamorphism and describe the role of each.

17. Distinguish between regional and contact metamorphism.

18. Which feature would easily distinguish schist and gneiss from quartzite and marble?

19. In what ways do metamorphic rocks differ from the igneous and sedimentary rocks from which they formed?

COMPANION WEBSITE

The *Foundations of Earth Science* Website uses the resources and flexibility of the Internet to aid in your study of the topics in this chapter. Written and developed by the authors and other Earth science instructors, this site will help improve your understanding of Earth science. Visit **www.mygeoscienceplace.com** in order to:

• **Review** key chapter concepts.

• **Read** with links to the ebook and to chapter-specific web resources.

• **Visualize** and comprehend challenging topics using learning activities in *GEODe: Earth Science*.

• **Test** yourself with online quizzes.

GEODe: EARTH SCIENCE

GEODe: Earth Science is a valuable and easy to use learning aid that can be accessed from your book's Companion Website **www.mygeoscienceplace.com.** It is a dynamic instructional tool that promotes understanding and reinforces important concepts by using tutorials, animations, and exercises that actively engage the student.

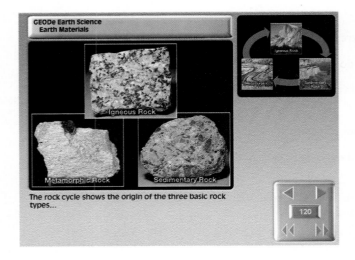

The rock cycle shows the origin of the three basic rock types...

For example, along oceanic ridges seawater circulates through hot basaltic rocks, transforming the existing iron-rich minerals into metamorphic minerals such as serpentine and talc.

LANDSCAPES
FASHIONED BY WATER

FOCUS ON LEARNING

To assist you in learning the important concepts in this chapter, you will find it helpful to focus on the following questions:

1. What is the role of *external processes* in the rock cycle?

2. What role does mass wasting play in the development of landforms?

3. What is the controlling force of mass wasting, and what factors might trigger mass-wasting processes?

4. What is the hydrologic cycle? What is the source of energy that powers the cycle?

5. What are the factors that determine the velocity of water in a stream?

6. The work of a stream involves what three processes?

7. How does base level influence a stream's ability to erode?

8. What common drainage patterns do streams produce?

9. What is the importance of groundwater as a resource and as a geologic agent?

10. What is groundwater, and how does it move?

11. What are some common natural phenomena associated with groundwater?

12. What are some environmental problems associated with groundwater?

Sunset along the Li River in China's Guilin District. The rock "towers" formed over a long time span when weakly acidic groundwater dissolved large volumes of soluble limestone leaving these residual rock masses. For more about this landscape, see the section on "Tower Karst" near the end of the chapter. (Photo by Moodboard/Corbis)

C H A P T E R

3

E arth is a dynamic planet. Volcanic and other internal forces elevate the land, while opposing external processes continually wear it down. The Sun and gravity drive external processes occurring at Earth's surface. Rock is disintegrated and decomposed, moved to lower elevations by gravity, and carried away by water, wind, or ice. In this manner, the physical landscape is sculptured.

EARTH'S EXTERNAL PROCESSES

Weathering, mass wasting, and erosion are called **external processes** because they occur at or near Earth's surface and are powered by energy from the Sun. External processes are a basic part of the rock cycle because they are responsible for transforming solid rock into sediment.

To the casual observer, the face of Earth may appear to be without change, unaffected by time. In fact, 200 years ago most people believed that mountains, lakes, and deserts were permanent features of an Earth that was thought to be no more than a few thousand years old. Today we know Earth is about 4.6 billion years old and that mountains eventually succumb to weathering and erosion, lakes fill with sediment or are drained by streams, and deserts come and go with changes in climate.

Earth is a dynamic body. Some parts of Earth's surface are gradually elevated by mountain building and volcanic activity. These **internal processes** derive their energy from Earth's interior. Meanwhile, opposing external processes are continually breaking rock apart and moving the debris to lower elevations. The latter processes include:

1. **Weathering**—the physical breakdown (disintegration) and chemical alteration (decomposition) of rock at or near Earth's surface.

2. **Mass wasting**—the transfer of rock and soil downslope under the influence of gravity.

3. **Erosion**—the physical removal of material by a mobile agent such as flowing water, waves, wind, or ice.

Weathering processes were treated in Chapter 2. In this chapter, we will focus on mass wasting and on two important erosional processes—running water and groundwater. Chapter 4 will examine the geologic work of two other significant erosional processes—glacial ice and wind.

MASS WASTING: THE WORK OF GRAVITY

Earth's surface is never perfectly flat but instead consists of slopes. Some are steep and precipitous; others are moderate or gentle. Some are long and gradual; others are short and abrupt. Some slopes are mantled with soil and covered by vegetation; others consist of barren rock and rubble. Their form and variety are great.

Although most slopes appear to be stable and unchanging, they are not static features, because the force of gravity causes material to move downslope. At one extreme, the movement may be gradual and practically imperceptible. At the other extreme, it may consist of a roaring debris flow or a thundering rock avalanche (**FIGURE 3.1**). Landslides are a worldwide, natural hazard. When these natural processes lead to loss of life and property, they become natural disasters.

DID YOU KNOW?

Although many people, including geologists, frequently use the word *landslide*, the term has no specific definition in geology. Rather, it is a popular nontechnical term used to describe all relatively rapid forms of mass wasting.

FIGURE 3.1 On August 6, 2006, photographer Herb Dunn witnessed this rockfall along the Merced River in California's Yosemite National Park. It appears to have been an event that had no discernible trigger (see "Landslides without Triggers" on p. 77). **A.** The impact of falling rock produces an explosion of dust and debris. **B.** The rockfall triggers a chain reaction. A debris avalanche moves down the slope knocking down trees along the way. (©2006 DunnRight Photograph)

FIGURE 3.2 Aerial view of a large debris flow at Caraballeda, Venezuela, in December 1999. Heavy rains triggered thousands of debris flows and other types of mass wasting in the adjacent mountains. Once created, these moving masses of mud and rock coalesced to form giant debris flows that moved rapidly through steep, narrow canyons and engulfed the city. The result was severe property damage and the tragic loss of an estimated 19,000 lives. (Kimberly White/ REUTERS/ CORBIS/ Bettmann)

Mass Wasting and Landform Development

Events such as those pictured in **FIGURES 3.1** and **3.2** are spectacular examples of a common geologic process called mass wasting. *Mass wasting* is the downslope movement of rock and soil under the direct influence of gravity. It is distinct from the erosional processes because mass wasting does not require a transporting medium such as water, wind, or glacial ice. There is a broad array of mass-wasting processes. Four are illustrated in **FIGURE 3.3**.

The Role of Mass Wasting

Mass wasting is the step that follows weathering in the evolution of most landforms. Once weathering weakens and breaks rock apart, mass wasting transfers the debris downslope, where a stream, acting as a conveyor belt, usually carries it away (**FIGURE 3.4**). Although there may be many intermediate stops along the way, the sediment is eventually transported to its ultimate destination: the sea. It is the combined effects of mass wasting and running water that produce stream valleys, which are the most common and conspicuous landforms at Earth's surface and the focus of a later part of this chapter.

If streams alone were responsible for creating the valleys in which they flow, valleys would be very narrow features. However, the fact that most river valleys are much

FIGURE 3.3 The four processes illustrated here are all considered to be relatively rapid forms of mass wasting. Because material in slumps **A.** and rockslides **B.** move along well-defined surfaces, they are said to move by sliding. By contrast, when material moves downslope as a viscous fluid, the movement is described as a flow. Debris flow **C.** and earthflow **D.** advance downslope in this manner.

Geologist's Sketch

FIGURE 3.4 The walls of the Grand Canyon extend far from the channel of the Colorado River. This results primarily from the transfer of weathered debris downslope to the river and its tributaries by mass-wasting processes. (Photo by Bryan Brazil/Shuttersotck)

wider than they are deep is a strong indication of the significance of mass-wasting processes in supplying material to streams. The walls of a canyon extend far from the river because of the transfer of weathered debris downslope to the river and its tributaries by mass-wasting processes. In this manner, streams and mass wasting combine to modify and sculpture the surface. Of course, glaciers, groundwater, waves, and wind are also important agents in shaping landforms and developing landscapes.

Slopes Change through Time

Most rapid and spectacular mass-wasting events occur in areas of rugged, geologically young mountains. Newly formed mountains are rapidly eroded by rivers and glaciers into regions characterized by steep and unstable slopes. It is in such settings that massive destructive landslides occur. As mountain building subsides, mass wasting and erosional processes lower the land. Over time, steep and rugged

mountain slopes give way to gentler, more subdued terrain. Thus, as a landscape ages, massive and rapid mass-wasting processes give way to smaller, less dramatic downslope movements.

Controls and Triggers of Mass Wasting

Gravity is the controlling force of mass wasting, but several factors play an important role in overcoming inertia and creating downslope movements. Long before a landslide occurs, various processes work to weaken slope material, gradually making it more and more susceptible to the pull of gravity. During this span, the slope remains stable but gets closer and closer to being unstable. Eventually, the strength of the slope is weakened to the point that something causes it to cross the threshold from stability to instability. Such an event that initiates downslope movement is called a *trigger*. Remember that the trigger is not

FIGURE 3.5 The Angle of repose for this granular material is about 30°. (Photo by G. Leavens/Photo Researchers, Inc.)

the sole cause of the mass-wasting event, but just the last of many causes. Among the common factors that trigger mass-wasting processes are saturation of material with water, oversteepening of slopes, removal of anchoring vegetation, and ground vibrations from earthquakes.

The Role of Water

Mass wasting is sometimes triggered when heavy rains or periods of snowmelt saturate surface materials. Such a situation is shown in Figure 3.2.

When the pores in sediment become filled with water, the cohesion among particles is destroyed, allowing them to slide past one another with relative ease. For example, when sand is slightly moist, it sticks together quite well. However, if enough water is added to fill the openings between the grains, the sand will ooze out in all directions. Thus, saturation reduces the internal resistance of materials, which are then easily set in motion by the force of gravity. When clay is wetted, it becomes very slick—another example of the "lubricating" effect of water. Water also adds considerable weight to a mass of material. The added weight in itself may be enough to cause the material to slide or flow downslope.

Oversteepened Slopes

Oversteepening of slopes is another trigger of many mass movements. This takes place in many situations in nature. A stream undercutting a valley wall and waves pounding against the base of a cliff are two familiar examples. Furthermore, through their activities, people often create oversteepened and unstable slopes that become prime sites for mass wasting.

Unconsolidated, granular (sand-size or coarser) particles assume a stable slope called the **angle of repose**, the steepest angle at which material remains stable (**FIGURE 3.5**). Depending on the size and shape of the particles, the angle varies from 25 to 40 degrees. The larger, more angular particles maintain the steepest slopes. If the angle is increased, the rock debris will adjust by moving downslope.

Oversteepening is important not only because it triggers movements of because it unconsolidated granular materials, but also because it produces unstable slopes and mass movements in cohesive soils, regolith (weathered rock debris), and bedrock. The response will not be immediate, as with loose, granular material, but sooner or later one or more mass-wasting processes will eliminate the oversteepening and restore stability to the slope.

Removal of Vegetation

Plants protect against erosion and contribute to the stability of slopes because their root systems bind soil and regolith together. Where plants are lacking, mass wasting is enhanced, especially if slopes are steep and water is plentiful. When anchoring vegetation is removed by forest fires or by people (for timber, farming, or development), surface materials frequently move downslope.

Earthquakes as Triggers

Among the more important and dramatic mass-wasting triggers are earthquakes. An earthquake and its aftershocks can dislodge enormous volumes of rock and unconsolidated material. In many areas that are jolted by earthquakes, it is not ground vibrations directly but landslides and ground subsidence triggered by the vibrations that cause the greatest damage.

Landslides without Triggers?

Do rapid mass-wasting events always require some sort of trigger such as heavy rains or an earthquake? The answer is no. Many rapid mass-wasting events occur without a discernible trigger. The rockfall shown in Figure 3.1 is an example. Slope materials gradually weaken over time under the influence of long-term weathering, infiltration of water, and other physical processes. Eventually, if the strength falls below what is necessary to maintain slope stability, a landslide will occur. The timing of such events is random and accurate prediction is not possible.

THE HYDROLOGIC CYCLE

Sculpturing Earth's Surface
▼ Hydrologic Cycle

All the rivers run into the sea; yet the sea is not full;
unto the place from whence the rivers come, thither
they return again.

Ecclesiastes 1:7

As the perceptive writer of Ecclesiastes implied, water is continually on the move, from the ocean to the atmosphere to the land and back again in an endless cycle called the **hydrologic cycle**. The remainder of this chapter deals with that part of the cycle that returns water to the sea. Some water travels by way of rivers, and some moves more slowly beneath the surface. We will examine the factors that influence the distribution and movement of water, as well as look at how water sculptures the landscape. The Grand Canyon, Niagara Falls, Old Faithful geyser, and Mammoth Cave all owe their existence to the action of water on its way to the sea.

Water is almost everywhere on Earth—in the oceans, glaciers, rivers, lakes, air, soil, and living tissue. All of these "reservoirs" constitute Earth's hydrosphere. In all, the water content of the hydrosphere is an estimated 1.36 billion cubic kilometers (326 million cubic miles). The vast bulk of it, about 97 percent, is stored in the global ocean. Ice sheets and glaciers account for more than 2 percent, leaving less than 1 percent to be divided among lakes, streams, groundwater, and the atmosphere (see Figure I.4, p. 7). Although the percentage of Earth's total water found in each of the latter sources is just a small fraction of the total inventory, the absolute quantities are great.

The hydrologic cycle is a gigantic, worldwide system powered by energy from the Sun in which the atmosphere provides the vital link between the oceans and continents (**FIGURE 3.6**). Water evaporates into the atmosphere from the ocean and to a much lesser extent from the continents. Winds transport this moisture-laden air, often great distances. Complex processes of cloud formation eventually result in precipitation. The precipitation that falls into the ocean has completed its cycle and is ready to begin another. The water that falls on the continents, however, must make its way back to the ocean.

What happens to precipitation once it has fallen on land? A portion of the water soaks into the ground (called **infiltration**), slowly moving downward, then laterally, finally seeping into lakes, streams, or directly into the ocean. When the rate of rainfall exceeds Earth's ability to absorb it, the surplus water flows over the surface into lakes and streams, a process called **runoff**. Much of the water that infiltrates or runs off eventually returns to the atmosphere because of evaporation from the soil, lakes, and streams. Also, some of the water that soaks into the ground is absorbed by plants, which then release it into the atmosphere. This process is called **transpiration**.

When precipitation falls in very cold places—at high elevations or high latitudes the water may not immediately soak in, run off, or evaporate. Instead, it may become part of a snowfield or a glacier. In this way, glaciers store large quantities of water on land. If present-day glaciers were to melt and release all their water, sea level would rise by several dozen meters. This would submerge many heavily populated coastal areas. As you will see in Chapter 4, over the past 2 million years, huge ice sheets have formed and melted on several occasions, each time affecting the balance of the water cycle.

Figure 3.6 also shows Earth's overall *water balance,* or the volume that passes through each part of the cycle annually. The amount of water vapor in the air at any one time is just a tiny fraction of Earth's total water supply. But the *absolute* quantities that are cycled through the atmosphere over a one-year period are immense—some 380,000 cubic kilometers (91,000 cubic miles)—enough to cover Earth's entire surface to a depth of about 1 meter (39 inches).

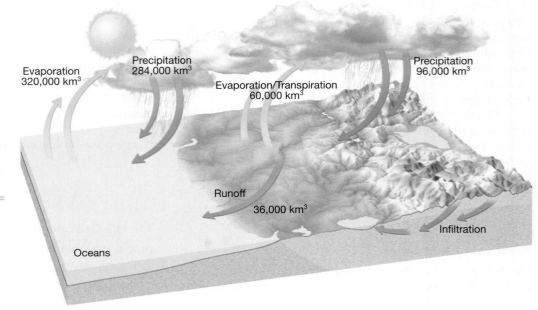

FIGURE 3.6   Earth's water balance. Each year, solar energy evaporates about 320,000 cubic kilometers of water from the oceans, and evaporation and transpiration from the land (including lakes and streams) contribute 60,000 cubic kilometers of water. Of this total of 380,000 cubic kilometers of water, about 284,000 cubic kilometers fall back to the ocean, and the remaining 96,000 cubic kilometers fall on the land surface. Of those 96,000 cubic kilometers, only 60,000 cubic kilometers of water return to the atmosphere by evaporation and transpiration, leaving 36,000 cubic kilometers of water to erode the land during the journey back to the oceans.

Each year, a field of crops may transpire the equivalent of a water layer 60 cm (2 ft) deep over the entire field. The same area of trees may pump twice this amount into the atmosphere.

RUNNING WATER

Sculpturing Earth's Surface
▼ *Running Water*

Recall that most of the precipitation that falls on land either enters the soil (infiltration) or remains at the surface, moving downslope as runoff. The amount of water that runs off rather than soaking into the ground depends on several factors: (1) intensity and duration of rainfall, (2) amount of water already in the soil, (3) nature of the surface material, (4) slope of the land, and (5) the extent and type of vegetation. When the surface material is highly impermeable, or when it becomes saturated, runoff is the dominant process. Runoff is also high in urban areas because large areas are covered by impermeable buildings, roads, and parking lots.

Runoff initially flows in broad, thin sheets across hillslopes. This unconfined flow eventually develops threads of current that form tiny channels called *rills*. Rills meet to form *gullies*, which join to form streams. At first streams are small, but as one intersects another, larger and larger ones form. Eventually rivers develop that carry water from a broad region.

Drainage Basins

The land area that contributes water to a river system is called a **drainage basin** (FIGURE 3.7). The drainage basin of one stream is separated from the drainage basin of another by an imaginary line called a **divide** (Figure 3.7). Divides range in scale from a ridge separating two small gullies on a hillside to a *continental divide*, which splits whole continents

It is important to know that the water cycle is *balanced*. Because the total amount of water vapor in the atmosphere remains about the same, the average annual precipitation worldwide must be equal to the quantity of water evaporated. However, for all of the continents taken together, precipitation exceeds evaporation. Conversely, over the oceans, evaporation exceeds precipitation. Because the level of the world ocean is not dropping, the system must be in balance. In Figure 3.6, the 36,000 cubic kilometers (8600 cubic miles) of water that annually makes its way from the land to the ocean causes enormous erosion. In fact, this immense volume of moving water is *the single most important agent sculpturing Earth's land surface.*

To summarize, the hydrologic cycle is the continuous movement of water from the oceans to the atmosphere, from the atmosphere to the land, and from the land back to the sea. The land-back-to-the-sea step is the primary action that wears down Earth's land surface. In the rest of this chapter, we will observe the work of water running over the surface, including floods, erosion, and the formation of valleys. Then we will look underground at the slow labors of groundwater as it forms springs and caverns and provides drinking water on its long migration to the sea.

FIGURE 3.7 A *drainage basin* is the land area drained by a stream and its tributaries. *Divides* are the boundaries separating drainage basins. Drainage basins and divides exist for all streams, regardless of size. The drainage basin of the Yellowstone River is one of many that contribute water to the Missouri River, which, in turn, is one of many that make up the drainage basin of the Mississippi River. The drainage basin of the Mississippi River, North America's largest, covers about 3 million square kilometers.

into enormous drainage basins. The Mississippi River has the largest drainage basin in North America. Extending between the Rocky Mountains in the West and the Appalachian Mountains in the East, the Mississippi River and its tributaries collect water from more than 3.2 million square kilometers (1.2 million square miles) of the continent.

River Systems

River systems involve not only a network of stream channels, but the entire drainage basin. Based on the dominant processes operating within them, river systems can be divided into three zones: *sediment production*—where erosion dominates, *sediment transport*, and *sediment deposition* (**FIGURE 3.8**). It is important to recognize that sediment is being eroded, transported, and deposited along the entire length of a stream, regardless of which process is dominant within each zone.

The zone of *sediment production*, where most of the water and sediment is derived, is located in the headwater region of the river system. Much of the sediment carried by streams begins as bedrock that is subsequently broken down by weathering, then transported downslope by mass wasting and overland flow. Bank erosion can also contribute significant amounts of sediment. In addition, scouring of the channel bed deepens the channel and adds to the stream's sediment load.

Sediment acquired by a stream is then transported through the channel network along sections referred to as *trunk streams*. When trunk streams are in balance, the amount of sediment eroded from their banks equals the amount deposited elsewhere in the channel. Although trunk streams rework their channels over time, they are not a source of sediment nor do they accumulate or store it.

When a river reaches the ocean, or another large body of water, it slows and the energy to transport sediment is

greatly reduced. Most of the sediments accumulate at the mouth of the river to form a delta, are reconfigured by wave action to form a variety of coastal features, or are moved far offshore by ocean currents. Because coarse sediments tend to be deposited upstream, it is primarily the fine sediments (clay and fine sand) that eventually reach the ocean. Taken together, erosion, transportation, and deposition are the processes by which rivers move Earth's surface materials and sculpt landscapes.

STREAMFLOW

Water may flow in one of two ways, either as **laminar flow** or **turbulent flow**. In slow-moving streams, the flow is often laminar, and the water moves in roughly straight-line paths that parallel the stream channel. However, streamflow is usually turbulent, with the water moving in an erratic fashion that can be characterized as a swirling motion. Strong, turbulent flow may be seen in whirlpools and eddies, as well as rolling whitewater rapids. Even streams that appear smooth on the surface often exhibit turbulent flow near the bottom and sides of the channel. Turbulence contributes to the stream's ability to erode its channel because it acts to lift sediment from the streambed.

Water makes its way to the sea under the influence of gravity. The time required for the journey depends on the velocity of the stream. Velocity is the distance that water travels in a unit of time. Some sluggish streams flow at less than 1 kilometer (0.6 mile) per hour, whereas a few rapid ones may exceed 30 kilometers (19 miles) per hour. Velocities are measured at gaging stations (**FIGURE 3.9A**). Along straight stretches, the highest velocities are near the center of the channel just below the surface, where friction is lowest (Figure 3.9B). But when a stream curves, its zone of maximum speed shifts (Figure 3.9C).

The ability of a stream to erode and transport material depends on its velocity. Even slight variations can lead to significant changes in the load of sediment that water can transport. Several factors influence the velocity of a stream, including (1) gradient; (2) shape, size, and roughness of the channel; and (3) the volume of water flowing in the channel.

Gradient and Channel Characteristics

The slope of a stream channel expressed as the vertical drop of a stream over a specified distance is **gradient**. Portions of the lower Mississippi River have very low

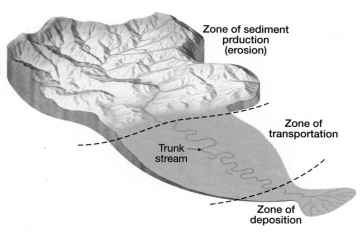

FIGURE 3.8 A river system can be divided into three zones based on the dominant process operating within each zone. These are the zone of sediment production (erosion), the zone of sediment transport, and the zone of sediment deposition.

A. Gaging station

Conical cups

Sounding weight

Maximum velocity

B.

Maximum velocity

C.

FIGURE 3.9 **A.** Continuous records of stage and discharge are collected by the U.S. Geological Survey at more than 7000 gaging stations in the United States. Average velocities are determined by using measurements from several spots across the stream. This station is on the Rio Grande south of Taos, New Mexico. (Photo by E. J. Tarbuck) **B.** Along straight stretches, stream velocity is highest at the center of the channel. **C.** When a stream curves, its zone of maximum speed shifts.

Discharge

Streams vary in size from small headwater creeks less than a meter wide to large rivers with widths of several kilometers. The size of a stream channel is largely determined by the amount of water supplied from the drainage basin. The measure most often used to compare the sizes of streams is **discharge**—the volume of water flowing past a certain point in a given unit of time. Discharge, usually measured in cubic meters per second or cubic feet per second, is determined by multiplying a stream's cross-sectional area by its velocity.

The largest river in North America, the Mississippi, discharges an average of 17,300 cubic meters (611,000 cubic feet) per second. Although this is a huge quantity of water, it is dwarfed by the mighty Amazon in South America, the world's largest river. Fed by a vast rainy region that is nearly three-fourths the size of the conterminous United States, the Amazon discharges 12 times more water than the Mississippi.

The discharges of most rivers are far from constant. This is true because of such variables as rainfall and snowmelt. In areas with seasonal variations in precipitation, streamflow will tend to be highest during the wet season, or during spring snowmelt, and lowest during the dry season or during periods when high temperatures increase the water losses through evaporation. However, not all channels maintain a continuous flow of water. Streams that exhibit flow only during wet periods are referred to as *intermittent streams*. In arid climates, many streams carry water only occasionally after a heavy rainstorm and are called *ephemeral streams*.

gradients of 10 centimeters per kilometer or less. By contrast, some mountain stream channels decrease in elevation at a rate of more than 40 meters per kilometer— a gradient 400 times steeper than the lower Mississippi (**FIGURE 3.10**). Gradient varies not only among different streams but also over a particular stream's length. The steeper the gradient, the more energy available for streamflow. If two streams were identical in every respect except gradient, the stream with the higher gradient would obviously have the greater velocity.

A stream's channel is a conduit that guides the flow of water, but the water encounters friction as it flows. The shape, size, and roughness of the channel affect the amount of friction. Larger channels have more efficient flow because a smaller proportion of water is in contact with the channel. A smooth channel promotes a more uniform flow, whereas an irregular channel filled with boulders creates enough turbulence to slow the stream significantly.

DID YOU KNOW?

The Amazon River is responsible for about 20 percent of all the water reaching the ocean via rivers. Its nearest rival, Africa's Congo River, delivers about 4 percent of the total.

FIGURE 3.10   Rapids are common in mountain streams where the gradient is steep and the channel is rough and irregular. (Photo by Fogstock Lic/Photolibrary)

Changes from Upstream to Downstream

One useful way of studying a stream is to examine its *longitudinal profile*—a cross-sectional view of a stream from its source area (called the *head* or *headwaters)* to its *mouth,* the point downstream where the river empties into another water body. By examining **FIGURE 3.11** you can see that the most obvious feature of a typical profile is a constantly decreasing gradient from the head to the mouth. Although

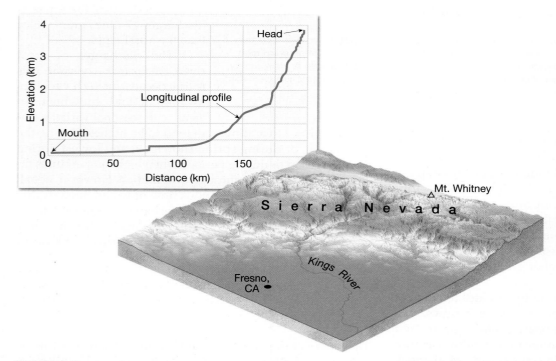

FIGURE 3.11   Longitudinal profile of California's Kings River. It originates in the Sierra Nevada and flows westward into the San Joaquin Valley. A longitudinal profile is a cross-section along the length of a stream. Note the concave curve of the profile, with a steeper gradient upstream and a gentler gradient downstream.

many local irregularities may exist, the overall profile is a relatively smooth concave curve.

The profile shows that the gradient decreases downstream. To see how other factors change in a downstream direction, observations and measurements must be made. When data are collected from several gaging stations along a river, they show that in a humid region, discharge increases from the head toward the mouth. This should come as no surprise because as we move downstream, more and more tributaries contribute water to the main channel. Furthermore, in most humid regions, additional water is added from the groundwater supply. Thus, as you move downstream, the stream's width, depth, and velocity change in response to the increased volume of water carried by the stream.

Streams that begin in mountainous areas where precipitation is abundant and then flow through arid regions may experience the opposite situation. Discharge may actually decrease downstream because of water loss due to evaporation, infiltration into the streambed, and removal by irrigation. The Colorado River in the southwestern United States is such an example.

THE WORK OF RUNNING WATER

Streams are Earth's most important erosional agents. Not only do they have the ability to downcut and widen their channels, but streams also have the capacity to transport the enormous quantities of sediment that are delivered to them by sheet flow, mass wasting, and groundwater. Eventually, much of this material is deposited to create a variety of depositional features.

Erosion

A stream's ability to accumulate and transport soil and weathered rock is aided by the work of raindrops, which knock sediment particles loose. When the ground is saturated, rainwater begins to flow downslope, transporting some of the material it has dislodged. On barren slopes the flow of muddy water, called *sheet flow,* will often erode small channels, or *rills,* which in time may evolve into larger *gullies.*

Once the surface flow reaches a stream, its ability to erode is greatly enhanced by the increase in water volume. When the flow of water is sufficiently strong, it can dislodge particles from the channel and lift them into the moving water. In this manner, the force of running water swiftly erodes poorly consolidated materials on the bed and sides of a stream channel. On occasion, the banks of the channel may be undercut, dumping even more loose debris into the water to be carried downstream.

In addition to eroding unconsolidated materials, the hydraulic force of streamflow can also cut a channel into solid bedrock. A stream's ability to erode bedrock is greatly enhanced by the particles it carries. These particles vary in size, from large gravel in fast-flowing waters to sand in somewhat slower flows. Just as the particles of grit on sandpaper can wear away a piece of wood, so too can the sand and gravel carried by a stream abrade a bedrock channel. Moreover, pebbles caught in swirling eddies can act like "drills" and bore circular *potholes* into the channel floor (**FIGURE 3.12**).

Transportation

All streams regardless of size transport some rock material. Streams also sort the solid sediment they transport because finer, lighter material is carried more readily than larger, heavier particles. Streams transport their load of sediment in three ways: (1) in solution (**dissolved load**), (2) in suspension (**suspended load**), and (3) sliding or rolling along the bottom (**bed load**).

Dissolved Load

Most of the *dissolved load* is brought to a stream by groundwater and is dispersed throughout the flow. When water percolates through the ground, it acquires soluble soil compounds. Then it seeps through cracks and pores in bedrock, dissolving additional mineral matter. Eventually, much of this mineral-rich water finds its way into streams.

Velocity has essentially no effect on a stream's ability to carry its dissolved load—material in solution goes wherever the water flows. Deposition (precipitation) of the dissolved mineral matter occurs when the chemistry of the water changes. In arid regions the water may enter an inland lake or sea and evaporate, leaving the dissolved load behind.

Suspended Load

Most streams carry the largest part of their load in *suspension*. Indeed, the visible cloud of sediment suspended in the water is the most obvious portion of a stream's load. Usually, only fine particles consisting of silt and clay can be carried this way, but during a flood, larger particles can also be transported in suspension. Also, during a flood, the total quantity of material carried in suspension increases dramatically, as can be verified by anyone whose home has been a site for the deposition of this material.

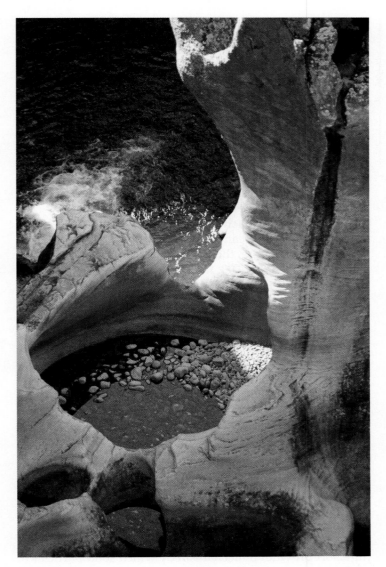

FIGURE 3.12 Potholes in the bed of a stream. The rotational motion of swirling pebbles acts ike a drill to create potholes. (Photo by Elmari Joubert/Alamy)

Bed Load

A portion of a stream's load consists of sand, gravel, and occasionally large boulders. These coarser particles, which are too large to be carried in suspension, move along the bottom (bed) of the stream channel and constitute the *bed load*. Unlike the suspended and dissolved loads, which are constantly in motion, the bed load is in motion only intermittently, when the force of the water is sufficient to move the larger particles. The smaller particles, mainly sand and gravel, are moved by *saltation*, which resembles a series of jumps or skips. Larger particles either roll or slide along the bottom, depending on their shape.

Competence and Capacity

Streams vary in their ability to carry a load. Their ability is determined by two criteria. First, the **competence** of a stream measures the maximum size of particles it is capable of transporting. The stream's velocity determines its competence. If the velocity of a stream doubles, its competence increases four times; if the velocity triples, its competence increases nine times; and so forth. This explains how large boulders that seem immovable can be transported during a flood, which greatly increases a stream's velocity.

Second, the **capacity** of a stream is the maximum load of solid particles a stream can transport per unit of time. The greater the discharge, the greater the stream's capacity for hauling sediment (**FIGURE 3.13**).

By now it should be clear why the greatest erosion and transportation of sediment occur during flood. The increase in discharge results in a greater capacity, and the increase in velocity results in greater competence. With rising velocity, the water becomes more turbulent, and larger and larger particles are set in motion. In just a few days or perhaps a few hours, a stream in flood stage can erode and transport more sediment than it does during months of normal flow.

Deposition

Whenever a stream slows down, the situation reverses. As its velocity decreases, its competence is reduced and sediment begins to drop out, largest particles first. Each particle size has a *critical settling velocity*. As stream flow drops below the critical setting velocity of a certain particle size, sediment in that category begins to settle out. Thus, stream transport provides a mechanism by which solid particles of various sizes are separated. This process, called **sorting**, explains why particles of similar size are deposited together.

The material deposited by a stream is called **alluvium**, the general term for any stream-deposited sediment. Many different depositional features are composed of alluvium. Some occur within stream channels, some occur on the valley floor adjacent to the channel, and some exist at the mouth of the stream. We will consider the nature of these features in the next section.

STREAM CHANNELS

A basic characteristic of streamflow that distinguishes it from overland flow is that it is confined to a channel. A stream channel can be thought of as an open conduit consisting of the streambed and banks that act to confine the flow except during floods.

Although somewhat oversimplified, we can divide stream channels into two types. *Bedrock channels* are those in which the streams are actively cutting into solid rock. In contrast, when the bed and banks are composed mainly of unconsolidated sediment, the channel is called an *alluvial channel*.

FIGURE 3.13   The Colorado River in Grand Canyon National Park. The muddy appearance is a result of suspended sediment. (Photo by Michael Collier)

Bedrock Channels

In their headwaters, where the gradient is steep, most rivers cut into bed rock. These streams typically transport coarse particles that actively abrade the bedrock channel. Potholes are often visible evidence of the erosional forces at work.

Bedrock channels typically alternate between relatively gently sloping segments where alluvium tends to accumulate, and steeper segments where bedrock is exposed. These steeper areas may contain rapids or occasionally a waterfall. The channel pattern exhibited by streams cutting into bedrock is controlled by the underlying geologic structure. Even when flowing over rather uniform bedrock, streams tend to exhibit a winding or irregular pattern rather than flowing in a straight channel. Anyone who has gone on a white-water rafting trip has observed the steep, winding nature of a stream flowing in a bedrock channel.

Alluvial Channels

Many stream channels are composed of loosely consolidated sediment (alluvium) and therefore can undergo significant changes in shape because the sediments are continually being eroded, transported, and redeposited. The major factors affecting the shapes of these channels is the average size of the sediment being transported, as well as the channel's gradient and discharge.

Alluvial channel patterns reflect a stream's ability to transport its load at a uniform rate, while expending the least amount of energy. Thus, the size and type of sediment being carried help determine the nature of the stream channel. Two common types of alluvial channels are *meandering channels* and *braided channels*.

Meandering Channels

Streams that transport much of their load in suspension generally move in sweeping bends called **meanders.** These streams flow in relatively deep, smooth channels and transport mainly mud (silt and clay). The lower Mississippi River exhibits a channel of this type.

Because of the cohesiveness of consolidated mud, the banks of stream channels carrying fine particles tend to resist erosion. As a consequence, most of the erosion in such channels occurs on the outside of the meander, where velocity and turbulence are greatest. In time, the outside bank is undermined, especially during periods of high water. Because the outside of a meander is a zone of active erosion, it is often referred to as the *cut bank* (**FIGURE 3.14**).

FIGURE 3.14 When a stream meanders, its zone of maximum speed shifts toward the outer bank. A point bar is deposited where the water on the inside of a meander slows. The point bar shown here is on the White River near Vernal, Utah. The black and white photo shows erosion of a cut bank along the Newaukum River in Washington State. By eroding its outer bank and depositing material on the inside of the bend, a stream is able to shift its channel. (Point bar photo by Michael Collier; cut bank photo by P.A. Glancy, U.S. Geological Survey)

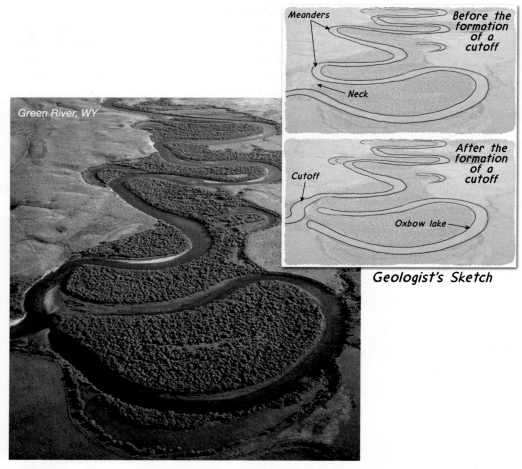

Geologist's Sketch

FIGURE 3.15 Oxbow lakes occupy abandoned meanders. As they fill with sediment, oxbow lakes gradually become swampy meander scars. Aerial view of an oxbow lake created by the meandering Green River near Bronx, Wyoming. (Photo by Michael Collier)

The debris acquired by the stream at the cut bank moves downstream with the coarser material generally being deposited as *point bars* in zones of decreased velocity on the insides of meanders. In this manner, meanders migrate laterally by eroding the outside of the bends and depositing on the inside.

In addition to migrating laterally, the bends in a channel also migrate down the valley. This occurs because erosion is more effective on the downstream (downslope) side of the meander. The downstream migration of a meander is sometimes slowed when it reaches a more resistant material. This allows the next meander upstream to "catch up" and overtake it as shown in **FIGURE 3.15**. The neck of land between the meanders is gradually narrowed. Eventually, the river may erode through the narrow neck of land to the next loop. The new, shorter channel segment is called a **cutoff** and, because of its shape, the abandoned bend is called an **oxbow lake** (Figure 3.15).

Braided Channels

Some streams consist of a complex network of converging and diverging channels that thread their way among numerous islands or gravel bars (**FIGURE 3.16**). Because these channels have an interwoven appearance, they are said to be **braided.** Braided channels form where a large proportion of the stream's load consists of coarse material (sand and gravel) and the stream has a highly variable discharge. Because the bank material is readily erodable, braided channels are wide and shallow.

One circumstance in which braided streams form is at the end of a glacier where there is a large seasonal variation in discharge. Here, large amounts of ice-eroded sediment are dumped into the meltwater streams flowing away from the glacier. When flow is sluggish, the stream is unable to move all of the sediment and therefore deposits the coarsest material as bars that force the flow to split and follow several paths. Usually the laterally shifting channels completely rework most of the surface sediments each year, thereby transforming the entire streambed. In some braided streams, however, the bars have built up to form islands that are anchored by vegetation.

In summary, meandering channels develop where the load consists largely of fine-grained particles that are transported as suspended load in a deep, smooth channel. By contrast, wide, shallow braided channels develop where coarse-grained alluvium is transported as bedload.

BASE LEVEL AND STREAM EROSION

Streams cannot endlessly erode their channels deeper and deeper. There is a lower limit to how deep a stream can erode, and that limit is called **base level**. Most often, a stream's base level occurs where a stream enters the ocean, a lake, or another stream.

Two general types of base level are recognized. Sea level is considered the *ultimate base level,* because it is the lowest level to which stream erosion could lower the land. *Temporary,* or *local, base levels* include lakes, resistant layers of rock, and main streams that act as base level for their tributaries. For example, when a stream enters a lake, its velocity quickly approaches zero and its ability to erode ceases. Thus, the lake prevents the stream from eroding below its level at any point upstream from the lake. However, because the outlet of the lake can cut downward and drain the lake, the lake is only a temporary hindrance to the stream's ability to downcut its channel. In a similar manner, the layer of resistant rock at the lip of the waterfall in **FIGURE 3.17** acts as a temporary base level. Until the ledge of hard rock is eliminated, it will limit the amount of downcutting upstream.

Any change in base level will cause a corresponding readjustment of stream activities. When a dam is built along a stream, the reservoir that forms behind it raises the base level of the stream (**FIGURE 3.18**). Upstream from the dam, the gradient is reduced, lowering the stream's velocity and, hence, its sediment-transporting ability. The stream, now having too little energy to transport its entire load, will deposit sediment. This builds up its channel. Deposition will be the dominant process until the stream's gradient increases sufficiently to transport its load.

FIGURE 3.16 The Knik River is a classic braided stream with multiple channels separated by migrating gravel bars. The river is choked with sediment carried by meltwater from four glaciers in the Chugach Mountains north of Anchorage, Alaska. (Photo by Michael Collier)

SHAPING STREAM VALLEYS

Streams, with the aid of weathering and mass wasting, shape the landscape through which they flow. As a result, streams continuously modify the valleys that they occupy.

A **stream valley** consists of not only the channel but also the surrounding terrain that directly contributes water to the stream. Thus, it includes the valley bottom, which is the lower, flatter area that is partially or totally occupied by the stream channel, and the sloping valley walls that rise above the valley bottom on both sides. Most stream valleys are much broader at the top than is the width of their channel at the bottom. This would not be the case if the only agent responsible for eroding valleys were the streams flowing through them. The sides of most valleys are shaped by a combination of weathering, overland flow, and mass wasting. In some arid regions, where weathering is slow and where rock is particularly resistant, narrow valleys having nearly vertical walls are common.

Stream valleys can be divided into two general types—narrow V-shaped valleys and wide valleys with flat floors—with many gradations between.

FIGURE 3.17 This series of diagrams illustrates what would happen if displacement along a fault raises a layer of resistant rock across the path of a stream. **A.** Stream course with a smooth profile prior to faulting. **B.** After faulting the resistant layer acts as a temporary base level and forms a waterfall. Because of the steep gradient, the stream's erosive energy is concentrated on the resistant bed. **C.** The waterfall evolves to rapids. **D.** Eventually the river reestablishes a smooth profile.

FIGURE 3.18 When a dam is built and a reservoir forms, the stream's base level is raised. This reduces the stream's velocity and leads to deposition and a reduction of the gradient upstream from the reservoir.

Valley Deepening

When a stream's gradient is steep and the channel is well above base level, downcutting is the dominant activity. Abrasion caused by bed-load sliding and rolling along the bottom, and the hydraulic power of fast-moving water, slowly lower the streambed. The result is usually a V-shaped valley with steep sides. A classic example of a V-shaped valley is located in the section of Yellowstone River shown in **FIGURE 3.19**.

The most prominent features of a V-shaped valley are *rapids* and *waterfalls*. Both occur where the stream's gradient increases significantly, a situation usually caused by variations in the erodability of the bedrock into which a stream channel is cutting. Resistant beds create rapids by acting as a temporary base level upstream while allowing downcutting to continue downstream. In time, erosion usually eliminates the resistant rock. Waterfalls are places where the stream makes an abrupt vertical drop.

Valley Widening

Once a stream has cut its channel closer to base level, downward erosion becomes less dominant. At this point, the stream's channel takes on a meandering pattern, and

DID YOU KNOW?

The world's highest uninterrupted waterfall is Angel Falls on Venezuela's Churun River. Named for American aviator Jimmie Angel, who first sighted the falls from the air in 1933, the river plunges 979 m (3212 ft).

more of the stream's energy is directed from side to side. The result is a widening of the valley as the river cuts away first at one bank and then at the other (**FIGURE 3.20**). The continuous lateral erosion caused by shifting of the stream's meanders produces an increasingly broader, flat valley floor covered with alluvium. This feature, called a **floodplain**, is appropriately named because when a river overflows its banks during flood stage, it inundates the floodplain.

Over time, the floodplain will widen to the point that the stream is only actively eroding the valley walls in a few places. In fact, in large rivers such as the lower Mississippi River valley, the distance from one valley wall to another can exceed 160 kilometers (100 miles).

FIGURE 3.19 V-shaped valley of the Yellowstone River. The rapids and waterfalls indicate that the river is vigorously downcutting. (Photo by Lane V. Erickson/Shutterstock.)

FIGURE 3.20   Stream eroding its floodplain.

commonly referred to as **bars**. Such features, however, are only temporary, as the material will be picked up again and eventually carried to the ocean. In addition to sand and gravel bars, streams also create other depositional features that have somewhat longer life spans. These include deltas and natural levees.

Deltas

When a stream enters the relatively still waters of an ocean or lake, its velocity drops abruptly, and the resulting deposits form a **delta** (**FIGURE 3.22**). As the delta grows outward, the stream's gradient continually lessens. This circumstance eventually causes the channel to become choked with sediment deposited from the slowing water. As a consequence, the river seeks a shorter, higher-gradient route to base level, as illustrated in Figure 3.22B. This illustration shows the main channel dividing into several smaller ones, called **distributaries**. Most deltas are characterized by these shifting channels that act in an opposite way to that of tributaries.

Changing Base Level and Incised Meanders

We usually expect a stream with a highly meandering course to be on a floodplain in a wide valley. However, certain rivers exhibit meandering channels that flow in steep, narrow valleys. Such meanders are called **incised** (*incisum* = to cut into) **meanders** (**FIGURE 3.21**). How do such features form?

Originally, the meanders probably developed on the floodplain of a stream that was relatively near base level. Then, a change in base level caused the stream to begin downcutting. One of two events could have occurred. Either base level dropped or the land upon which the river flowed was uplifted.

An example of the first circumstance happened during the Ice Age when large quantities of water were withdrawn from the ocean and locked up in glaciers on land. The result was that sea level (ultimate base level) dropped, causing rivers flowing into the ocean to begin to downcut.

Regional uplift of the land, the second cause for incised meanders, is exemplified by the Colorado Plateau in the southwestern United States. As the plateau was gradually uplifted, numerous meandering rivers adjusted to being higher above base level by downcutting.

DEPOSITIONAL LANDFORMS

Recall that streams continually pick up sediment in one part of their channels and redeposit it downstream. These channel deposits are most often composed of sand and gravel and are

FIGURE 3.21   Incised meanders of the Colorado River in Canyonlands National Park, Utah. Here, as the Colorado Plateau was gradually uplifted, the meandering river adjusted to being higher above base level by downcutting. (Photo by Michael Collier)

A.

B.

FIGURE 3.22 **A.** Structure of a simple delta that forms in the relatively quiet waters of a lake. **B.** Growth of a simple delta. As a stream extends its channel, the gradient is reduced. During flood stage, the river is frequently diverted to a higher-gradient route, forming a new distributary. Old, abandoned distributaries are gradually invaded by aquatic vegetation and fill with sediment. (After Ward's Natural Science Establishment, Inc., Rochester, NY)

Rather than carrying water into the main channel, distributaries carry water away from the main channel. After numerous shifts of the channel, a delta may grow into a roughly triangular shape like the Greek letter delta (Δ), for which it is named. Note, however, that many deltas do not exhibit the idealized shape. Differences in the configurations of shorelines and variations in the nature and strength of wave activity result in many shapes. Many large rivers have deltas extending over thousands of square kilometers. The delta of the Mississippi River is one example. It resulted from the accumulation of huge quantities of sediment derived from the vast region drained by the river and its tributaries. Today, New Orleans rests where there was ocean less than 5000 years ago. **FIGURE 3.23** shows that portion of the Mississippi delta that has been built over the past 6000 years. As you can see, the delta is actually a series of seven coalescing subdeltas. Each formed when the river left its existing channel in favor of a

DID YOU KNOW?

Not all rivers have deltas. Some streams that transport large sediment loads lack deltas because ocean waves and powerful currents redistribute the sediment. The Columbia River in the Pacific Northwest is one example. In other cases, rivers do not carry sufficient quantities of sediment to build a delta. The St. Lawrence River, for example, does not acquire much sediment between Lake Ontario and its mouth at the Gulf of St. Lawrence.

FIGURE 3.23 During the past 6000 years, the Mississippi River has built a series of seven coalescing subdeltas. The numbers indicate the order in which the subdeltas were deposited. The present birdfoot delta (number 7) represents the activity of the past 500 years. Without ongoing human efforts, the present course will shift and follow the path of the Atchafalaya River. The inset on the left shows the point where the Mississippi may someday break through (arrow) and the shorter path it would take to the Gulf of Mexico. (After C. R. Kolb and J. R. Van Lopik; satellite image NASA/GSFC)

shorter, more direct path to the Gulf of Mexico. The individual subdeltas interfinger and partially cover one another to produce a very complex structure. The present subdelta, called a *bird-foot* delta because of the configuration of its distributaries, has been built by the Mississippi in the past 500 years.

Natural Levees

Meandering rivers that occupy valleys with broad floodplains tend to build **natural levees** that parallel their channels on both banks (**FIGURE 3.24**). Natural levees are built by successive floods over many years. When a stream overflows its banks, its velocity immediately diminishes, leaving coarse sediment deposited in strips bordering the channel. As the water spreads out over the valley, a lesser amount of fine sediment is deposited over the valley floor. This uneven distribution of material produces the very gentle slope of the natural levee.

The natural levees of the lower Mississippi rise 6 meters (20 feet) above the floodplain. The area behind the levee is characteristically poorly drained for the obvious reason that water cannot flow over the levee and into the river. Marshes called **backswamps** result. A tributary stream that cannot enter a river because levees block the way often has to flow parallel to the river until it can breach the levee. Such streams are called **yazoo tributaries** after the Yazoo River, which parallels the Mississippi for more than 300 kilometers (about 190 miles).

DRAINAGE PATTERNS

Sculpturing Earth's Surface
▼ Running Water

Drainage systems are networks of streams that together form distinctive patterns. The nature of a drainage pattern can vary greatly from one type of terrain to another, primarily in response to the kinds of rock on which the streams developed and/or the structural pattern of faults and folds.

The most commonly encountered drainage pattern is the **dendritic pattern** (**FIGURE 3.25A**). This pattern of irregularly branching tributary streams resembles the branching pattern of a deciduous tree. In fact, the word *dendritic* means "treelike." The dendritic pattern forms where the underlying material is relatively uniform. Because the surface material is essentially uniform in its resistance to erosion, it does not control the pattern of streamflow. Rather, the pattern is determined chiefly by the direction of slope of the land.

When streams diverge from a central area like spokes from the hub of a wheel, the pattern is said to be **radial** (Figure 3.25B). This pattern typically develops on isolated volcanic cones and domal uplifts.

Figure 3.25C illustrates a **rectangular** pattern, in which many right-angle bends can be seen. This pattern develops when the bedrock is criss-crossed by a series of joints and/or faults. Because these structures are eroded more

FIGURE 3.24 Natural levees are gently sloping landforms created by repeated floods. The diagrams on the right show the sequence of development. Because the ground next to the stream channel is higher than the adjacent floodplain, back swamps and yazoo tributaries may develop.

A. Dendritic pattern develops on highly uniform bedrock

B. Radial pattern develops on isolated volcanic cones or domes

Volcano

C. Rectangular pattern develops on highly jointed bedrock

Valleys cut in less-resistant rock

Ridges of resistant rock

D. Trellis pattern develops in areas of alternating weak and resistant bedrock

FIGURE 3.25 Drainage patterns. **A.** Dendritic **B.** Radial **C.** Rectangular **D.** Trellis

easily than unbroken rock, their geometric pattern guides the directions of valleys.

Figure 3.25D illustrates a **trellis** drainage pattern, a rectangular pattern in which tributary streams are nearly parallel to one another and have the appearance of a garden trellis. This pattern forms in areas underlain by alternating bands of resistant and less-resistant rock.

FLOODS AND FLOOD CONTROL

When the discharge of a stream becomes so great that it exceeds the capacity of its channel, it overflows its banks as a **flood.** Floods are among the most common and most destructive of all geologic hazards. They are, nevertheless, simply part of the *natural* behavior of streams.

Causes of Floods

Rivers flood because of the weather. Rapid melting of snow in the sping and/or major storms that bring heavy rains over a large region cause most floods. Exceptional rains caused the devastating floods in the upper Mississippi River Valley during the summer of 1993 (**FIGURE 3.26**).

Unlike the extensive regional floods just mentioned, *flash floods* are more limited in extent. Flash floods occur with little warning and can be deadly because they produce a rapid rise in water levels and can have a devastating flow velocity. Several factors influence flash flooding. Among

them are rainfall intensity and duration, surface conditions, and topography. Urban areas are susceptible to flash floods because a high percentage of the surface area is composed of impervious roofs, streets, and parking lots, where runoff is very rapid. Mountainous areas are susceptible because steep slopes can funnel runoff into narrow canyons.

Human interference with the stream system can worsen or even cause floods. A prime example is the failure of a dam or an artificial levee. These structures are built for flood protection. They are designed to contain floods of a certain magnitude. If a larger flood occurs, the dam or levee is overtopped. If the dam or levee fails or is washed out, the water behind it is released to become a flash flood. The bursting of a dam in 1889 on the Little Conemaugh River caused the devastating Johnstown, Pennsylvania, flood that took some 3000 lives. A second dam failure occured there in 1977 and caused 77 fatalities.

DID YOU KNOW?

Humans have covered an amazing amount of land with buildings, parking lots, and roads. A recent study indicated that the area of such impervious surfaces in the United States (excluding Alaska and Hawaii) amounts to more than 112,600 sq km (nearly 44,000 sq mi), which is slightly less than the area of the state of Ohio.

FIGURE 3.26 Satellite views of the Missouri River flowing into the Mississippi River. St. Louis is just south of their confluence. The upper image shows the rivers during a drought that occurred in summer 1988. The lower image depicts the peak of the record-breaking 1993 flood. Exceptional rains produced the wettest spring and early summer of the twentieth century in the upper Mississippi River basin. In all, nearly 14 million acres were inundated, displacing at least 50,000 people. (Photos courtesy of Spaceimaging.com)

Flood Control

Several strategies have been devised to eliminate or lessen the catastrophic effects of floods. Engineering efforts include the construction of artificial levees, the building of flood-control dams, and river channelization.

Artificial Levees

Artificial levees are earthen mounds built on the banks of a river to increase the volume of water the channel can hold. These most common of stream-containment structures have been used since ancient times and continue to be used today. Artificial levees are usually easy to distinguish from natural levees because their slopes are much steeper. Many artificial levees were not built to withstand periods of extreme flooding. For example, levee failures were numerous in the Midwest during summer 1993, when the upper Mississippi and many of its tributaries experienced record floods (**FIGURE 3.27**).

Flood-Control Dams

Flood-control dams are built to store floodwater and then let it out slowly. This lowers the flood crest by spreading it out over a longer time span. Ever since the 1920s, thousands of dams have been built on nearly every major river in the United States. Many dams have significant non-flood-related functions such as providing water for irrigated agriculture and for hydroelectric power generation. Many reservoirs are also major regional recreational facilities.

Although dams may reduce flooding and provide other benefits, building these structures also has significant costs and consequences. For example, reservoirs created by dams may cover fertile farmland, useful forests, historic sites, and scenic valleys. Of course, dams trap sediment. Therefore, deltas and floodplains downstream erode because they are no longer replenished with silt during floods. Large dams can also cause significant ecologic damage to river environments that took thousands of years to establish.

Building a dam is not a permanent solution to flooding. Sedimentation behind a dam means that the volume of its reservoir will gradually diminish, reducing the effectiveness of this flood-control measure.

Channelization

Channelization involves altering a stream channel to speed the flow of water to prevent it from reaching flood height. This may simply involve clearing a channel of obstructions or dredging a channel to make it wider and deeper.

A more radical alteration involves straightening a channel by creating *artificial cutoffs*. The idea is that by shortening the stream, the gradient and hence the velocity are increased. By increasing velocity, the larger discharge associated with flooding can be dispersed more rapidly.

Beginning in the early 1930s, the U.S. Army Corps of Engineers created many artificial cutoffs on the Mississippi for the purpose of increasing the efficiency of the channel and reducing the threat of flooding. In all, the river has been shortened more than 240 kilometers (150 miles). The program has been somewhat successful in reducing the height of the river in flood stage. However, because the river's tendency toward meandering still exists, preventing the river from returning to its previous course has been difficult.

A Nonstructural Approach

All of the flood-control measures described so far have involved structural solutions aimed at "controlling" a river. These solutions are expensive and often give people residing on the floodplain a false sense of security.

Today, many scientists and engineers advocate a nonstructural approach to flood control. They suggest that an alternative to artificial levees, dams, and channelization is sound floodplain management. By identifying high-risk areas,

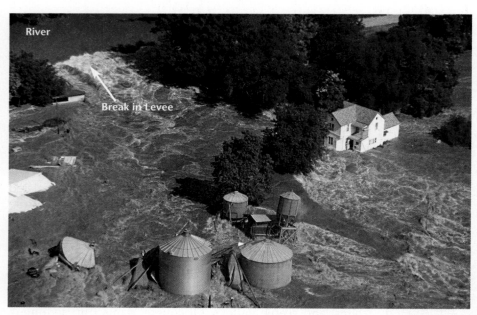

FIGURE 3.27 Water rushes through a break in an artificial levee in Monroe County, Illinois. During the record-breaking 1993 Midwest floods, many artificial levees could not withstand the force of the floodwaters. Sections of many weakened structures were overtopped or simply collapsed. (Photo by James A. Finley/AP/Wide World Photos)

appropriate zoning regulations can be implemented to minimize development and promote more appropriate land use.

GROUNDWATER: WATER BENEATH THE SURFACE

Sculpturing Earth's Surface
▼ Groundwater

Groundwater is one of our most important and widely available resources. Yet people's perceptions of the subsurface environment from which it comes are often unclear and incorrect. The reason is that groundwater is hidden from view except in caves and mines, and the impressions people gain from these subsurface openings are often misleading. Observations on the land surface give an impression that Earth is "solid." This view is not changed very much when we enter a cave and see water flowing in a channel that appears to have been cut into solid rock.

Because of such observations, many people believe that groundwater occurs only in underground "rivers." But actual rivers underground are extremely rare. In reality, most of the subsurface environment is not "solid" at all. Rather, it includes countless tiny *pore spaces* between grains of soil and sediment plus narrow joints and fractures in bedrock. Together, these spaces add up to an immense volume. It is in these tiny openings that groundwater collects and moves.

The Importance of Groundwater

Considering the entire hydrosphere, or all of Earth's water, only about six-tenths of 1 percent occurs underground. Nevertheless, this small percentage, stored in the rocks and sediments beneath Earth's surface, is a vast quantity. When the oceans are excluded and only sources of freshwater are considered, the significance of groundwater becomes more apparent.

FIGURE 3.28 contains estimates of the distribution of freshwater in the hydrosphere. Clearly, the largest volume occurs as glacial ice. Second in rank is groundwater, with slightly more than 14 percent of the total. However, when ice is excluded and just liquid water is considered, more than 94 percent is groundwater. Without question, *groundwater represents the largest reservoir of freshwater that is readily available to humans.* Its value in terms of economics and human well-being is incalculable.

Worldwide, wells and springs provide water for cities, crops, livestock, and industry. In the United States, groundwater is the source of about 40 percent of the water used for all purposes (except hydroelectric power generation and power plant cooling). Groundwater is the drinking water for more than 50 percent of the population, is 40 percent of the water for irrigation, and provides more than 25 percent of industry's needs. In some areas, however, overuse of this basic resource has caused serious problems, including streamflow depletion, land subsidence, and increased pumping costs. In addition, groundwater contamination resulting from human activities is a real and growing threat in many places.

Groundwater's Geologic Roles

Geologically, groundwater is important as an erosional agent. The dissolving action of groundwater slowly removes rock, allowing surface depressions known as sinkholes to form as well as creating subterranean caverns (**FIGURE 3.29**).

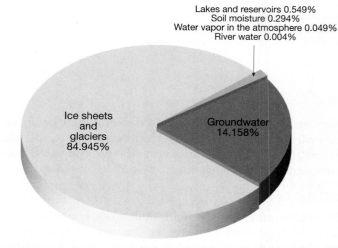

Lakes and reservoirs 0.549%
Soil moisture 0.294%
Water vapor in the atmosphere 0.049%
River water 0.004%

Ice sheets and glaciers 84.945%

Groundwater 14.158%

FIGURE 3.28 Estimated distribution of freshwater in the hydrosphere, according to the U.S. Geological Survey.

Groundwater is also an equalizer of streamflow. Much of the water that flows in rivers is not direct runoff from rain and snowmelt. Rather, a large percentage of precipitation soaks in and then moves slowly underground to stream channels. Groundwater is thus a form of storage that sustains streams during periods when rain does not fall. When we see water flowing in a river during a dry period, it is water from rain that fell at some earlier time and was stored underground.

DISTRIBUTION AND MOVEMENT OF GROUNDWATER

Sculpturing Earth's Surface
▼ Groundwater

When rain falls, some of the water runs off, some returns to the atmosphere by evaporation and transpiration, and the remainder soaks into the ground. This last path is the primary source of practically all groundwater. The amount of water that takes each of these paths, however, varies greatly from time to time and place to place. Influential factors include steepness of the slope, nature of the surface material, intensity of the rainfall, and type and amount of vegetation. Heavy rains falling on steep slopes underlain by impervious materials will obviously result in a high percentage of the water running off. Conversely, if rain falls steadily and gently on more gradual slopes composed of materials that are more easily penetrated by water, a much larger percentage of the water soaks into the ground.

Distribution

Some of the water that soaks in does not travel far, because it is held by molecular attraction as a surface film on soil particles. This near-surface zone is called the *belt of soil moisture*. It is crisscrossed by roots, voids left by decayed roots, and animal and worm burrows that enhance the infiltration of rainwater into the soil. Soil water is used by plants for life functions and transpiration. Some of this water also evaporates directly back into the atmosphere.

Water that is not held as soil moisture penetrates downward until it reaches a zone where all the open spaces in sediment and rock are completely filled with water. This is the **zone of saturation**. Water within it is called **groundwater**. The upper limit of this zone is known as the **water table**. The area above the water table where the soil, sediment, and rock are not saturated is called the

A.

B.

FIGURE 3.29   A. A view of the interior of New Mexico's Carlsbad Caverns. The dissolving action of groundwater created the caverns. Later, groundwater deposited the limestone decorations. (Photo by Clint Farlinger/Alamy) **B.** Groundwater was responsible for creating these sinkholes west of Timaru on New Zealand's South Island. (Photo by G. R. "Dick" Roberts/NSIL/Getty Images)

unsaturated zone (**FIGURE 3.30**). Although a considerable amount of water can be present in the unsaturated zone, this water cannot be pumped by wells because it clings too tightly to rock and soil particles. By contrast, below the water table, the water pressure is great enough to allow water to enter wells, thus permitting groundwater to be withdrawn for use. We will examine wells more closely later in the chapter.

The water table is rarely level, as we might expect a table to be. Instead, its shape is usually a subdued replica of the surface, reaching its highest elevations beneath hills and decreasing in height toward valleys (Figure 3.30). The water table of a wetland (swamp) is right at the surface. Lakes and streams generally occupy areas low enough that the water table is above the land surface.

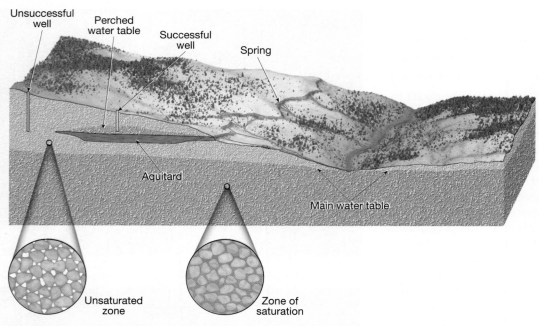

FIGURE 3.30   This diagram illustrates the relative positions of many features associated with subsurface water.

to 50 percent of the sediment's total volume. Pore space depends on the size and shape of the grains; how they are packed together; the degree of sorting; and in sedimentary rocks, the amount of cementing material. Most igneous and metamorphic rocks, as well as some sedimentary rocks, are composed of tightly interlocking crystals so the voids between grains may be negligible. In these rocks, fractures must provide the voids.

Permeability

Porosity alone cannot measure a material's capacity to yield groundwater. Rock or sediment may be very porous and still prohibit water from moving through it. The **permeability** of a material indicates its ability to *transmit* a fluid. Groundwater moves by twisting and turning through interconnected small openings. The smaller the pore spaces, the slower the groundwater moves. If the spaces between particles are too small, water cannot move at all. For example, clay's ability to store water can be great, owing to its high porosity, but its pore spaces are so small that water is unable to move through it. Thus, we say that clay is *impermeable.*

Aquitards and Aquifers

Impermeable layers such as clay that hinder or prevent water movement are termed **aquitards** (*aqua* = water, *tard* = slow). In contrast, larger particles, such as sand or gravel, have larger pore spaces. Therefore, water moves with relative ease. Permeable rock strata or sediments that transmit groundwater freely are called **aquifers** ("water carriers"). Aquifers are important because they are the water-bearing layers sought after by well drillers.

Several factors contribute to the irregular surface of the water table. One important influence is the fact that groundwater moves very slowly. Because of this, water tends to "pile up" beneath high areas between stream valleys. If rainfall were to cease completely, these water "hills" would slowly subside and gradually approach the level of the adjacent valleys. However, new supplies of rainwater are usually added often enough to prevent this. Nevertheless, in times of extended drought, the water table may drop enough to dry up shallow wells. Other causes for the uneven water table are variations in rainfall and permeability of Earth materials from place to place.

Factors Influencing the Storage and Movement of Groundwater

The nature of subsurface materials strongly influences the rate of groundwater movement and the amount of groundwater that can be stored. Two factors are especially important—porosity and permeability.

Porosity

Water soaks into the ground because bedrock, sediment, and soil contain countless voids or openings. These openings are similar to those of a sponge and are often called *pore spaces*. The quantity of groundwater that can be stored depends on the **porosity** of the material, which is the percentage of the total volume of rock or sediment that consists of pore spaces. Voids most often are spaces between sedimentary particles, but also common are joints, faults, cavities formed by the dissolving of soluble rock such as limestone, and vesicles (voids left by gases escaping from lava).

Variations in porosity can be great. Sediment is commonly quite porous, and open spaces may occupy 10 percent

Groundwater Movement

The movement of most groundwater is exceedingly slow, from pore to pore. A typical rate is a few centimeters per day. The energy that makes the water move is provided by the force of gravity. In response to gravity, water moves from areas where the water table is high to zones where the water table is lower.

DID YOU KNOW?

Because of its high porosity, excellent permeability, and great size, the Ogallala Formation, the largest aquifer in the United States, accumulated huge amounts of groundwater—enough freshwater to fill Lake Huron.

FIGURE 3.31 Arrows indicate groundwater movement through uniformly permeable material. The looping curves may be thought of as a compromise between the downward pull of gravity and the tendency of water to move toward areas of reduced pressure.

This means that water usually gravitates toward a stream channel, lake, or spring. Although some water takes the most direct path down the slope of the water table, much of the water follows long, curving paths toward the zone of discharge.

FIGURE 3.31 shows how water percolates into a stream from all possible directions. Some paths clearly turn upward, apparently against the force of gravity, and enter through the bottom of the channel. This is easily explained: The deeper you go into the zone of saturation, the greater the water pressure. Thus, the looping curves followed by water in the saturated zone may be thought of as a compromise between the downward pull of gravity and the tendency of water to move toward areas of reduced pressure.

SPRINGS

Sculpturing Earth's Surface
▼ Groundwater

Springs have aroused the curiosity and wonder of people for thousands of years. The fact that springs were (and to some people still are) rather mysterious phenomena is not difficult to understand, for here is water flowing freely from the ground in all kinds of weather in seemingly inexhaustible supply but with no obvious source. Today, we know that the source of springs is water from the zone of saturation and that the ultimate source of this water is precipitation.

Whenever the water table intersects Earth's surface, a natural outflow of groundwater results, which we call a **spring.** Springs such as the one pictured in **FIGURE 3.32** form when an aquitard blocks the downward movement of groundwater and forces it to move laterally. Where the permeable bed (aquifer) outcrops, a spring or several springs result.

Another situation that can produce a spring is illustrated in Figure 3.30. Here an aquitard is situated above the main water table. As water percolates downward, a portion of it is intercepted by the aquitard, thereby creating a localized zone of saturation and *a perched water table.* Springs, however, are not confined to places where a perched water table creates a flow at the surface. Many geologic situations lead to the formation of springs because subsurface conditions vary greatly from place to place.

FIGURE 3.32   Thousand Springs along the Snake River in Hagerman Valley, Idaho. (Photo by David Frazier)

Hot Springs

By definition, the water in **hot springs** is 6° to 9°C (10° to 15°F) warmer than the average annual air temperature for the localities where they occur. In the United States alone, there are well over 1000 such springs.

Temperatures in deep mines and oil wells usually rise with increasing depth, an average of about 2°C per 100 meters (1°F per 100 feet). Therefore, when groundwater circulates at great depths, it becomes heated. If it rises to the surface, the water may emerge as a hot spring. The water of some hot springs in the eastern United States is heated in this manner. The great majority (more than 95 percent) of the hot springs (and geysers) in the United States are found in the West. The reason for such a distribution is that the source of heat for most hot springs is cooling igneous rock, and it is in the West that igneous activity has occurred most recently.

Geysers

Geysers are intermittent hot springs or fountains in which columns of water are ejected with great force at various intervals, often rising 30 to 60 meters (100 to 200 feet) into the air. After the jet of water ceases, a column of steam rushes out, often with a thunderous roar. Perhaps the most famous geyser in the world is Old Faithful in Yellowstone National Park, which erupts about once each hour (**FIGURE 3.33**). Geysers are also found in other parts of the world, notably New Zealand and Iceland. In fact, the Icelandic word *geysa,* to gush, gives us the name *geyser.*

Geysers occur where extensive underground chambers exist within hot igneous rocks. As relatively cool groundwater enters the chambers, it is heated by the

FIGURE 3.33 A wintertime eruption of Old Faithful, one of the world's most famous geysers. During a typical eruption it emits as much as 45,000 liters (almost 12,000 gallons) of hot water and steam. (Photo by Art Director & Trip/Alamy)

Many people think that Old Faithful Geyser in Wyoming's Yellowstone National Park erupts so reliably—every hour on the hour—that you can set your watch by it. So goes the legend, but it's not true. Time spans between eruptions vary from about 65 minutes to more than 90 minutes, and have generally increased over the years thanks to changes in the geyser's plumbing.

WELLS

Sculpturing Earth's Surface
▼ Groundwater

The most common method for removing groundwater is the **well**, a hole bored into the zone of saturation. Wells serve as small reservoirs into which groundwater migrates and from which it can be pumped to the surface. The use of wells dates back many centuries and continues to be an important method of obtaining water. By far the single greatest use of this water in the United States is irrigation for agriculture. More than 65 percent of the groundwater used each year is for this purpose. Industrial uses rank a distant second, followed by the amount used by homes in cities and rural areas.

The water-table level may fluctuate considerably during the course of a year, dropping during dry seasons and rising following periods of precipitation. Therefore, to ensure a continuous supply of water, a well must penetrate below the water table. Whenever a substantial amount of water is withdrawn from a well, the water table around the well is lowered. This effect, termed **drawdown**, decreases with increasing distance from the well. The result is a depression in the water table, roughly conical in shape, known as a **cone of depression** (FIGURE 3.34). For most small domestic wells, the cone of depression is negligible. However, when wells are used for irrigation or for industrial purposes, the withdrawal of water can be great enough to create a very wide and steep cone of depression that may substantially lower the water table in an area and cause nearby shallow wells to become dry. Figure 3.34 illustrates this situation.

ARTESIAN WELLS

Sculpturing Earth's Surface
▼ Groundwater

In most wells, water cannot rise on its own. If water is first encountered at 30 meters (100 feet) depth, it remains at that level, fluctuating perhaps a meter or two with seasonal wet and dry periods. However, in some wells, water rises, sometimes overflowing at the surface.

The term **artesian** is applied to any situation in which groundwater rises in a well above the level where it was initially encountered. For such a situation to occur, two conditions must exist (FIGURE 3.35): (1) Water must be confined to an

surrounding rock. At the bottom of the chamber, the water is under great pressure because of the weight of the overlying water. This great pressure prevents the water from boiling at the normal surface temperature of 100°C (212°F). For example, at the bottom of a 300-meter (1000-foot) water-filled chamber, water must attain a temperature of nearly 230°C (450°F) before it will boil. The heating causes the water to expand, with the result that some is forced out at the surface. This loss of water reduces the pressure on the remaining water in the chamber, which lowers the boiling point. A portion of the water deep within the chamber quickly turns to steam and causes the geyser to erupt. Following the eruption, cool groundwater again seeps into the chamber, and the cycle begins anew.

Before heavy pumping

After heavy pumping

Well drilling rig

FIGURE 3.34 Wells are the most common means by which people acquire groundwater. A cone of depression in the water table often forms around a pumping well. If heavy pumping lowers the water table, some wells may be left dry. (Photo by ASP/ YPP/ age fotostock)

FIGURE 3.35 Artesian systems occur when an inclined aquifer is surrounded by impermeable beds. Such an aquifer is called a *confined aquifer*. The photo shows a flowing artesian well. (Photo by James E. Patterson)

FIGURE 3.36   City water systems can be considered artificial artesian systems.

aquifer that is inclined so that one end is exposed at the surface, where it can receive water; and (2) aquitards both above and below the aquifer must be present to prevent the water from escaping. Such an aquifer is called a **confined aquifer**. When such a layer is tapped, the pressure created by the weight of the water above will force the water to rise. If there were no friction, the water in the well would rise to the level of the water at the top of the aquifer. However, friction reduces the height of this pressure surface. The greater the distance from the recharge area (area where water enters the inclined aquifer), the greater the friction and the smaller the rise of water.

In Figure 3.35, Well 1 is a *no flowing artesian well,* because at this location the pressure surface is below ground level. When the pressure surface is above the ground and a well is drilled into the aquifer, *a flowing artesian well* is created (Well 2, Figure 3.35).

Artesian systems act as "natural pipelines," transmitting water from remote areas of recharge great distances to the points of discharge. In this manner, water that fell in central Wisconsin years ago is now taken from the ground and used by communities many kilometers to the south in Illinois. In South Dakota, such a system brings water from the western Black Hills eastward across the state.

On a different scale, city water systems may be considered examples of artificial artesian systems (**FIGURE 3.36**). The water tower, into which water is pumped, may be considered the area of recharge, the pipes the confined aquifer, and the faucets in homes the flowing artesian wells.

ENVIRONMENTAL PROBLEMS OF GROUNDWATER

As with many of our valuable natural resources, groundwater is being exploited at an increasing rate. In some areas, overuse threatens the groundwater supply. In other places, groundwater withdrawal has caused the ground and everything resting upon it to sink. Still other localities are concerned with the possible contamination of their groundwater supply.

Treating Groundwater as a Nonrenewable Resource

Many natural systems tend to establish a condition of equilibrium. The groundwater system is no exception. The water table's height reflects a balance between the rate of water added by precipitation and the rate of water removed by discharge and withdrawal. An imbalance will either raise or lower the water table. A long-term drop in the water table can occur if there is either a decrease in recharge due to prolonged drought or an increase in groundwater discharge or withdrawal.

For many people, groundwater appears to be an endlessly renewable resource, for it is continually replenished by rainfall and melting snow. But in some regions, groundwater has been and continues to be treated as a *nonrenewable* resource because the amount of water available to recharge the aquifer is significantly less than the amount being withdrawn.

The High Plains, a relatively dry region that extends from the western Dakotas to western Texas, provides one example of an extensive agricultural economy that is largely dependent on irrigation (**FIGURE 3.37**). Underlying about 111 million acres (450,000 square kilometers or 174,000 square miles) in parts of eight states, the High Plains Aquifer is one of the largest and most agriculturally significant aquifers in the United States. It accounts for about 30 percent of all groundwater withdrawn for irrigation in the country. In the southern part of this region, which includes the Texas panhandle, the natural recharge of the aquifer is very slow and the problem of declining groundwater levels is acute. In fact, in years of average or below-average precipitation, recharge is negligible because all or nearly all of the meager rainfall is returned to the atmosphere by evaporation and transpiration.

Therefore, where intense irrigation has been practiced for an extended period, depletion of groundwater can be severe. Declines in the water table at rates as great as 1 meter per year have led to an overall drop of between 15 and 60 meters (50 and 200 feet) in some areas. Under these circumstances, it can be said that the groundwater is literally being "mined." Even if pumping were to cease immediately, it would take thousands of years for the groundwater to be fully replenished.

Groundwater depletion has been a concern in the High Plains and other areas of the West for many years, but it is worth pointing out that the problem is not confined to this part of the country. Increased demands on groundwater resources have overstressed aquifers in many areas, not just in arid and semiarid regions.

Land Subsidence Caused by Groundwater Withdrawal

As you will see later in this chapter, surface subsidence can result from natural processes related to groundwater. However, the ground may also sink when water is pumped from wells faster than natural recharge processes can replace it. This effect is particularly pronounced in areas underlain by thick layers of loose sediments. As water is withdrawn, the water pressure drops and the weight of the overburden is transferred to the sediment. The greater

A.

B.

FIGURE 3.37 The High Plains Aquifer underlies about 111 million acres in parts of eight western states. It is one of the largest and most agriculturally significant aquifers in the United States. **A.** Satellite image of circular crop fields irrigated by center pivot irrigation. Resembling a work of modern art, crop circles cover what was once short grass prairie in southwestern Kansas. Three different crops are being grown—corn, wheat, and sorghum. Each is at a different point of development that accounts for the varying shades of green and yellow. (NASA) **B.** Groundwater provides nearly 216 billion liters (57 billion gallons) per day in support of the agricultural economy of the United States. (Photo by Clark Dunbar/ Corbis)

Groundwater Contamination

The pollution of groundwater is a serious matter, particularly in areas where aquifers provide a large part of the water supply. One common source of groundwater pollution is sewage emanating from an ever increasing number of septic tanks. Other sources are inadequate or broken sewer systems and farm wastes.

If sewage water, which is contaminated with bacteria, enters the groundwater system, it may become purified through natural processes. The harmful bacteria may be mechanically filtered by the sediment through which the water percolates, destroyed by chemical oxidation, and/or assimilated by other organisms. For purification to occur, however, the aquifer must be of the correct composition. For example, extremely permeable aquifers (such as highly fractured crystalline rock, coarse gravel, or cavernous limestone) have such large openings that contaminated groundwater may travel long distances without being cleansed. In this case, the water flows too rapidly and is not in contact with the surrounding material long enough for purification to occur. This is the problem at Well 1 in **FIGURE 3.39A**.

pressure packs the sediment grains more tightly together and the ground subsides.

Many areas can be used to illustrate such land subsidence. A classic example in the United States occurred in the San Joaquin Valley of California (**FIGURE 3.38**). Other well-known cases of land subsidence resulting from groundwater pumping in the United States include Las Vegas, Nevada; New Orleans and Baton Rouge, Louisiana; and the Houston-Galveston area of Texas. In the low-lying coastal area between Houston and Galveston, land subsidence ranges from 1.5 to 3 meters (5 to 10 feet). The result is that about 78 square kilometers (30 square miles) are permanently flooded.

Outside the United States, one of the most spectacular examples of subsidence occurred in Mexico City, which is built on a former lake bed. In the first half of the twentieth century, thousands of wells were sunk into the water-saturated sediments beneath the city. As water was withdrawn, portions of the city subsided by as much as 6 meters (20 feet) or more.

Conversely, when the aquifer consists of sand or permeable sandstone, the water can sometimes be purified after traveling only a few dozen meters through it. The openings between sand grains are large enough to permit water movement, yet the movement of the water is slow enough to allow ample time for its purification (Well 2, Figure 3.39B).

Other sources and types of contamination also threaten groundwater supplies (**FIGURE 3.40**). These include widely used substances such as highway salt, fertilizers that are spread across the land surface, and pesticides. In addition, a wide array of chemicals and industrial materials may leak from pipelines, storage tanks, landfills, and holding ponds. Some of these pollutants are classified as *hazardous*, meaning that they are either flammable, corrosive, explosive, or toxic. As rainwater oozes through the refuse, it may dissolve a variety of potential contaminants. If the leached material reaches the water table, it will mix with the groundwater and contaminate the supply.

Because groundwater movement is usually slow, polluted water may go undetected for a long time. In fact, contamination is sometimes discovered only after drinking water has been affected and people become ill. By this time, the volume of polluted water could be quite large, and even if the source of contamination is removed immediately, the problem is not solved. Although the sources of groundwater contamination are numerous, the solutions are relatively few.

Once the source of the problem has been identified and eliminated, the most common practice is simply to abandon the water supply and allow the pollutants to be flushed away gradually. This is the least costly and easiest solution, but the aquifer must remain unused for many years. To accelerate this process, polluted water is sometimes pumped out and treated. Following removal of the tainted water, the aquifer is allowed to recharge naturally or, in some cases, the treated water or other fresh water is pumped back in. This process is costly, time consuming, and possibly risky because there is no way to be certain that all of the contamination has been removed. Clearly, the most effective solution to groundwater contamination is prevention.

THE GEOLOGIC WORK OF GROUNDWATER

Groundwater dissolves rock. This fact is key to understanding how caverns and sinkholes form. Because soluble rocks, especially limestone, underlie millions of square kilometers of Earth's surface, it is here that groundwater carries on its important role as an erosional agent. Limestone is nearly insoluble in pure water but is quite easily dissolved by water containing small quantities of carbonic acid, and most groundwater contains this acid. It forms because rainwater readily dissolves carbon dioxide from the air and from decaying plants. Therefore, when groundwater comes in contact with limestone, the carbonic acid reacts with calcite (calcium carbonate) in the rocks to form calcium bicarbonate, a soluble material that is then carried away in solution.

Caverns

The most spectacular results of groundwater's erosional handiwork are limestone **caverns**. In the United States alone, about 17,000 caves have been discovered. Although most are relatively small, some have spectacular dimensions. Carlsbad Caverns in southeastern New Mexico and Mammoth Cave in Kentucky are famous examples. One chamber in Carlsbad

FIGURE 3.38 The shaded area on the map shows California's San Joaquin Valley. This important agricultural region relies heavily on irrigation. The marks on the utility pole in the photo indicate the level of the surrounding land in preceding years. Between 1925 and 1975, this part of the San Joaquin Valley subsided almost 9 meters (30 feet) because of the withdrawal of groundwater and the resulting compaction of sediments. (Photo courtesy of U.S. Geological Survey, U.S. Department of the Interior)

FIGURE 3.39 **A.** Although the contaminated water has traveled more than 100 meters (330 feet) before reaching Well 1, the water moves too rapidly through the cavernous limestone to be purified. **B.** As the discharge from the septic tank percolates through the permeable sandstone, it is purified in a relatively short distance.

A.   **B.**

FIGURE 3.40   Sometimes agricultural chemicals **A.** and materials leached from landfills **B.** find their way into the groundwater. These are two of the potential sources of groundwater contamination. (Photo A by Michael Collier; Photo B by F. Rossotto/The Stock Market)

Caverns has an area equivalent to 14 football fields and enough height to accommodate the U.S. Capitol Building. At Mammoth Cave, the total length of interconnected caverns extends for more than 540 kilometers (340 miles).

Most caverns are created at or just below the water table in the zone of saturation. Acidic groundwater follows lines of weakness in the rock, such as joints and bedding planes. As time passes, the dissolving process slowly creates cavities and gradually enlarges them into caverns. Material that is dissolved by the groundwater is eventually discharged into streams and carried to the ocean.

Certainly, the features that arouse the greatest curiosity for most cavern visitors are the stone formations that give some caverns a wonderland appearance. These are not erosional features, like the caverns in which they reside, but depositional features. They are created by the seemingly endless dripping of water over great spans of time. The calcium carbonate that is left behind produces the limestone we call travertine. These cave deposits, however, are also commonly called *dripstone*, an obvious reference to their mode of origin.

Although the formation of caverns takes place in the zone of saturation, the deposition of dripstone is not possible until the caverns are above the water table, in the unsaturated zone. This commonly occurs as nearby streams cut their valleys deeper, lowering the water table as the elevation of the rivers drops. As soon as the chamber is filled with air, the conditions are right for the decoration phase of cavern building to begin.

Of the various dripstone features found in caverns, perhaps the most familiar are **stalactites**. These icicle-like pendants hang from the ceiling of the cavern and form where water seeps through cracks above. When water reaches air in the cave, some of the dissolved carbon dioxide

escapes from the drop and calcite begins to precipitate. Deposition occurs as a ring around the edge of the water drop. As drop after drop follows, each leaves an infinitesimal trace of calcite behind, and a hollow limestone tube is created. Water then moves through the tube, remains suspended momentarily at the end, contributes a tiny ring of calcite, and falls to the cavern floor.

The stalactite just described is appropriately called a *soda straw* (**FIGURE 3.41A**). Often the hollow tube of the soda straw becomes plugged or its supply of water increases. In either case, the water is forced to flow and deposit along the outside of the tube. As deposition continues, the stalactite takes on the more common conical shape.

Formations that develop on the floor of a cavern and reach upward toward the ceiling are called **stalagmites** (Figure 3.41B). The water supplying the calcite for stalagmite growth falls from the ceiling and splatters over the surface. As a result, stalagmites do not have a central tube and are usually more massive in appearance and more rounded on their upper ends than are stalactites. Given enough time, a downward-growing stalactite and an upward-growing stalagmite may join to form a *column*.

DID YOU KNOW?

America's largest bat colonies are found in caves. For example, Braken Cave in central Texas is the summer home of 20 million Mexican free-tail bats. They spend their days in total darkness more than 3 Km (2 mi) inside the cave. Each night, they leave the cave to feed, consuming more than 200,000 Km (220 tons) of insects.

A.

B.

FIGURE 3.41 **A.** Live soda-straw stalactite in Chinn Springs Cave, Independence County, Arkansas. (Photo by Dante Fenolio/Photo Researchers, Inc.) **B.** Stalactites, stalagmites, and columns in New Mexico's Carlsbad Caverns National Park. (Photo by Tbkmedia.de/Alamy).

Karst Topography

Many areas of the world have landscapes that, to a large extent, have been shaped by the dissolving power of groundwater. Such areas are said to exhibit **karst topography**, named for the *Krs* region in the border area between Slovenia and Italy where such topography is strikingly developed. In the United States, karst landscapes occur in many areas that are underlain by limestone, including portions of Kentucky, Tennessee, Alabama, southern Indiana, and central and northern Florida (**FIGURE 3.42**). Generally, arid and semiarid areas do not develop karst topography because there is insufficient groundwater. When solution features exist in such regions, they are likely to be remnants of a time when rainier conditions prevailed.

Sinkholes

Karst areas typically have irregular terrain punctuated with many depressions called **sinkholes** or, simply, **sinks** (see Figure 3.29B, p. 95). In the limestone areas of Florida,

Kentucky, and southern Indiana, literally tens of thousands of these depressions vary in depth from just a meter or two to a maximum of more than 50 meters.

Sinkholes commonly form in one of two ways. Some develop gradually over many years without any physical disturbance to the rock. In these situations, the limestone immediately below the soil is dissolved by downward-seeping rainwater that is freshly charged with carbon dioxide. These depressions are usually not deep and are characterized by relatively gentle slopes. By contrast, sinkholes can also form suddenly and without warning when the roof of a cavern collapses under its own weight. Typically, the depressions created in this manner are steep sided and deep. When they form in populous areas, they may represent a serious geologic hazard. Such a situation is clearly the case in **FIGURE 3.43**.

In addition to a surface pockmarked by sinkholes, karst regions characteristically show a striking lack of surface drainage (streams). Following a rainfall, runoff is quickly funneled belowground through sinks. It then flows through caverns until it finally reaches the water table. Where streams do exist at the surface, their paths are usually short. The names of such streams often give a clue to their fate. In the Mammoth Cave area of Kentucky, for example, there is Sinking Creek, Little Sinking Creek, and Sinking Branch. Some sinkholes become plugged with clay and debris, creating small lakes or ponds.

FIGURE 3.43 This small sinkhole formed suddenly in 1991 when the roof of a cavern collapsed, destroying this home in Frostproof, Florida. (Photo by *St. Petersburg Times*/Liaison Agency, Inc.)

Tower Karst Landscapes

Some regions of karst development exhibit landscapes that look very different from the sinkhole-studded terrain depicted in Figure 3.42. One striking example is an extensive region in southern China that is described as exhibiting *tower karst*. As the chapter-opening photograph shows, the term *tower* is appropriate because the landscape consists of a maze of isolated steep-sided hills that rise abruptly from the ground. Each is riddled with interconnected caves and passageways. This type of karst topography forms in wet tropical and subtropical regions having thick beds of highly jointed limestone. In such settings groundwater dissolves large volumes of limestone, leaving only these residual towers. Karst development is more rapid in tropical climates due to the abundant rainfall and greater availability of carbon dioxide from the decay of lush tropical vegetation. The extra carbon dioxide in the soil means there is more carbonic acid for dissolving limestone. Other tropical areas of advanced karst development include portions of Puerto Rico, western Cuba, and northern Vietnam.

THE CHAPTER IN REVIEW

- Weathering, mass wasting, and erosion are responsible for transforming solid rock into sediment. They are called external processes because they occur at or near Earth's surface and are powered by energy from the Sun. By contrast, internal processes, such as volcanism and mountain building, derive their energy from Earth's interior.

- Mass wasting is the downslope movement of rock and soil under the direct influence of gravity. Gravity is the controlling force of mass wasting, but water often influences mass wasting by saturating the pore spaces and destroying the cohesion between particles. Oversteepening of slopes can trigger mass wasting.

- The *hydrologic cycle* describes the continuous interchange of water among the oceans, atmosphere, and continents. Powered by energy from the Sun, it is a global system in which the atmosphere provides the link between the oceans and continents. The processes involved in the hydrologic cycle include *precipitation, evaporation, infiltration* (the movement of water into rocks or soil through cracks and pore spaces), *runoff* {water that flows over the land rather than infiltrating into the ground), and *transpiration* (the release of water vapor to the atmosphere by plants).

- The factors that determine a stream's *velocity* are *gradient* (slope of the stream channel); *shape, size,* and *roughness* of the channel; and the stream's *discharge* (amount of water passing a given point per unit of time). Most often, the gradient and roughness of a stream decrease downstream, whereas width, depth, discharge, and velocity increase.

- The land area that contributes water to a stream is its *drainage basin.* Drainage basins are separated by imaginary lines called *divides.*

- River systems are divided into three zones. In the zone of *sediment production,* erosion dominates. Farther downstream are the zones of *sediment transport* and *sediment deposition.*

- Streams transport their load of sediment in solution (*dissolved load*), in suspension (*suspended load*), and along the bottom of the channel *(bed load).* Much of the dissolved load is contributed by groundwater. Most streams carry the greatest part of their load in suspension. The bed load moves only intermittently and is usually the smallest portion of a stream's load.

- A stream's ability to transport solid particles is described using two criteria: *capacity* (the maximum load of solid particles a stream can carry) and *competence* (the maximum particle size a stream can transport). Competence increases as the square of stream velocity, so if velocity doubles, the water's force increases fourfold.

- Streams deposit sediment when velocity slows and competence is reduced. This results in *sorting,* the process by which like-sized particles are deposited together. Stream deposits are called *alluvium* and may occur as channel deposits called *bars;* as floodplain deposits, which include *natural levees;* and as *deltas* at the mouths of streams.

- Stream channels are of two basic types: *bedrock channels* and *alluvial channels.* Bedrock channels are most common in headwaters regions where gradients are steep. Rapids and waterfalls are common features. Two types of alluvial channels are *meandering channels* and *braided channels.*

- The two general types of *base level* (the lowest point to which a stream may erode its channel) are (1) *ultimate base level* and (2) *temporary,* or *local base level.* Any change in base level will cause a stream to adjust and establish a new balance. Lowering base level will cause a stream to downcut, whereas raising base level results in deposition of material in the channel.

- When a stream has cut its channel closer to base level, its energy is directed from side to side, and erosion produces a flat valley floor, or *floodplain.* Streams that flow upon floodplains often move in sweeping bends called *meanders.* Widespread meandering may result in shorter channel segments, called *cutoffs,* and/or abandoned bends, called *oxbow lakes.*

- Common *drainage patterns* produced by streams include (1) *dendritic,* (2) *radial,* (3) *rectangular,* and (4) *trellis.*

- *Floods* are triggered by heavy rains and/or snowmelt. Sometimes human interference can worsen or even cause floods. Flood-control measures include the building of *artificial levees* and dams, as well as *channelization,* which could involve creating *artificial cutoffs.* Many scientists and engineers advocate a nonstructural approach to flood control that involves more appropriate land use.

- As a resource, *groundwater* represents the largest reservoir of freshwater that is readily available to humans. Geologically, the dissolving action of groundwater produces caves and sinkholes. Groundwater is also an equalizer of streamflow.

- Groundwater is water that occupies the pore spaces in sediment and rock in a zone beneath the surface, called the *zone of saturation.* The upper limit of this zone is the *water table.* The *unsaturated zone* is above the water table where the soil, sediment, and rock are not saturated. The quantity of water that can be stored depends on the *porosity* (the volume of open spaces) of the material. *The permeability* (the ability to transmit a fluid through interconnected pore spaces) of a material is a key factor affecting the movement of groundwater.

- *Springs* occur whenever the water table intersects the land surface and a natural flow of groundwater results. *Wells,* openings bored into the zone of saturation, withdraw groundwater and create roughly conical depressions in the water table, known as *cones of depression. Artesian wells* occur when water rises above the level where it was initially encountered.

- When groundwater circulates at great depths, it becomes heated. If it rises, the water may emerge as a *hot spring. Geysers* occur when groundwater is heated in underground chambers, and expands, and some water quickly changes to steam, causing the geyser to erupt. The source of heat for most hot springs and geysers is hot igneous rock.

• Some of the current environmental problems involving groundwater include (1) *overuse* by intense irrigation, (2) *land subsidence* caused by groundwater withdrawal, and (3) *contamination* by pollutants.

• Most *caverns* form in limestone at or below the water table when acidic groundwater dissolves this soluble rock. *Karst topography* exhibits an irregular terrain punctuated with many depressions, called *sinkholes*.

KEY TERMS

alluvium (p. 84)
angle of repose (p. 77)
aquifer (p. 96)
aquitard (p. 96)
artesian well (p. 98)
backswamp (p. 91)
bar (p. 89)
base level (p. 86)
bed load (p. 83)
braided channels (p. 86)
capacity (p. 84)
cavern (p. 102)
competence (p. 83)
cone of depression (p. 98)
confined aquifer (p. 100)
cutoff (p. 86)

delta (p. 89)
dendritic pattern (p. 91)
discharge (p. 81)
dissolved load (p. 83)
distributary (p. 89)
divide (p. 79)
drainage basin (p. 79)
drawdown (p. 98)
erosion (p. 74)
external process (p. 74)
flood (p. 92)
floodplain (p. 88)
geyser (p. 97)
gradient (p. 80)
groundwater (p. 95)

hot spring (p. 97)
hydrologic cycle (p. 78)
incised meander (p. 89)
infiltration (p. 78)
internal process (p. 74)
karst topography (p. 104)
laminar flow (p. 80)
mass wasting (p. 74)
meander (p. 85)
natural levee (p. 91)
oxbow lake (p. 86)
permeability (p. 96)
porosity (p. 96)
radial pattern (p. 91)
rectangular pattern (p. 91)
runoff (p. 78)

sinkhole (sink) (p. 104)
sorting (p. 84)
spring (p. 97)
stalactite (p. 103)
stalagmite (p. 103)
stream valley (p. 87)
suspended load (p. 83)
transpiration (p. 78)
trellis pattern (p. 92)
turbulent flow (p. 80)
unsaturated zone (p. 95)
water table (p. 95)
weathering (p. 74)
well (p. 98)
yazoo tributary (p. 91)
zone of saturation (p. 95)

QUESTIONS FOR REVIEW

1. Describe the role of external processes in the rock cycle.
2. What is the controlling force of mass wasting? What other factors can influence or trigger mass-wasting processes?
3. What role does mass wasting play in sculpting Earth's landscapes?
4. Describe the movement of water through the hydrologic cycle. Once precipitation has fallen on land, what paths might it take?
5. What are the three main parts (zones) of a river system?
6. A stream starts out 2000 meters above sea level and travels 250 kilometers to the ocean. What is its average gradient in meters per kilometer?
7. Suppose that the stream mentioned in Question 6 developed extensive meanders so that its course was lengthened to 500 kilometers. Calculate its new gradient. How does meandering affect gradient?

8. When the discharge of a stream increases, what happens to the stream's velocity?
9. In what three ways does a stream transport its load?
10. If you collect a jar of water from a stream, which part of its load will settle to the bottom of the jar? Which portion will remain in the water? Which portion of a stream's load would probably not be present in your sample?
11. Differentiate between competency and capacity.
12. Are bedrock channels more likely to be found near the head or near the mouth of a stream?
13. Describe a situation that might cause a stream channel to become braided.
14. Define base level. Name the main river in your area. For what streams does it act as base level? What is base level for the Mississippi River? The Missouri River?
15. Describe two situations that would trigger the formation of incised meanders.

16. Briefly describe the formation of a natural levee. How is this feature related to backswamps and yazoo tributaries?

17. List and briefly describe three basic flood-control strategies. What are some drawbacks of each?

18. Each of the following statements refers to a particular drainage pattern. Identify the pattern.
    a. Streams diverge from a central high area, such as a volcano.
    b. Streams form a branching, "treelike" pattern.
    c. Bedrock is crisscrossed by joints and faults.

19. What percentage of freshwater is groundwater? (See Figure 3.28, p. 94). If glacial ice is excluded and only liquid freshwater is considered, about what percentage is groundwater?

20. Geologically, groundwater is important as an erosional agent. Name another significant geologic role of groundwater.

21. Define groundwater and relate it to the water table.

22. How do porosity and permeability differ?

23. What is the source of heat for most hot springs and geysers? How is this reflected in the distribution of these features?

24. What is meant by the term *artesian?* Under what circumstances do artesian wells form?

25. Which problem is associated with the pumping of groundwater for irrigation in the southern part of the High Plains?

26. Briefly explain what happened in California's San Joaquin Valley, Mexico City, and other places as the result of excessive groundwater withdrawal.

27. Which aquifer would be most effective in purifying polluted groundwater: one composed mainly of coarse gravel, one consisting of sand, or one of cavernous limestone?

28. Differentiate between stalactites and stalagmites. How do these features form?

29. If you were to explore an area that exhibited karst topography, what features might you find? This area would probably be underlain by what rock type?

COMPANION WEBSITE

The *Foundations of Earth Science* Website uses the resources and flexibility of the Internet to aid in your study of the topics in this chapter. Written and developed by the authors and other Earth science instructors, this site will help improve your understanding of Earth science. Visit **www.mygeoscienceplace.com** in order to:

• **Review** key chapter concepts.

• **Read** with links to the ebook and to chapter-specific web resources.

• **Visualize** and comprehend challenging topics using learning activities in *GEODe: Earth Science*.

• **Test** yourself with online quizzes.

GEODe: EARTH SCIENCE

GEODe: Earth Science is a valuable and easy to use learning aid that can be accessed from your book's Companion Website: **www.mygeoscienceplace.com.** It is a dynamic instructional tool that promotes understanding and reinforces important concepts by using tutorials, animations, and exercises that actively engage the student.

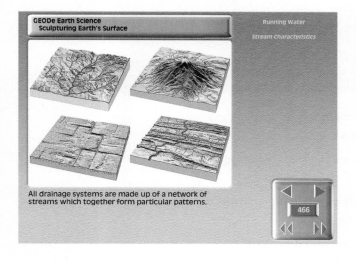

All drainage systems are made up of a network of streams which together form particular patterns.

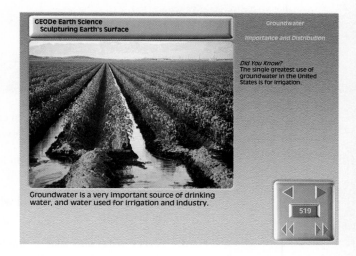

Groundwater is a very important source of drinking water, and water used for irrigation and industry.

GLACIAL AND ARID LANDSCAPES

To assist you in learning the important concepts in this chapter, you will find it helpful to focus on the following questions:

1. What is a glacier? Where on Earth are the two general types of glaciers located today?

2. How do glaciers move, and what are the various processes of glacial erosion?

3. What materials make up the features created by glacial deposition? What are the most widespread features?

4. What is some evidence for the Ice Age? What indirect effects did Ice Age glaciers have on the land and sea?

5. What are the causes of deserts in both the lower and middle latitudes?

6. What are the roles of water and wind in arid climates?

7. How did many of the landscapes in the dry Basin and Range region of the United States evolve?

8. What are the ways that wind erodes?

9. What are some depositional features produced by wind?

Wind commonly deposits sand in mounds or ridges called *dunes*. These dunes are some of the largest in the world and are located in Africa's Namib Desert. For more about this place, see the "Did You Know" at the end of the chapter. (Photo by Paul Souders/ WorldFoto/Aurora Photos)

Like the running water and groundwater that were the focus of Chapter 3, glaciers and wind are significant erosional processes. They are responsible for creating many different landforms and are part of an important link in the rock cycle in which the products of weathering are transported and deposited as sediment.

Climate has a strong influence on the nature and intensity of Earth's external processes. This fact is dramatically illustrated in this chapter. The existence and extent of glaciers are largely controlled by Earth's changing climate. Another excellent example of the strong link between climate and geology is seen when we examine the development of arid landscapes.

Today, glaciers cover nearly 10 percent of Earth's land surface; however, in the recent geologic past, ice sheets were three times more extensive, covering vast areas with ice thousands of meters thick. Many regions still bear the mark of these glaciers. The first part of this chapter will examine glaciers and the erosional and depositional features they create. The second part will explore dry lands and the geologic work of wind. Because desert and near-desert conditions prevail over an area as large as that affected by the massive glaciers of the Ice Age, the nature of such landscapes is indeed worth investigating.

GLACIERS: A PART OF TWO BASIC CYCLES

Sculpturing Earth's Surface
▼ Glaciers

Many present-day landscapes were modified by the widespread glaciers of the most recent Ice Age and still strongly reflect the handiwork of ice. The basic features of such diverse places as the Alps, Cape Cod, and Yosemite Valley were fashioned by now vanished masses of glacial ice. Moreover, Long Island, New York; the Great Lakes; and the fiords of Norway and Alaska all owe their existence to glaciers. Glaciers, of course, are not just a phenomenon of the geologic past. As you will see, they are still sculpturing and depositing in many regions today.

Glaciers are a part of two of Earth's basic cycles—the hydrologic cycle and the rock cycle. In the hydrologic cycle, when precipitation falls at high elevations or high latitudes, the water may not immediately make its way back toward the sea. Instead, it may become part of a glacier. Although the ice will eventually melt, allowing the water to continue its path to the sea, water can be stored as glacial ice for tens, hundreds, or even thousands of years. During the time that the water is part of a glacier, the moving mass of ice can do enormous amounts of work—scouring the land surface and acquiring, transporting, and depositing great quantities of sediment. This activity is a basic part of the rock cycle (**FIGURE 4.1**).

A **glacier** is a thick ice mass that forms over hundreds or thousands of years. It originates on land from the accumulation, compaction, and recrystallization of snow. A glacier appears to be motionless, but it is not—glaciers move

very slowly. Like running water, groundwater, wind, and waves, glaciers are dynamic erosional agents that accumulate, transport, and deposit sediment. Although glaciers are found in many parts of the world today, most are located in remote areas, either near Earth's poles or in high mountains.

Valley (Alpine) Glaciers

Literally thousands of relatively small glaciers exist in lofty mountain areas, where they usually follow valleys originally occupied by streams. Unlike the rivers that previously flowed in these valleys, the glaciers advance slowly, perhaps only a few centimeters per day. Because of their location, these moving ice masses are termed **valley glaciers** or **alpine glaciers** (see Figure 4.1). Each glacier is a stream of ice, bounded by precipitous rock walls, that flows downvalley from a snow accumulation center near its head. Like rivers, valley glaciers can be long or short, wide or narrow, single or with branching tributaries. The widths of alpine glaciers are generally small compared to their lengths. In length, some extend for just a fraction of a kilometer, whereas others go on for many tens of kilometers. The west branch of the Hubbard Glacier, for example, runs through 112 kilometers (70 miles) of mountainous terrain in Alaska and Canada's Yukon Territory.

Ice Sheets

In contrast to valley glaciers, **ice sheets** exist on a much larger scale. These enormous masses flow out in all directions from one or more centers and completely obscure all but the highest areas of underlying terrain. Although many ice sheets have existed in the past, just two achieve this status at present (**FIGURE 4.2**). In the Northern Hemisphere, Greenland is covered by an imposing ice sheet averaging nearly 1500 meters (5000 feet) thick. It occupies 1.7 million square kilometers (more than 660 thousand square miles) or about 80 percent of this large island.

In the Southern Hemisphere, the huge Antarctic ice sheet attains a maximum thickness of nearly 4300 meters (14,000 feet) and covers an area of more than 13.9 million

FIGURE 4.1   Kennicott Glacier is a 43-kilometer (27-mile) long valley glacier that is sculpting the mountains in Alaska's Wrangell-St. Elias National Park. The dark stripes of sediment are called *medial moraines* (see p. 122). The transport and deposition of sediment make glaciers a basic part of the rock cycle. (Photo by Michael Collier)

square kilometers (5.4 million square miles). Because of the proportions of these huge features, they are often called *continental ice sheets*. Indeed, the combined areas of present-day continental ice sheets represent almost 10 percent of Earth's land area.

Along portions of the Antarctic coast, glacial ice flows into the adjacent ocean, creating features called **ice shelves**. These are large, relatively flat masses of floating ice that extend seaward from the coast but remain attached to the land along one or more sides. The shelves are thickest on their landward sides, and they become thinner seaward. They are sustained by ice from the adjacent ice sheet as well as being nourished by snowfall and the freezing of seawater to their bases. Antarctica's ice shelves extend over approximately 1.4 million square kilometers (0.6 million square miles). The Ross and Filchner ice shelves are the largest, with the Ross Ice Shelf alone covering an area approximately the size of Texas (see Figure 4.2).

Other Types of Glaciers

In addition to valley glaciers and ice sheets, other types of glaciers have also been identified. Covering some uplands and plateaus are masses of glacial ice called **ice caps**. Like ice sheets, ice caps completely bury the underlying landscape but are much smaller than the continental-scale features. Ice caps occur in many places, including Iceland and several of the large islands in the Arctic Ocean (**FIGURE 4.3A**). Another type, known as **piedmont glaciers**, occupy broad lowlands at the bases of steep mountains and form when one

FIGURE 4.2 The only present-day continental ice sheets are those covering Greenland and Antarctica. Their combined areas represent almost 10 percent of Earth's land area. Greenland's ice sheet occupies 1.7 million square kilometers, or about 80 percent of the island. The area of the Antarctic ice sheet is almost 14 million square kilometers. Ice shelves occupy an additional 1.4 million square kilometers adjacent to the Antarctic ice sheet.

or more valley glaciers emerge from the confining walls of mountain valleys. The advancing ice spreads out to form a broad sheet. The size of individual piedmont glaciers varies greatly. Among the largest is the broad Malaspina Glacier along the coast of southern Alaska. It covers more than 5000 square kilometers (2000 square miles) of the flat coastal plain at the foot of the lofty St. Elias range (**FIGURE 4.3B**).

DID YOU KNOW?

The Greenland ice sheet is long enough to extend from Key West, Florida, to 100 mi north of Portland, Maine. Its width could reach from Washington, D.C., to Indianapolis, Indiana. Put another way, the ice sheet is 80 percent as big as the entire United States east of the Mississippi. The area of Antarctica's ice sheet is more than eight times this great!

FIGURE 4.3 **A.** Iceland's Vatnajökull ice cap. In 1996 the Grimsvötn volcano erupted beneath the ice cap, an event that triggered melting and floods. (NASA) **B.** Malaspina Glacier in southern Alaska is a classic piedmont glacier. Piedmont glaciers occur where valley glaciers exit a mountain range onto broad lowlands, are no longer laterally confined, and spread to become wide lobes. (NASA/JPL)

HOW GLACIERS MOVE

GEODe
EARTH SCIENCE

Sculpturing Earth's Surface
▼ Glaciers

The movement of glacial ice is generally referred to *as flow*. The fact that glacial movement is described in this way seems paradoxical—how can a solid flow? The way in which ice flows is complex and of two basic types. One mechanism involves plastic movement within the ice. Ice behaves as a brittle solid until the pressure upon it is equivalent to the weight of about 50 meters (165 feet) of ice. Once that load is surpassed, ice behaves as a plastic material and flow begins. A second and often equally important mechanism of glacial movement occurs when the entire ice mass slips along the ground. The lowest portions of most glaciers probably move by this sliding process.

The uppermost 50 meters (165 feet) of a glacier is appropriately referred to as the *zone of fracture*. Because there is not enough overlying ice to cause plastic flow, this upper part of the glacier consists of brittle ice. Consequently, the ice in this zone is carried along piggyback-style by the ice below. When the glacier moves over irregular terrain, the zone of fracture is subjected to tension, resulting in cracks called **crevasses**. These gaping cracks, which often make travel across glaciers dangerous, may extend to depths of 50 meters (165 feet). Below this depth, plastic flow seals them off.

Observing and Measuring Movement

Unlike streamflow, glacial movement is not obvious. If we could watch a valley glacier move, we would see that like the water in a river, all of the ice does not move downstream at the same rate. Flow is greatest in the center of the glacier because of the drag created by the walls and floor of the valley.

Early in the nineteenth century, the first experiments involving the movement of glaciers were designed and carried out in the Alps. Markers were placed in a straight line across an alpine glacier. The position of the line was marked on the valley walls so that if the ice moved, the change in position could be detected. The positions of the markers were noted periodically, revealing the movement just described. Although most glaciers move too slowly for direct visual detection, the experiments succeeded in demonstrating that movement nevertheless occurs. The experiment illustrated in **FIGURE 4.4A** was carried out at Switzerland's Rhône Glacier later in the nineteenth century. It not only traced the movement of markers within the ice but also mapped the position of the glacier's terminus.

For many years, time lapse photography has allowed us to observe glacial movement. Images are taken from the same vantage point on a regular basis (e.g., once per day) over an extended span and then played back like a movie. More recently, satellites let us track the movement of glaciers and observe glacial behavior (**FIGURE 4.4B**). This is especially useful because the remoteness and extreme weather associated with many glacial areas limits on-site study.

How rapidly does glacial ice move? Average rates vary considerably from one glacier to another. Some move so slowly that trees and other vegetation may become well established in the debris that accumulates on the glacier's surface. Others advance up to several meters each day.

Movement of some glaciers is characterized by periods of extremely rapid advance followed by periods during which movement is practically nonexistent.

Budget of a Glacier: Accumulation versus Wastage

Snow is the raw material from which glacial ice originates. Therefore, glaciers form in areas where more snow falls in winter than can melt during the summer. Glaciers are constantly gaining and losing ice.

FIGURE 4.4 A. Ice movement and changes in the terminus of Rhône Glacier, Switzerland. In this classic study of a valley glacier, the movement of stakes clearly shows that glacial ice moves and that movement along the sides of the glacier is slower than movement in the center. Also notice that even though the ice front was retreating, the ice within the glacier was advancing. **B.** This satellite image provides detailed information about the movement of Antarctica's Lambert Glacier. Ice velocities are determined from pairs of images obtained 24 days apart using radar data. (NASA)

Glacial Zones

Snow accumulation and ice formation occur in the **zone of accumulation** (FIGURE 4.5). The addition of snow thickens the glacier and promotes movement. Beyond this area of ice formation is the **zone of wastage**, where there is a net loss to the glacier as all of the snow from the previous winter melts, as does some of the glacial ice (Figure 4.5).

In addition to melting, glaciers also waste as large pieces of ice break off the front of a glacier in a process called *calving*. Calving creates *icebergs* when glaciers reach the sea (FIGURE 4.6). Because icebergs are just slightly less dense than seawater, they float very low in the water, with more than 80 percent of their mass submerged. The margins of the Greenland ice sheet produce thousands of icebergs each year. Many drift southward and find their way into the North Atlantic, where they are a hazard to navigation.

Glacial Budget

Whether the margin of a glacier is advancing, retreating, or remaining stationary depends on the *budget of the glacier.* That is, it depends on the balance or lack of balance between accumulation on the one hand and wastage on the other. If ice accumulation exceeds wastage, the glacial front advances until the two factors balance. At this point, the terminus of the glacier becomes stationary. If a warming trend increases wastage and/or if a drop in snowfall decreases accumulation, the ice

Geologist's Sketch

FIGURE 4.6 Icebergs are created when large pieces break off the front of a glacier after it reaches a water body, a process known as *calving*. The photo shows an iceberg in Canada's Labrador Sea. As the drawing illustrates, only about 20 percent (or less) of an iceberg protrudes above the waterline. (Photo by Radius Images/Photolibrary)

front will retreat. As the terminus of the glacier retreats, the extent of the zone of wastage diminishes. Therefore, in time a new balance will be reached between accumulation and wastage, and the ice front will again become stationary.

Zone of accumulation
More snow falls each winter than melts each summer

Zone of wastage
All the snow from the previous winter melts along with some glacial ice

Snowline

Direction of ice movement

Crevasses

Iceberg formed by calving

FIGURE 4.5 The snowline separates the zone of accumulation and the zone of wastage. Above the snowline, more snow falls each winter than melts each summer. Below the snowline, the snow from the previous winter completely melts as does some of the underlying ice. Whether the margin of a glacier advances, retreats, or remains stationary depends on the balance between accumulation and wastage. When a glacier moves across irregular terrain, crevasses form in the brittle upper portion.

1941

2004

FIGURE 4.7 Two images taken 63 years apart from the same vantage point in Alaska's Glacier Bay National Park. Muir Glacier, which is prominent in the 1941 photo, has retreated out of the field of view in the 2004 image. Also Riggs Glacier (upper right) has thinned and retreated significantly. (Photos courtesy of National Snow and Ice Data Center)

Whether the margin of a glacier is advancing, retreating, or stationary, the ice within the glacier continues to flow forward. In the case of a receding glacier, the ice simply does not flow forward rapidly enough to offset wastage. This point is illustrated in Figure 4.4A. While the line of stakes within the Rhône Glacier continued to advance downvalley, the terminus of the glacier slowly retreated upvalley.

FIGURE 4.8 Glaciers are capable of great erosion. As the terminus of this Alaskan glacier wastes away, it deposits large quantities of unsorted sediment called *till*. (Photos by Michael Collier)

Glaciers in Retreat

Because glaciers are sensitive to changes in temperature and precipitation, they provide clues about changes in climate. With few exceptions, valley glaciers around the world have been retreating at unprecedented rates over the last century (**FIGURE 4.7**). Many valley glaciers have disappeared altogether. For example, 150 years ago, there were 147 glaciers in Montana's Glacier National Park. Today, only 37 remain and these may vanish by 2030.

GLACIAL EROSION

GEODe
EARTH
SCIENCE

Sculpturing Earth's Surface
▼ Glaciers

Glaciers erode tremendous volumes of rock. For anyone who has observed the terminus of an alpine glacier, the evidence of its erosive force is plain. You can witness firsthand the release of rock fragments of various sizes from the ice as it melts (**FIGURE 4.8**). All signs lead to the conclusion that the ice has scraped, scoured, and torn rock debris from the floor and walls of the valley and carried it downvalley. Indeed, as a transporter of sediment, ice has no equal.

Once rock debris is acquired by the glacier, it cannot settle out as does the load carried by a stream or by the wind. Consequently, glaciers can carry huge blocks that no other erosional agent could possibly budge. Although today's glaciers are of limited importance as erosional agents, many landscapes that were modified by the widespread glaciers of the recent Ice Age still reflect to a high degree the work of ice.

How Glaciers Erode

Glaciers erode land primarily in two ways—by plucking and abrasion. First, as a glacier flows over a fractured bedrock surface, it loosens and lifts blocks of rock and incorporates them into the ice. This process, known as **plucking**, occurs when meltwater penetrates the cracks and joints along the rock floor of the glacier and freezes. As the water freezes, it expands and exerts tremendous leverage that pries rock loose. In this manner, sediment of all sizes becomes part of the glacier's load.

The second major erosional process is **abrasion**. As the ice and its load of rock fragments move over bedrock, they function like sandpaper to smooth and polish the surface below. The pulverized rock produced by the glacial "grist mill" is appropriately called **rock flour**. So much rock flour may be produced that meltwater streams leaving a glacier often have the grayish appearance of skim milk—visible evidence of the grinding power of the ice.

When ice at the bottom of a glacier contains larger rock fragments, long scratches and grooves called **glacial striations** may be gouged into the bedrock (**FIGURE 4.9A**). These linear scratches provide clues to the direction of ice flow. By mapping the striations over large areas, patterns of glacial flow can often be reconstructed.

Not all abrasive action produces striations. The rock surfaces over which the glacier moves may become highly polished by the ice and its load of finer particles. The broad expanses of smoothly polished granite in California's Yosemite National Park provide an excellent example (**FIGURE 4.9B**).

As is the case with other agents of erosion, the rate of glacial erosion is highly variable. This differential erosion by ice is largely controlled by four factors: (1) rate of glacial movement; (2) thickness of the ice; (3) shape, abundance, and hardness of the rock fragments contained in the ice at the base of the glacier; and (4) the erodibility of the surface beneath the glacier. Variations in any or all of these factors from time to time and/or from place to place mean that the features, effects, and degree of landscape modification in glaciated regions can vary greatly.

Landforms Created by Glacial Erosion

Although the erosional accomplishments of ice sheets can be tremendous, landforms carved by these huge ice masses usually do not inspire the same awe as do the erosional features created by valley glaciers. In regions where the erosional effects of ice sheets are significant, glacially scoured surfaces and subdued terrain are the rule. By contrast, in mountainous areas, erosion by valley glaciers produces many truly spectacular features. Much of the rugged mountain scenery so celebrated for its majestic beauty is the product of erosion by valley glaciers.

Take a moment to study **FIGURE 4.10** which shows a mountain setting before, during, and after glaciation. You will refer to this figure often in the following discussion.

Glaciated Valleys

Prior to glaciation, alpine valleys are characteristically V-shaped because streams are well above base level and are therefore downcutting (Figure 4.10A). However, in mountainous regions that have been glaciated, the valleys are no longer narrow. As a glacier moves down a valley once occupied by a stream, the ice modifies it in three ways: The glacier widens, deepens, and straightens the valley, so that what was once a narrow V-shaped valley is transformed into a U-shaped **glacial trough** (Figure 4.10C).

The amount of glacial erosion depends in part on the thickness of the ice. Consequently, main glaciers, also called *trunk glaciers*, cut their valleys deeper than do their smaller tributary glaciers. Thus, after the ice has receded, the valleys of tributary glaciers are left standing above the main glacial trough and are termed **hanging valleys**. Rivers flowing through

A.

B.

FIGURE 4.9 **A.** Glacial abrasion created the scratches and grooves in this bedrock. Cove Glacier, Prince William Sound, northeast of Whittier, Alaska. **B.** Glacially polished granite in California's Yosemite National Park. (Photos by Michael Collier)

FIGURE 4.10   These diagrams of a hypothetical area show the development of erosional landforms created by alpine glaciers. The unglaciated landscape in part **A** is modified by valley glaciers in part **B.** After the ice recedes, in part **C,** the terrain looks very different than it did before glaciation. (Arête photo from James E. Patterson Collection; Cirque photo by Marli G. Miller; Hanging Valley photo by Marc Muench)

hanging valleys may produce spectacular waterfalls, such as those in Yosemite National Park, California (Figure 4.10).

Cirques

At the head of a glacial valley is a characteristic and often imposing feature associated with an alpine glacier—a **cirque**. As Figure 4.10 illustrates, these hollowed-out, bowl-shaped depressions have precipitous walls on three sides but are open on the downvalley side. The cirque is the focal point of the glacier's growth because it is the area of snow accumulation and ice formation. Cirques begin as irregularities in the mountainside that are subsequently enlarged by frost wedging

and plucking along the sides and bottom of the glacier. The glacier, in turn, acts as a conveyor belt that carries the debris away. After the glacier has melted away, the cirque basin is often occupied by a small lake called a *tarn*.

Arêtes and Horns

The Alps, Northern Rockies, and many other mountain landscapes carved by valley glaciers reveal more than glacial troughs and cirques. In addition, sinuous, sharp-edged ridges called **arêtes** and sharp, pyramid-like peaks called **horns** project above the surroundings (Figure 4.10C). Both features can originate from the same basic process—the enlargement of cirques produced by plucking and frost action. Cirques around a single high mountain create the spires of rock called horns. As the cirques enlarge and converge, an isolated horn is produced. A famous example is the Matterhorn in the Swiss Alps (**FIGURE 4.11**).

Arêtes can form in a similar manner except that the cirques are not clustered around a point but rather exist on opposite sides of a divide. As the cirques grow, the divide separating them is reduced to a very narrow, knifelike partition. An arête may also be created when the area separating two parallel glacial valleys is narrowed as the glaciers scour and widen their valleys.

Fiords

Fiords are deep, often spectacular, steep-sided inlets of the sea that exist in many high-latitude areas of the world where mountains are adjacent to the ocean (**FIGURE 4.12**). Norway, British Columbia, Greenland, New Zealand, Chile, and Alaska all have coastlines characterized by fiords. They are glacial troughs that became submerged as the ice left the valley and sea level rose following the Ice Age.

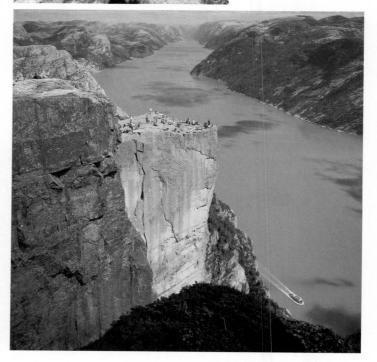

FIGURE 4.12 The coast of Norway is known for its many fiords. Frequently these ice-sculpted inlets of the sea are hundreds of meters deep. (Satellite images courtesy of NASA; photo by Wolfgang Meier/Photography)

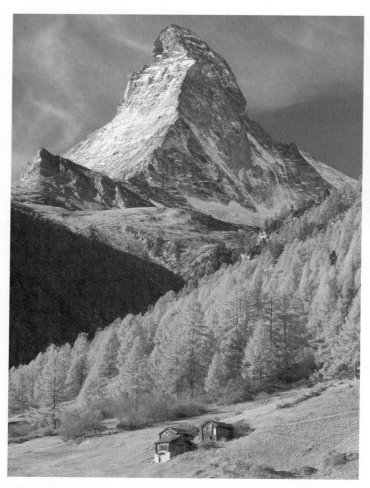

FIGURE 4.11 Horns are sharp, pyramid-like peaks that are fashioned by alpine glaciers. This example is the famous Matterhorn in the Swiss Alps. (Photo by Andy Selinger/age footstock)

DID YOU KNOW?

If all of Earth's glaciers melted, sea level would rise approximately 70 m (230 ft) worldwide.

The depth of some fiords exceeds 1000 meters (3300 feet). However, the great depths of these flooded troughs are only partly explained by the post-Ice Age rise in sea level. Unlike the situation governing the downward erosional work of rivers, sea level does not act as base level for glaciers. As a consequence, glaciers are capable of eroding their beds far below the surface of the sea. For example, a valley glacier 300 meters (1000 feet) thick can carve its valley floor more than 250 meters (800 feet) below sea level before downward erosion ceases and the ice begins to float.

GLACIAL DEPOSITS

Sculpturing Earth's Surface
▼ Glaciers

Glaciers pick up and transport a huge load of debris as they slowly advance across the land. These materials are ultimately deposited when the ice melts. Glacial sediment can play a truly significant role in forming the physical landscape in regions where it is deposited. For example, in many areas once covered by the ice sheets of the recent Ice Age, the bedrock is rarely exposed because glacial deposits that are tens or even hundreds of meters thick completely bury the terrain. The general effect of these deposits is to level the topography. Indeed, many of today's familiar rural landscapes—rocky pastures in New England, wheat fields in the Dakotas, rolling farmland in the Midwest—resulted directly from glacial deposition.

Types of Glacial Drift

Long before the theory of an extensive Ice Age was proposed, much of the soil and rock debris covering portions of Europe was recognized as coming from elsewhere. At the time, these foreign materials were believed to have "drifted" into their present positions by floating ice during an ancient flood. As a consequence, the term *drift* was applied to this sediment. Although rooted in a concept that was not correct, this term was so well established by the time the true glacial origin of the debris became widely recognized that it remained in the glacial vocabulary. **Glacial drift** is an all-embracing term for sediments of glacial origin, no matter how, where, or in what form they were deposited.

Glacial drift is divided into two distinct types: (1) materials deposited directly by the glacier, which are known as *till,* and (2) sediments laid down by glacial meltwater, called *stratified drift.* Here is the difference: **Till** is deposited as glacial ice melts and drops its load of rock fragments. Unlike moving water and wind, ice cannot sort the sediment it carries; therefore, deposits of till are characteristically unsorted mixtures of many particle sizes (**FIGURE 4.13**). **Stratified drift** is sorted according to the size and weight of the fragments. Because ice is not capable of such sorting activity, these sediments are not deposited directly by the glacier. Rather, they reflect the sorting action of glacial meltwater.

Some deposits of stratified drift are made by streams coming directly from the glacier. Other stratified deposits involve sediment that was originally laid down as till and later picked up, transported, and redeposited by meltwater beyond the margin of the ice. Accumulations of stratified drift often consist largely of sand and gravel, because the meltwater is not capable of moving larger material and because the finer rock flour remains suspended and is commonly carried far from the glacier. An indication that stratified drift consists primarily of sand and gravel can be seen in many areas where these deposits are actively mined as aggregate for roadwork and other construction projects.

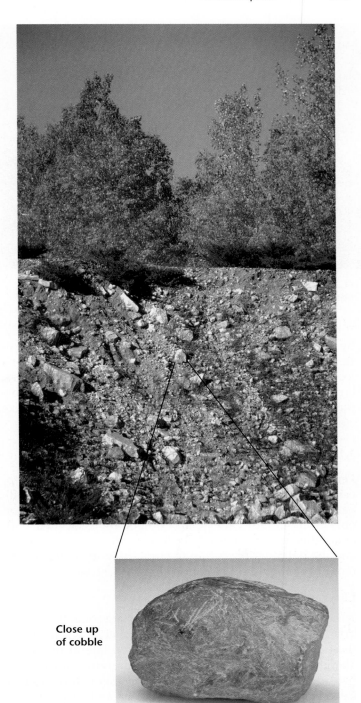

Close up of cobble

FIGURE 4.13   Glacial till is an unsorted mixture of many different sediment sizes. A close examination often reveals cobbles that have been scratched as they were dragged along by the glacier. (Photos by E. J. Tarbuck)

Boulders found in the till or lying free on the surface are called **glacial erratics** if they are different from the bedrock below (**FIGURE 4.14**). Of course, this means that they must have been derived from a source outside the area where they are found. Although the locality of origin for most erratics is unknown, the origin of some can be determined. Therefore,

FIGURE 4.14   A large, glacially transported boulder in Denali National Park, Alaska. Such boulders are called *glacial erratics*. (Photo by Michael Collier)

by studying glacial erratics as well as the mineral composition of the till, geologists can sometimes trace the path of a lobe of ice. In portions of New England as well as other areas, erratics can be seen dotting pastures and farm fields. In some places, these rocks are cleared from fields and piled to make stone walls and fences.

Moraines, Outwash Plains, and Kettles

Perhaps the most widespread features created by glacial deposition are *moraines,* which are simply layers or ridges of till. Several types of moraines are identified; some are common only to mountain valleys, and others are associated with areas affected by either ice sheets or valley glaciers. Lateral and medial moraines fall in the first category, whereas end moraines and ground moraines are in the second.

Lateral and Medial Moraines

The sides of a valley glacier accumulate large quantities of debris from the valley walls. When the glacier wastes away, these materials are left as ridges, called **lateral moraines**, along the sides of the valley. **Medial moraines** form when two advancing valley glaciers come together to form a single ice stream. The till that was once carried along the edges of each glacier joins to form a single dark stripe of debris within the newly enlarged glacier. The creation of these dark stripes within the ice stream is one obvious proof that glacial ice moves, because the medial moraine could not form if the ice did not flow downvalley. It is common to see several dark debris stripes within a large alpine glacier because one will form each time a tributary glacier joins the main valley. Kennicott Glacier in Figure 4.1 (p. 113) provides an excellent example.

End Moraines and Ground Moraines

An **end moraine** is a ridge of till that accumulates at the terminus of a glacier. These relatively common landforms are deposited when a state of equilibrium is attained between wastage and ice accumulation. That is, the end moraine forms when the ice is melting near the end of the glacier at a rate equal to the forward advance of the glacier from its region of nourishment. Although the terminus of the glacier is stationary, the ice continues to flow forward, delivering a continuous supply of sediment in the same manner a conveyor belt delivers goods to the end of a production line. As the ice melts, the till is dropped and the end moraine grows. The longer the ice front remains stable, the larger the ridge of till will become.

Eventually, the time comes when wastage exceeds nourishment. At this point, the front of the glacier begins to recede in the direction from which it originally advanced. As the ice front retreats, however, the conveyor-belt action of the glacier continues to provide fresh supplies of sediment to the terminus. In this manner, a large quantity of till is deposited as the ice melts away, creating a rock-strewn, undulating plain. This gently rolling layer of till deposited as the ice front recedes is termed **ground moraine**. Ground moraine has a leveling effect, filling in low spots and clogging old stream channels, often leading to a derangement of the existing drainage system. In areas where this layer of till is still relatively fresh, such as the northern Great Lakes region, poorly drained swampy lands are quite common.

Periodically, a glacier will retreat to a point where wastage and nourishment once again balance. When this happens, the ice front stabilizes and a new end moraine forms.

The pattern of end moraine formation and ground moraine deposition may be repeated many times before the glacier has completely vanished. Such a pattern is illustrated by **FIGURE 4.15**. The very first end moraine to form marks the farthest advance of the glacier and is called the *terminal end moraine.* Those end moraines that form as the ice front occasionally stabilizes during retreat are termed *recessional end moraines.* Terminal and recessional moraines are essentially alike; the only difference between them is their relative positions.

End moraines deposited by the most recent major stage of Ice Age glaciation are prominent features in many parts of the Midwest and Northeast. In Wisconsin, the wooded, hilly terrain of the Kettle Moraine near Milwaukee is a particularly picturesque example. A well-known example in the Northeast is Long Island. This linear strip of glacial sediment that extends northeastward from New York City is part of an end moraine complex that stretches from eastern Pennsylvania to Cape Cod, Massachusetts.

FIGURE 4.16 represents a hypothetical area during and following glaciation. It shows the end moraines that were just described as well as the depositional features that are discussed in the sections that follow. This figure depicts landscape features similar to those that might be encountered if you were traveling in the upper Midwest or New England. As you read about other glacial deposits, you will be referred to this figure again.

Outwash Plains and Valley Trains

At the same time that an end moraine is forming, meltwater emerges from the ice in rapidly moving streams that are often choked with suspended material and carrying a substantial

End moraines:
Wisconsinan Age
End moraines:
Illinoian Age

0 ——————— 150 mi
0 ——————— 150 km

Driftless
area

Extent of
Wisconsinan
glaciation

Extent of
Illinoian glaciation

FIGURE 4.15 End moraines of the Great Lakes region. Those deposited during the most recent stage of glaciation (a span called the Wisconsinan stage) are most prominent.

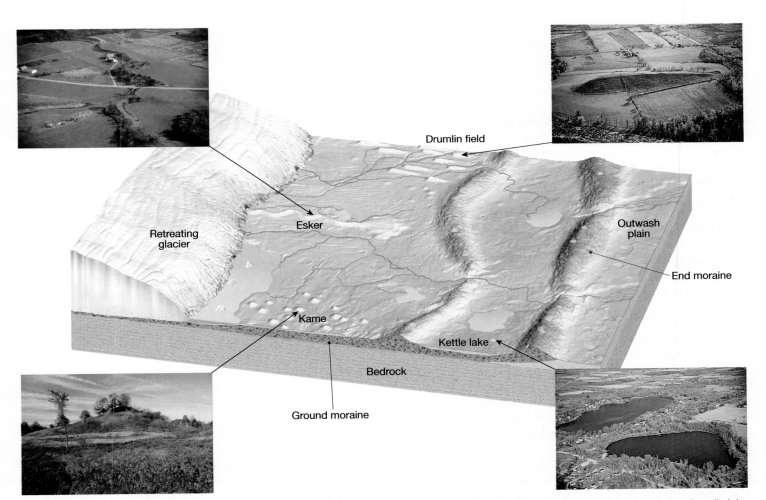

Drumlin field

Retreating
glacier

Esker

Outwash
plain

End moraine

Kame

Kettle lake

Bedrock

Ground moraine

FIGURE 4.16 This hypothetical area illustrates many common depositional landforms. The outermost end moraine marks the limit of glacial advance and is called the *terminal end moraine*. End moraines that form as the ice front occasionally becomes stationary during retreat are called *recessional end moraines*. (Drumlin photo courtesy of Ward's Natural Science Establishment; Kame, Esker, and Kettle photos by Richard P. Jacobs/JLM Visuals) bed load. As the water leaves the glacier, it rapidly loses velocity and much of its bed load is dropped. In this way, a broad, ramplike accumulation of stratified drift is built adjacent to the downstream edge of most end moraines. When the feature is formed in association with an ice sheet, it is termed an **outwash plain**, and when it is confined to a mountain valley, it is commonly referred to as a **valley train** (Figure 4.16).

Kettles

Often, end moraines, outwash plains, and valley trains are pockmarked with basins or depressions known as **kettles** (Figure 4.16). Kettles form when blocks of stagnant ice become buried in drift and eventually melt, leaving pits in the glacial sediment. Most kettles do not exceed 2 kilometers (1.25 miles) in diameter and the typical depth of most kettles is less than 10 meters (33 feet). Water often fills the depression and forms a pond or lake. One well-known example is Walden Pond near Concord, Massachusetts. It is here that Henry David Thoreau lived alone for two years in the 1840s and about which he wrote *Walden,* his American literature classic.

Drumlins, Eskers, and Kames

Moraines are not the only landforms deposited by glaciers. Some landscapes are characterized by numerous elongate parallel hills made of till. Other areas exhibit conical hills and relatively narrow winding ridges composed mainly of stratified drift.

Drumlins

Drumlins are streamlined asymmetrical hills composed of till (Figure 4.16). They range in height from 15 to 60 meters (50 to 200 feet) and average 0.4 to 0.8 kilometer (0.25 to 0.50 mile) in length. The steep side of the hill faces the direction from which the ice advanced, while the gentler slope points in the direction the ice moved. Drumlins are not found singly but rather occur in clusters, called *drumlin fields.* One such cluster, east of Rochester, New York, is estimated to contain about 10,000 drumlins. Their streamlined shape indicates that they were molded in the zone of flow within an active glacier. It is thought that drumlins originate when glaciers advance over previously deposited drift and reshape the material.

Eskers and Kames

In some areas that were once occupied by glaciers, sinuous ridges composed largely of sand and gravel may be found. These ridges, called **eskers**, are deposits made by streams flowing in tunnels beneath the ice, near the terminus of a glacier (Figure 4.16). They may be several meters high and extend for many kilometers. In some areas, they are mined for sand and gravel and for this reason eskers are disappearing in some localities.

Kames are steep-sided hills that, like eskers, are composed largely of stratified drift (Figure 4.16). Kames originate when glacial meltwater washes sediment into openings and depressions in the stagnant wasting terminus of a glacier. When the ice eventually melts away, the stratified drift is left behind as mounds or hills.

OTHER EFFECTS OF ICE AGE GLACIERS

In addition to the massive erosional and depositional work carried on by Ice Age glaciers, ice sheets had other, sometimes profound, effects on the landscape. For example, as the ice advanced and retreated, animals and plants were forced to migrate. This led to stresses that some organisms could not tolerate. Furthermore, many present-day stream courses bear little resemblance to their preglacial routes. The Missouri River once flowed northward toward Hudson Bay in Canada. The Mississippi River followed a path through central Illinois, and the head of the Ohio River reached only as far as Indiana (**FIGURE 4.17**). A comparison of the two parts of Figure 4.17 shows that the Great Lakes were created by glacial erosion during the Ice Age. Prior to the Pleistocene, the basins occupied by these huge lakes were lowlands with rivers that ran eastward to the Gulf of St. Lawrence.

In areas that were centers of ice accumulation, such as Scandinavia and northern Canada, the land has been slowly rising for the past several thousand years. The land had downwarped under the tremendous weight of 3-kilometer-thick (almost 2-mile-thick) masses of ice. Following the removal of this immense load, the crust has been adjusting by gradually rebounding upward ever since.

Ice sheets and alpine glaciers can act as dams to create lakes by trapping glacial meltwater and blocking the flow of rivers. Some of these lakes are relatively small and short-lived. Others can be large and exist for hundreds or thousands of years.

FIGURE 4.18 is a map of Lake Agassiz—the largest lake to form during the Ice Age in North America. With the retreat of the ice sheet came enormous volumes of meltwater. The Great Plains generally slope upward to the west. As the terminus of the ice sheet receded northeastward, meltwater was trapped between the ice on one side and the sloping land on the other, causing Lake Agassiz to deepen and spread across the landscape. It came into existence about 12,000 years ago and lasted for about 4500 years. Such water bodies are termed *proglacial lakes,* referring to their position just beyond the outer limits of a glacier or ice sheet.

A far-reaching effect of the Ice Age was the worldwide change in sea level that accompanied each advance and retreat of the ice sheets. The snow that nourishes

FIGURE 4.17 **A.** This map shows the Great Lakes and the familiar present-day pattern of rivers in the central United States. Pleistocene ice sheets played a major role in creating this pattern. **B.** Reconstruction of drainage systems in the central United States prior to the Ice Age. The pattern was very different from today's, and there were no Great Lakes.

FIGURE 4.18 Map showing the extent of glacial Lake Agassiz. This proglacial lake came into existence about 12,000 years ago and lasted for about 4500 years. It was an immense feature—bigger than all of the present-day Great Lakes combined. The modern-day remnants of this water body are still major landscape features.

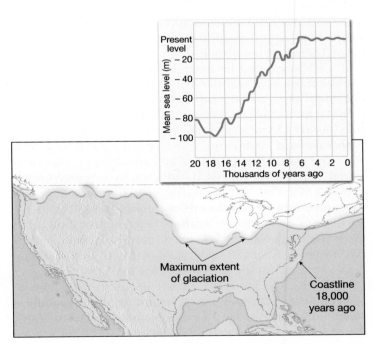

FIGURE 4.19 Changing sea level during the past 20,000 years. About 18,000 years ago, when the most recent ice advance was at a maximum, sea level was nearly 100 meters (330 feet) lower than at present. Thus, land that is presently covered by the ocean was exposed and the shoreline looked very different than today. As the ice sheets melted, sea level rose and the shoreline shifted.

glaciers ultimately comes from moisture evaporated from the oceans. Therefore, when the ice sheets increased in size, sea level fell and the shoreline moved seaward (**FIGURE 4.19**). Estimates suggest that sea level was as much as 100 meters (330 feet) lower than it is today. Consequently, the Atlantic Coast of the United States was located more than 100 kilometers (60 miles) to the east of New York City. Moreover, France and Britain were joined where the English Channel is today. Alaska and Siberia were connected across the Bering Strait, and Southeast Asia was tied by dry land to the islands of Indonesia.

The formation and growth of ice sheets was an obvious response to significant changes in climate. But the existence of the glaciers themselves triggered climatic changes in the regions beyond their margins. In arid and semiarid areas on all continents, temperatures were lower, which meant evaporation rates were also lower. At the same time, precipitation was moderate. This cooler, wetter climate resulted in the formation of many lakes called **pluvial lakes** (from the Latin term *pluvia* meaning "rain"). In North America, pluvial lakes were concentrated in the vast Basin and Range region of Nevada and Utah. Although most are now gone, a few remnants remain, the largest being Utah's Great Salt Lake.

GLACIERS OF THE ICE AGE

During the Ice Age, ice sheets and alpine glaciers were far more extensive than they are today. There was a time when the most popular explanation for drift was that the material had been brought by icebergs or perhaps simply swept across the landscape by a catastrophic flood. During the nineteenth century, however, field investigations by many scientists provided convincing proof that an extensive Ice Age was responsible for these deposits and for many other features.

By the beginning of the twentieth century, geologists had largely determined the extent of Ice Age glaciation. Further, they discovered that many glaciated regions did not have just one layer of drift, but several. Close examination of these older deposits showed well-developed zones of chemical weathering and soil formation as well as the remains of plants that require warm temperatures. The evidence was clear: There had not been just one glacial advance but several, each separated by extended periods when climates were as warm as or warmer than at present. The Ice Age had not simply been a time when the ice advanced over the land, lingered for a while, and then receded. Rather, it was a complex period characterized by a number of advances and withdrawals of glacial ice.

The glacial record on land is punctuated by many erosional gaps. This makes it difficult to reconstruct the episodes of the Ice Age. But sediment on the ocean floor provides an uninterrupted record of climate cycles for this period. Studies of these seafloor sediments show that glacial/interglacial cycles have occurred about every 100,000 years. About 20 such cycles of cooling and warming were identified for the span we call the Ice Age.

During the Ice Age, ice left its imprint on almost 30 percent of Earth's land area, including about 10 million square kilometers (nearly 4 million square miles) of North America, 5 million square kilometers (2 million square miles) of Europe, and 4 million square kilometers (1.6 million square miles) of Siberia (**FIGURE 4.20**). The amount of glacial ice in the Northern Hemisphere was roughly twice that in the Southern Hemisphere. The primary reason is that the Southern Hemisphere has little land in the middle latitudes, and, therefore, the southern polar ice could not spread far beyond the margins of Antarctica. By contrast, North America and Eurasia provided great expanses of land for the spread of ice sheets.

We now know that the Ice Age began between 2 million and 3 million years ago. This means that most of the

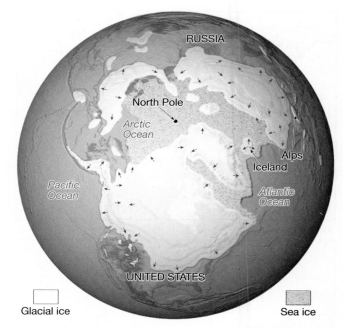

FIGURE 4.20 Maximum extent of glaciation in the Northern Hemisphere during the Ice Age. Sea ice (the ice surrounding the North Pole in the Arctic Ocean) is *not* glacial ice. Rather, it is the frozen upper portion of the ocean.

major glacial episodes occurred during a division of the geologic time scale called the **Pleistocene epoch**. Although the Pleistocene is commonly used as a synonym for the Ice Age, this epoch does not encompass it all. The Antarctic Ice Sheet, for example, formed at least 30 million years ago.

DESERTS

 Sculpturing Earth's Surface
▼ Deserts

The dry regions of the world encompass about 42 million square kilometers (more than 16 million square miles), a surprising 30 percent of Earth's land surface. No other climate group covers so large a land area. The word *desert* literally means "deserted" or "unoccupied." For many dry regions, this is a very appropriate description. Yet where water is available in deserts, plants and animals thrive. Nevertheless, the world's dry regions are among the least familiar land areas on Earth outside of the polar realm.

Desert landscapes frequently appear stark. Their profiles are not softened by a carpet of soil and abundant plant life. Instead, barren rocky outcrops with steep, angular slopes are common. Some rocks are tinted orange and red; others in different locations are gray and brown and streaked with black. For many visitors, desert scenery exhibits a striking beauty; to others, the terrain seems bleak. No matter which feeling is elicited, it is clear that deserts are very different from the more humid places where most people live.

As you will see, arid regions are not dominated by a single geologic process. Rather, the effects of tectonic (mountain-building) forces, running water, and wind are all apparent. Because these processes combine in different ways from place to place, the appearance of desert landscapes varies a great deal as well (**FIGURE 4.21**).

Distribution and Causes of Dry Lands

We all recognize that deserts are dry places, but just what is meant by the word *dry*? That is, how much rain defines the boundary between humid and dry regions?

Sometimes, it is arbitrarily defined by a single rainfall figure—for example, 25 centimeters (10 inches) per year of precipitation. However, the concept of dryness is relative; it refers to *any situation in which a water deficiency exists.*

Climatologists define *dry climate* as one in which yearly precipitation is less than the potential loss of water by evaporation.

Within these water-deficient regions, two climatic types are commonly recognized: **desert**, or arid, and **steppe**, or semiarid. The two categories have many features in common; their differences are primarily a matter of degree. The steppe is a marginal and more humid variant of the desert and represents a transition zone that surrounds the desert and separates it from bordering humid climates. The world map showing

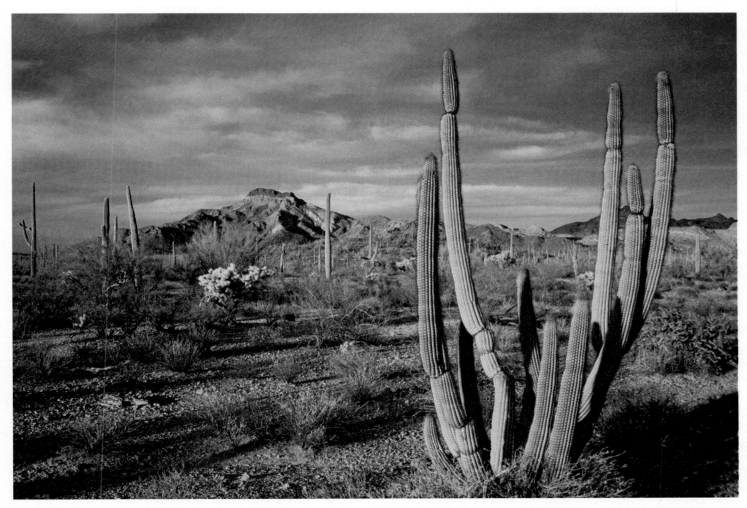

FIGURE 4.21 A scene in Organ Pipe Cactus National Monument near the Arizona–Mexico border. The appearance of desert landscapes varies a great deal from place to place. (Photo by Marek Zuk/Alamy)

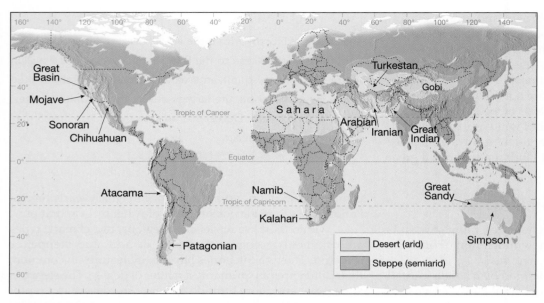

FIGURE 4.22 Arid and semiarid climates cover about 30 percent of Earth's land surface. No other climate group covers so large an area. Lower latitude deserts, such as the Sahara, Kalahari, and Great Sandy, are associated with the dry subsiding air masses of Earth's subtropical high-pressure belts. Middle-latitude deserts, such as the Gobi and Great Basin, are in the deep interior of continents and in the rainshadow of mountains.

the distribution of desert and steppe regions reveals that dry lands are concentrated in the subtropics and in the middle latitudes (**FIGURE 4.22**).

Deserts in places such as Africa, Arabia, and Australia are primarily the result of the prevailing global distribution of air pressure and winds (**FIGURE 4.23**). Coinciding with dry regions in the lower latitudes are zones of high air pressure known as the *subtropical highs*. These pressure systems are characterized by subsiding air currents. When air sinks, it is compressed and warmed. Such conditions are just the opposite of what is needed to produce clouds and precipitation. Consequently, these regions are known for their clear skies, sunshine, and ongoing drought.

Middle-latitude deserts and steppes exist principally because they are sheltered in the deep interiors of large landmasses. They are far removed from the ocean, which is the ultimate source of moisture for cloud formation and precipitation. In addition, the presence of high mountains across the paths of prevailing winds further acts to separate these areas from water-bearing, maritime air masses, In North America, the Coast Ranges, Sierra Nevada, and Cascades are the foremost mountain barriers to moisture from the Pacific (**FIGURE 4.24**). In their rainshadow lies the dry and expansive Basin and Range region of the American West.

Middle-latitude deserts provide an example of how mountain-building processes affect climate. Without mountains, wetter climates would prevail where dry regions exist today.

The Role of Water in Arid Climates

Permanent streams are normal in humid regions, but practically all desert streambeds are dry most of the time (**FIGURE 4.25A**). Deserts have **ephemeral streams**, which means that they carry water only in response to specific episodes of rainfall. A typical ephemeral stream may flow only a few days or perhaps just a few hours during the year. In some years, the channel might carry no water at all.

This fact is obvious even to the casual traveler who notices the numerous bridges with no streams beneath them,

FIGURE 4.23 In this view of Earth from space, North Africa's Sahara Desert, the adjacent Arabian Desert, and the Kalahari and Namib deserts in southern Africa are clearly visible as tan-colored, cloud-free zones. These low-latitude deserts are dominated by the dry, subsiding air associated with pressure belts known as the *subtropical highs*. By contrast, the band of clouds that extends across central Africa and the adjacent oceans coincides with the equatorial low-pressure belt, the rainiest region on Earth. (NASA)

DID YOU KNOW?

All deserts are not hot. Cold temperatures are experienced in middle-latitude deserts. For example, at Ulan Bator in Mongolia's Gobi Desert, the average *high* temperature on January days is only −19°C (−2°F)!

Sierra Nevada
Range

Coast Range | Rainshadow

Windward (wet) | Leeward (dry) | Great Basin

Wind

FIGURE 4.24 Mountains contribute to the formation of middle-latitude dry regions by creating a rainshadow. As moving air meets a mountain barrier, it is forced to rise. Clouds and precipitation on the windward side result. Air descending the leeward side is much drier. The mountains effectively cut the leeward side off from the source of moisture, creating a rainshadow. The Great Basin desert is a rainshadow desert that covers nearly all of Nevada and portions of adjacent states. (Left photo by Dean Pennala/Shutterstock; right photo by Dennis Tasa)

humid regions. A flood on a river like the Mississippi may take many days to reach its crest and then subside. But desert floods arrive suddenly and subside quickly. Because much surface material in a desert is not anchored by vegetation, the amount of erosional work that occurs during a single short-lived rain event is impressive.

In the dry western United States, different names are used for ephemeral streams, including *wash* and *arroyo*. In other parts of the world, a dry desert stream may be a *wadi* (Arabia and North Africa), a *donga* (South America), or a *nullah* (India).

Humid regions are notable for their well-developed drainage systems. But in arid regions, streams usually lack an extensive system of tributaries. In fact, a basic characteristic of desert streams is that they are small and die out before reaching the sea. Because the water table is usually far below the surface, few desert streams can draw upon it as streams do in humid regions. Without a steady supply of water, the combination of evaporation and soaking in soon depletes the stream.

or numerous dips in the road where dry channels cross. However, when the rare heavy showers do occur, so much rain falls in such a short time that it cannot all soak in. Because desert vegetative cover is sparse, runoff is largely unhindered and, therefore, rapid, often creating flash floods along valley floors (**FIGURE 4.25B**). These floods are quite unlike floods in

The few permanent streams that do cross arid regions, such as the Colorado and Nile rivers, originate *outside* the desert, often in mountains where precipitation is plentiful. The supply of water must be great to compensate for the losses that occur as the stream crosses the desert. For example, after the Nile leaves its headwaters in the lakes and mountains of central Africa, it crosses almost 3000 kilometers (nearly 1900 miles) of the Sahara Desert *without a single tributary*.

It should be emphasized that *running water, although infrequent, nevertheless is responsible for most of the erosional work in deserts*. This is contrary to a common belief that wind is the most important erosional agent sculpturing desert landscapes. Although wind erosion is indeed more significant in dry areas than elsewhere, most desert landforms are carved by running water. The main role of wind, as you will see later in this chapter, is in the transportation and deposition of sediment, which creates and shapes the ridges and mounds we call dunes.

FIGURE 4.25 A. Most of the time, desert stream channels are dry. **B.** This photo shows an ephemeral stream shortly after a heavy shower. Although such floods are short-lived, large amounts of erosion occur. (Photos by E.J. Tarbuck)

A.

B.

BASIN AND RANGE: THE EVOLUTION OF A MOUNTAINOUS DESERT LANDSCAPE

Because arid regions typically lack permanent streams, they are characterized as having **interior drainage**. This means that they have a discontinuous pattern of intermittent streams that do not flow out of the desert to the ocean. In the United States, the dry Basin and Range region provides an excellent example. The region includes southern Oregon, all of Nevada, western Utah, southeastern California, southern Arizona, and southern New Mexico. The name Basin and Range is an apt description for this almost 800,000-square-kilometer (312,000-square-mile) region, as it is characterized by more than 200 relatively small mountain ranges that rise 900 to 1500 meters (3000 to 5000 feet) above the basins that separate them.

In this region, as in others like it around the world, most erosion occurs without reference to the ocean (ultimate base level), because the interior drainage never reaches the sea. Even where permanent streams flow to the ocean, few tributaries exist, and only a narrow strip of land adjacent to the stream has sea level as its ultimate level of land reduction.

The block models in **FIGURE 4.26** depict how the landscape has evolved in the Basin and Range region. During and following uplift of the mountains, running water carves the elevated masses and deposits large quantities of sediment in the basin. In this early stage, relief (difference in elevation between high and low points in an area) is greatest. As erosion lowers the mountains and sediment fills the basins, elevation differences diminish.

When the occasional torrents of water produced by sporadic rains or periods of snowmelt move down the mountain canyons, they are heavily loaded with sediment. Emerging from the confines of the canyon, the runoff spreads over the gentler slopes at the base of the mountains and quickly loses velocity. Consequently, most of its sediment load is dumped within a short distance. The result is a cone of debris known as an **alluvial fan** at the mouth of a canyon. Over the years, a fan enlarges, eventually coalescing with fans from adjacent canyons to produce an apron of sediment, called a **bajada**, along the mountain front.

On the rare occasions of abundant rainfall, streams may flow across the alluvial fans to the center of the basin, converting the basin floor into a shallow **playa lake**. Playa lakes last only a few days or weeks, before evaporation and infiltration remove the water. The dry, flat lake bed that remains is termed a *playa*. Playas occasionally become encrusted with salts (*salt flats*) that are left behind when the water in which they were dissolved evaporates. **FIGURE 4.27** is a satellite image of a portion of California's Death Valley, a classic Basin and Range landscape. Many of the features just described are prominent, including a bajada (left side of valley), alluvial fans, a playa lake, and extensive salt flats.

FIGURE 4.26 Stages of landscape evolution in a mountainous desert such as the Basin and Range region of the West. As erosion of the mountains and deposition in the basins continue, relief diminishes. **A.** Early stage. **B.** Middle stage. **C.** Late stage.

FIGURE 4.27 Satellite image of a portion of Death Valley, California, a classic Basin and Range landscape. Shortly before this image was taken in February 2005, heavy rains led to the formation of a playa lake—the pool of greenish water on the basin floor. By May 2005, the lake had reverted to a salt-covered playa. (NASA)

With the ongoing erosion of the mountain mass and the accompanying sedimentation, the local relief continues to diminish. Eventually, nearly the entire mountain mass is gone. Thus, by the late stages of erosion, the mountain areas are reduced to a few large bedrock knobs (called *inselbergs*) projecting above the sediment-filled basin.

DID YOU KNOW?

The Atacama Desert of Chile is the world's driest desert. This narrow belt of arid land extends for about 1200 km (750 mi) along South America's Pacific Coast (see Figure 4.22). It is said that some portions of the Atacama have not received rain for more than 400 years! One must view such pronouncements skeptically. Nevertheless, for places where records have been kept, Arica, Chile, in the northern part of the Atacama, has experienced a span of 14 years without measurable rainfall.

Each of the stages of landscape evolution in an arid climate depicted in Figure 4.26 can be observed in the Basin and Range region. Recently uplifted mountains in an early stage of erosion are found in southern Oregon and northern Nevada. Death Valley, California, and southern Nevada fit into the more advanced middle stage, whereas the late stage, with its inselbergs, can be seen in southern Arizona.

WIND EROSION

EARTH SCIENCE

Sculpturing Earth's Surface
▼ Deserts

Moving air, like moving water, is turbulent and able to pick up loose debris and transport it to other locations. Just as in a river, the velocity of wind increases with height above the surface. Also like a river, wind transports fine particles in suspension while heavier ones are carried as bed load (**FIGURE 4.28**). However, the transport of sediment by wind differs from that by running water in two significant ways. First, wind's lower density compared to water renders it less

A.

B.

FIGURE 4.28 **A.** This satellite image shows thick plumes of dust from the Sahara Desert blowing across the Red Sea on June 30, 2009. Such dust storms are common in arid North Africa. In fact, this region is the largest dust source in the world. Satellites are an excellent tool for studying the transport of dust on a global scale. They show that dust storms can cover huge areas and that dust can be transported great distances. (NASA) **B.** The bed load carried by wind consists of sand grains, many of which move by bouncing along the surface. Sand never travels far from the surface, even when winds are very strong. (Photo by imagebroker/Alamy)

capable of picking up and transporting coarse materials. Second, because wind is not confined to channels, it can spread sediment over large areas, as well as high into the atmosphere.

Compared to running water and glaciers, wind is a relatively insignificant erosional agent. Recall that even in deserts, most erosion is performed by intermittent running water, not by the wind. Wind erosion is more effective in arid lands than in humid areas because in humid places moisture binds particles together and vegetation anchors the soil. For wind to be an effective erosional force, dryness and scanty vegetation are important prerequisites. When such circumstances exist, wind may pick up, transport, and deposit great quantities of fine sediment. During the 1930s, parts of the Great Plains experienced vast dust storms (**FIGURE 4.29**). The plowing under of the natural vegetative cover for farming, followed by severe

FIGURE 4.29 A dust storm blackens the Colorado sky in this historic image from the Dust Bowl of the 1930s. (Photo courtesy U.S.D.A./Natural Resources Conservation Service)

drought, exposed the land to wind erosion and led to the area being labeled the Dust Bowl.

Deflation, Blowouts, and Desert Pavement

One way that wind erodes is by **deflation**, the lifting and removal of loose material. Wind can suspend only fine sediment such as clay and silt. Larger grains of sand are rolled or skipped along the surface (a process called *saltation*) and comprise the bed load. Particles larger than sand are usually not transported by wind. Deflation sometimes is difficult to notice because the entire surface is being lowered at the same time, but it can be significant.

The most noticeable result of deflation in some places is shallow depressions called **blowouts** (**FIGURE 4.30**). In the Great Plains region, from Texas north to Montana, thousands of blowouts can be seen. They range from small dimples less than 1 meter (3 feet) deep and 3 meters (10 feet) wide to depressions that are more than 45 meters (150 feet) deep and several kilometers across.

In portions of many deserts, the surface is characterized by a layer of coarse pebbles and cobbles that are too large to be moved by the wind. This stony veneer, called

DID YOU KNOW?

Deserts do not necessarily consist of mile after mile of drifting sand dunes. Surprisingly, sand accumulations represent only a small percentage of the total desert area. In the Sahara, dunes cover only one-tenth of its area. The sandiest of all deserts, the Arabian, is one-third sand covered.

FIGURE 4.30 **A.** Blowouts are depressions created by deflation. Land that is dry and largely unprotected by anchoring vegetation is particularly susceptible. **B.** In this example, deflation has removed about 4 feet of soil—the distance from the man's outstretched arm to his feet. (Photo courtesy of U.S.D.A./Natural Resources Conservation Service)

FIGURE 4.31 Two models of desert pavement formation. **A.** This model portrays an area with poorly sorted surface deposits. Coarse particles gradually become concentrated into a tightly packed layer as deflation lowers the surface by removing sand and silt. Here desert pavement is the result of wind erosion. **B.** This model shows the formation of desert pavement on a surface initially covered with coarse pebbles and cobbles. Wind-blown dust accumulates at the surface and gradually sifts downward through spaces between coarse particles. Infiltrating rainwater aids the process. This depositional process raises the surface and produces a layer of coarse pebbles and cobbles underlain by a substantial layer of fine sediment.

blown away. Eventually, a continuous cover of coarse particles remains.

Studies have shown that the process depicted in Figure 4.31A is not an adequate explanation for all environments in which desert pavement exists. As a result, an alternate explanation was formulated and is illustrated in **FIGURE 4.31B**. This hypothesis suggests that pavement develops on a surface that initially consists of coarse pebbles. Over time, protruding cobbles trap fine wind-blown grains that settle and sift downward through the spaces between the larger surface stones. The process is aided by infiltrating rainwater.

Once desert pavement becomes established, a process that might take hundreds of years, the surface is effectively protected from further deflation if left undisturbed. However, as the layer is only one or two stones thick, the passage of vehicles or animals can dislodge the pavement and expose the fine-grained material below. If this happens, the surface is no longer protected from deflation.

Wind Abrasion

Like glaciers and streams, wind erodes in part by *abrasion*. In dry regions as well as along some beaches, windblown sand will cut and polish exposed rock surfaces. Abrasion is often given credit for accomplishments beyond its actual capabilities. Such features as balanced rocks that stand high atop narrow pedestals and intricate detailing on tall pinnacles are not the results of abrasion by windblown sand. Sand is seldom lifted more than a meter above the surface, so the wind's sandblasting effect is obviously limited in vertical extent. But in areas prone to such activity, telephone poles have actually been cut through near their bases. For this reason, collars are often fitted on the poles to protect them from being "sawed" down.

desert pavement, may form as deflation lowers the surface by removing sand and silt from poorly sorted materials. As **FIGURE 4.31A** illustrates, the concentration of larger particles at the surface gradually increases as the finer particles are

WIND DEPOSITS

Sculpturing Earth's Surface
▼ Deserts

Although wind is relatively unimportant in carving erosional features, significant depositional landforms are created by the wind in some regions. Accumulations of windblown sediment are particularly conspicuous in the world's dry lands and along many sandy coasts. Wind deposits are of two distinctive types: (1) extensive blankets of silt, called *loess,* that once were carried in suspension, and (2) mounds and ridges of sand from the wind's bed load, which we call *dunes.*

Loess

In some parts of the world the surface topography is mantled with deposits of windblown silt, called **loess.** Dust

A.

B.

C.

Windblown dust

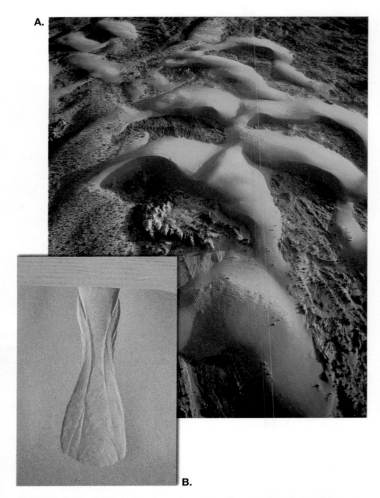

A.

B.

FIGURE 4.33   A. The White Point dunes near Preston Mesa, Arizona. Strong winds move sand up the more gentle windward slopes. As sand accumulates near the dune crest, the slope becomes steeper. (Photo by Michael Collier) **B.** Eventually, some of the sand slides down the *slip face.* (Photo by Christopher Liu/ChinaStock Photo Library)

storms deposited this material over thousands of years. When loess is breached by streams or road cuts, it tends to maintain vertical cliffs and lacks any visible layers, as you can see in **FIGURE 4.32A.**

The distribution of loess worldwide indicates two primary sources for this sediment: deserts and glacial deposits of stratified drift. The thickest and most extensive loess deposits occur in western and northern China

FIGURE 4.32   A. This vertical loess bluff near the Mississippi River in southern Illinois is about 3 meters (10 feet) high. (Photo by James E. Patterson) **B.** In parts of China, loess has sufficient structural strength to permit the excavation of cavelike dwellings. (Photo by Betty Crowell) **C.** This satellite image from November 1, 2006, shows streamers of windblown dust moving southward into the Gulf of Alaska. It illustrates a process similar to the one that created many loess deposits in the American Midwest during the Ice Age. Fine silt is produced by the grinding action of glaciers and then transported beyond the margin of the ice by running water and deposited. Later, the fine silt is picked up by strong winds and later deposited as loess. (NASA)

(FIGURE 4.32B). They were blown there from the extensive desert basins of central Asia. Accumulations of 30 meters (100 feet) are not uncommon, and thicknesses of more than 100 meters (300 feet) have been measured. It is this fine, buff-colored sediment that gives the Yellow River (Huang He) its name.

In the United States, deposits of loess are significant in many areas, including South Dakota, Nebraska, Iowa, Missouri, and Illinois, as well as portions of the Columbia Plateau in the Pacific Northwest. Unlike the deposits in China, which originated in deserts, the loess in the United States and Europe is an indirect product of glaciation. Its source is deposits of stratified drift. During the retreat of the ice sheets, many river valleys were choked with glacial sediment. Strong winds sweeping across the barren floodplains picked up the finer sediment and dropped it as a blanket on areas adjacent to the valleys (FIGURE 4.32C).

Sand Dunes

Like running water, wind releases its load of sediment when its velocity falls and the energy available for transport diminishes. Thus, sand begins to accumulate wherever an obstruction across the path of the wind slows its movement. Unlike deposits of loess, which form blanketlike layers over broad areas, winds commonly deposit sand in mounds or ridges called **dunes** (FIGURE 4.33).

As moving air encounters an object, such as a clump of vegetation or a rock, the wind sweeps around and over it, leaving a shadow of more slowly moving air behind the obstacle as well as a smaller zone of quieter air just in front of the obstacle. Some of the sand grains moving with the wind come to rest in these *wind shadows*. As the accumulation of sand continues, it forms an increasingly efficient wind barrier to trap even more sand. If there is a sufficient supply of sand and the wind blows steadily long enough, the mound of sand grows into a dune.

Many dunes have an asymmetrical profile, with the leeward (sheltered) slope being steep and the windward slope more gently inclined. Sand is rolled up the gentle slope on the windward side by the force of the wind. Just beyond the crest of the dune, the wind velocity is reduced and the sand accumulates. As more sand collects, the slope

FIGURE 4.34 **A.** and **B.** Dunes commonly have an asymmetrical shape. The steeper leeward side is called the *slip face*. Sand grains deposited on the slip face create the cross bedding of the dunes. **C.** Over time, a complex pattern develops. Also notice that when dunes are buried and become part of the sedimentary record, the cross bedded structure is preserved. **D.** Cross beds are an obvious characteristic of the Navajo Sandstone in Zion National Park, Utah. (Photo by Dennis Tasa)

steepens and eventually some of it slides under the pull of gravity. In this way, the leeward slope of the dune, called the **slip face**, maintains a relatively steep angle. Continued sand accumulation, coupled with periodic slides down the slip face, results in the slow migration of the dune in the direction of air movement (Figure 4.33).

As sand is deposited on the slip face, it forms layers inclined in the direction the wind is blowing. These sloping layers are called **cross beds**. When the dunes are eventually buried under layers of sediment and become part of the sedimentary rock record, their asymmetrical shape is destroyed, but the cross beds remain as a testimony to their origin. Nowhere is cross bedding more prominent than in the sandstone walls of Zion Canyon in southern Utah (**FIGURE 4.34**).

THE CHAPTER IN REVIEW

• A *glacier* is a thick mass of ice originating on the land from the compaction and recrystallization of snow. It shows evidence of past or present movement. Today, *valley*, or *alpine glaciers*, are found in mountain areas where they usually follow valleys originally occupied by streams. *Ice sheets* exist on a much larger scale, covering most of Greenland and Antarctica. Other categories include *ice caps* and *piedmont glaciers*.

• Glaciers move in part by flowing. On the surface of a glacier, ice is brittle. However, below about 50 meters (165 feet), pressure is great and ice behaves like *a plastic material and flows*. A second important mechanism of glacial movement consists of the whole ice mass *slipping* along the ground.

• Glaciers form in areas where more snow falls in winter than melts during summer. Snow accumulation and ice formation occur in the *zone of accumulation*. Beyond this area is the *zone of wastage*, where there is a net loss to the glacier. The *glacial budget* is the balance, or lack of balance, between accumulation at the upper end of the glacier and loss at the lower end.

• Glaciers erode land by *plucking* (lifting pieces of bedrock out of place) and *abrasion* (grinding and scraping of a rock surface). Erosional features produced by valley glaciers include *glacial troughs, hanging valleys, cirques, arêtes, horns,* and *fiords*.

• Any sediment of glacial origin is called *drift*. The two distinct types of glacial drift are (a) *till,* which is material deposited directly by the ice, and (b) *stratiified drifi,* which is sediment laid down by meltwater from a glacier.

• The most widespread features created by glacial deposition are layers or ridges of till, called *moraines*. Associated with valley glaciers are *lateral moraines,* formed along the sides of the valley, and *medial moraines,* formed between two valley glaciers that have joined. *End moraines,* which mark the former position of the front of a glacier, and *ground moraines,* undulating layers of till deposited as the ice front retreats, are common to both valley glaciers and ice sheets.

• Perhaps the most convincing evidence for several glacial advances during the *Ice Age* is the widespread existence of *multiple layers of drift* on land and an uninterrupted record of climate cycles preserved in *seafloor sediments*. In addition to massive erosional and depositional work, other effects of Ice Age glaciers included the *forced migration* of animals, *changes in river courses, adjustment of the crust* by rebounding after the removal of the immense load of ice, and *climate changes* caused by the existence of the glaciers themselves. In the sea, the most far-reaching effect of the Ice Age was the *worldwide change in sea level* that accompanied each advance and retreat of the ice sheets.

• Deserts in the lower latitudes coincide with zones of high air pressure known as *subtropical highs.* Middle-latitude deserts exist because of their positions in the deep interiors of large continents, far removed from oceans. Mountains also act to shield these regions from marine air masses.

• Practically all desert streams are dry most of the time and are said to be *ephemeral.* Nevertheless, *running water is responsible for most of the erosional work in a desert.* Although wind erosion is more significant in dry areas than elsewhere, the main role of wind in a desert is the transportation and deposition of sediment.

• Many of the landscapes of the Basin and Range region of the western United States are characterized by *interior drainage* with streams eroding uplifted mountain blocks and depositing the sediment in interior basins. *Alluvial fans, bajadas, playas, playa lakes,* and *inselbergs* are features often associated with these landscapes.

• For wind erosion to be effective, dryness and scant vegetation are essential. *Deflation,* the lifting and removal of loose material, often produces shallow depressions called *blowouts* and can also lower the surface by removing sand and silt. *Abrasion,* the "sandblasting" effect of wind, is often given too much credit for producing desert features. However, abrasion does cut and polish rock near the surface.

• Wind deposits are of two distinct types: (1) extensive *blankets of silt,* called *loess,* that were carried by wind in *suspension,* and (2) *mounds and ridges of sand,* called *dunes,* formed from sediment that was carried as part of the wind's *bed load.*

KEY TERMS

abrasion (p. 118)
alluvial fan (p. 130)
alpine glacier (p. 112)
arête (p. 119)
bajada (p. 130)
blowout (p. 132)
cirque (p. 119)
crevasses (p. 115)
cross beds (p. 136)
deflation (p. 132)
desert (p. 127)
desert pavement (p. 133)
drumlin (p. 124)

dune (p. 135)
end moraine (p. 122)
ephemeral stream (p. 128)
esker (p. 124)
fiord (p. 120)
glacial drift (p. 121)
glacial erratic (p. 121)
glacial striations (p. 118)
glacial trough (p. 118)
glacier (p. 112)
ground moraine (p. 122)
hanging valley (p. 118)
horn (p. 119)

ice cap (p. 113)
ice sheet (p. 112)
ice shelf (p. 113)
interior drainage (p. 130)
kame (p. 124)
kettle (p. 124)
lateral moraine (p. 122)
loess (p. 134)
medial moraine (p. 122)
outwash plain (p. 124)
piedmont glacier (p. 113)
playa lake (p. 130)
Pleistocene epoch (p. 126)

plucking (p. 117)
pluvial lake (p. 125)
rock flour (p. 118)
slip face (p. 136)
steppe (p. 127)
stratified drift (p. 121)
till (p. 121)
valley glacier (p. 112)
valley train (p. 124)
zone of accumulation (p. 116)
zone of wastage (p. 116)

QUESTIONS FOR REVIEW

1. What is a glacier? What percentage of Earth's land area do glaciers cover?

2. Contrast valley glaciers and ice sheets.

3. Describe how glaciers fit into the hydrologic cycle. What role do they play in the rock cycle?

4. Describe the two components of glacial flow. At what rates do glaciers move? In a valley glacier, does all of the ice move at the same rate? Explain.

5. Why do crevasses form in the upper portion of a glacier but not below a depth of about 50 meters (165 feet)?

6. Under what circumstances will the terminus of a glacier advance? Retreat? Remain stationary?

7. Describe two basic processes by which glaciers erode.

8. How does the shape of a glaciated mountain valley differ from that of an unglaciated mountain valley?

9. List and describe the erosional features you might expect to see in an area where valley glaciers exist or have recently existed.

10. What is glacial drift? What is the difference between till and stratified drift? What general effect do glacial deposits have on the landscape?

11. List and briefly describe the four basic moraine types. What do all moraines have in common?

12. List and briefly describe four depositional features other than moraines.

13. How does a kettle form?

14. About what percentage of Earth's land surface was covered at some time by Pleistocene glaciers? How does this compare to the area presently covered by ice sheets and glaciers? (Check your answer with that for Question 1.)

15. List three indirect effects of Ice Age glaciers.

16. How extensive are Earth's dry regions?

17. Most desert streams are said to be ephemeral. What does that mean?

18. What is the most important erosional agent in deserts?

19. Describe the features and characteristics associated with each of the stages in the evolution of a mountainous desert region such as the Basin and Range region in the American West.

20. Why is wind erosion relatively more important in dry regions than in humid areas?

21. List two types of wind erosion and the features that may result from each.

22. Although sand dunes are the best-known wind deposits, accumulations of loess are very significant in some parts of the world. What is loess? Where are such deposits found? What are the origins of this sediment?

23. How do sand dunes migrate?

COMPANION WEBSITE

The *Foundations of Earth Science* Website uses the resources and flexibility of the Internet to aid in your study of the topics in this chapter. Written and developed by the authors and other Earth science instructors, this site will help improve your understanding of Earth science. Visit **www.mygeoscienceplace .com** in order to:

• **Review** key chapter concepts.

• **Read** with links to the ebook and to chapter-specific web resources

• **Visualize** and comprehend challenging topics using learning activities in *GEODe: Earth Science.*

• **Test** yourself with online quizzes.

GEODe: EARTH SCIENCE

GEODe: Earth Science is a valuable and easy to use learning aid that can be accessed from your book's Companion Website: **www.mygeoscienceplace.com.** It is a dynamic instructional tool that promotes understanding and reinforces important concepts by using tutorials, animations, and exercises that actively engage the student.

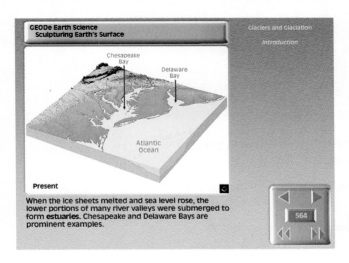

When the ice sheets melted and sea level rose, the lower portions of many river valleys were submerged to form **estuaries**. Chesapeake and Delaware Bays are prominent examples.

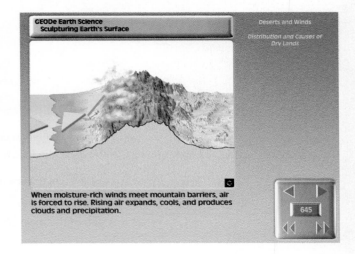

When moisture-rich winds meet mountain barriers, air is forced to rise. Rising air expands, cools, and produces clouds and precipitation.

PLATE TECTONICS
A SCIENTIFIC THEORY
UNFOLDS

FOCUS ON LEARNING

To assist you in learning the important concepts in this chapter, you will find it helpful to focus on the following questions:

1. What lines of evidence were used to support the continental drift hypothesis?

2. What was one of the main objections to the continental drift hypothesis?

3. What is the theory of plate tectonics?

4. In what major way does the plate tectonics theory depart from the continental drift hypothesis?

5. What are the three types of plate boundaries?

6. What is the evidence used to support the plate tectonics theory?

7. What models have been proposed to explain the driving mechanism for plate motion?

Hikers in the Himalayas. A continental collision created these mountains.
(Photo by Jake Norton/Mountain World Photography/
Aurora Photos)

Prior to the 1960s most geologists held the view that the ocean basins and continents had fixed geographic positions and were of great antiquity. Less than a decade later researchers came to realize that Earth's continents are not static, instead they gradually migrate across the globe. Because of these movements, blocks of continental material collide, deforming the intervening crust, thereby creating Earth's great mountain chains (**FIGURE 5.1**). Furthermore, landmasses occasionally split apart. As the continental blocks separate, a new ocean basin emerges between them. Meanwhile, other portions of the seafloor plunge into the mantle. In short, a dramatically different model of Earth's tectonic processes emerged.*

This profound reversal in scientific thought has been appropriately described as a *scientific revolution*. The revolution began early in the twentieth century as a relatively straightforward proposal called *continental drift*. For more than 50 years the idea that continents were capable of movement was categorically rejected by the scientific establishment.** Continental drift was particularly distasteful to North American geologists, perhaps because much of the supporting evidence had been gathered from the continents of Africa, South America, and Australia, with which most North American geologists were unfamiliar.

Following World War II, modern instruments replaced rock hammers as the tools of choice for many researchers. Armed with these more advanced tools, geologists and a new breed of researchers including *geophysicists* and *geochemists* made several surprising discoveries that began to rekindle interest in the drift hypothesis. By 1968 these developments led to the unfolding of a far more encompassing explanation known as the *theory of plate tectonics*.

In this chapter, we will examine the events that led to this dramatic reversal of scientific opinion in an attempt to provide insight into how science works. We will also briefly trace the development of the continental drift hypothesis, examine why it was first rejected, and consider the evidence that finally led to the acceptance of its direct descendant—the theory of plate tectonics.

*Tectonic processes are those that deform Earth's crust to create major structural features such as mountains, continents, and ocean basins.

**A few geologists including Alexander du Toit of South Africa and Arthur Homers in England supported the continental drift hypothesis. But they were clearly in the minority.

FIGURE 5.1   Climbers (left) camping on a shear rock face of a mountain known as K7 in Pakistan's Karakoram, a part of the Himalayas. These mountains formed as India collided with Eurasia. (Photo by Jimmy Chin/National Geographic/Getty)

CONTINENTAL DRIFT: AN IDEA BEFORE ITS TIME

The idea that continents, particularly South America and Africa, fit together like pieces of a jigsaw puzzle came about during the 1600s as better world maps became available. However, little significance was given to this notion until 1915, when Alfred Wegener (1880–1930), a German meteorologist and geophysicist, wrote *The Origin of Continents and Oceans*. This book, published in several editions, set forth the basic outline of Wegener's hypothesis called **continental drift**— which dared to challenge the long-held assumption that the continents and ocean basins had fixed geographic positions.

Wegener suggested that a single **supercontinent** consisting of all Earth's landmasses once existed.* He named this giant landmass **Pangaea** (pronounced Pan-jee-ah; meaning "all lands") (**FIGURE 5.2**). Wegener further hypothesized that about 200 million years ago, during the early part of the Mesozoic era, this supercontinent began to fragment into smaller landmasses. These continental blocks then "drifted" to their present positions over a span of millions of years. The inspiration for continental drift is believed to have come to Wegener when he observed the breakup of sea ice during a Danish-led expedition to Greenland.

Wegener and others who advocated the continental drift hypothesis collected substantial evidence to support their

*Wegener was not the first person to conceive of a long-vanished supercontinent. Edward Suess (1831–1914), a distinguished nineteenth-century geologist pieced together evidence for a giant landmass consisting of the continents of South America, Africa, India, and Australia.

point of view. The fit of South America and Africa and the geographic distribution of fossils and ancient climates all seemed to buttress the idea that these now separate landmasses were once joined. Let us examine some of this evidence.

Evidence: The Continental Jigsaw Puzzle

Like a few others before him, Wegener suspected that the continents might once have been joined when he noticed the remarkable similarity between the coastlines on opposite sides of the Atlantic Ocean. However, Wegener's use of present-day shorelines to fit these continents together was challenged immediately by other Earth scientists. These opponents correctly argued that shorelines are continually modified by wave erosion and depositional processes. Even if continental displacement had taken place, a good fit today would be unlikely. Because Wegener's original jigsaw fit of the continents was crude, it is assumed that he was aware of this problem (Figure 5.2B).

Scientists later determined that a much better approximation of the outer boundary of a continent is the seaward edge of its continental shelf, which lies submerged a few hundred meters below sea level. In the early 1960s, Sir Edward Bullard and two associates constructed a map that pieced together the edges of the continental shelves of South America and Africa at depths of 900 meters (**FIGURE 5.3**). The remarkable fit that was obtained was more precise than even these researchers had expected. As shown in Figure 5.3 there are a few places where the continents overlap. Some of these overlaps are related to the process of stretching and thinning of the continental margins as they drifted apart. Others can be explained by the work of major river systems. For example, since the break-up of Pangaea the Niger River has built an extensive delta that enlarged the continental shelf of Africa.

Evidence: Fossils Match across the Seas

Although the seed for Wegener's hypothesis came from the remarkable similarities of the continental margins on opposite sides of the Atlantic, it was when he learned that identical fossil organisms had been discovered in rocks from both South America and Africa that his pursuit of continental drift became more focused. Through a review of the literature, Wegener learned that most paleontologists (scientists who study the fossilized remains of ancient organisms) were in agreement that some type of land connection was needed to explain the existence of similar Mesozoic age life forms on widely separated landmasses. Just as modern life forms native to North America are quite different from those of Africa and Australia, one would expect that during the Mesozoic era, organisms on widely separated continents would be distinct.

A. Modern reconstruction of Pangaea

B. Wegener's Pangaea

FIGURE 5.2 Reconstruction of Pangaea as it is thought to have appeared 200 million years ago. **A.** Modern reconstruction. **B.** Reconstruction done by Wegener in 1915.

Continental shelf

AFRICA

Modern Equator

SOUTH AMERICA

Modern Equator

■ Overlap

FIGURE 5.3   This figure shows the best fit of South America and Africa along the continental slope at a depth of 500 fathoms (about 900 meters [3000 feet]). The areas where continental blocks overlap appear in brown. (After A. G. Smith, "Continental Drift," in *Understanding the Earth*, edited by I. G. Gass.)

Mesosaurus

To add credibility to his argument, Wegener documented cases of several fossil organisms that were found on different landmasses despite the unlikely possibility that their living forms could have crossed the vast ocean presently separating them (**FIGURE 5.4**). A classic example is *Mesosaurus,* an aquatic fish-catching reptile whose fossil remains are limited to black shales of the Permian period (about 260 million years ago) in eastern South America and southwestern Africa (Figure 5.4).

If *Mesosaurus* had been able to make the long journey across the South Atlantic, its remains would likely be more widely distributed. As this is not the case, Wegener asserted that South America and Africa must have been joined during that period of Earth history.

How did opponents of continental drift explain the existence of identical fossil organisms in places separated by thousands of kilometers of open ocean? Rafting, transoceanic land bridges (isthmian links), and island stepping stones were the most widely invoked explanations for these migrations (**FIGURE 5.5**). We know, for example, that during the Ice Age that ended about 8000 years ago, the lowering of sea level allowed mammals (including humans) to cross the narrow Bering Strait that separates Russia and Alaska. Was it possible that land bridges once connected Africa and South America but later subsided below sea level? Modern maps of the seafloor substantiate Wegener's contention that if land bridges of this magnitude once existed, their remnants would still lie below sea level.

Glossopteris

Wegener also cited the distribution of the fossil "seed fern" *Glossopteris* as evidence for the existence of Pangaea (Figure 5.4). This plant, identified by its tongue-shaped leaves and seeds that were too large to be carried by the wind, was known to be widely dispersed among Africa, Australia, India, and South America. Later, fossil remains of *Glossopteris* were also discovered in Antarctica.* Wegener also learned that these seed ferns and associated flora grew only in a subpolar climate. Therefore, he concluded that when these landmasses were joined, they were located much closer to the South Pole.

*In 1912 Captain Robert Scott and two companions froze to death lying beside 35 pounds of rock on their return from a failed attempt to be the first to reach the South Pole. These samples, collected on the moraines of Beardmore Glacier, contained fossil remains of *Glossopteris*.

C. Lystrosaurus

Mesosaurus

Lystrosaurus

Glossopteris

A. Mesosaurus

B. Glossopteris

FIGURE 5.4   Fossil evidence supporting continental drift. **A.** Fossils of *Mesosaurus* are found only in nonmarine deposits in eastern South America and western Africa. *Mesosaurus* was a freshwater reptile incapable of swimming the 5000 kilometers of open ocean that now separate these continents. **B.** Remains of *Glossopteris* and related flora are found in Australia, Africa, South America, Antarctica, and India, landmasses that currently have quite varied climates. However, when *Glossopteris* inhabited these regions during the late Paleozoic era, their climates were all subpolar. **C.** Fossils of *Lystrosaurus,* a land-dwelling reptile, are also found on three of these landmasses.

FIGURE 5.5   These sketches by John Holden illustrate various explanations for the occurrence of similar species on landmasses that are presently separated by vast oceans. (Reprinted with permission of John Holden)

Evidence: Rock Types and Geologic Features

Anyone who has worked a jigsaw puzzle knows that its successful completion requires that you fit the pieces together while maintaining the continuity of the picture. The "picture" that must match in the "continental drift puzzle" is

one of rock types and geologic features such as mountain belts. If the continents were once together, the rocks found in a particular region on one continent should closely match in age and type those found in adjacent positions on the once adjoining continent. Wegener found evidence of 2.2-billion-year-old igneous rocks in Brazil that closely resembled similarly aged rocks in Africa.

Similar evidence can be found in mountain belts that terminate at one coastline, only to reappear on landmasses across the ocean. For instance, the mountain belt that includes the Appalachians trends northeastward through the eastern United States and disappears off the coast of Newfoundland (**FIGURE 5.6A**). Mountains of comparable age and structure are found in the British Isles and Scandinavia. When these landmasses are reassembled, as in **FIGURE 5.6B**, the mountain chains form a nearly continuous belt.

Wegener described how the similarities in geologic features on both sides of the Atlantic linked these landmasses when he said, "It is just as if we were to refit the torn pieces of a newspaper by matching their edges and then check whether the lines of print run smoothly across. If they do, there is nothing left but to conclude that the pieces were in fact joined in this way."*

---

* Alfred Wegener, *The Origin of Continents and Oceans*, translated from the 4th revised German ed. of 1929 by J. Birman (London: Methuen, 1966).

A.

B.

FIGURE 5.6   Matching mountain ranges across the North Atlantic. **A.** The Appalachian Mountains trend along the eastern flank of North America and disappear off the coast of Newfoundland. Mountains of comparable age and structure are found in the British Isles, and Scandinavia. **B.** When these landmasses are placed in their predrift locations, these ancient mountain chains form a nearly continuous belt. These folded mountain belts formed roughly 300 million years ago as the landmasses collided during the formation of the supercontinent of Pangaea.

Evidence: Ancient Climates

Because Alfred Wegener was a student of world climates, he suspected that **paleoclimatic** (*paleo* = ancient, *climatic* = climate) **data** might also support the idea of mobile continents. His assertion was bolstered when he learned that evidence for a glaciation that dated to the late Paleozoic had been discovered in southern Africa, South America, Australia, and India (**FIGURE 5.7A**). This meant that about 300 million years ago, vast ice sheets covered extensive portions of the Southern Hemisphere as well as India (**FIGURE 5.7B**). Much of the land area that contains evidence of this period of Paleozoic glaciation presently lies within 30 degrees of the equator in subtropical or tropical climates.

How could extensive ice sheets form near the Equator? One proposal suggested that our planet experienced a period of extreme global cooling. Wegener rejected this explanation because during the same span of geologic time, large tropical swamps existed in several locations in the Northern Hemisphere. The lush vegetation in these swamps was eventually buried and converted to coal. Today these deposits comprise major coal fields in the eastern United States, Northern Europe, and Asia. Many of the fossils found in these coal-bearing rocks were produced by tree ferns that possessed large fronds; a fact consistent with a warm, moist climate. Furthermore, these fern trees lacked growth rings, a characteristic of tropical plants that grow in regions having minimal yearly fluctuations in temperature. By contrast, trees that inhabit the middle latitudes, such as those found in most of the United States, develop multiple tree rings—one for each growing season.

Wegener suggested that a more plausible explanation for the late Paleozoic glaciation was provided by the supercontinent of Pangaea. In this configuration the southern continents are joined together and located near the South Pole (**FIGURE 5.7C**). This would account for the conditions necessary to generate extensive expanses of glacial ice over much of these landmasses. At the same time, this geography would place today's northern continents nearer the equator and account for the tropical swamps that generated the vast coal deposits. Wegener was so convinced that his explanation was correct that he wrote, "This evidence is so compelling that by comparison all other criteria must take a back seat."

How does a glacier develop in hot, arid central Australia? How do land animals migrate across wide expanses of ocean? As compelling as this evidence may have been, 50 years passed before most of the scientific community

A.

B.

FIGURE 5.7   Paleoclimatic evidence for continental drift. **A.** Glacial striations (scratches) and grooves like these are produced as glaciers drag rock debris across the underlying bedrock. The direction of glacial movement can be deduced from the distinctive patterns of aligned scratches and grooves. (Photo by Gregory S. Springer) **B.** Near the end of the Paleozoic era (about 300 million years ago), ice sheets covered extensive areas of the Southern Hemisphere and India. Arrows show the direction of ice movement that can be inferred from glacial grooves in the bedrock. **C.** The continents restored to their predrift position when they were part of Pangaea. This configuration accounts for the conditions necessary to generate a vast glacial ice sheet and also explains the direction of ice movements that radiated away from the South Pole.

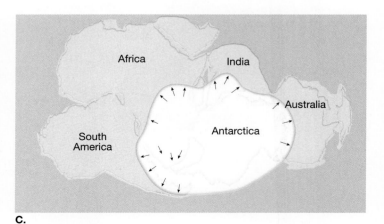

C.

accepted the concept of continental drift and the logical conclusions to which it led.

THE GREAT DEBATE

Wegener's proposal did not attract much open criticism until 1924, when his book was translated into English, French, Spanish, and Russian. From that point until his death in 1930, the drift hypothesis encountered a great deal of hostile criticism. The respected American geologist R. T. Chamberlain stated, "Wegener's hypothesis in general is of the foot-loose type, in that it takes considerable liberty with our globe, and is less bound by restrictions or tied down by awkward, ugly facts than most of its rival theories. Its appeal seems to lie in the fact that it plays a game in which there are few restrictive rules and no sharply drawn code of conduct."*

A quote attributed to W. B. Scott, former president of the American Philosophical Society, expressed the prevalent American view of continental drift in fewer words when he described the hypothesis as "utter damned rot!"

Rejection of the Continental Drift Hypothesis

One of the main objections to Wegener's hypothesis stemmed from his inability to identify a credible mechanism for continental drift. Wegener proposed that gravitational forces of the Moon and Sun that produce Earth's tides were also capable of gradually moving the continents across the globe. However, the prominent physicist Harold Jeffreys correctly countered that tidal forces of the magnitude needed to displace the continents would bring Earth's rotation to a halt in a matter of a few years.

Wegener also incorrectly suggested that the larger and sturdier continents broke through thinner oceanic crust, much like ice breakers cut through ice. However, no evidence existed to suggest that the ocean floor was weak enough to permit passage of the continents without the continents being appreciably deformed in the process.

In 1930 Wegener made his fourth and final trip to the Greenland ice sheet. Although the primary focus of this expedition was to study the harsh winter polar climate on the ice-covered island, Wegener continued to test his continental drift hypothesis. Like earlier expeditions, he used astronomical methods in an attempt to verify that Greenland had drifted westward with respect to Europe.

While returning from Eismitte (an experimental station located in the center of Greenland), Wegener perished along with a companion. His intriguing idea, however, did not die. Following Wegener's death, Danish workers continued to take measurements of Greenland's position (1936, 1938, and 1948), but found no evidence of drift. Thus, Wegener's final

*A. Hallam. *A Revolution in the Earth Sciences*. New York, Oxford University ress, 1973, p 25.

DID YOU KNOW?

Alfred Wegener, best known for his continental drift hypothesis, also wrote numerous scientific papers on weather and climate. Following his interest in meteorology, Wegener made four extended trips to the Greenland ice sheet to study its harsh winter weather. In November 1930, while making a month-long trek across the ice sheet, Wegener and a companion perished.

test proved to be a failure. Today the Global Positioning System (GPS) allows scientists to measure the extremely gradual displacement of the continents that Wegener had worked so diligently, but unsuccessfully, to detect.

PLATE TECTONICS

Forces Within
▼ Plate Tectonics

Following World War II, oceanographers equipped with new marine tools and ample funding from the U.S. Office of Naval Research embarked on an unprecedented period of oceanographic exploration. Over the next two decades, a much better picture of large expanses of the seafloor slowly and painstakingly began to emerge. From this work came the discovery of a global **oceanic ridge system** that winds through all of the major oceans in a manner similar to the seams on a baseball (**FIGURE 5.8**).

In other parts of the ocean, new discoveries were also being made. Earthquake studies conducted in the western Pacific demonstrated that tectonic activity was occurring at great depths beneath deep-ocean trenches. Of equal importance was the fact that dredging of the seafloor did not bring up any oceanic crust that was older than 180 million years. Further, sediment accumulations in the deep-ocean basins were found to be thin, not the thousands of meters that were predicted.

By 1968, these developments, among others, led to the unfolding of a far more encompassing theory than continental drift, known as **plate tectonics**. The implications of plate

DID YOU KNOW?

A group of scientists proposed an interesting although incorrect explanation for the cause of continental drift. This proposal suggested that early in Earth's history, our planet was only about half its current diameter and completely covered by continental crust. Through time, Earth expanded, causing the continents to split into their current configurations, while new seafloor "filled in" the spaces as they drifted apart.

FIGURE 5.8   A mosaic of rigid plates constitutes Earth's outer shell. (After W. B. Hamilton and others)

A. Divergent boundary

tectonics are so far-reaching that this theory is today the framework within which to view most geologic processes.

According to the plate tectonics model, the uppermost mantle, along with the overlying crust, behave as a strong, rigid layer, known as the **lithosphere** (*lithos* = stone, *sphere* =

a ball) which is broken into segments commonly referred to as **plates** (**FIGURE 5.9**). The lithosphere is thinnest in the oceans where it varies from as little as a few kilometers along the axis of the oceanic ridge system to about 100 kilometers (60 miles) in the deep-ocean basins. By contrast, continental

North American plate

Canadian Shield

Rocky Mountains

Basin and Range

Juan de Fuca plate

San Andreas Fault

Appalachian Mts.

Caribbean plate

Iceland

Eurasian plate

Alps

African plate

Mid-Atlantic Ridge

Cocos plate

Antilles Arc

Pacific plate

Galapagos Ridge

East Pacific Rise

South American plate

Andes Mountains

Nazca plate

Chile Ridge

Scotia plate

Antarctic plate

Continental volcanic arc

Trench

Oceanic crust

Continental lithosphere

Subducting oceanic lithosphere

B. Convergent boundary

Oceanic lithosphere

C. Transform fault boundary

lithosphere is generally thicker than 100 kilometers and may extend to depths of 200 to 300 kilometers in some regions.

The lithosphere, in turn, overlies a weak region in the mantle known as the **asthenosphere** (*asthenos* = weak, *sphere* = a ball). The temperatures and pressures in the upper asthenosphere (100 to 200 kilometers in depth) are such that the rocks there are very near their melting temperatures and, hence, respond to stress by flowing. As a result, Earth's rigid outer shell is effectively detached from the layers below, which permit it to move independently.

FIGURE 5.9 Illustration of some of Earth's lithospheric plates.

Earth's Major Plates

The lithosphere is composed of about 20 segments having irregular sizes and shapes called **lithospheric** or **tectonic plates** that are in constant motion with respect to one another. As shown in Figure 5.8, seven major lithospheric plates are recognized. These plates, which account for 94 percent of Earth's surface area, include the *North American, South American, Pacific, African, Eurasian, Australian-Indian,* and *Antarctic plates.* The largest is the Pacific plate, which encompasses a significant portion of the Pacific Ocean basin. The six other large plates include an entire continent plus a significant amount of ocean floor. Notice in Figure 5.8 that the South American plate encompasses almost all of South America and about one-half of the floor of the South Atlantic. This is a major departure from Wegener's continental drift hypothesis, which proposed that the continents moved through the ocean floor, not with it. Note also that none of the plates are defined entirely by the margins of a single continent.

Intermediate-sized plates include the *Caribbean, Nazca, Philippine, Arabian, Cocos, Scotia,* and *Juan de Fuca plates.* These plates, with the exception of the Arabian plate, are composed mostly of oceanic lithosphere. In addition, there are several smaller plates (*microplates*) that have been identified but are not shown in Figure 5.8.

Plate Boundaries

One of the main tenets of the plate tectonic theory is that plates move as semicoherent units relative to all other plates. As plates move, the distance between two locations on different plates, such as New York and London, gradually changes whereas the distance between sites on the same plate—New York and Denver, for example—remains relatively constant.

Because plates are in constant motion relative to each other, most major interactions among them (and, therefore, most deformation) occur along their *boundaries.* In fact, plate boundaries were first established by plotting the locations of earthquakes and volcanoes. Moreover, plates are bounded by three distinct types of boundaries, which are differentiated by the type of movement they exhibit. These boundaries are depicted at the bottom of Figure 5.8 and are briefly described here:

1. **Divergent boundaries** (*constructive margins*)—where two plates move apart, resulting in upwelling of hot material from the mantle to create new seafloor (Figure 5.8A).
2. **Convergent boundaries** (*destructive margins*)—where two plates move together, resulting in oceanic lithosphere descending beneath an overriding plate, eventually to be reabsorbed into the mantle, or possibly in the collision of two continental blocks to create a mountain system (Figure 5.8B).
3. **Transform fault boundaries** (*conservative margins*)—where two plates grind past each other without the production or destruction of lithosphere (Figure 5.8C).

Divergent and convergent plate boundaries each account for about 40 percent of all plate boundaries. Transform faults account for the remaining 20 percent. In the following sections we will summarize the nature of the three types of plate boundaries.

DID YOU KNOW?

An observer on another planet would notice, after only a few million years, that all of the continents and ocean basins on Earth are indeed moving. The Moon, on the other hand, is tectonically dead, so it would look virtually unchanged millions of years into the future.

DIVERGENT BOUNDARIES

Forces Within
▼ Plate Tectonics

Most **divergent** (*di* = apart, *vergere* = to move) **boundaries** are located along the crests of oceanic ridges and can be thought of as *constructive plate margins* since this is where new ocean floor is generated (**FIGURE 5.10**). Divergent boundaries are also called **spreading centers**, because seafloor spreading occurs at these boundaries. Here, two adjacent plates are moving away from each other, producing long, narrow fractures in the ocean crust. As a result, hot rock from the mantle below migrates upward to fill the voids left as the crust is being ripped apart. This molten material gradually cools to produce new slivers of seafloor. In a slow, yet unending manner, adjacent plates spread apart and new oceanic lithosphere forms between them.

Oceanic Ridges and Seafloor Spreading

Most divergent plate boundaries are associated with *oceanic ridges*: elevated areas of the seafloor that are characterized by high heat flow and volcanism. The global ridge system is the longest topographic feature on Earth's surface, exceeding 70,000 kilometers (43,000 miles) in length. As shown in Figure 5.8 various segments of the global ridge system have been named, including the Mid-Atlantic Ridge, East Pacific Rise, and Mid-Indian Ridge.

Representing 20 percent of Earth's surface, the oceanic ridge system winds through all major ocean basins like the seam on a baseball. Although the crest of the oceanic ridge is commonly 2 to 3 kilometers higher than the adjacent ocean basins, the term *ridge* may be misleading because this feature is not narrow but has widths that vary from 1000 to more than 4000 kilometers. Further, along the axis of some ridge segments is a deep down-faulted structure called a **rift valley** (Figure 5.10). This structure is evidence that tensional forces are actively pulling the ocean crust apart at the ridge crest.

The mechanism that operates along the oceanic ridge system to create new seafloor is appropriately called **seafloor spreading**. Typical rates of spreading average around 5 centimeters (2 inches) per year. This is roughly the same rate at which human fingernails grow. Comparatively slow spreading rates of 2 centimeters per year are found along the Mid-Atlantic Ridge, whereas spreading rates exceeding 15 centimeters (6 inches) per year have been measured along sections of the East Pacific Rise. Although these rates of seafloor production are slow on a human time scale, they are nevertheless rapid enough to have generated all of Earth's ocean basins within the last 200 million years. In fact, none of the ocean floor that has been dated thus far exceeds 180 million years in age.

The primary reason for the elevated position of the oceanic ridge is that newly created oceanic crust is hot, making it less dense than cooler rocks found away from the ridge axis. As soon as new lithosphere forms, it is slowly yet continually displaced away from the zone of upwelling. Thus, it begins to cool and contract, thereby increasing in density. This thermal contraction accounts for the increase in ocean depths away from the ridge crest. It takes about 80 million years for the temperature of the crust to stabilize and contraction to cease. By this time, rock that was once part of the elevated oceanic ridge system is located in the deep-ocean basin, where it may be buried by substantial accumulations of sediment.

In addition, cooling strengthens the hot material directly below the oceanic crust, thereby adding to the plate's thickness. Stated another way, the thickness of oceanic lithosphere is age-dependent. The older (cooler) it is, the greater its thickness. Oceanic lithosphere that exceeds 80 million years in age is about 100 kilometers thick: about its maximum thickness.

Continental Rifting

Divergent boundaries can also develop within a continent, in which case the landmass may split into two or more smaller segments separated by an ocean basin. Continental rifting occurs where opposing tectonic forces act to pull the lithosphere apart. The initial stage of rifting tends to include mantle upwelling

FIGURE 5.10 Most divergent plate boundaries are situated along the crests of oceanic ridges.

FIGURE 5.11 Continental rifting and the formation of a new ocean basin. **A.** The initial stage of continental rifting tends to include upwelling in the mantle that is associated with broad doming of the lithosphere. Tensional forces and buoyant uplifting of the heated lithosphere cause the crust to be broken into large slabs. **B.** As the crust is pulled apart, large slabs of rock sink, generating a rift valley. **C.** Further spreading generates a narrow sea, similar to the present-day Red Sea. **D.** Eventually, an expansive ocean basin and ridge system are created.

molten rock to ascend from the mantle. Evidence for recent volcanic activity includes several large volcanic mountains including Mount Kilimanjaro and Mount Kenya, the tallest peaks in Africa. Research suggests that if rifting continues, the rift valley will lengthen and deepen, eventually extending out to the margin of the landmass (**FIGURE 5.11C**). At this point, the rift will become a narrow sea with an outlet to the ocean. The Red Sea, which formed when the Arabian Peninsula split from Africa, is a modern example of such a feature. Consequently, the Red Sea provides us with a view of how the Atlantic Ocean may have looked in its infancy (**FIGURE 5.11D**).

CONVERGENT BOUNDARIES

Forces Within
Plate Tectonics

New lithosphere is constantly being produced at the oceanic ridges; however, our planet is not growing larger—its total surface area remains constant. A balance is maintained because older, denser portions of oceanic lithosphere descend into the mantle at a rate equal to seafloor production. This activity occurs along **convergent** (*con* = together, *vergere* = to move) **boundaries**, where two plates move toward each other and the leading edge of one is bent downward, as it slides beneath the other.

Convergent boundaries are also called **subduction zones**, because they are sites where lithosphere is descending (being subducted) into the mantle. Subduction occurs because the density of the descending tectonic plate is greater than the density of the underlying asthenosphere. In general, oceanic lithosphere is more dense than the asthenosphere, whereas continental lithosphere is less dense and resists subduction. As a consequence, only oceanic lithosphere will subduct to great depths.

that is associated with broad upwarping of the overlying lithosphere (**FIGURE 5.11A**). As a result, the lithosphere is stretched, causing the brittle crustal rocks to break into large slabs. As the tectonic forces continue to pull the crust apart, these crustal fragments sink, generating an elongated depression called a **continental rift** (**FIGURE 5.11B**).

A modern example of an active continental rift is the East African Rift (**FIGURE 5.12**). Whether this rift will eventually result in the breakup of Africa is a topic of continued research. Nevertheless, the East African Rift is an excellent model of the initial stage in the breakup of a continent. Here, tensional forces have stretched and thinned the crust, allowing

DID YOU KNOW?

The remains of some of the earliest humans, *Homo habilis* and *Homo erectus*, were discovered by Louis and Mary Leakey in the East African Rift. Scientists consider this region to be the "birthplace" of the human race.

FIGURE 5.12   East African rift valleys and associated features.

thicken and increase in density. In parts of the western Pacific, some oceanic lithosphere is 180 million years old. This is the thickest and densest in today's oceans. The very dense slabs in this region typically plunge into the mantle at angles approaching 90 degrees. This largely explains the fact that most trenches in the western Pacific are deeper than trenches in the eastern Pacific.

Although all convergent zones have the same basic characteristics, they are highly variable features. Each is controlled by the type of crustal material involved and the tectonic setting. Convergent boundaries can form between *two oceanic plates, one oceanic and one continental plate,* or *two continental plates.*

Oceanic–Continental Convergence

Whenever the leading edge of a plate capped with continental crust converges with a slab of oceanic lithosphere, the buoyant continental block remains "floating," and the denser oceanic slab sinks into the mantle (**FIGURE 5.14A**). When a descending oceanic slab reaches a depth of about 100 kilometers (60 miles), melting is triggered within the wedge of hot asthenosphere that lies above it. But how does the subduction of a cool slab of oceanic lithosphere cause mantle rock to melt? The answer lies in the fact that water contained in the descending plate acts like salt does to melt ice. That is, "wet" rock in a high-pressure environment, melts at substantially lower temperatures than does "dry" rock of the same composition.

Sediments and oceanic crust contain a large amount of water that is carried to great depths by a subducting plate. As the plate plunges downward, heat and pressure drive water from the voids in the rock. At a depth of roughly 100 kilometers, the wedge of mantle rock is sufficiently hot that the introduction of water from the slab below leads to some melting. This process, called **partial melting**, is thought to generate about 10 percent molten material, which is intermixed with unmelted mantle rock. Being less dense than the surrounding mantle, this hot mobile material gradually rises toward the surface. Depending on the environment, these mantle-derived masses of molten rock may ascend through the crust and give rise to a volcanic eruption. However, much of this material never reaches the surface; rather, it solidifies at depth—a process that thickens the crust.

The volcanoes of the towering Andes are the product of molten rock generated by the subduction of the Nazca plate beneath the South American continent (**FIGURE 5.14B**). Mountain systems such as the Andes, which are produced in part by volcanic activity associated with the subduction of

Deep-ocean trenches are the surface manifestations produced as oceanic lithosphere descends into the mantle (**FIGURE 5.13**). These linear depressions are remarkably long and deep. The Peru-Chile trench along the west coast of South America is more than 4500 kilometers (3000 miles) long and its base is as much as 8 kilometers (5 miles) below sea level. The trenches in the western Pacific, including the Mariana and Tonga trenches, tend to be even deeper than those of the eastern Pacific.

Slabs of oceanic lithosphere descend into the mantle at angles that vary from a few degrees to nearly vertical (90 degrees). The angle at which oceanic lithosphere descends depends largely on its density. For example, when a spreading center is located near a subduction zone, as is the case along the Peru-Chile trench, the subducting lithosphere is young and, therefore, warm and buoyant. Because of this, the angle of descent is small, which results in considerable interaction between the descending slab and the overriding plate. Consequently, the region around the Peru-Chile trench experiences great earthquakes, including the 1960 Chilean earthquake—the largest on record.

As oceanic lithosphere ages (gets farther from the spreading center), it gradually cools, which causes it to

FIGURE 5.13 Distribution of the world's oceanic trenches, ridge system, and transform faults. Where transform faults offset ridge segments, they permit the ridge to change direction (curve) as can be seen in the Atlantic Ocean.

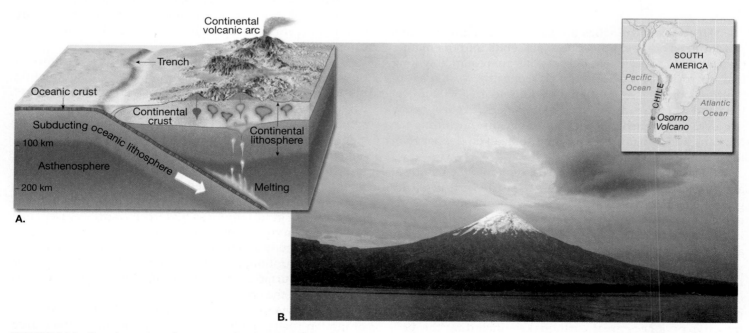

FIGURE 5.14 Oceanic–continental convergent plate boundary. **A.** Illustration of dense oceanic lithosphere subducting beneath a buoyant continental block. Melting in the asthenosphere generates molten rock that rises toward the surface. This activity produces a chain of volcanic structures built on the overriding landmass, called a *continental volcanic arc.* **B.** Osorno Volcano is one of the most active volcanoes in the southern Chilean Andes, having erupted 11 times between 1575 and 1869. Located on the shore of Lake Llanquihue, Osorno is similar in appearance to Japan's Mount Fuji. (Photo by Michael Collier)

oceanic lithosphere, are called **continental volcanic arcs**. The Cascade Range of Washington, Oregon, and California is another volcanic arc that consists of several well-known volcanic mountains, including Mount Rainier, Mount Shasta, and Mount St. Helens. This active volcanic arc also extends into Canada, where it includes Mount Garibaldi, Mount Silverthrone, and others.

Oceanic–Oceanic Convergence

An *oceanic–oceanic convergent boundary* has many features in common with oceanic–continental plate margins. Where two oceanic slabs converge, one descends beneath the other, initiating volcanic activity by the same mechanism that operates at all subduction zones (**FIGURE 5.15A**). Water squeezed from the subducting slab of oceanic lithosphere triggers melting in the hot wedge of mantle rock above. In this setting, volcanoes grow up from the ocean floor, rather than upon a continental platform. When subduction is sustained, it will eventually build a chain of volcanic structures large enough to emerge as islands. The volcanic islands tend to be spaced at intervals of about 80 kilometers (50 miles). This newly formed land consisting of an arc-shaped chain of volcanic islands is called a **volcanic island arc**, or simply an **island arc** (**FIGURE 5.15B**).

The Aleutian, Mariana, and Tonga islands are examples of relatively young volcanic island arcs. Island arcs are generally located 100 to 300 kilometers (60 to 200 miles) from a deep-ocean trench. Located adjacent to the island arcs just mentioned are the Aleutian trench, the Mariana trench, and the Tonga trench.

Most volcanic island arcs are located in the western Pacific. Only two are located in the Atlantic—the Lesser Antilles arc, on the eastern margin of the Caribbean Sea and the Sandwich Islands located off the tip of South America. The Lesser Antilles are a product of the subduction of the Atlantic seafloor beneath the Caribbean plate. Located within this volcanic arc are the United States and British Virgin Islands as well as the island of Martinique, where Mount Pelée erupted in 1902, destroying the town of St. Pierre and killing an estimated 28,000 people. This chain of islands also includes Montserrat, where there has been recent volcanic activity.*

Relatively young island arcs are fairly simple structures made of numerous volcanic cones that are underlain by oceanic crust that is generally less than 20 kilometers (12 miles) thick. By contrast, older island arcs are more complex and are underlain by highly deformed crust that may reach 35 kilometers in thickness. Examples include the islands that make up the countries of Japan, Indonesia, and the Philippines. These island arcs are built upon material generated by earlier episodes of subduction or on small slivers of continental crust.

Continental–Continental Convergence

The third type of convergent boundary results when one landmass moves toward the margin of another because of subduction of the intervening seafloor (**FIGURE 5.16A**). Whereas oceanic lithosphere tends to be dense and sink into the mantle, the buoyancy of continental material inhibits it from being subducted. Consequently, a collision between two converging continental fragments ensues

*More on these volcanic events is found in Chapter 7.

FIGURE 5.15 Oceanic–oceanic convergent plate boundaries. **A.** When oceanic plates converge, one descends beneath the other, initiating volcanic activity in the overriding plate. In this setting, a volcanic island arc is built. **B.** These four volcanic structures are part of the Aleutian Islands, a string of both active and dormant volcanoes fed by magma created by the subduction of the Pacific plate. Steam plumes have recently been observed emanating from Cleveland Volcano (center), evidence of their recent activity. (Photo courtesy of NASA)

FIGURE 5.16 The ongoing collision of India and Asia, starting about 50 million years ago, produced the majestic Himalayas. **A.** Converging plates generated a subduction zone, while partial melting triggered by the subducting oceanic slab produced a continental volcanic arc. Sediments scraped from the subducting plate were added to the edge of the continent. **B.** Position of India in relation to Eurasia at various times. (Modified after Peter Molnar) **C.** The two landmasses eventually collided, deforming and elevating the sediments that had been deposited along their continental margins.

(**FIGURE 5.16C**). This event folds and deforms the accumulation of sediments and sedimentary rocks along the continental margins as if they had been placed in a gigantic vise. The result is the formation of a new mountain range composed of deformed sedimentary and metamorphic rocks that often contains slivers of oceanic crust.

Such a collision began about 50 million years ago when the subcontinent of India "rammed" into Asia, producing the Himalayas—the most spectacular mountain range on Earth (Figure 5.16C). During this collision, the continental crust buckled and fractured, and was generally shortened and thickened. In addition to the Himalayas, several other major mountain systems, including the Alps, Appalachians, and Urals, formed as continental fragments collided. (This topic will be considered further in Chapter 6.)

TRANSFORM FAULT BOUNDARIES

Forces Within
▼ Plate Tectonics

Along **transform** (*trans* = across, *forma* = form) **fault boundaries**, plates slide horizontally past one another without the production or destruction of lithosphere (*conservative plate margins*). The nature of transform faults was discovered in 1965 by Canadian geologist J. Tuzo Wilson, who proposed that these large faults connected two spreading centers (divergent boundaries), or less commonly two trenches (convergent boundaries). Most transform faults are found on the ocean floor (**FIGURE 5.17A**). Here they offset segments of the oceanic ridge system, producing a steplike plate margin.

FIGURE 5.17 Transform fault boundaries. **A.** Most transform faults offset segments of a spreading center, producing a steplike plate margin. The zigzag shape of the Mid-Atlantic Ridge roughly reflects the shape of the zone of rifting that produced the breakup of Pangaea. **B.** Fracture zones are long, narrow fractures in the seafloor that are nearly perpendicular to the offset ridge segments. They include both the active transform fault and its "fossilized" trace, where oceanic crust of different ages is juxtaposed. The offsets between ridge segments (transform faults) do not change in length over time.

Notice that the zigzag shape of the Mid-Atlantic Ridge in Figure 5.9 roughly reflects the shape of the original rifting that caused the beakup of the supercontinent of Pangaea. (Compare the shapes of the continental margins of the landmasses on both sides of the Atlantic with the shape of the Mid-Atlantic Ridge.)

Typically, transform faults are part of prominent linear breaks in the seafloor known as **fracture zones**, which include both the active transform faults as well as their inactive extensions into the plate interior (**FIGURE 5.17B**). Active transform faults lie *only between* the two offset ridge segments and are generally defined by weak, shallow earthquakes. Here seafloor produced at one ridge axis moves in the opposite direction as seafloor produced at an opposing ridge segment. Thus, between the ridge segments these adjacent slabs of oceanic crust are grinding past each other along a transform fault. Beyond the ridge crests are inactive zones, where the fractures are preserved as linear topographic depressions. The trend of these fracture zones roughly parallels the direction of plate motion at the time of their formation. Thus, these structures are useful in mapping the direction of plate motion in the geologic past.

In another role, transform faults provide the means by which the oceanic crust created at ridge crests can be transported to a site of destruction—the deep-ocean trenches. **FIGURE 5.18** illustrates this situation. Notice that the Juan de Fuca plate moves in a southeasterly direction, eventually being subducted under the west coast of the United States. The southern end of this plate is bounded by a transform fault called the Mendocino fault. This transform boundary connects the Juan de Fuca ridge to the Cascadia subduction zone (Figure 5.18). Therefore, it facilitates the movement of the crustal material created at the Juan de Fuca ridge to its destination beneath the North American continent (Figure 5.18).

Like the Mendocino fault, most transform fault boundaries are located within the ocean basins; however, a few cut through continental crust. Two examples are the earthquake-prone San Andreas Fault of California and New Zealand's Alpine Fault. Notice in Figure 5.18 that the San Andreas Fault connects a spreading center

FIGURE 5.18 The Mendocino transform fault permits seafloor generated at the Juan de Fuca ridge to move southeastward past the Pacific plate and beneath the North American plate. Thus, this transform fault connects a divergent boundary to a subduction zone. Furthermore, the San Andreas Fault, also a transform fault, connects two spreading centers: the Juan de Fuca Ridge and a divergent zone located in the Gulf of California.

FIGURE 5.19 Along the San Andreas Fault, the Pacific plate is moving toward the northwest, relative to the North American plate. This aerial view shows the offset in the dry channel of Wallace Creek near Taft, California. (Photo by Michael Collier)

Another consequence of plate motion is that boundaries also migrate. For example, the position of the Peru-Chile trench, which is the result of the Nazca plate being bent downward as it descends beneath the South American plate, has changed over time (see Figure 5.9). Because of the westward drift of the South American plate relative to the Nazca plate, the position of the Peru-Chile trench has migrated in a westerly direction as well.

New plate boundaries can also be created or destroyed in response to changes in the forces acting on the lithosphere. Recall that the Red Sea is the site of a relatively new spreading center. It came into existence less than 20 million years ago when the Arabian Peninsula began to split from Africa. At other locations, plates carrying continental crust are presently moving toward one another. Eventually these continental fragments may collide and be sutured together. This could occur, for example, in the South Pacific where Australia is moving northward toward southern Asia. Should Australia continue its northward migration, the boundary separating it from Asia will disappear as these plates become one.

located in the Gulf of California to the Cascadia subduction zone and the Mendocino fault located along the northwest coast of the United States. Along the San Andreas Fault, the Pacific plate is moving toward the northwest, past the North American plate (**FIGURE 5.19**). If this movement continues, that part of California west of the fault zone, including the Baja Peninsula of Mexico, will become an island off the West Coast of the United States and Canada. It could eventually reach Alaska. However, a more immediate concern is the earthquake activity triggered by movements along this fault system.

HOW DO PLATES AND PLATE BOUNDARIES CHANGE?

Although the total surface area of Earth does not change, the size and shape of individual plates are constantly changing. For example, the African and Antarctic plates are mainly bounded by divergent boundaries—sites of seafloor production. Thus, the African and Antarctic plates are continually growing in size as new lithosphere is added to their margins. By contrast, the Pacific plate is being consumed into the mantle along its northern and western flanks much faster that it is growing along the East Pacific Rise and thus is diminishing in size.

TESTING THE PLATE TECTONICS MODEL

With the development of the theory of plate tectonics, researchers from all of the Earth sciences began testing this new model of how Earth works. Some of the evidence supporting continental drift and seafloor spreading has already been presented. Although new supporting data were obtained, it was often new interpretations of already existing data that swayed the tide of opinion.

DID YOU KNOW?

The Great Alpine Fault of New Zealand is a transform fault that runs down South Island, marking the line where two plates meet. The northwestern part of South Island sits on the Australian plate, whereas the rest of the island lies on the Pacific plate. Like its sister fault, California's San Andreas, displacement has been measured in hundreds of miles.

Thickness of sediments increase
with distance from the ridge crest

Age of seafloor

Drilling ship collects core samples of
seafloor sediments and basaltic crust

Ocean crust (basalt)

FIGURE 5.20   Since 1968, drilling ships have gathered core samples of seafloor sediment and crustal rocks at hundreds of sites. Results from these efforts show that the ocean floor is indeed youngest at the ridge axis. This was the first direct evidence supporting the seafloor spreading hypothesis and the broader theory of plate tectonics.

Evidence from Ocean Drilling

Some of the most convincing evidence for seafloor spreading came from the Deep Sea Drilling Project, which operated from 1968 until 1983. One of the early goals was to gather samples of the ocean floor in order to establish its age. To accomplish this, the *Glomar Challenger*, a drilling ship capable of working in water thousands of meters deep, was built. Hundreds of holes were drilled through the layers of sediments that blanket the ocean crust, as well as into the basaltic rocks below. Rather than radiometrically dating the crustal rocks, researchers used the fossil remains of microorganisms found in the sediments resting directly on the crust to date the seafloor at each site.*

When the oldest sediment from each drill site was plotted against its distance from the ridge crest, the plot showed that the sediments increased in age with increasing distance from the ridge (**FIGURE 5.20**). This finding supported the seafloor-spreading hypothesis, which predicted that the youngest oceanic crust would be found at the ridge crest, the site of seafloor production, and the oldest oceanic crust would be located adjacent to the continents.

The data collected by the Deep Sea Drilling Project also reinforced the idea that the ocean basins are geologically young because no seafloor with an age in excess of 180 million years was ever found. By comparison, most continental crust exceeds several hundred million years in age and some has been located that exceeds 4 billion years in age.

The thickness of ocean-floor sediments provided additional verification of seafloor spreading. Drill cores from the *Glomar Challenger* revealed that sediments are almost entirely absent on the ridge crest and that sediment thickness increases with increasing distance from the ridge

(Figure 5.20). This pattern of sediment distribution should be expected if the seafloor-spreading hypothesis is correct.

The Ocean Drilling Program, the successor to the Deep Sea Drilling Project, employed a more technologically advanced drilling ship, the *JOIDES Resolution,* to continue the work of the *Glomar Challenger* (**FIGURE 5.21**). Although the Deep Sea Drilling Project validated many of the major tenets of the theory of plate tectonics, the *JOIDES Resolution* was able to probe deeper into the oceanic crust. This allowed for the study of earthquake-generating zones at convergent plate margins and for the direct examination of oceanic plateaus and seamounts. The Ocean Drilling Program has also extended our knowledge of long- and short-term climatic changes.

In October 2003, the *JOIDES Resolution* became part of a new program, the Integrated Ocean Drilling Program (IODP). This new international effort uses multiple vessels for exploration, including the massive 210-meter-long (nearly 770-foot-) *Chikyu* (meaning "planet Earth" in Japanese), which began operations in 2007. (see Figure I.1B, p. 4) One of the goals of the IODP is to drill a complete section of the ocean crust.

Hot Spots and Mantle Plumes

Mapping volcanic islands and seamounts (submarine volcanoes) in the Pacific Ocean revealed several linear chains of volcanic structures. One of the most studied chains consists of at least 129 volcanoes that extend from the Hawaiian Islands to Midway Island and continue northward toward the Aleutian trench (**FIGURE 5.22**). Radiometric dating of this structure, called the *Hawaiian Island–Emperor Seamount chain,* showed that the volcanoes increase in age with increasing distance from the "big island" of Hawaii. The youngest volcanic island in the chain (Hawaii), rose from the ocean floor less than a million years ago, whereas Midway Island is 27 million years old, and Suiko Seamount, near the Aleutian trench, is about 65 million years old (Figure 5.22).

Most researchers are in agreement that cylindrically shaped upwelling of hot rock, called a **mantle plume**, is located beneath the island of Hawaii. As the hot, rocky plume ascends through the mantle the confining pressure drops, which triggers partial melting. (This process, called *decompression melting,* is discussed in Chapter 7.) The surface manifestation of this activity is a **hot spot**, an area of volcanism, high heat flow, and crustal uplifting that is a few hundred kilometers across. As the Pacific plate moved over the hot spot, a chain of volcanic structures known as a **hot-spot track** was built. As shown in Figure 5.22, the age of each volcano indicates how much time has elapsed since it was situated over the mantle plume.

Taking a closer look at the five largest Hawaiian Islands, we see a similar pattern of ages from the volcanically active island of Hawaii to the inactive volcanoes that make

*Radiometric dates of the ocean crust itself are unreliable because of the alteration of basalt by seawater.

A.

B.

FIGURE 5.21 The *JOIDES Resolution*. **A.** *JOIDES Resolution*, one of the drilling ships of the Integrated Ocean Drilling Program. (Photo courtesy of Ocean Drilling Program) **B.** The *JOIDES Resolution* has a tall metal derrick that is used to conduct rotary drilling, while the ship's thrusters hold it in a fixed position at sea. Individual sections of drill pipe are fitted together to make a single string of pipe up to 8200 meters (27,000 feet) long. The drill bit, located at the end of the pipe string, rotates as it is pressed against the ocean bottom and can drill up to 2100 meters (6900 feet) into the seafloor. Like twirling a drinking straw into a layer cake, the drilling operation cuts through sediments and rock and retains a cylinder of material (a core sample) on the inside of the hollow pipe, which can then be raised onboard the ship and analyzed in state-of-the-art laboratory facilities.

up the oldest island, Kauai (Figure 5.22). Five million years ago, when Kauai was positioned over the hot spot, it was the *only* Hawaiian Island in existence (Figure 5.22). Visible evidence of the age of Kauai can be seen by examining its extinct volcanoes, which have been eroded into jagged peaks and vast canyons. By contrast, the relatively young island of Hawaii exhibits many fresh lava flows, and one of its five major volcanoes, Kilauea, remains active today.

Research suggests that at least some mantle plumes originate at great depth, perhaps at the core-mantle boundary. Others, however, may have a much shallower origin. Of the 40 or so hot spots that have been identified worldwide, more than a dozen are located near spreading centers. For example, the mantle plume located beneath Iceland is responsible for the vast accumulation of volcanic rocks found along this exposed section of the Mid-Atlantic Ridge.

DID YOU KNOW?

Olympus Mons is a huge volcano on Mars that strongly resembles the Hawaiian shield volcanoes. Rising 25 km (16 mi) above the surrounding plains, Olympus Mons owes its massiveness to the fact that plate tectonics *does not* operate on Mars. Consequently, instead of being carried away from the hot spot by plate motion, as occurred with the Hawaiian volcanoes, Olympus Mons remained fixed and grew to a gigantic size.

Evidence: Paleomagnetism

Anyone who has used a compass to find direction knows that Earth's magnetic field has a north and south magnetic pole. Today these magnetic poles align closely, but not exactly, with the geographic poles. (The geographic poles are located where Earth's rotational axis intersects the surface.) Earth's magnetic field is similar to that produced by a simple bar magnet. Invisible lines of force pass through the planet and extend from one magnetic pole to the other (**FIGURE 5.23**). A compass needle, itself a small magnet free to rotate on an axis, becomes aligned with the magnetic lines of force and points to the magnetic poles.

Unlike the pull of gravity, we cannot feel Earth's magnetic field, yet its presence is revealed because it deflects a compass needle. In addition, some naturally occurring minerals are magnetic and hence are influenced by Earth's magnetic field. One of the most common is the iron-rich mineral *magnetite*, which is abundant in lava flows of basaltic composition.* Basaltic lavas erupt at the surface at temperatures greater than 1000°C, exceeding a threshold temperature for magnetism known as the **Curie point** (about 585°C). Consequently, the magnetite grains in molten lava are nonmagnetic. However, as the lava cools these iron-rich grains become magnetized and align themselves in the direction of the existing magnetic lines of force.

*Some sediments and sedimentary rocks contain enough iron-bearing mineral grains to acquire a measurable amount of magnetization.

Kauai
3.8—5.6

Oahu
2.2–3.3

Molokai
1.3–1.8

Maui
less than 1.0

Hawaii
0.7 to present

Ages given
in millions of
years

Suiko
65 my

Emperor
Seamount chain

Hawaiian chain

Midway
Islands
27 my

Hawaii

Plate motion

Extinct
volcano

Hot spot
volcanism

Rising
mantle
plume

FIGURE 5.22   The chain of islands and seamounts that extends from Hawaii to the Aleutian trench results from the movement of the Pacific plate over an apparently stationary hot spot. Radiometric dating of the Hawaiian Islands shows that the volcanic activity decreases in age toward the island of Hawaii.

Once the minerals solidify, the magnetism they possess will usually remain "frozen" in this position. Thus, they act like a compass needle because they "point" toward the position of the magnetic poles at the time of their formation. Rocks that formed thousands or millions of years ago and contain a "record" of the direction of the magnetic poles at the time of their formation are said to possess **fossil magnetism**, or **paleomagnetism**. During the 1950s paleomagnetic data was collected from lava flows around the globe.

Apparent Polar Wandering

A study of rock magnetism conducted in Europe by S. K. Runcorn and his associates led to an interesting discovery. The magnetic alignment of iron-rich minerals in lava flows of different ages indicated that the position of the paleomagnetic poles had changed through time. A plot of the location of the magnetic north pole with respect to Europe revealed that during the past 500 million years, the pole had gradually wandered from a location near Hawaii northward to its present location near the North Pole (**FIGURE 5.24A**). This was strong evidence that either the magnetic poles had migrated, an idea known as *polar wandering*, or that the lava flows moved—in other words, Europe had drifted in relation to the poles.

Although the magnetic poles are known to move in an erratic path around the geographic poles, studies of paleomagnetism from numerous locations show that the positions of the magnetic poles, averaged over thousands of years, correspond closely to the positions of the geographic poles. Therefore, a more acceptable explanation for the apparent polar wandering paths was provided by

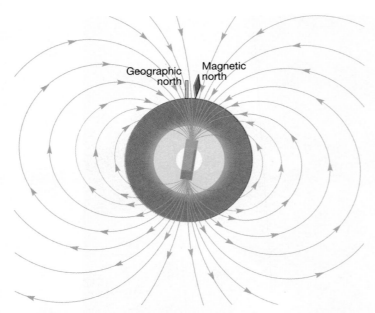

FIGURE 5.23 Earth's magnetic field consists of lines of force much like those a giant bar magnet would produce if placed at the center of Earth.

FIGURE 5.24 Simplified apparent polar wandering paths as established from North American and Eurasian paleomagnetic data. **A.** The more westerly path determined from North American data is thought to have been caused by the westward drift of North America by about 24 degrees from Eurasia. **B.** The positions of the wandering paths when the landmasses are reassembled in their predrift locations.

Wegener's hypothesis. If the magnetic poles remain stationary, their *apparent movement* is produced by continental drift.

Further evidence for continental drift came a few years later when a polar-wandering path was constructed for North America (Figure 5.24A). For the first 300 million years or so, the paths for North America and Europe were found to be similar in direction, but separated by about 5000 kilometers (3000 miles). Then, during the middle of the Mesozoic era (180 million years ago) they began to converge on the present North Pole. Because the North Atlantic Ocean is about 5000 kilometers wide, the explanation for these curves was that North America and Europe were joined until the Mesozoic, when the Atlantic began to open. From this time forward, these continents continuously moved apart. When North America and Europe are moved back to their predrift positions, as shown in **FIGURE 5.24B**, these apparent wandering paths coincide.

Magnetic Reversals and Seafloor Spreading

Additional evidence surfaced when geophysicists discovered that over periods of hundreds of thousands of years, Earth's magnetic field periodically reverses polarity. During a **magnetic reversal** the north magnetic pole becomes the south magnetic pole, and vice versa. Lava solidifying during a period of reverse polarity will be magnetized with the polarity opposite that of volcanic rocks being formed today.

DID YOU KNOW?

When all of the continents were joined to form Pangaea, the rest of Earth's surface was covered with a huge ocean called *Panthalassa* (*pan* = all, *thalassa* = sea). Today, all that remains of Panthalassa is the Pacific Ocean, which has been decreasing in size since the breakup of Pangaea.

When rocks exhibit the same magnetism as the present magnetic field, they are said to possess **normal polarity**, whereas rocks exhibiting the opposite magnetism are said to have **reverse polarity**.

Once the concept of magnetic reversals was confirmed, researchers set out to establish a time scale for these occurrences. The task was to measure the magnetic polarity of hundreds of lava flows and use radiometric dating techniques to establish the age of each flow. **FIGURE 5.25** shows the **magnetic time scale** established for the past few million years. The major divisions of the magnetic time scale are called *chrons* and last for roughly 1 million years. As more measurements became available, researchers realized that several, short-lived reversals (less than 200,000 years long) often occurred during a single chron.

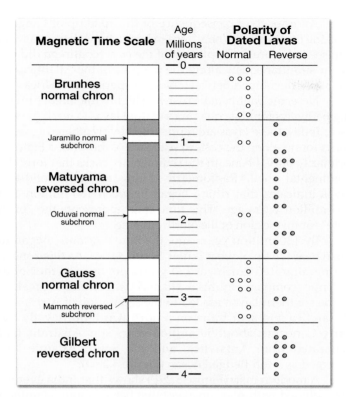

FIGURE 5.25   Time scale of Earth's magnetic field in the recent past. This time scale was developed by establishing the magnetic polarity for lava flows of known age. (Data from Allen Cox and G. B. Dalrymple)

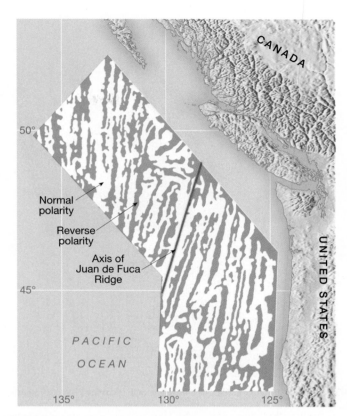

FIGURE 5.26   Pattern of alternating stripes of high- and low-intensity magnetism discovered off the Pacific Coast of North America.

Meanwhile, oceanographers had begun to do magnetic surveys of the ocean floor in conjunction with their efforts to construct detailed maps of seafloor topography. These magnetic surveys were accomplished by towing very sensitive instruments, called **magnetometers,** behind research vessels. The goal of these geophysical surveys was to map variations in the strength of Earth's magnetic field that arise from differences in the magnetic properties of the underlying crustal rocks.

The first comprehensive study of this type was carried out off the Pacific Coast of North America and had an unexpected outcome. Researchers discovered alternating stripes of high- and low-intensity magnetism as shown in **FIGURE 5.26.** This relatively simple pattern of magnetic variation defied explanation until 1963, when Fred Vine and D. H. Matthews demonstrated that the high- and low-intensity stripes supported the concept of seafloor spreading. Vine and Matthews suggested that the stripes of high-intensity magnetism are regions where the paleomagnetism of the ocean crust exhibits normal polarity (**FIGURE 5.27**). Consequently, these rocks *enhance* (reinforce) Earth's magnetic field. Conversely, the low-intensity stripes are regions where the ocean crust is polarized in the reverse direction and therefore *weaken* the existing magnetic field. But how do parallel stripes of normally and reversely magnetized rock become distributed across the ocean floor?

Vine and Matthews reasoned that as magma solidifies along narrow rifts at the crest of an oceanic ridge, it is magnetized with the polarity of the existing magnetic field

(**FIGURE 5.28**). Because of seafloor spreading, this strip of magnetized crust would gradually increase in width. When Earth's magnetic field reverses polarity, any newly formed seafloor (having the opposite polarity) would form in the middle of the old strip. Gradually, the two halves of the old strip are carried in opposite directions away from the ridge crest. Subsequent reversals would build a pattern of normal and reverse magnetic stripes as shown in Figure 5.28. Because new rock is added in equal amounts to both trailing edges of the spreading ocean floor, we should expect that the pattern of stripes (size and polarity) found on one side of an oceanic ridge to be a mirror image of the other side. A few years later a survey across the Mid-Atlantic Ridge just south of Iceland revealed a pattern of magnetic stripes exhibiting a remarkable degree of symmetry to the ridge axis.

THE BREAKUP OF PANGAEA

Wegener used evidence from fossils, rock types, and ancient climates to create a jigsaw-puzzle fit of the continents, thereby creating his supercontinent of Pangaea. In a similar manner, but employing modern tools not available to Wegener, geologists have recreated the steps in the breakup of this supercontinent, an event that began nearly 200 million years ago. From this work, the dates when individual crustal fragments separated from one another and their relative motions have been well established (**FIGURE 5.29**).

FIGURE 5.27 The ocean floor as a magnetic tape recorder. Magnetic intensities recorded as a magnetometer is towed across a segment of the oceanic ridge. Notice the symmetrical stripes of low- and high-intensity magnetism that parallel the ridge crest. Vine and Matthews suggested that the stripes of high-intensity magnetism occur where normally magnetized oceanic rocks enhanced the existing magnetic field. Conversely, the low-intensity stripes are regions where the crust is polarized in the reverse direction, which weakens the existing magnetic field.

FIGURE 5.28 As new basalt is added to the ocean floor at mid-ocean ridges, it is magnetized according to Earth's existing magnetic field. Hence, it behaves much like a tape recorder as it records each reversal of the planet's magnetic field.

An important consequence of the breakup of Pangaea was the creation of a "new" ocean basin: the Atlantic. As you can see in Figure 5.29, splitting of the supercontinent did not occur simultaneously along the margins of the Atlantic. The first split developed between North America and Africa.

Here, the continental crust was highly fractured, providing pathways for huge quantities of fluid lavas to reach the surface. Today, these lavas are represented by weathered igneous rocks found along the eastern seaboard of the United States—primarily buried beneath the sedimentary rocks that form the continental shelf. Radiometric dating of these solidified lavas indicates that rifting began between 180 million and 165 million years ago. This time span represents the "birth date" for this section of the North Atlantic.

By 130 million years ago, the South Atlantic began to open near the tip of what is now South Africa. As this zone of rifting migrated northward, it gradually opened the South Atlantic (compare Figures 5.29B and C). Continued breakup of the southern landmass led to the separation of Africa and Antarctica and sent India on a northward journey. By the early Cenozoic, about 50 million years ago, Australia had separated from Antarctica, and the South Atlantic had emerged as a full-fledged ocean (Figure 5.29D).

A modern map (Figure 5.29F) shows that India eventually collided with Asia, an event that began about 50 million years ago and created the Himalayas as well as the Tibetan Highlands. About the same time, the separation of Greenland from Eurasia completed the breakup of the northern landmass. During the past 20 million years or so of Earth's history, Arabia rifted from Africa to form the Red Sea, and Baja California separated from Mexico to form the Gulf of California (Figure 5.29E). Meanwhile, the Panama Arc joined North America and South America to produce our globe's familiar, modern appearance.

WHAT DRIVES PLATE MOTIONS?

The plate tectonics theory *describes* plate motion and the role that this motion plays in generating and modifying the major features of Earth's crust. Therefore, acceptance of plate tectonics does not rely on knowing precisely what drives plate motion. This is fortunate, because none of the models yet proposed can account for all major facets of plate tectonics.

Plate-Mantle Convection

From geophysical evidence, we have learned that although the mantle consists almost entirely of solid rock, it is hot and weak enough to exhibit fluidlike convective flow. The

DID YOU KNOW?

Researchers have estimated that continents join to form supercontinents roughly every 500 million years. Since it has been about 200 million years since Pangaea broke up, we have only 300 million years to wait before the next supercontinent is completed.

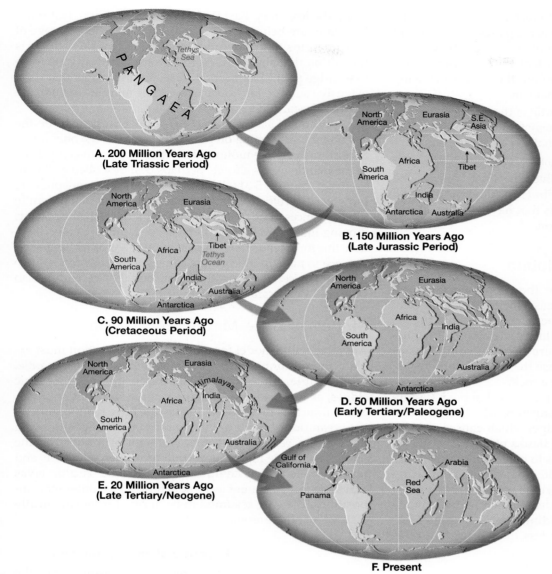

**A. 200 Million Years Ago
(Late Triassic Period)**

**B. 150 Million Years Ago
(Late Jurassic Period)**

**C. 90 Million Years Ago
(Cretaceous Period)**

**D. 50 Million Years Ago
(Early Tertiary/Paleogene)**

**E. 20 Million Years Ago
(Late Tertiary/Neogene)**

F. Present

FIGURE 5.29 Several views of the breakup of Pangaea over a period of 200 million years.

was upwelling that came from deep in the mantle. Upon reaching the base of the lithosphere, this flow was thought to spread laterally and drag the plates along. Thus, plates were viewed as being carried passively by convective flow in the mantle. Based on physical evidence, however, it became clear that upwelling beneath oceanic ridges is quite shallow and not related to deep circulation in the lower mantle. It is the horizontal movement of lithospheric plates away from the ridge that causes mantle upwelling, not the other way around. Thus, modern models have plates being an integral part of mantle convection and perhaps even its most active component.

Although convection in the mantle is still poorly understood, researchers generally agree on the following:

1. Convective flow in the rocky 2900-kilometer-thick mantle—in which warm, buoyant rock rises and cooler, denser material sinks—is the underlying driving force for plate movement.

simplest type of convection is analogous to heating a pot of water on a stove (**FIGURE 5.30**). Heating the base causes the material to rise in relatively thin sheets or blobs that spread out at the surface and cool. Eventually, the surface layer thickens (increases in density) and sinks back to the bottom where it is reheated until it achieves enough buoyancy to rise again.

Mantle convection is considerably more complex than the model just described. The shape of the mantle does not resemble that of a cooking pot. Rather it is a spherically shaped zone with a much larger upper boundary (Earth's surface) than lower boundary (core-mantle boundary). Furthermore, mantle convection is driven by a combination of three thermal processes: heating at the bottom by heat loss from Earth's core; heating from within by the decay of radioactive isotopes; and cooling from the top that creates thick, cold lithospheric slabs that sink into the mantle.

When seafloor spreading was first introduced, geologists proposed that the main driving force for plate motion

FIGURE 5.30 Convection is a type of heat transfer that involves the actual movement of a substance. Here the stove warms the water in the bottom of a cooking pot. The heated water expands, becomes less dense (more buoyant), and rises. Simultaneously, the cooler, denser water near the top sinks.

2. Mantle convection and plate tectonics are part of the same system. Subducting oceanic plates drive the cold downward-moving portion of convective flow while shallow upwelling of hot rock along the oceanic ridge and buoyant mantle plumes are the upward-flowing arms of the convective mechanism.

3. Convective flow in the mantle is the primary mechanism for transporting heat away from Earth's interior to the surface where it is eventually radiated into space.

What is not known with any high degree of certainty is the exact structure of this convective flow. First, we will look at some of the forces that contribute to plate motion and then we will examine two models that have been proposed to describe plate-mantle convection.

Forces that Drive Plate Motion

There is general agreement that the subduction of cold, dense slabs of oceanic lithosphere is a major driving force of plate motion (**FIGURE 5.31**). As these slabs sink into the asthenosphere, they "pull" the trailing plate along. This phenomenon, called slab pull, occurs because cold slabs of oceanic lithosphere are more dense than the underlying asthenosphere and hence "sink like a rock."

Another important driving force is **ridge push** (Figure 5.31). This gravity-driven mechanism results from the elevated position of the oceanic ridge, which causes slabs of lithosphere to "slide" down the flanks of the ridge. Ridge push appears to contribute far less to plate motions than slab pull. The primary evidence for this comes from comparing rates of seafloor spreading along ridge segments having different elevations. For example, despite its greater average height above the seafloor, spreading rates along the Mid-Atlantic Ridge are considerably less than spreading rates

along the less steep East Pacific Rise. In addition, fast-moving plates are being subducted along a larger percentage of their margins than slow-moving plates. This fact supports the notion that slab pull is a more significant driving force than ridge push. Examples of fast-moving plates that have extensive subduction zones along their margins include the Pacific, Nazca, and Cocos plates.

Although slab pull and ridge push appear to be the dominant forces acting on plates, they are not the only forces that influence plate motion. Beneath plates, convective flow in the mantle exerts a force, perhaps best described as "mantle drag" (Figure 5.31). When flow in the asthenosphere is moving at a velocity that exceeds that of the plate, mantle drag enhances plate motion. However, if the asthenosphere is moving more slowly than the plate, or in the opposite direction, this force tends to resist plate motion. Another type of resistance to plate motion occurs along subduction zones. Here friction between the overriding plate and the descending slab generates significant earthquake activity.

Models of Plate-Mantle Convection

Any acceptable model for plate-mantle convection must explain compositional variations known to exist in the mantle. For example, the basaltic lavas that erupt along oceanic ridges, as well as those that are generated by hot-spot volcanism, such as those found in Hawaii, have mantle sources. Yet ocean ridge basalts are very uniform in composition and depleted in certain elements. Hot-spot eruptions, on the other hand, have high concentrations of these elements and tend to have varied compositions. Because basaltic lavas that arise from different tectonic settings have different compositions, they are assumed to be derived from chemically distinct mantle reservoirs.

Layering at 660 Kilometers

Some researchers argue that the mantle resembles a "giant layer cake" divided at a depth of 660 kilometers. As shown in **FIGURE 5.32A**, this layered model has two zones of convection—a thin, dynamic layer in the upper mantle and a thick, sluggish one located below. This model successfully explains why basaltic lavas that erupt along the oceanic ridges have a different chemical make-up than those that erupt in Hawaii as a result of hot-spot activity. The mid-ocean ridge basalts come from the upper convective layer, which is well mixed, whereas the mantle plume that feeds the Hawaiian volcanoes taps a deeper, more primitive magma source that resides in the lower convective layer.

However, data gathered from the study of earthquake waves have

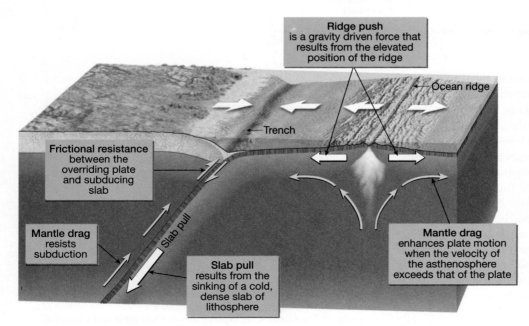

FIGURE 5.31 Illustration of some of the forces that act on plates.

A. Layering at 660 kilometers

B. Whole mantle convection

FIGURE 5.32 Proposed models for mantle convection. **A.** This model consists of two convection layers—a thin, convective layer above 660 kilometers (410 miles) and a thick one below. **B.** In this whole-mantle convection model, cold, oceanic lithosphere descends into the lowermost mantle whereas hot mantle plumes transport heat toward the surface.

shown that at least some subducting oceanic slabs penetrate the 660-kilometer boundary and descend deep into the mantle. The subducting lithosphere should serve to mix the upper and lower layers together, thereby destroying the layered structure proposed in this model.

Whole-Mantle Convection

Other researchers favor some type of *whole-mantle convection* in which cold oceanic lithosphere sinks to great depths and stirs the entire mantle (**FIGURE 5.32B**). One whole-mantle model suggests that the burial ground for subducting slabs is the core-mantle boundary. Over time, this material melts and buoyantly rises toward the surface as a mantle plume, thereby transporting hot material toward the surface (Figure 5.32B).

Recent work has predicted that whole-mantle convection would cause the entire mantle to completely mix in a matter of a few hundred million years. This, in turn, would eliminate chemically distinct magma sources—those that are observed in hot-spot volcanism and those associated with volcanic activity along oceanic ridges. Thus, the whole-mantle model also has shortcomings.

Although there is still much to be learned about the mechanisms that cause Earth's tectonic plates to migrate across the globe, one thing is clear. The unequal distribution of heat in Earth's interior generates some type of thermal convection that ultimately drives plate-mantle motion.

DID YOU KNOW?

Because plate tectonic processes are powered by heat from Earth's interior, the forces that drive plate motion will cease sometime in the distant future. The work of external forces (wind, water, and ice), however, will continue to erode Earth's surface. Eventually, landmasses will be nearly flat. What a different world it will be—an Earth with no earthquakes, no volcanoes, and no mountains.

THE CHAPTER IN REVIEW

• In the early 1900s, *Alfred Wegener* set forth his *continental drift* hypothesis. One of its major tenets was that a supercontinent called *Pangaea* began breaking apart into smaller continents about 200 million years ago. The smaller continental fragments then *drifted* to their present positions. To support the claim that the now-separate continents were once joined,

Wegener and others used the *fit of South America and Africa, the distribution of ancient climates, fossil evidence,* and *rock structures.*

• One of the main objections to the continental drift hypothesis was the inability of its supporters to provide an acceptable mechanism for the movement of continents.

• The theory of *plate tectonics,* a far more encompassing theory than continental drift, holds that Earth's rigid outer shell, called the *lithosphere,* consists of seven large and numerous smaller segments called *plates* that are in motion relative to one another. Most of Earth's *seismic activity, volcanism,* and *mountain building* occur along the dynamic margins of these plates.

• A major departure of the plate tectonics theory from the continental drift hypothesis is that large plates contain both continental and ocean crust and the entire plate moves. By contrast, in continental drift, Wegener proposed that the sturdier continents "drifted" by breaking through the oceanic crust, much like ice breakers cut through ice.

• *Divergent plate boundaries* occur where plates move apart, resulting in upwelling of material from the mantle to create new seafloor. Most divergent boundaries occur along the axis of the oceanic ridge system and are associated with seafloor spreading, which occurs at rates between about 2 and 15 centimeters (1 and 6 inches) per year. New divergent boundaries may form within a continent (for example, the East African rift valleys), where they may fragment a landmass and develop a new ocean basin.

• *Convergent plate boundaries* occur where plates move together, resulting in the subduction of oceanic lithosphere into the mantle along a deep-ocean trench. Convergence between oceanic and continental blocks results in subduction of the oceanic slab and the formation of a *continental volcanic arc* such as the Andes of South America. Oceanic–oceanic convergence results in an arc-shaped chain of volcanic islands called a *volcanic island arc.* When two plates carrying continental crust converge, both plates are too buoyant to be subducted. The result is a "collision" resulting in the formation of a mountain belt such as the Himalayas.

• *Transform fault boundaries* occur where plates grind past each other without the production or destruction of lithosphere. Most transform faults join two segments of a mid-ocean ridge. Others connect spreading centers to subduction zones and thus facilitate the transport of oceanic crust created at a ridge crest to its site of destruction, at a deep-ocean trench. Still others, like the San Andreas Fault, cut through continental crust.

• The theory of plate tectonics is supported by the ages and thickness of *sediments* from the floors of the deep-ocean basins and the existence of island chains that formed over *hot spots* and provide a frame of reference for tracing the direction of plate motion.

• Two basic models for mantle convection are currently being evaluated. Mechanisms that contribute to this convective flow are slab pull and ridge push. *Slab pull* occurs where cold, dense oceanic lithosphere is subducted and pulls the trailing lithosphere along. *Ridge push* results when gravity sets the elevated slabs astride oceanic ridges in motion. Hot, buoyant *mantle plumes* are considered the upward flowing arms of mantle convection. One model suggests that mantle convection occurs in two layers separated at a depth of 660 kilometers (410 miles). Another model proposes whole-mantle convection that stirs the entire 2900-kilometer-thick (1800-mile-thick) rocky mantle.

KEY TERMS

asthenosphere (p. 149)

continental drift (p. 143)

continental rift (p. 152)

continental volcanic arc (p. 155)

convergent boundary (p. 152)

Curie point (p. 160)

deep-ocean trench (p. 153)

divergent boundary (p. 151)

fossil magnetism (p. 161)

fracture zone (p. 157)

hot spot (p. 159)

hot-spot track (p. 159)

island arc (p. 155)

lithosphere (p. 147)

lithospheric plates (p. 150)

magnetic reversal (p. 162)

magnetic time scale (p. 162)

magnetometer (p. 163)

mantle plume (p. 159)

normal polarity (p. 162)

oceanic ridge system (p. 147)

paleoclimatic data (p. 146)

paleomagnetism (p. 161)

Pangaea (p. 143)

partial melting (p. 153)

plate (p. 148)

plate tectonics (p. 147)

reverse polarity (p. 162)

ridge push (p. 166)

rift valley (p. 151)

seafloor spreading (p. 151)

spreading center (p. 151)

subduction zone (p. 152)

supercontinent (p. 143)

tectonic plates (p. 149)

transform fault boundary (p. 156)

volcanic island arc (p. 155)

QUESTIONS FOR REVIEW

1. Who is credited with developing the continental drift hypothesis?

2. What was probably the first evidence that led some to suspect the continents were once connected?

3. What was Pangaea?

4. List the evidence that Wegener and his supporters gathered to substantiate the continental drift hypothesis.

5. Explain why the discovery of the fossil remains of *Mesosaurus* in both South America and Africa, but nowhere else, supports the continental drift hypothesis.

6. Early in this century, what was the prevailing view of how land animals migrated across vast expanses of ocean?

7. How did Wegener account for the existence of glaciers in the southern landmasses, while at the same time areas in North America, Europe, and Siberia supported lush tropical swamps?

8. On what basis were plate boundaries first established?

9. What are the three major types of plate boundaries? Describe the relative plate motion at each of these boundaries.

10. What is seafloor spreading? Where is active seafloor spreading occurring today?

11. What is a subduction zone? With what type of plate boundary is it associated?

12. Where is lithosphere being consumed? Why must the production and destruction of lithosphere be going on at approximately the same rate?

13. Briefly describe how the Himalaya Mountains formed.

14. Differentiate between transform faults and the other two types of plate boundaries.

15. Some predict that California will sink into the ocean. Is this idea consistent with the theory of plate tectonics?

16. Define the term *paleomagnetism*.

17. How does the continental drift hypothesis account for the apparent wandering of Earth's magnetic poles?

18. What is the age of the oldest sediments recovered by deep-ocean drilling? How do the ages of these sediments compare to the ages of the oldest continental rocks?

19. How do hot spots and the plate tectonics theory account for the fact that the Hawaiian Islands vary in age?

20. Briefly describe the three mechanisms that drive plate motion.

21. With which of the three types of plate boundaries are the following places or features associated: Himalayas, Aleutian Islands, Red Sea, Andes Mountains, San Andreas Fault, Iceland, Japan, Mount St. Helens?

COMPANION WEBSITE

The *Foundations of Earth Science* Website uses the resources and flexibility of the Internet to aid in your study of the topics in this chapter. Written and developed by the authors and other Earth science instructors, this site will help improve your understanding of Earth science. Visit **www.mygeoscienceplace.com** in order to

- **Review** key chapter concepts.
- **Read** with links to the ebook and to chapter-specific web resources

- **Visualize** and comprehend challenging topics using learning activities in *GEODe: Earth Science*.
- **Test** yourself with online quizzes.

GEODe: EARTH SCIENCE

GEODe: Earth Science is a valuable and easy to use learning aid that can be accessed from your book's Companion Website: **www.mygeoscienceplace.com**. It is a dynamic instructional tool that promotes understanding and reinforces important concepts by using tutorials, animations, and exercises that actively engage the student.

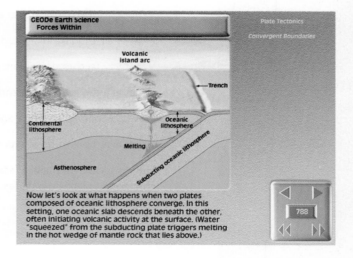

RESTLESS EARTH
EARTHQUAKES, GEOLOGIC STRUCTURES, AND MOUNTAIN BUILDING

To assist you in learning the important concepts in this chapter, you will find it helpful to focus on the following questions:

1. What is an earthquake?

2. What are the types of earthquake waves?

3. How is the epicenter of an earthquake determined?

4. Where are Earth's principal earthquake zones?

5. How is earthquake magnitude expressed?

6. What key factors determine the destructiveness of an earthquake?

7. What are the four major zones of Earth's interior?

8. How do continental crust and oceanic crust differ?

9. What are the two basic types of rock deformation?

10. How is mountain building associated with the various kinds of convergent plate boundaries?

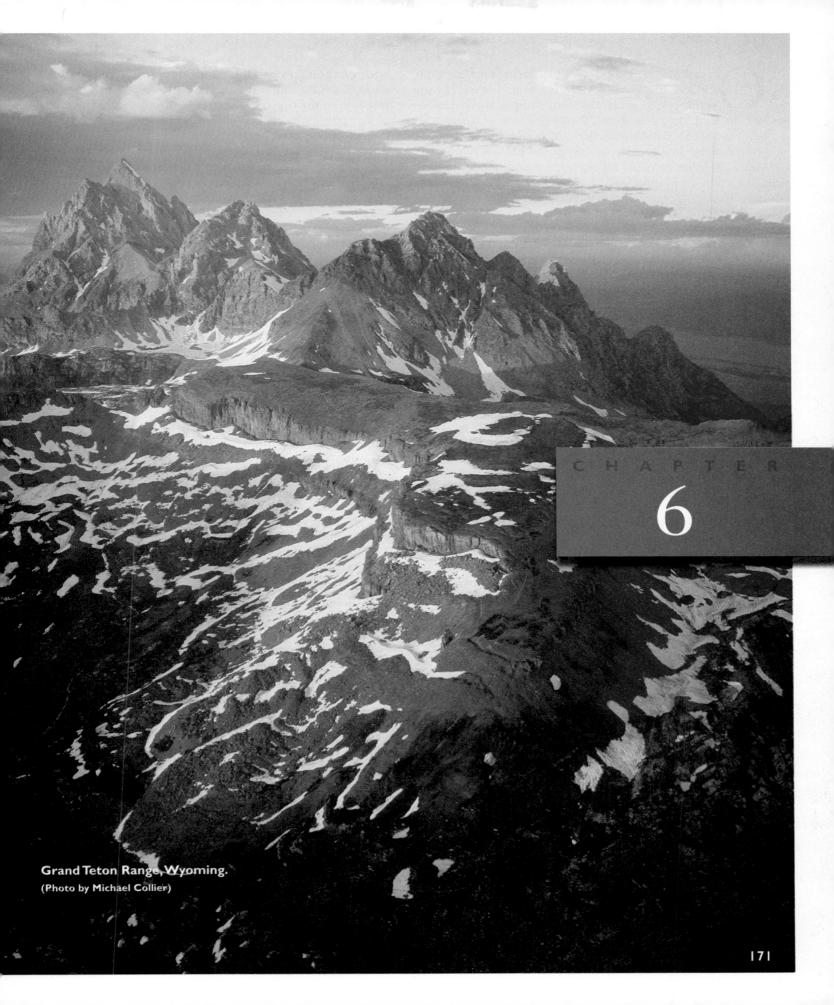

Grand Teton Range, Wyoming.
(Photo by Michael Collier)

On October 17, 1989, at 4:04 P.M. Pacific daylight time, millions of television viewers around the world were settling in to watch the third game of the World Series. Instead, they saw their TV sets go black as tremors hit San Francisco's Candlestick Park. Although the earthquake was centered in a remote section of the Santa Cruz Mountains, 100 kilometers (62 miles) to the south, major damage occurred in the Marina District of San Francisco.

The most tragic result of the violent shaking was the collapse of some double-decked sections of Interstate 880, also known as the Nimitz Freeway. The ground motions caused the upper deck to sway, shattering the concrete support columns along a mile-long section of the freeway. The upper deck then collapsed onto the lower roadway, flattening cars as if they were aluminum cans. This earthquake, named the Loma Prieta quake for its point of origin, claimed 67 lives.

In mid-January 1994, less than five years after the Loma Prieta earthquake devastated portions of the San Francisco Bay area, a major earthquake struck the Northridge area of Los Angeles. Although not the fabled "Big One," this moderate 6.7 magnitude earthquake left 57 dead, more than 5000 injured, and tens of thousands of households without water and electricity. The damage exceeded $40 billion and was attributed to an apparently unknown fault that ruptured 18 kilometers (11 miles) beneath Northridge.

The Northridge earthquake, which occurred northwest of downtown Los Angeles, began at 4:31 A.M. and lasted roughly 40 seconds. During this brief period, the quake terrorized the entire Los Angeles area. The three-story Northridge Meadows apartment complex, where 16 people died, was devastated. Most of the deaths resulted when sections of the upper floors collapsed onto the first-floor units. In addition, nearly 300 schools were seriously damaged and a dozen major roadways buckled. Among these were two of California's major arteries—the Golden State Freeway (Interstate 5), where an overpass collapsed, completely blocking the roadway, and the Santa Monica Freeway. Fortunately, these roadways had practically no traffic at this early morning hour.

In nearby Granada Hills, broken gas lines were set ablaze while the streets flooded from broken water mains. In Los Angeles County alone, more than 100 calls were made to the fire department. Seventy homes burned in the Sylmar area. A 64-car freight train derailed, including some cars carrying hazardous cargo. Despite the huge economic losses, it is remarkable that the destruction was not greater. Unquestionably, the upgrading of structures to meet the requirements of building codes developed for this earthquake-prone area helped minimize what could have been a much greater human tragedy.

WHAT IS AN EARTHQUAKE?

Forces Within
▼ Earthquakes

Earthquakes are natural geologic phenomena caused by the sudden and rapid movement of a large volume of rock (**FIGURE 6.1**). The violent shaking and destruction associated

with earthquakes are the result of rupture and slippage along fractures in Earth's crust called **faults**. Larger quakes result from the rupture of larger fault segments. The origin of an earthquake occurs at depths between 5 and 700 kilometers, at the **focus** (foci = a point). The point at the surface directly above the focus is called the **epicenter** (**FIGURE 6.2**).

During large earthquakes, a massive amount of energy is released as heat and **seismic waves**—a form of elastic energy that causes vibrations in the material that transmits them. Seismic waves are analogous to waves produced when a stone is dropped into a calm pond. Just as the impact of the stone creates a pattern of waves in motion, an earthquake generates waves that radiate outward in all directions from the focus. Even though seismic energy dissipates rapidly with increasing distance, sensitive instruments located around the world detect and record these events.

More than 30,000 earthquakes that are strong enough to be felt by humans occur worldwide annually. Fortunately, most are minor tremors that have little impact on our lives. Nevertheless, over geologic time earthquakes help shape our landscape.

Only about 75 strong earthquakes are recorded each year, and many of these occur in remote regions. Occasionally, a large earthquake is triggered near a major population center. Such events are among the most destructive natural forces on Earth. The shaking of the ground, coupled with the liquefaction of soils, wreaks havoc on buildings, roadways, and other structures. In addition, when a quake occurs in a populated area, power and gas lines are often ruptured, causing numerous fires. In the famous 1906 San Francisco earthquake, much of the damage was caused by fires that became uncontrollable when broken water mains left firefighters with only trickles of water (**FIGURE 6.3**).

Discovering the Causes of Earthquakes

The energy released by atomic explosions or by the movement of magma in Earth's crust can generate earthquake-like waves, but these events are generally quite weak. What mechanism produces a destructive earthquake? As you have learned, Earth is not a static planet. We know that large sections of Earth's crust have been thrust upward, because fossils of marine organisms have been discovered thousands of meters above the sea level. Other regions exhibit evidence of extensive subsidence. In addition to these vertical displacements, offsets in fence lines, roads, and other structures indicate that horizontal movements are also common (**FIGURE 6.4**).

The actual mechanism of earthquake generation eluded geologists until H. F. Reid of Johns Hopkins University conducted a study following the great 1906 San Francisco earthquake. The earthquake was accompanied by horizontal surface displacements of several meters along the northern portion of the San Andreas Fault. Field studies determined that during this single earthquake, the Pacific plate lurched as much as 4.7 meters (15 feet) northward past the adjacent North American plate.

FIGURE 6.1 Much of the city of Port-au-Prince, Haiti, including this concrete school building, was devastated by the 7.0 magnitude earthquake that struck on January 14, 2010. Inadequate building codes contributed greatly to the tragic loss of life. (AP Photo/Gerald Herbert)

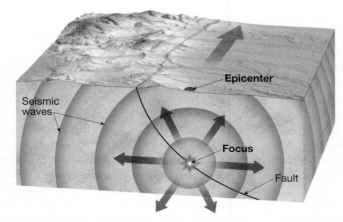

FIGURE 6.2 Earthquake focus and epicenter. The *focus* is the zone within Earth where the initial displacement occurs. The *epicenter* is the surface location directly above the focus.

What Reid concluded from his investigations is illustrated in **FIGURE 6.5**. Tectonic stresses acting over tens to hundreds of years slowly deform the crustal rocks on both sides of a fault. When deformed by differential stress, rocks bend and store elastic energy, much like a wooden stick does if bent (Figure 6.5B). Eventually, the frictional resistance holding the rocks in place is overcome. Slippage allows the deformed (strained) rock to "snap back" to its original, stress-free, shape (Figure 6.5C, D). The "springing back" was termed **elastic rebound** by Reid because the rock behaves elastically, much like a stretched rubber band does when it is released. The vibrations we know as an earthquake are generated by the rock elastically returning to its original shape.

In summary, *earthquakes are produced by the rapid release of elastic energy stored in rock that has been deformed by differential stresses*. Once the strength of the rock is exceeded, it suddenly ruptures, causing the vibrations of an earthquake.

FIGURE 6.3 San Francisco in flames after the 1906 earthquake. (Reproduced from the collection of the Library of Congress) Inset photo shows fire triggered when a gas line ruptured during the Northridge earthquake in southern California in 1994. (AFP/Getty Images)

FIGURE 6.4 Slippage along a fault produced an offset in this orange grove located east of Calexico, California. (Photo by John S. Shelton) Inset photo shows a fence offset 2.5 meters (8.5 feet) during the 1906 San Francisco earthquake. (Photo by G. K. Gilbert, U.S. Geological Survey)

DID YOU KNOW?

Literally thousands of earthquakes occur daily! Fortunately, the majority of them are too small to be felt by people, and the majority of larger ones occur in remote regions. Their existence is known only because of sensitive seismographs.

Aftershocks and Foreshocks

Strong earthquakes are followed by numerous smaller tremors, called **aftershocks**, that gradually diminish in frequency and intensity over a period of several months. Within 24 hours of the massive 1964 Alaskan earthquake, 28 aftershocks were recorded, 10 of which had magnitudes that exceeded 6. More than 10,000 aftershocks with magnitudes of 3.5 or above occurred in the following 69 days and thousands of minor tremors were recorded over a span of 18 months. Because aftershocks happen mainly on the section of the fault that has slipped, they provide geologists with data that is useful in establishing the dimensions of the rupture surface.

Although aftershocks are weaker than the main earthquake, they can trigger the destruction of already weakened structures. This occurred in northwestern Armenia (1988)

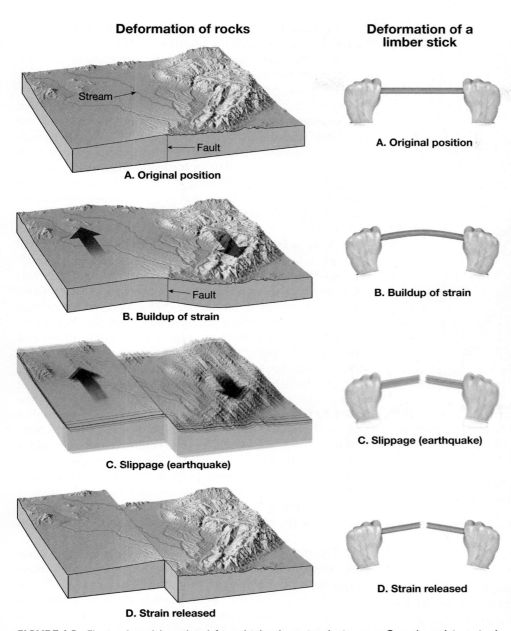

Deformation of rocks

A. Original position

Stream

Fault

B. Buildup of strain

Fault

C. Slippage (earthquake)

D. Strain released

Deformation of a limber stick

A. Original position

B. Buildup of strain

C. Slippage (earthquake)

D. Strain released

FIGURE 6.5 Elastic rebound. As rock is deformed, it bends, storing elastic energy. Once the rock is strained beyond its breaking point, it ruptures, releasing the stored-up energy in the form of earthquake waves.

which is the *transform fault boundary* that separates two great sections of Earth's lithosphere: the North American plate and the Pacific plate. Other faults are small and capable of producing only minor earthquakes.

Most of the displacement that occurs along faults can be satisfactorily explained by the plate tectonics theory, which states that large slabs of Earth's lithosphere are in continual slow motion. These mobile plates interact with neighboring plates, straining and deforming the rocks at their margins. Faults associated with plate boundaries are the source of most large earthquakes.

Most large faults are not perfectly straight or continuous; instead, they consist of numerous branches and smaller fractures that display kinks and offsets. Such a pattern is displayed in **FIGURE 6.6**, which shows the San Andreas Fault as a system of several faults of various sizes.

The San Andreas is undoubtedly the most studied fault system in the world. Over the years, research has shown that displacement occurs along discrete segments that behave somewhat differently from one another. A few sections of the San Andreas exhibit a slow, gradual displacement known as fault creep, which occurs without the build up of significant strain. These sections produce only minor seismic shaking. Other segments slip at regular intervals, producing small to moderate earthquakes. Still other segments remain locked and store energy for a few hundred years before rupturing in great earthquakes. Earthquakes that occur along locked segments of the San Andreas Fault tend to be repetitive. As soon as one is over, the continuous motion of the plates begins building strain anew. Decades or centuries later, the fault fails again.

where many people lived in large apartment buildings constructed of brick and concrete slabs. After a moderate earthquake of magnitude 6.9 weakened the buildings, a strong aftershock of magnitude 5.8 completed the demolition.

In contrast to aftershocks, small earthquakes called **foreshocks** often precede a major earthquake by days, or in some cases, by several years. Monitoring of foreshocks to predict forthcoming earthquakes has been attempted with limited success.

Earthquakes and Faults

Earthquakes take place along faults both new and old that occur in places where differential stresses have ruptured Earth's crust. Some faults are large and capable of generating major earthquakes. One example is the San Andreas Fault,

DID YOU KNOW?

Humans have inadvertently triggered earthquakes. In 1962, Denver began experiencing frequent tremors. The earthquakes were located near an army waste-disposal well used to inject waste into the ground. Investigators concluded that the pressurized fluids made their way along a buried fault surface, which reduced friction and triggered fault slippage and earthquakes. Sure enough, when the pumping halted, so did the tremors.

FIGURE 6.6 Map showing the extent of the San Andreas Fault system and the Eastern California Shear Zone.

SEISMOLOGY: THE STUDY OF EARTHQUAKE WAVES

Forces Within
▼ Earthquakes

The study of earthquake waves, **seismology**, dates back to attempts made by the Chinese almost 2000 years ago to determine the direction from which these waves originated. Modern **seismographs**, instruments that record earthquake waves, are similar to the instruments used by the Chinese. Seismographs have a weight freely suspended from a support that is securely attached to bedrock (**FIGURE 6.7**). When vibrations from an earthquake reach the instrument, the inertia of the weight keeps it relatively stationary while Earth and the support move. (*Inertia* is the tendency of objects at rest to stay at rest and objects in motion to remain in motion.)

DID YOU KNOW?

The first instrument to detect earthquakes was developed in about A.D. 132 in China by Chang Heng. (China has a long history of devastating earthquakes.) Chang Heng's instrument is thought to have detected unfelt earthquakes and estimated the direction to the epicenters.

To detect very weak earthquakes, or a great earthquake that has occurred in another part of the world, most seismographs are designed to amplify ground motion. Other instruments are designed to withstand the violent shaking that occurs very near the focus.

The records obtained from seismographs, called **seismograms**, provide useful information about the nature of seismic waves. Seismograms reveal that two main groups of seismic waves are generated by the slippage of a rock mass. One of these wave types, called **surface waves**, travels along the outer part of Earth. Others travel through Earth's interior and are called **body waves**. Body waves are divided into two types—called **primary**, or **P**, **waves** and **secondary**, or **S**, **waves**.

Body waves are identified by their mode of travel through intervening materials. P waves are "push-pull" waves—they momentarily *push* (squeeze) and *pull* (stretch) rocks in the direction the wave is traveling (**FIGURE 6.8A**). This wave motion is similar to that generated by human vocal cords as they move air to create sound. Solids, liquids, and gases resist a change in volume when compressed and will elastically spring back once the force is removed. Therefore, P waves can travel through all these materials.

On the other hand, S waves "shake" the particles at right angles to their direction of travel. This can be illustrated by fastening one end of a rope and shaking the other end, as shown in **FIGURE 6.8C**. Unlike P waves, which temporarily change the *volume* of intervening material by alternately squeezing and stretching it, S waves change the *shape* of the material that transmits them. Because fluids (gases and liquids) do not resist stresses that cause changes in shape—meaning fluids will not return to their original shape once the stress is removed—they will not transmit S waves.

The motion of surface waves is somewhat more complex. As surface waves travel along the ground, they cause the ground and anything resting upon it to move, much like ocean swells toss a ship. In addition to their up-and-down motion, surface waves have a side-to-side motion similar to an S wave oriented in a horizontal plane. This latter motion is particularly damaging to the foundations of structures.

By examining the "typical" seismic record shown in **FIGURE 6.9**, you can see a major difference among seismic waves—their speed of travel. P waves are the first to arrive at a recording station, then S waves, and finally surface waves. The velocity of P waves through the crustal rock granite is about 6 kilometers per second and increases to nearly 13 kilometers per second at the base of the mantle. P waves can pass through Earth's mantle in about 20 minutes. Generally, in any solid material, P waves travel about 1.7 times faster than S waves, and surface waves are roughly 10 percent slower than S waves.

In addition to velocity differences, notice in Figure 6.9 that the height, or *amplitude,* of these wave types also varies. S waves have slightly greater amplitudes than P waves, and surface waves exhibit even greater amplitudes. Surface waves also retain their maximum amplitude longer than P and S waves. As a result, surface waves tend to cause greater

A.

B.

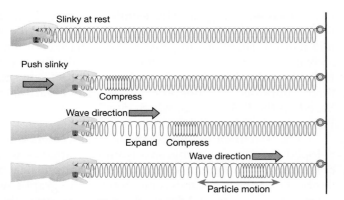

A. P waves generated using a slinky

B. P waves traveling along the surface

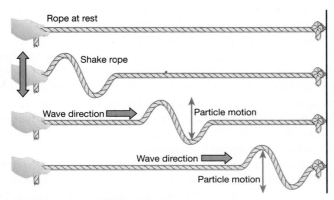

C. S waves generated using a rope

D. S waves traveling along the surface

FIGURE 6.8 Types of seismic waves and their characteristic motion. (Note that during a strong earthquake, ground shaking consists of a combination of various kinds of seismic waves.) **A.** As illustrated by a slinky, P waves are compressional waves that alternately compress and expand the material through which they pass. **B.** The back-and-forth motion produced as compressional waves travel along the surface can cause the ground to buckle and fracture and may cause power lines to break. **C.** S waves cause material to oscillate at right angles to the direction of wave motion. **D.** Because S waves can travel in any plane, they produce up-and-down and sideways shaking of the ground.

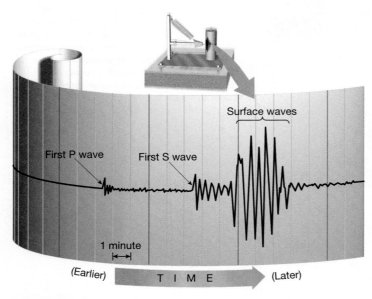

FIGURE 6.9 Typical seismogram. Note the time interval (about 5 minutes) between the arrival of the first P wave and the arrival of the first S wave.

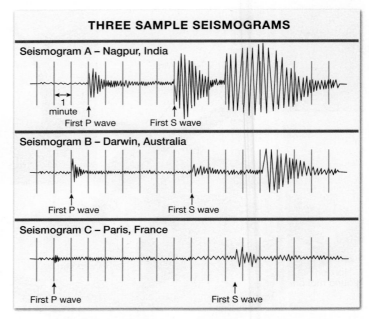

FIGURE 6.10 Simplified seismograms of the same earthquake recorded in three different cities. **A.** Nagpur, India. **B.** Darwin, Australia. **C.** Paris, France.

DID YOU KNOW?

Some of the most interesting uses of seismographs involve the reconstruction of unfortunate events, such as airline crashes, pipeline explosions, and mining disasters. For example, a seismologist helped with the investigation of Pan Am Flight 103, which was brought down in 1988 over Lockerbie, Scotland, by a terrorist's bomb. Nearby seismographs recorded six separate impacts, indicating that the plane had broken into that many large pieces before it crashed.

ground shaking, and hence, greater destruction, than either P or S waves.

Seismic waves are useful in determining the location and magnitude of earthquakes. In addition, seismic waves provide an important tool for probing Earth's interior.

LOCATING AN EARTHQUAKE

 Forces Within
▼ Earthquakes

When analyzing an earthquake, the first task seismologists undertake is determining its *epicenter*, the point on Earth's surface directly above the focus (see Figure 6.2). The method used for locating an earthquake's epicenter relies on the fact that P waves travel faster than S waves.

The method is analogous to the results of a race between two autos, one faster than the other. The first P wave, like the faster auto, always wins the race, arriving ahead of

the first S wave. The greater the length of the race, the greater the difference in their arrival times at the finish line (the seismic station). Therefore, the greater the interval between the arrival of the first P wave and the arrival of the first S wave, the greater the distance to the epicenter. **FIGURE 6.10** shows three simplified seismograms for the same earthquake. Based on the P-S interval, which city, Nagpur, Darwin, or Paris, is farthest from the epicenter?

The system for locating earthquake epicenters was developed by using seismograms from earthquakes whose epicenters could be easily pinpointed from physical evidence. From these seismograms, travel-time graphs were constructed (**FIGURE 6.11**). Using the sample seismogram for Nagpur, India, in Figure 6.10A and the travel-time curve in Figure 6.11, we can determine the distance separating the recording station from the earthquake in two steps: (1) Using the seismogram, determine the time interval between the arrival of the first P wave and the arrival of the first S wave, and (2) using the travel-time graph, find the P-S interval on the vertical axis and use that information to determine the distance to the epicenter on the horizontal axis. Following this procedure, we can determine that the earthquake occurred 3400 kilometers (2100 miles) from the recording instrument in Nagpur, India.

Now we know the *distance*, but what about *direction*? The epicenter could be in any direction from the seismic station. Using a method called *triangulation*, the precise location can be determined when the distance is known from three or more seismic stations (**FIGURE 6.12**). On a globe, a circle is drawn around each seismic station. The radius of these circles is equal to the distance from the seismic station to the epicenter. The point where the three circles intersect is the epicenter of the quake.

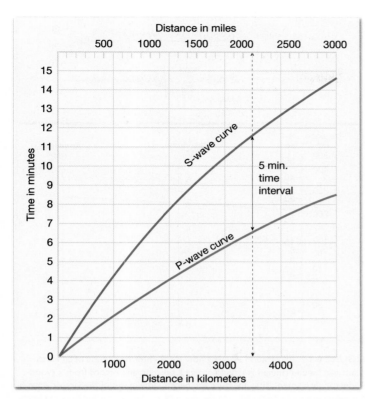

FIGURE 6.11   A travel-time graph is used to determine the distance to the epicenter. The difference in arrival times of the first P and S waves in the example is 5 minutes. Thus, the epicenter is roughly 3400 kilometers (2100 miles) away.

FIGURE 6.12   Determining an earthquake epicenter using the distances obtained from three or more siesmic stations—a method called *trangulation*.

DID YOU KNOW?

During the 1811–1812 New Madrid earthquake, the ground subsided as much as 4.5 meters (15 feet) and created Lake St. Francis west of the Mississippi and enlarged Reelfoot Lake to the east. Other regions rose, creating temporary waterfalls in the bed of the Mississippi River.

MEASURING THE SIZE OF EARTHQUAKES

Historically, seismologists have employed a variety of methods to determine two fundamentally different measures that describe the size of an earthquake—intensity and magnitude. The first of these to be used was **intensity**—a measure of the degree of earthquake shaking at a given locale based on observed damage. Later, with the development of seismographs, it became possible to measure ground motion using instruments. This quantitative measurement, called **magnitude**, relies on data gleaned from seismic records to estimate the amount of energy released at an earthquake's source.

Intensity and magnitude provide useful, though different, information about earthquake strength. Consequently, both measures are used to describe earthquake severity.

Intensity Scales

Until a little more than a century ago, historical records provided the only accounts of the severity of earthquake shaking and destruction. Perhaps the first attempt to "scientifically" describe the aftermath of an earthquake came following the great Italian earthquake of 1857. By systematically mapping effects of the earthquake, a measure of the intensity of ground shaking was established. The map generated by this study employed lines to connect places of equal damage and hence equal ground shaking. Using this technique, zones of intensity were identified, with the zone of highest intensity located near the center of maximum ground shaking and often (but not always) the earthquake epicenter (**FIGURE 6.13**).

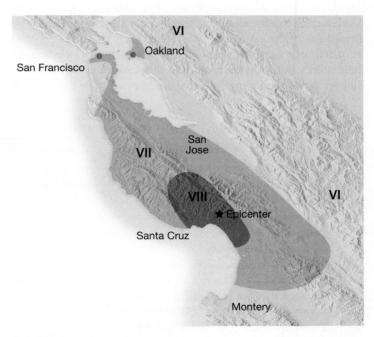

FIGURE 6.13   Zones of destruction associated with the Loma Prieta earthquake that devastated portions of California's San Francisco Bay Area, January 1994. Intensity levels based on the Modified Mercalli Intensity Scale. Note the areas of heavy destruction in San Francisco and Oakland, located almost 100 kilometers (60 miles) from the epicenter.

In 1902, Giuseppe Mercalli developed a more reliable intensity scale, which in a modified form is still used today. The **Modified Mercalli Intensity Scale**, shown in Table 6.1, was developed using California buildings as its standard. For example, if some well-built wood structures and most masonry buildings were destroyed by an earthquake, the affected area would be assigned an intensity of X (ten) on the Mercalli scale (Table 6.1).

Despite their usefulness in providing seismologists with a tool to compare earthquake severity, intensity scales have significant drawbacks. Such intensity scales are based on effects (largely destruction) that depend not only on the severity of ground shaking but also on factors such as building design and the nature of surface materials. For example, the modest 6.9-magnitude 1988 Armenian earthquake mentioned earlier was extremely destructive, mainly because of inferior building practices. A quake that struck Mexico City in 1985 was deadly because of the soft sediment upon which part of the city rests. Thus, the destruction wrought by an earthquake is frequently not a good measure of the amount of energy that was unleashed.

Magnitude Scales

To more accurately compare earthquakes across the globe, a measure was needed that does not rely on parameters that vary considerably from one part of the world to another. As a consequence, a number of magnitude scales were developed.

Richter Magnitude

In 1935 Charles Richter of the California Institute of Technology developed the first magnitude scale using seismic records. As shown in **FIGURE 6.14** (top), the **Richter scale** is based on the amplitude of the largest seismic wave (P, S, or surface wave) recorded on a seismogram. Because seismic waves weaken as the distance between the focus and the seismograph increases, Richter developed a method that accounts for the decrease in

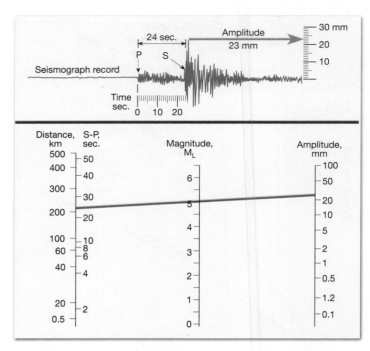

FIGURE 6.14 Illustration showing how the Richter magnitude of an earthquake can be determined graphically using a seismograph record from a Wood-Anderson instrument. First, measure the height (amplitude) of the largest wave on the seismogram (23 mm) and then the distance to the focus using the time interval between S and P waves (24 seconds). Next, draw a line between the distance scale (left) and the wave amplitude scale (right). By doing this, you should obtain the Richter magnitude (M_L) of 5. (Data from California Institute of Technology)

wave amplitude with increasing distance. Theoretically, as long as equivalent instruments are used, monitoring stations at various locations will obtain the same Richter magnitude for each recorded earthquake. In practice, however, different recording stations often obtain slightly different Richter magnitudes for the same earthquake—a consequence of the variations in rock types through which the waves travel.

Table 6.1   Modified Mercalli Intensity Scale

I	Not felt except by a very few under especially favorable circumstances.
II	Felt only by a few persons at rest, especially on upper floors of buildings.
III	Felt quite noticeably indoors, especially on upper floors of buildings, but many people do not recognize it as an earthquake.
IV	During the day felt indoors by many, outdoors by few. Sensation like heavy truck striking building.
V	Felt by nearly everyone, many awakened. Disturbances of trees, poles, and other tall objects sometimes noticed.
VI	Felt by all; many frightened and run outdoors. Some heavy furniture moved; few instances of fallen plaster or damaged chimneys. Damage slight.
VII	Everybody runs outdoors. Damage negligible in buildings of good design and construction; slight-to-moderate in well-built ordinary structures; considerable in poorly built or badly designed structures.
VIII	Damage slight in specially designed structures; considerable in ordinary substantial buildings with partial collapse; great in poorly built structures. (Fall of chimneys, factory stacks, columns, monuments, walls.)
IX	Damage considerable in specially designed structures. Buildings shifted off foundations. Ground cracked conspicuously.
X	Some well-built wooden structures destroyed. Most masonry and frame structures destroyed. Ground badly cracked.
XI	Few, if any, (masonry) structures remain standing. Bridges destroyed. Broad fissures in ground.
XII	Damage total. Waves seen on ground surfaces. Objects thrown upward into air.

Earthquakes vary enormously in strength, and great earthquakes produce wave amplitudes that are thousands of times larger than those generated by weak tremors (**FIGURE 6.15**). To accommodate this wide variation, Richter used a *logarithmic scale* to express magnitude, in which a *tenfold* increase in wave amplitude corresponds to an increase of 1 on the magnitude scale. Thus, the degree of ground shaking for a 5-magnitude earthquake is 10 times greater than that produced by an earthquake having a Richter magnitude of 4.

In addition, each unit of Richter magnitude equates to roughly a *32-fold energy increase.* Thus, an earthquake with a magnitude of 6.5 releases 32 times more energy than one with a magnitude of 5.5, and roughly 1000 times (32 × 32) more energy than a 4.5-magnitude quake. A major earthquake with a magnitude of 8.5 releases millions of times more energy than the smallest earthquakes felt by humans (Figure 6.15).

Although the Richter scale has no upper limit, the largest magnitude recorded was 8.9. Great shocks such as these release an amount of energy that is roughly equivalent to the detonation of 1 billion tons of explosives. Conversely, earthquakes with a Richter magnitude of less than 2.0 are generally not felt by humans.

Richter's original goal was modest in that he only attempted to rank shallow earthquakes in southern California into groups of large, medium, and small magnitude. Hence, Richter magnitude was designed to classify relatively local earthquakes and is designated by the symbol (M_L)—where M is for *magnitude* and L is for *local.*

The convenience of describing the size of an earthquake by a single number that can be calculated quickly from seismograms makes the Richter scale a powerful tool. Further, unlike intensity scales that can only be applied to populated areas of the globe, Richter magnitudes could be assigned to earthquakes in more remote regions and even to events that occur in the ocean basins. In time, seismologists modified Richter's work and developed new Richter-like magnitude scales.

Despite its usefulness, the Richter scale is not adequate for describing very large earthquakes. For example, the 1906 San Francisco earthquake and the 1964 Alaskan earthquake had roughly the same Richter magnitudes. However, based on the relative size of the affected areas and the associated tectonic changes, the Alaskan earthquake released considerably more energy than the San Francisco quake. Thus, the Richter scale is said to be *saturated* for major earthquakes because it cannot distinguish among them.

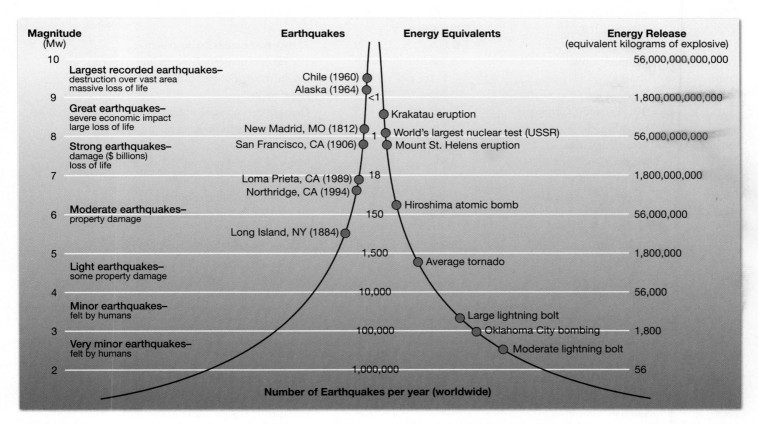

FIGURE 6.15 The size or magnitude of an earthquake (left side) compared to the number of earthquakes of various magnitudes that occur worldwide each year. The largest quakes occur less than once a year, whereas strong earthquakes happen more than once a month and weak quakes, those less than magnitude 2, occur hundreds of times per day. (Data from IRIS Consortium, www.iris.edu)

Moment Magnitude

In recent years, seismologists have come to favor a newer measure called **moment magnitude** (M_W), which determines the strain energy released from the entire fault surface. Because moment magnitude estimates the total energy released, it is better for measuring or describing very large earthquakes. In light of this, seismologists have recalculated the magnitudes of older, strong earthquakes using the moment magnitude scale. For example, the 1964 Alaskan earthquake was originally given a Richter magnitude of 8.3, but a recent recalculation using the moment magnitude scale resulted in an upgrade to 9.2. Similarly, the 1906 San Francisco earthquake which had a Richter magnitude of 8.3 was degraded to a M_W 7.9. The strongest earthquake on record is the 1960 Chilean subduction zone earthquake, with a moment magnitude of 9.5 (Table 6.2).

Moment magnitude can be calculated from geologic fieldwork by measuring the average amount of slip on the fault, the area of the fault surface that slipped, and the strength of the faulted rock. The area of the fault plane can be roughly calculated by multiplying the surface-rupture length by the depth of the aftershocks. Moment magnitude can also be calculated using data from seismograms.

DID YOU KNOW?

The greatest loss of life attributed to an earthquake occurred in northern China. The Chinese made their homes here by carving numerous structures into a powdery, windblown material called *loess*. Early on the morning of January 23, 1556, an earthquake struck the region, collapsing the cavelike structures and killing about 830,000 people. Sadly, in 1920, a similar event collapsed loess structures in much the same way, taking about 200,000 lives.

Table 6.2   Some notable earthquakes

Year	Location	Deaths(est)	Magnitude[†]	Comments
1556	Shensi, China	830,000		Possibly the greatest natural disaster.
1756	Lisbon, Portugal	70,000		Tsunami damage extensive
*1811–1812	New Madrid, Missouri	Few	7.9	Three major earthquakes
*1886	Charleston, South Carolina	60		Greatest historical earthquake in the eastern United States.
*1906	San Francisco, California	3,000	7.8	Fires caused extensive damage.
1908	Messina, Italy	120,000		
1923	Tokyo, Japan	143,000	7.9	Fire caused extensive destruction.
1960	Southern Chile	5,700	9.5	The largest-magnitude earthquake ever recorded.
*1964	Alaska	131	9.2	Greatest North American earthquake.
1970	Peru	70,000	7.9	Great rockslide.
*1971	San Fernando, California	65	6.5	Damage exceeded $1 billion.
1975	Liaoning Province, China	1,328	7.5	First major earthquake to be predicted.
1976	Tangshan China	255,000	7.5	Not predicted.
1985	Mexico City	9,500	8.1	Major damage occurred 400 km from epicenter.
1988	Armenia	25,000	6.9	Poor construction practices.
*1989	San Francisco Bay area	62	7.1	Damages exceeded $6 billion.
1990	Iran	50,000	7.4	Landslides and poor construction practices caused great damage.
1993	Latur, India	10,000	6.4	Located in stable continental interior.
*1994	Northridge, California	51	6.7	Damages in excess of $15 billion.
1995	Kobe, Japan	5,472	6.9	Damages estimated to exceed $100 billion.
1999	Izmit, Turkey	17,127	7.4	Nearly 44,000 injured and more than 250,000 displaced.
1999	Chi-Chi, Taiwan	2,300	7.6	Severe destruction; 8,700 injuries.
2001	Bhuj, India	25,000+	7.9	Millions homeless.
2003	Bam, Iran	41,000+	6.6	Ancient city with poor construction.
2004	Indian Ocean (Sumatra)	230,000	9.1	Devastating tsunami damage.
2005	Pakistan/Kashmir	86,000	7.6	Many landslides; 4 million homeless.
2008	Sichuan, China	70,000	7.9	Millions homeless, some towns will not be rebuilt.
2010	Port-au-Prince Haiti	230,000	7.0	Tens of thousands injured, hundreds of thousands homeless.

SOURCE: U.S. Geological Survey.
* U.S. earthquakes.
† Widely differing magnitudes have been estimated for some of these earthquakes. When available, moment magnitudes are used.

EARTHQUAKE BELTS AND PLATE BOUNDARIES

About 95 percent of the energy released by earthquakes originates in the few relatively narrow zones shown in **FIGURE 6.16**. The zone of greatest seismic activity, called the *circum-Pacific belt*, encompasses the coastal regions of Chile, Central America, Indonesia, Japan, and Alaska, including the Aleutian Islands (Figure 6.16). Most earthquakes in the circum-Pacific belt occur along convergent plate boundaries where one plate slides at a low angle beneath another. The zone of contact between the subducting and overlying plates forms a huge thrust fault called a *megathrust*, along which Earth's largest earthquakes are generated. Because subduction zone earthquakes usually happen beneath the ocean they may also generate destructive waves called *tsunami*. For example, the 2004 quake off the coast of Sumatra produced a tsunami that claimed an estimated 230,000 lives.

Another major concentration of strong seismic activity, referred to as the *Alpine-Himalayan belt*, runs through the mountainous regions that flank the Mediterranean Sea and extends past the Himalayan Mountains (Figure 6.16). Tectonic activity in this region is mainly attributed to the collision of the African plate with Eurasia and the collision of the Indian plate with southeast Asia. These plate interactions created faults that remain active. In addition, numerous faults located away from these plate boundaries have been reactivated as India continues its northward advance into Asia. For example, slippage on a complex fault system in 2008 in the Sichuan Province of China killed at least 70,000 people and left 1.5 million others homeless. The "culprit" is the Indian subcontinent, which shoves the Tibetan Plateau eastward against the rocks of the Sichuan Basin.

Figure 6.16 shows another continuous earthquake belt that extends for thousands of kilometers through the world's oceans. This zone coincides with the oceanic ridge

system, which is an area of frequent but low-intensity seismic activity caused by seafloor spreading. The remaining seismic activity in this zone is associated with slippage along transform faults located between ridge segments.

Transform faults and related faults also run through continental crust where they may generate large earthquakes that tend to occur on a cyclical basis. Examples include California's San Andreas Fault, New Zealand's Alpine Fault, and Turkey's North Anatolian Fault, which produced a deadly earthquake in 1999.

EARTHQUAKE DESTRUCTION

The most violent earthquake to jar North America in the last 100 years—the Good Friday Alaskan earthquake—occurred in 1964. Felt throughout that state, the earthquake had a moment magnitude (M_W) of 9.2 and reportedly lasted three to four minutes. This brief event left 131 people dead, thousands homeless, and the economy of the state badly disrupted (**FIGURE 6.17**). Had the schools and business districts been open on this holiday, the toll surely would have been higher. Within 24 hours of the initial shock, 28 aftershocks were recorded, 10 of which exceeded a magnitude of 6 on the Richter scale.

Destruction from Seismic Vibrations

The 1964 Alaskan earthquake provided geologists with insights into the role of ground shaking as a destructive force. As the energy released by an earthquake travels along Earth's surface, it causes the ground to vibrate in a complex manner by moving up and down as well as from side to side. The amount of damage to human-made structures attributable to the vibrations depends on several factors, including (1) the intensity and (2) the duration of the vibrations, (3) the nature of the material upon which the structure rests,

FIGURE 6.16 Distribution of nearly 15,000 earthquakes with magnitudes equal to or greater than 5 for a 10-year period. (Data from U.S. Geological Survey)

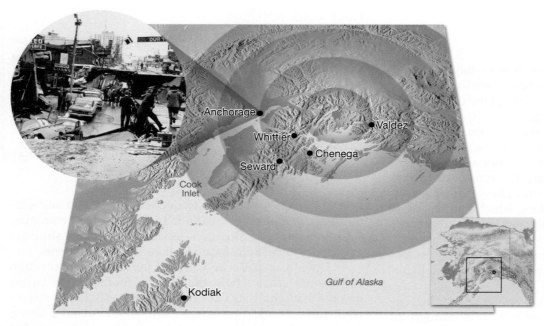

FIGURE 6.17   Region most affected by the Good Friday earthquake of 1964. Note the location of the epicenter (red dot). (After U.S. Geological Survey)

Amplification of Seismic Waves

Although the region near the epicenter will experience about the same intensity of ground shaking, destruction may vary considerably within this area. Such differences are usually attributable to the nature of the ground on which the structures are built. Soft sediments, for example, generally amplify the vibrations more than solid bedrock. Thus, the buildings in Anchorage that were situated on unconsolidated sediments experienced heavy structural damage. By contrast, most of the town of Whittier, although much nearer the epicenter, rested on a firm foundation of solid bedrock and suffered much less damage from seismic vibrations. Following the quake, however, Whittier was damaged by a tsunami—a phenomenon that will be described later in the chapter.

Liquefaction

In areas where unconsolidated materials are saturated with water, earthquake vibrations can turn stable soil into a mobile fluid, a phenomenon known as **liquefaction**. As a result, the ground is not capable of supporting buildings and underground storage tanks and sewer lines may literally float toward the surface (**FIGURE 6.19**). During the 1989 Loma Prieta

DID YOU KNOW?

In Japanese folklore, earthquakes were caused by a giant catfish that lived beneath the ground. Whenever the catfish flopped about, the ground shook. Meanwhile, people in Russia's Kamchatka Peninsula believed that earthquakes occurred when a mighty dog, Kozei, shook freshly fallen snow from its coat.

and (4) the nature of building materials and the construction practices of the region.

All of the multistory structures in Anchorage were damaged by the vibrations. The more flexible wood-frame residential buildings fared best. However, many homes were destroyed when the ground failed. A striking example of how construction variations affect earthquake damage is shown in **FIGURE 6.18**. You can see that the steel-frame building on the left withstood the vibrations, whereas the poorly designed JC Penney building was badly damaged. Engineers have learned that buildings built of blocks and bricks that are not reinforced with steel rods are the most serious safety threat in earthquakes.

Most large structures in Anchorage were damaged, even though they were built according to the earthquake provisions of the Uniform Building Code. Perhaps some of that destruction can be attributed to the unusually long duration of this earthquake. Most quakes involve tremors that last less than a minute. For example, the 1994 Northridge earthquake was felt for about 40 seconds, and the strong vibrations of the 1989 Loma Prieta earthquake lasted less than 15 seconds. But the Alaska quake reverberated for 3 to 4 minutes.

FIGURE 6.18   Damage to the five-story JCPenney building, Anchorage, Alaska. Very little structural damage was incurred by the adjacent building. (Courtesy of NOAA)

FIGURE 6.19 Effects of liquefaction. This tilted building rests on unconsolidated sediment that imitated quicksand during a major 1985 Mexican earthquake. (Photo by James L. Beck)

A.

B.

FIGURE 6.20 Liquefaction. **A.** These "mud volcanoes" were produced by the Loma Prieta earthquake of 1989. They formed when geysers of sand and water shot from the ground, an indication that liquefaction occurred. (Photo by Richard Hilton, courtesy of Dennis Fox) **B.** Students experiencing the nature of liquefaction. (Photo by M. Miller)

earthquake, in San Francisco's Marina District, foundations failed and geysers of sand and water shot from the ground, indicating that liquefaction had occurred (**FIGURE 6.20**).

Landslides and Ground Subsidence

The greatest damage to structures is often caused by landslides and ground subsidence triggered by earthquake vibrations. This was the case during the 1964 Alaskan earthquake in Valdez and Seward, where the violent shaking caused deltaic sediments to slump, carrying both waterfronts away. In Valdez, 31 people on a dock died when it slid into the sea. Because of the threat of recurrence, the entire town of Valdez was relocated to more stable ground about 7 kilometers away.

Much of the damage in the city of Anchorage was attributed to landslides. Homes were destroyed in Turnagain Heights when a layer of clay lost its strength and over 200 meters of land slid toward the ocean (**FIGURE 6.21**). A portion of this spectacular landslide was left in its natural condition as a reminder of this destructive event. The site was appropriately named "Earthquake Park." Downtown Anchorage was also disrupted as sections of the main business district dropped by as much as 3 meters (10 feet).

Fire

More than 100 years ago, San Francisco was the economic center of the western United States, largely because of gold and silver mining. Then, at dawn on April 18, 1906, a violent earthquake struck unexpectedly, triggering an enormous firestorm. Much of the city was reduced to ashes and ruins. It is estimated that 3000 people died and 225,000 of the city's 400,000 residents were left homeless.

That historic earthquake reminds us of the formidable threat of fire. The central city contained mostly large, older wooden structures and brick buildings. Although many of the unreinforced brick buildings were extensively damaged by vibrations, the greatest destruction was caused by fires, which started when gas and electrical lines were severed. The fires raged out of control for three days and devastated over 500 blocks of the city. The initial

FIGURE 6.21 Turnagain Heights slide caused by the 1964 Alaskan earthquake. **A.** Vibrations from the earthquake caused cracks to appear near the edge of the bluff. **B.** Within seconds, blocks of land began to slide toward the sea on a weak layer of clay. In less than 5 minutes, as much as 200 meters (650 feet) of the Turnagain Heights bluff area had been destroyed. **C.** Photo of a small portion of the Turnagain Heights slide. (Photo courtesy of U.S. Geological Survey)

ground shaking, which broke the city's water lines into hundreds of disconnected pieces, made controlling the fires virtually impossible.

The fires were finally contained when buildings were dynamited along a wide boulevard to provide a fire break, similar to the strategy used in fighting forest fires. Only a few deaths were attributed to the San Francisco fires, but other earthquake-initiated fires have been more destructive and claimed many more lives. For example, a 1923 earthquake in Japan triggered an estimated 250 fires, which devastated the city of Yokohama and destroyed more than half the homes in Tokyo. More than 100,000 deaths were attributed to the fires, which were driven by unusually high winds.

What Is a Tsunami?

Large undersea earthquakes occasionally set in motion massive waves that scientists call seismic sea waves. You may be more familiar with the Japanese term **tsunami**, which is frequently used to describe these destructive phenomena. Because of Japan's location along the circum-Pacific belt and its expansive coastline, it is especially vulnerable to tsunami destruction.

Most tsunami are caused by the displacement of a slab of seafloor, or a large submarine landslide triggered by an earthquake (**FIGURE 6.22**). Once generated, a tsunami resembles the ripples formed when a pebble is dropped into a pond. In contrast to ripples, tsunami advance across the ocean at amazing speeds, between 500 and 950 kilometers per hour. Despite this striking characteristic, a tsunami in the open ocean can pass undetected because its height (amplitude) is usually less than 1 meter and the distance between wave crests is great, ranging from 100 to 700 kilometers. However, upon entering shallow coastal waters, these destructive waves "feel bottom" and slow,

FIGURE 6.22 Schematic drawing of a tsunami generated by displacement of the ocean floor. The speed of a wave column correlates with ocean depth. As shown, waves moving in deep water advance at speeds in excess of 800 kilometers per hour. Speed gradually slows to 50 kilometers per hour at depths of 20 meters. Decreasing depth slows the movement of the wave column. As waves slow in shallow water, they grow in height until they topple and rush onto shore with tremendous force. The size and spacing of these swells are not to scale.

causing the water to pile up (Figure 6.22). A few exceptional tsunami have reached 30 meters (100 feet) in height. As the crest of a tsunami approaches the shore, it appears as a rapid rise in sea level with a turbulent and chaotic surface (**FIGURE 6.23A**).

The first warning of an approaching tsunami is a rapid withdrawal of water from beaches. Some inhabitants of the Pacific basin have learned to heed this warning and move to higher ground. Approximately 5 to 30 minutes after the retreat of water, a surge capable of extending hundreds of meters inland occurs. In a successive fashion, each surge is followed by a rapid oceanward retreat of the sea.

Tsunami Damage from the 2004 Indonesian Earthquake

A massive undersea earthquake of moment magnitude 9.1 occurred near the island of Sumatra on December 26, 2004, and sent waves of water racing across the Indian Ocean and Bay of Bengal. It was one of the deadliest natural disasters of any kind in modern times, claiming more than 230,000 lives. As water surged several kilometers inland, cars and trucks were flung around like toys in a bathtub, and fishing boats were rammed into homes. In some locations, the backwash of water dragged bodies and huge amounts of debris out to sea.

The destruction was indiscriminate, destroying luxury resorts and poor fishing hamlets on the Indian Ocean coast (**FIGURE 6.23B**). Damages were reported as far away as the Somalia coast of Africa, 4100 kilometers (2500 miles) west of the earthquake epicenter.

The killer waves generated by this massive quake achieved heights as great as 10 meters (33 feet) and struck many unprepared areas during a three-hour span following the earthquake. Although the Pacific basin had a tsunami warning system in place, the Indian Ocean unfortunately did not. The rarity of tsunami in the Indian Ocean also contributed to a lack of preparedness. It should come as no surprise that a tsunami warning system for the Indian Ocean was subsequently established.

Tsunami Warning System

In 1946, a large tsunami struck the Hawaiian Islands without warning. A wave more than 15 meters (50 feet) high left several coastal villages in shambles. This destruction motivated the U.S. Coast and Geodetic Survey to establish a tsunami warning system for coastal areas of the Pacific. Seismic observatories throughout the region report large earthquakes to the Tsunami Warning Center in Honolulu. Scientists at the Center use deep-sea buoys equipped with pressure sensors to detect energy released by an earthquake. In addition, tidal gauges measure the rise and fall in sea level that accompany tsunami, resulting in warnings issued within the hour. Although tsunami travel very rapidly, there is sufficient time to evacuate all but the areas nearest

A.

B.

FIGURE 6.23 A massive earthquake of moment magnitude 9.1 off the Indonesian island of Sumatra sent a tsunami racing across the Indian Ocean and Bay of Bengal on December 26, 2004. **A.** Unsuspecting foreign tourists, who at first walked on the sand after the water receded, now rush toward shore as the first of six tsunami start to roll toward Hat Rai Lay Beach near Krabi in southern Thailand. (AFP/Getty Images, Inc.) **B.** Tsunami survivors walk among the debris from this earthquake-triggered event. (Photo by Kimmasa Mayama/Reuters/CORBIS) the epicenter. For example, a tsunami generated near the Aleutian Islands would take five hours to reach Hawaii, and one generated near the coast of Chile would travel 15 hours before reaching Hawaii (**FIGURE 6.24**).

FIGURE 6.24 Tsunami travel times to Honolulu, Hawaii, from selected locations throughout the Pacific. (Data from NOAA)

DID YOU KNOW?

During an earthquake near Port Royal, Jamaica, the water-saturated sand on which the city was built vigorously shook. As a result, the sand particles lost contact with one another, giving the mixture the consistency of a thick milk shake. Anything supported by the ground, such as buildings and people, either floated or sank. One eyewitness stated: "[W]hole streets with inhabitants were swallowed up. . . . Some were swallowed quite down, and cast up again by great quantities of water; others went down and were never more seen."

PROBING EARTH'S INTERIOR: "SEEING" SEISMIC WAVES

Forces Within
▼ Earth's Interior

Discovering the structure and properties of Earth's deep interior has not been easy. Light does not travel through rock, so we must find other ways to "see" into our planet. The best way to learn about Earth's interior is to dig or drill a hole and examine it directly. Unfortunately, this is only possible at shallow depths. The deepest a drilling rig has ever penetrated is only 12.3 kilometers (8 miles), which is about

DID YOU KNOW?

The tsunami generated in the 1964 Alaskan earthquake heavily damaged communities along the Gulf of Alaska and killed 107 people. By contrast, only nine people died in Anchorage as a direct result of the vibrations. Furthermore, despite a one-hour warning, 12 persons perished in Crescent City, California, from the fifth and most destructive tsunami wave generated by this quake.

1/500 of the way to Earth's center! Even this was an extraordinary accomplishment because temperature and pressure increase so rapidly with depth.

Fortunately, many earthquakes are large enough that their seismic waves travel all the way through Earth and can be recorded on the other side (**FIGURE 6.25**). This means that the seismic waves act like medical x-rays used to take images of a person's insides. There are about 100 to 200 earthquakes each year that are large enough (about $M_w > 6$) to be well recorded by seismographs all around the globe. These large earthquakes provide the means to "see" into our planet and have been the source of most of the data that allowed us to figure out the nature of Earth's interior.

Interpreting the waves recorded on seismograms in order to identify Earth structure is complicated by the fact that seismic waves usually do not travel along straight paths. Instead, seismic waves are *reflected, refracted,* and *diffracted* as they pass through our planet. They reflect off boundaries between different layers, they refract (or bend) when passing from one layer to another layer, and they diffract around any obstacles they encounter (Figure 6.25).

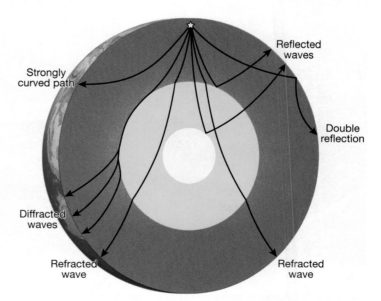

FIGURE 6.25 Slice through Earth's interior showing some of the ray paths that seismic waves from an earthquake would take. Notice that in the mantle, the rays follow curved (refracting) paths rather than straight paths because the seismic velocity of rocks increases with depth, a result of increasing pressure with depth.

These different wave behaviors have been used to identify the boundaries that exist within Earth.

One of the most noticeable behaviors of seismic waves is that they follow strongly curved paths (Figure 6.25). This occurs because the velocity of seismic waves generally increases with depth. In addition, seismic waves travel faster when rock is stiffer or less compressible. These properties of stiffness and compressibility are then used to interpret the composition and temperature of the rock. For instance, when rock is hotter, it becomes less stiff (imagine taking a frozen chocolate bar and then heating it up!), and waves travel more slowly. Waves also travel at different speeds through rocks of different compositions. Thus, the speed that seismic waves travel can help determine both the kind of rock that is inside Earth and how hot it is.

Formation of Earth's Layered Structure

As material accumulated to form Earth (and for a short period afterward), the high-velocity impact of nebular debris and the decay of radioactive elements caused the temperature of our planet to steadily increase. During this time of intense heating, Earth became hot enough that iron and nickel began to melt. Melting produced liquid blobs of heavy metal that sank toward the center of the planet. This process occurred rapidly on the scale of geologic time and produced Earth's dense iron-rich core.

The early period of heating resulted in another process of chemical differentiation, whereby melting formed buoyant masses of molten rock that rose toward the surface, where they solidified to produce a primitive crust. These rocky materials were rich in oxygen and "oxygen-seeking" elements, particularly silicon and aluminum, along with lesser amounts of calcium, sodium, potassium, iron, and magnesium. In addition, some heavy metals such as gold, lead, and uranium, which have low melting points or were highly soluble in the ascending molten masses, were scavenged from Earth's interior and concentrated in the developing crust. This early period of chemical segregation established the three basic divisions of Earth's interior—the iron-rich *core;* the thin *primitive crust;* and Earth's largest layer, called the *mantle,* which is located between the core and crust (**FIGURE 6.26**).

Earth's Internal Structure

In addition to these three compositionally distinct layers, Earth can be divided into layers based on physical properties. The physical properties used to define such zones include whether the layer is solid or liquid and how weak or strong it is. Knowledge of both types of layers is essential to our understanding of basic geologic processes, such as volcanism, earthquakes, and mountain building (Figure 6.26).

Earth's Crust

The **crust**, Earth's relatively thin, rocky outer skin, is of two types—continental crust and oceanic crust. Both share the word *crust,* but the similarity ends there. The oceanic crust is roughly 7 kilometers (4 miles) thick and composed of the dark igneous rock *basalt.* By contrast, the continental crust averages 35 to 40 kilometers (22 to 25 miles) thick but may exceed 70 kilometers (40 miles) in some mountainous regions such as the Rockies and Himalayas. Unlike the oceanic crust, which has a relatively homogeneous chemical composition, the continental crust consists of many rock types. Although the upper crust has an average composition of a *granitic rock* called *granodiorite,* it varies considerably from place to place.

Continental rocks have an average density of about 2.7 grams per cubic centimeter, and some are 4 billion years old. The rocks of the oceanic crust are younger (180 million years or less) and denser (about 3.0 grams per cubic centimeter) than continental rocks.*

Earth's Mantle

More than 82 percent of Earth's volume is contained in the **mantle**, a solid, rocky shell that extends to a depth of about 2900 kilometers (1800 miles). The boundary between the crust and mantle represents a marked change in chemical composition. The dominant rock type in the uppermost mantle is *peridotite,* which is richer in the metals magnesium and iron than the minerals found in either the continental or oceanic crust.

The upper mantle extends from the crust-mantle boundary down to a depth of about 660 kilometers (410 miles). The upper mantle can be divided into two different parts. The top portion of the upper mantle is part of the stiff *lithosphere,* and beneath that is the weaker *asthenosphere.* The **lithosphere** (sphere of rock) consists of the entire crust and uppermost mantle and forms Earth's relatively cool, rigid outer shell. Averaging about 100 kilometers (62 miles) in thickness, the lithosphere is more than 250 kilometers (155 miles) thick below the oldest portions of the continents (Figure 6.26). Beneath this stiff layer to a depth of about 350 kilometers (217 miles) lies a soft, comparatively weak layer known as the **asthenosphere** ("weak sphere"). The top portion of the asthenosphere has a temperature/pressure regime that results in a small amount of melting. Within this very weak zone, the lithosphere is mechanically detached from the layer below. The result is that the lithosphere is

---

*Liquid water has a density of 1 gram per cubic centimeter; therefore, the density of basalt is three times that of water.

FIGURE 6.26   Views of Earth's layered structure. The study of seismic waves and other geophysical techniques have shown Earth to be a dynamic planet with many interacting parts. The properties of Earth's layers include the physical state of the material (solid, liquid, or gas) as well as how stiff the material is (for example, the distinction between the lithosphere and asthenosphere). These studies have shown that Earth's layers are mainly determined by density, with the heaviest materials (iron) at the center and the lightest ones on the outside (gases and liquids).

able to move independently of the asthenosphere, a fact we will consider in the next chapter.

It is important to emphasize that the strength of various Earth materials is a function of both their composition and the temperature and pressure of their environment. The entire lithosphere does *not* behave like a brittle solid similar to rocks found on the surface. Rather, the rocks of the lithosphere get progressively hotter and weaker (more easily deformed) with increasing depth. At the depth of the uppermost asthenosphere, the rocks are close enough to their melting temperature that they are very easily deformed, and some melting may actually occur. Thus, the uppermost asthenosphere is weak because it is near its melting point, just as hot wax is weaker than cold wax.

From 660 kilometers (410 miles) deep to the top of the core, at a depth of 2900 kilometers (1800 miles), is the **lower mantle**. Because of an increase in pressure (caused by the weight of the rock above), the mantle gradually strengthens with depth. Despite their strength, however, the rocks within the lower mantle are very hot and capable of very gradual flow.

Earth's Core

The composition of the **core** is thought to be an iron-nickel alloy with minor amounts of oxygen, silicon, and sulfur—elements that readily form compounds with iron. At the extreme pressure found in the core, this iron-rich material has an average density of nearly 11 grams per cubic centimeter and approaches 14 times the density of water at Earth's center.

The core is divided into two regions that exhibit very different mechanical strengths. The **outer core** is a *liquid layer* 2270 kilometers (1410 miles) thick. It is the movement of metallic iron within this zone that generates Earth's magnetic field. The **inner core** is a sphere with a radius of 1216 kilometers (754 miles). Despite its higher temperature, the iron in the inner core is *solid* due to the immense pressures that exist in the center of the planet.

GEOLOGIC STRUCTURES

Forces Within
▼ Mountain Building

Earth is a dynamic planet. Shifting lithospheric plates continually change the face of our planet by moving continents across the globe. The results of this tectonic activity are perhaps most strikingly apparent in Earth's major mountain belts. Rock containing fossils of marine organisms are found thousands of meters above sea level and massive rock units are bent, contorted, overturned, and sometimes rife with fractures.

Before examining mountain building, we must first look at the nature of rock deformation and the structures that result.

Rock Deformation

Every body of rock, no matter how strong, has a point at which it will fracture or flow. **Deformation** (*de* = out, *forma* = form) is a general term that refers to all changes in the shape, position, or orientation of a rock mass. Significant crustal deformation occurs along plate margins. Plate motions and the interactions along plate boundaries generate the tectonic forces that cause rock to deform.

When rocks are subjected to forces (stresses) greater than their own strength, they begin to deform, usually by folding, flowing, or fracturing (**FIGURE 6.27**). It is easy to visualize how rocks break, because we normally think of them as being brittle. But how can rock masses be bent into intricate folds without being broken during the process? To answer this question, geologists performed laboratory experiments in which rocks were subjected to forces under conditions that simulated those existing at various depths within the crust.

Although each rock type deforms somewhat differently, the general characteristics of rock deformation were determined from these experiments. Geologists discovered that when stress is gradually applied, rocks first respond by deforming elastically. Changes that result from *elastic deformation* are recoverable; that is, like a rubber band, the rock will return to nearly its original size and shape when the force is removed. During elastic deformation the chemical bonds of the minerals within a rock are stretched, but do not break. Once the elastic limit (strength) of a rock is surpassed, it either flows (*ductile deformation*) or fractures (*brittle deformation*).

The factors that influence the strength of a rock and how it will deform include temperature, confining pressure, rock type, and time. Rocks near the surface, where temperatures and confining pressures are low, tend to behave like a brittle solid and fracture once their strength is exceeded. This type of deformation is called **brittle failure** or **brittle deformation**. From our everyday experience, we know that glass objects, wooden pencils, china plates, and even our bones exhibit brittle failure once their strength is surpassed. By contrast, at depth, where temperatures and confining pressures are high, rocks exhibit *ductile* behavior. **Ductile deformation**

FIGURE 6.27 Folded sedimentary layers exposed on the face of Mount Kidd, Alberta, Canada. (Photo by Tom Neversely/Photolibrary)

is a type of solid-state flow that produces a change in the size and shape of an object without fracturing. Ordinary objects that display ductile behavior include modeling clay, bee's wax, caramel candy, and most metals. For example, a copper penny placed on a railroad track will be flattened and deformed (without breaking) by the force applied by a passing train. Ductile deformation of a rock—strongly aided by high temperature and high confining pressure—is somewhat similar to the deformation of a penny flattened by a train. In rocks, ductile deformation is the result of some chemical bonds breaking, while others are forming, allowing minerals to change shape. Rocks that display evidence of ductile flow were usually deformed at great depth and may exhibit contorted folds that give the impression that the strength of the rock was akin to soft putty (**FIGURE 6.28**).

FIGURE 6.28 Rocks exhibiting ductile deformation. These rocks were deformed at great depth and were subsequently exposed at the surface. Vishnu Schist, Grand Canyon National Park, Arizona. (Photo by Michael Collier)

Folds

Along convergent plate boundaries, flat-lying sedimentary and volcanic rocks are often bent into a series of wavelike undulations called **folds**. Folds in sedimentary strata are much like those that would form if you were to hold the ends of a sheet of paper and then push them together. In nature, folds come in a wide variety of sizes and configurations. Some folds are broad flexures in which rock units hundreds of meters thick have been slightly warped. Others are very tight microscopic structures found in metamorphic rocks. Size differences notwithstanding, most folds are the result of *compressional forces that result in the shortening and thickening of the crust*.

Anticlines and Synclines

The two most common types of folds are anticlines and synclines (**FIGURE 6.29**). **Anticlines** usually arise by upfolding, or arching, of sedimentary layers and are sometimes spectacularly displayed along highways that have been cut through deformed strata. Almost always found in association with anticlines are downfolds, or troughs, called **synclines** (Figure 6.29).* Notice in Figure 6.29 that the limb of an anticline is also a limb of the adjacent syncline.

Depending on their orientation, these basic folds are described as *symmetrical* when the limbs are mirror images of each other and *asymmetrical* when they are not. An asymmetrical fold is said to be *overturned* if one, or both, limbs are tilted beyond the vertical (Figure 6.29). An overturned fold can also "lie on its side" so a plane extending through the axis of the fold would be horizontal. These *recumbent* folds are common in highly deformed mountainous regions such as the Alps.

*By strict definition, an anticline is a structure in which the oldest strata are found in the center. This most typically occurs when strata are upfolded. Further, a syncline is strictly defined as a structure in which the youngest strata are found in the center. This occurs most commonly when strata are downfolded.

Domes and Basins

Broad upwarps in basement rock may deform the overlying cover of sedimentary strata and generate large folds. When this upwarping produces a circular or elongated structure, the feature is called a **dome**. Downwarped structures having a similar shape are termed **basins**.

The Black Hills of western South Dakota is a large domed structure thought to be generated by upwarping. Erosion has stripped away the highest portions of the upwarped sedimentary beds, exposing older igneous and metamorphic rocks in the center (**FIGURE 6.30**). Remnants of these once continuous sedimentary layers are visible, flanking the crystalline core of these mountains.

Several large basins exist in the United States. The basins of Michigan and Illinois have very gently sloping beds similar to saucers. These basins are thought to be the result of large accumulations of sediment, whose weight caused the crust to subside.

Because large basins usually contain sedimentary beds sloping at very low angles, they are usually identified by the age of the rocks comprising them. The youngest rocks are found near the center, and the oldest rocks are at the flanks. This is just the opposite order of a domed structure, such as the Black Hills, where the oldest rocks form the core.

Faults

Faults are fractures in the crust along which appreciable displacement has taken place. Occasionally, small faults can be recognized in road cuts where sedimentary beds have been offset a few meters, as shown in **FIGURE 6.31**. Faults of this scale usually occur as single discrete breaks. By contrast, large faults, such as the San Andreas Fault in California, have displacements of hundreds of kilometers and consist of many interconnecting fault surfaces. These *fault zones* can be several kilometers wide and are often easier to identify from high-altitude photographs than at ground level.

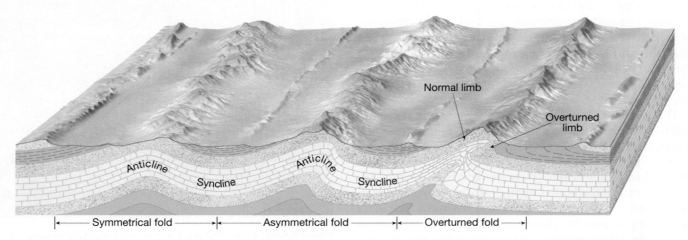

FIGURE 6.29   Block diagram of principal types of folded strata. The upfolded or arched structures are anticlines. The downfolds, or troughs, are synclines. Notice that the limb of an anticline is also the limb of the adjacent syncline.

FIGURE 6.30 The Black Hills of South Dakota, an example of a domal structure in which the resistant igneous and metamorphic central core has been exposed by erosion. Map view (above), and cross-sectional view from point X to point Y (below).

FIGURE 6.31 Faulting caused the displacement of these beds. Arrows show relative motion of rock units. (Photo by Fletcher & Baylis/Photo Researchers)

Dip-Slip Faults

Faults in which movement is primarily parallel to the *dip* (or inclination) of the fault surface are called **dip-slip faults**. It has become common practice to call the rock surface that is immediately above the fault the **hanging wall block** and to call the rock surface below, the **footwall block** (Figure 6.31).

This nomenclature arose from prospectors and miners who excavated shafts and tunnels along fault zones that were sites of ore deposits. In these tunnels, the miners would walk on the rocks below the mineralized fault zone (the footwall block) and hang their lanterns on the rocks above (the hanging wall block).

Vertical displacements along dip-slip faults may produce long, low cliffs called **fault scarps** (*scrape* = a slope). Fault scarps, such as the one shown in **FIGURE 6.32**, are produced by displacements that generate earthquakes.

Dip-slip faults are classified as **normal faults** when the hanging wall block moves down relative to the footwall block (**FIGURE 6.33**). Because of the downward motion of the hanging wall block, normal faults accommodate lengthening, or extension, of the crust.

Normal faults are found in a variety of sizes, some are small, having displacements of only a meter or so, like the one shown in the road cut in Figure 6.31. Others extend for tens of kilometers where they may sinuously trace the boundary of a mountain front. Most large, normal faults have relatively steep dips that tend to flatten out with depth.

In the western United States, large normal faults are associated with structures called **fault-block mountains**. Excellent examples of fault-block mountains are found in the Basin and Range Province, a region that encompasses Nevada and portions of the surrounding states (**FIGURE 6.34**). Here the crust has been elongated and broken to create more than 200 relatively small mountain ranges. Averaging about 80 kilometers in length, the ranges rise 900 to 1500 meters above the adjacent down-faulted basins.

The topography of the Basin and Range Province evolved in association with a system of roughly north-south trending normal faults. Movements along these faults produced alternating uplifted fault blocks called **horsts** and down-dropped blocks called **grabens** (*graben* = ditch). Horsts generate elevated topography, whereas grabens form basins. As Figure 6.34 illustrates, structures called *half-grabens*, which are titled fault blocks, also contribute to the alternating topographic highs and lows in the Basin and Range Province. The horsts and higher ends of the tilted fault blocks are the source of sediments that have accumulated in the basins created by the grabens and lower ends of the tilted blocks.

FIGURE 6.32   This *fault scarp* formed north of Landers, California, during an earthquake in 1992. It is the largest of several scarps that formed during this event. The scarp was created when land on one side of the fault dropped relative to the land on the opposite side. (Photo by Roger Ressmeyer/CORBIS)

that pull the crust apart. This "pulling apart" can be accomplished either by uplifting that causes the surface to stretch and break or by opposing horizontal forces.

Reverse and **thrust faults** are dip-slip faults in which the hanging wall block moves up relative to the footwall block (Figure 6.33B, C). Thrust faults are reverse faults having dips less than 45°, so the overlying block moves nearly horizontally over the underlying block.

Whereas normal faults occur in tensional environments, reverse faults result from strong compressional stresses. Because the hanging wall block moves up and over the footwall block, reverse and thrust faults accommodate horizontal shortening of the crust.

Most high-angle reverse faults are small and accommodate local displacements in regions dominated by other types of faulting. Thrust faults, on the other hand, exist at all scales with some large thrust faults having displacements on the order of tens to hundreds of kilometers.

In mountainous regions such as the Alps, Northern Rockies, Himalayas, and Appalachians, thrust faults have displaced strata as far as 100 kilometers (60 miles) over adjacent rock units. The result of this large-scale movement is that older strata end up overlying younger rocks.

Thrust faulting is most pronounced in subduction zones and other convergent boundaries where plates are colliding. Compressional forces generally produce folds as well as faults and result in a thickening and shortening of the material involved.

Strike-Slip Faults

Faults in which the dominant displacement is horizontal and parallel to the *trend* or *strike* of the fault surface is called a **strike-slip fault** (Figure 6.33D). The earliest scientific records of strike-slip faulting were made following surface ruptures that produced large earthquakes. One of the most noteworthy of these was the great San Francisco earthquake of 1906. During this strong earthquake, structures such as fences that were built across the San Andreas Fault were displaced as much as 4.7 meters (15 feet). Because movement along the San Andreas causes the crustal block on the opposite side of the fault to move to the right as you face the fault, it is called a *right-lateral* strike-slip fault.

The Great Glen Fault in Scotland is a well-known example of a *left-lateral* strike-slip fault, which exhibits the opposite sense of displacement. The total displacement along the Great Glen Fault is estimated to exceed 100 kilometers (60 miles). Also associated with this fault trace are numerous lakes, including Loch Ness, the home of the legendary monster.

DID YOU KNOW?

People have actually observed the creation of a fault scarp—and have lived to tell about it. In Idaho, a large earthquake in 1983 created a 3-meter (10-foot) fault scarp that was witnessed by several people, many of whom were knocked off their feet. More often, though, fault scarps are noticed only after they form.

Notice in Figure 6.34 that the slopes of the normal faults decrease with depth and eventually join to form a nearly horizontal fault called a *detachment fault*. These faults form a major boundary between the rocks below, which exhibit ductile deformation, and the rocks above, which exhibit brittle deformation.

Fault motion provides geologists with a method of determining the nature of the tectonic forces at work within Earth. Normal faults are associated with tensional forces

FIGURE 6.33 Block diagrams of four types of faults. **A.** Normal fault. **B.** Reverse fault. **C.** Thrust fault. **D.** Strike-slip fault.

A. Normal fault

Footwall block

Hanging wall block

B. Reverse fault

Hanging wall block

Footwall block

C. Thrust fault

Hanging wall block

Footwall block

D. Strike-slip fault

FIGURE 6.34 Normal faulting in the Basin and Range Province. Here, tensional stresses have elongated and fractured the crust into numerous blocks. Movement along these fractures has tilted the blocks, producing parallel mountain ranges called *fault-block mountains*. The downfaulted blocks (grabens) form basins, whereas the upfaulted blocks (horsts) are eroded to form rugged mountainous topography. In addition, numerous tilted blocks (half-grabens) form both basins and mountains. (Photo by Michael Collier)

Extension

Half graben

Horst

Graben

Horst

Detachment fault

Rather than a single fracture along which movement takes place, large strike-slip faults consist of a zone of roughly parallel fractures. The zone may be up to several kilometers wide. The most recent movement, however, is often along a strand only a few meters wide, which may offset features such as stream channels (see Figure 5.19, p. 158). Crushed and broken rocks produced during faulting are more easily eroded, so linear valleys or sag ponds often mark the locations of strike-slip faults. Because of their large size and linear nature, many strike-slip faults produce a trace that is visible over a great distance.

Some strike-slip faults cut through the lithosphere and accommodate motion between two large tectonic plates. Recall this special kind of strike-slip fault is called a **transform fault**. Numerous transform faults cut the oceanic lithosphere and link spreading oceanic ridges. Others accommodate displacement between continental plates that move horizontally with respect to each other. One of the best-known transform faults is California's San Andreas Fault. This plate-bounding fault can be traced for about 950 kilometers (600 miles) from the Gulf of California to a point along the Pacific Coast north of San Francisco, where it heads out to sea. Since its formation about 30 million years ago, displacement along the San Andreas Fault has exceeded 560 kilometers. This movement has accommodated the northward displacement of southwestern California and the Baja Peninsula of Mexico in relation to the remainder of North America.

MOUNTAIN BUILDING

GEODe
EARTH
SCIENCE

Forces Within
▼ Mountain Building

Mountain building has occurred in the recent geologic past in several locations around the world (**FIGURE 6.35**). One example is the American Cordillera, which runs along the western margin of the Americas from Cape Horn at the tip of South America to Alaska and includes the Andes and Rocky Mountains. Other examples include the Alpine–Himalaya chain, which extends along the margin of the Mediterranean, through Iran to northern India, and into Indochina; and the mountainous terrains of the western Pacific, which include volcanic island arcs that comprise Japan, the Philippines, and Sumatra. Most of these young mountain belts have come into existence within the last 100 million years. Some, including the Himalayas, began their growth as recently as 50 million years ago.

In addition to these young mountain belts, there are several chains of Paleozoic-age mountains found on Earth. Although these older structures are deeply eroded and topographically less prominent, they exhibit the same structural features found in younger mountains. The Appalachians in the eastern United States and the Urals in Russia are classic examples of this group of older and well-worn mountain belts.

The term for the processes that collectively produce a mountain belt is **orogenesis** (*oros* = mountain, *genesis* = to come into being). Most major mountain belts display striking visual evidence of great horizontal forces that have shortened and thickened the crust. These *compressional mountains* contain large quantities of preexisting sedimentary and crystalline rocks that have been faulted and

FIGURE 6.35   This peak is part of the Karakoram Range in the Pakistan-China border region. The Karakoram are part of the Himalayan system. (Photo by RonaldNear/age fotostock)

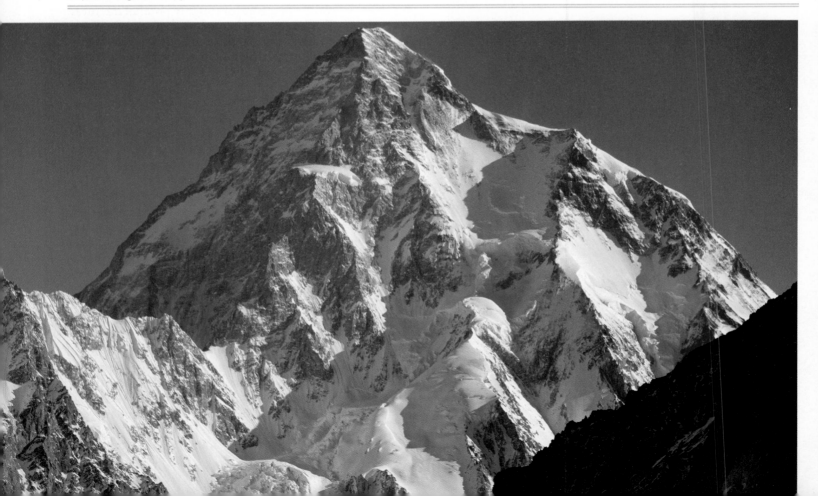

contorted into a series of folds. Although folding and thrust faulting are often the most conspicuous signs of orogenesis, varying degrees of metamorphism and igneous activity are always present.

How do mountain belts form? As early as the ancient Greeks, this question has intrigued some of the greatest philosophers and scientists. One early proposal suggested that mountains are simply wrinkles in Earth's crust, produced as the planet cooled from its original semimolten state. According to this idea, Earth contracted and shrank as it lost heat, which caused the crust to deform in a manner similar to how an orange peel wrinkles as the fruit dries out. However, neither this nor any other early hypothesis withstood scientific scrutiny.

With the development of the theory of plate tectonics, a model for orogenesis with excellent explanatory power has emerged. Its premise asserts the tectonic processes that generate Earth's major mountainous terrains begin at convergent plate boundaries, where oceanic lithosphere descends into the mantle.

Convergence and Subducting Plates

In their quest to unravel the events that produce mountains, researchers examine ancient mountain structures as well as sites where orogenesis is currently active. Of particular interest are convergent plate boundaries, where lithospheric plates subduct. The subduction of oceanic lithosphere generates Earth's strongest earthquakes and most explosive volcanic eruptions, as well as playing a pivotal role in generating many of Earth's mountain belts.

The subduction of oceanic lithosphere gives rise to two different types of tectonic structures. Where oceanic lithosphere subducts beneath an oceanic plate, a volcanic island arc and related tectonic features develop. Subduction beneath a continental block, on the other hand, results in the formation of a volcanic arc along the margin of a continent. Plate boundaries that generate continental volcanic arcs are referred to as Andean-type plate margins.

FIGURE 6.36 The development of a volcanic island arc by the convergence of two oceanic plates. Continuous subduction along these convergent zones results in the development of thick units of continental-type crust.

Volcanic Island Arcs

Island arcs result from the steady subduction of oceanic lithosphere, which may last for 200 million years or more (**FIGURE 6.36**). Periodic volcanic activity, the emplacement of igneous plutons at depth, and the accumulation of sediment that is scraped from the subducting plate gradually increase the volume of crustal material capping the upper plate. Some large volcanic island arcs, such as Japan, owe their size to having been built upon a preexisting fragment of continental crust.

The continued growth of a volcanic island arc can result in the formation of mountainous topography consisting of belts of igneous and metamorphic rocks. This activity, however, is viewed as just one phase in the development of a major mountain belt. As you will see later, some volcanic arcs are carried by a subducting plate to the margin of a large continental block, where they become involved in a large-scale mountain-building episode.

Mountain Building Along Andean-Type Margins

Mountain building along continental margins involves the convergence of an oceanic plate and a plate whose leading edge contains continental crust. Exemplified by the Andes Mountains, an *Andean-type convergent zone* results in the formation of a continental volcanic arc and related tectonic features inland of the continental margin.

The first stage in the development of an idealized Andean-type mountain belt occurs prior to the formation of the subduction zone. During this period, the continental margin is a **passive continental margin**; that is, it is not a plate boundary but a part of the same plate as the adjoining oceanic crust. The East Coast of North America provides a present-day example of a passive continental margin. Here, as at other passive continental margins surrounding the Atlantic, deposition of sediment on the continental shelf is producing a thick wedge of shallow-water sandstones, limestones, and shales (**FIGURE 6.37A**). Beyond the continental shelf, turbidity currents are depositing sediments on the continental slope and rise (see Chapter 9).

At some point, the continental margin becomes active. A subduction zone forms and the deformation process begins (**FIGURE 6.37B**). A good place to examine an **active continental margin** is the west coast of South America, where the Nazca plate is being subducted beneath the South American plate

FIGURE 6.37 Mountain building along an Andean-type subduction zone. **A.** Passive continental margin with an extensive platform of sediments. **B.** Plate convergence generates a subduction zone, and partial melting produces a volcanic arc. Continued convergence and igneous activity further deform and thicken the crust, elevating the mountain belt, while an accretionary wedge develops. **C.** Subduction ends and is followed by a period of uplift and erosion.

magma that intrudes the crust never reaches the surface—instead, it crystallizes at depth to form plutons. Eventually, uplifting and erosion exhume these igneous bodies and associated metamorphic rocks. Once they are exposed at the surface, these massive structures are called *batholiths* (**FIGURE 6.37C**). Composed of numerous plutons, batholiths form the core of the Sierra Nevada in California and are prevalent in the Peruvian Andes.

During the development of this continental volcanic arc, sediment derived from the land and scraped from the subducting plate is plastered against the landward side of the trench like piles of dirt in front of a bulldozer. This chaotic accumulation of sedimentary and metamorphic rocks with occasional scraps of ocean crust is called an **accretionary wedge** (Figure 6.37B). Prolonged subduction can build an accretionary wedge that is large enough to stand above sea level (Figure 6.37C).

Andean-type mountain belts are composed of two roughly parallel zones. The volcanic arc develops on the continental block. It consists of volcanoes and large intrusive bodies intermixed with high-temperature metamorphic rocks. The seaward segment is the accretionary wedge. It consists of folded and faulted sedimentary and metamorphic rocks (Figure 6.37C).

One of the best examples of an inactive Andean-type orogenic belt is found in the western United States. It includes the Sierra Nevada and the Coast Ranges in California. These parallel mountain belts were produced by the subduction of a portion of the Pacific Basin under the western edge of the North American plate. The Sierra Nevada batholith is a remnant of a portion of the continental volcanic arc that was produced by several surges of magma over tens of millions of years. Subsequent uplifting and erosion have removed most of the evidence of past volcanic activity and exposed a core of crystalline, igneous, and associated metamorphic rocks.

along the Peru-Chile trench. This subduction zone probably formed prior to the breakup of the supercontinent of Pangaea.

In an idealized Andean-type subduction, convergence of the continental block and the subducting oceanic plate leads to deformation and metamorphism of the continental margin. Once the oceanic plate descends to about 100 kilometers (62 miles), partial melting of mantle rock above the subducting slab generates magma that migrates upward (Figure 6.37B). Thick continental crust greatly impedes the ascent of magma. Consequently, a high percentage of the

In the trench region, sediments scraped from the subducting plate, plus those provided by the eroding continental volcanic arc, were intensely folded and faulted into an accretionary wedge. This chaotic mixture of rocks presently constitutes the Franciscan Formation of California's Coast Ranges. Uplifting of the Coast Ranges took place only recently, as evidenced by the young unconsolidated sediments that still mantle portions of these highlands.

In summary, *the growth of mountain belts at subduction zones is a response to crustal thickening caused by the addition of mantle-derived igneous rocks and sediments scrapped from the descending oceanic slab.*

Collisional Mountain Belts

Most major mountain belts are generated when one or more buoyant crustal fragments collide with a continental margin as a result of subduction. Oceanic lithosphere, which is relatively dense, readily subducts, whereas continental lithosphere, which contains significant amounts of low-density crustal rocks, is too buoyant to undergo subduction. Consequently, the arrival of a crustal fragment at a trench results in a collision with the margin of the overlying continental block and an end to subduction.

Terranes and Mountain Building

The process of collision and accretion (joining together) of comparatively small crustal fragments to a continental margin has generated many of the mountainous regions that rim the Pacific. Geologists refer to these accreted crustal blocks as terranes. **Terrane** refers to any crustal fragment that has a geologic history distinct from that of the adjoining terranes.

What is the nature of these crustal fragments, and where did they originate? Research suggests that prior to their accretion to a continental block, some of these fragments may have been microcontinents similar to the modern-day island of Madagascar, located east of Africa in the Indian Ocean. Many others were island arcs similar to Japan, the Philippines, and the Aleutian Islands. Still others may have been submerged oceanic plateaus created by massive outpourings of basaltic lavas associated with mantle plumes (see **FIGURE 6.38**). More than 100 of these comparatively small crustal fragments are presently known to exist.

As oceanic plates move, they carry embedded oceanic plateaus, volcanic island arcs, and microcontinents to an Andean-type subduction zone. When an oceanic plate contains small seamounts, these structures are generally subducted along with the descending oceanic slab. However, large thick units of oceanic crust, such as the Ontong Java Plateau, which is the size of Alaska, or an island arc composed of abundant "light" igneous rocks, render the oceanic lithosphere too buoyant to subduct. In these situations, a collision between the crustal fragment and the continental margin occurs.

The sequence of events that happen when an island arc reaches an Andean-type margin is shown in **FIGURE 6.39**. Rather than subduct, the upper crustal layers of these thickened zones are peeled from the descending plate and thrust in relatively thin sheets upon the adjacent continental block. Because subduction often continues for 100 million years or longer, several crustal fragments can be transported to the continental margin. Each collision displaces earlier accreted terranes further inland, adding to the zone of deformation as well as to the thickness and lateral extent of the continental margin.

The relationship between mountain building and the accretion of crustal fragments arose primarily from studies conducted in the North American Cordillera (**FIGURE 6.40**). Researchers determined that some of the rocks in the orogenic belts of Alaska and British Columbia contain fossil and paleomagnetic evidence that indicated these strata previously lay much closer to the equator.

It is now known that many of the terranes that make up the North American Cordillera were scattered throughout the eastern Pacific, like the island arcs and oceanic plateaus currently distributed in the western Pacific (see Figure 6.38). During the breakup of Pangaea, the eastern portion of the Pacific basin (Farallon plate) began to subduct under the western margin of North America. This activity resulted in the piecemeal addition of crustal

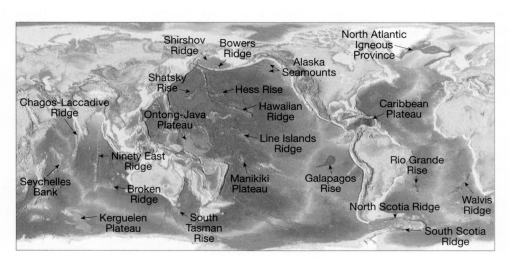

FIGURE 6.38 Distribution of present-day oceanic plateaus and other submerged crustal fragments. (Data from Ben-Avraham and others)

FIGURE 6.39 Sequence of events showing the collision and accretion of an island arc to a continental margin.

fragments to the entire Pacific margin of the continent—from Mexico's Baja Peninsula to northern Alaska (Figure 6.40). Geologists expect that many modern microcontinents will likewise be accreted to active continental margins, producing new orogenic belts.

Continental Collisions

The Himalayas, Appalachians, Urals, and Alps represent mountain belts that formed by the closure of major ocean basins. Continental collisions result in the development of mountains characterized by shortened and thickened crust achieved through folding and faulting. Some mountainous regions have crustal thicknesses that exceed 70 kilometers (40 miles).

The mountain-building episode that created the Himalayas began roughly 50 million years ago when India began to collide with Asia. Prior to the breakup of Pangaea, India was located between Africa and Antarctica in the Southern Hemisphere. As Pangaea fragmented, India moved rapidly, geologically speaking, a few thousand kilometers in a northward direction.

The subduction zone that facilitated India's northward migration was near the southern margin of Asia (**FIGURE 6.41A**). Continued subduction along Asia's margin created an Andean-type plate margin that contained a well-developed continental volcanic arc and an accretionary wedge. India's northern margin, on the other hand, was a passive continental margin consisting of a thick platform of shallow-water sediments and sedimentary rocks.

Geologists have determined that one, or perhaps more, small continental fragments were positioned on the subducting plate somewhere between India and Asia. During the closing of the intervening ocean basin, a small crustal fragment, which now forms southern Tibet, reached the trench. This event was followed by the docking of India itself. The tectonic forces involved in the collision of India

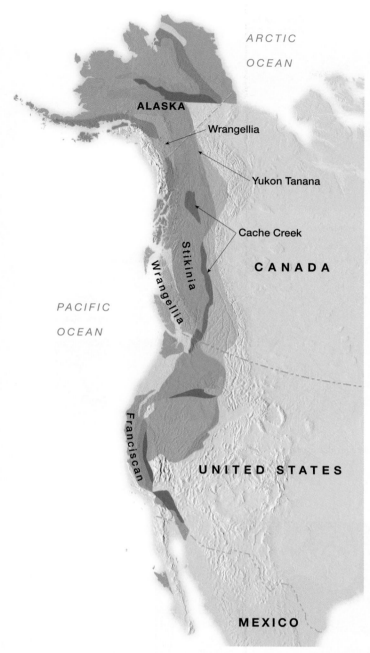

ARCTIC
OCEAN

ALASKA

Wrangellia

Yukon Tanana

Cache Creek

Stikinia

Wrangellia

CANADA

PACIFIC

OCEAN

Franciscan

UNITED STATES

MEXICO

FIGURE 6.40 Map showing terranes thought to have been added to western North America during the past 200 million years. (Redrawn after D. R. Hutchinson and others)

the deepest and most deformed region of the developing mountain belt produced magmas that intruded the overlying rocks. It is in these environments that the metamorphic and igneous cores of collisional mountains are generated.

The formation of the Himalayas was followed by a period of uplift that raised the Tibetan Plateau. Seismic evidence suggests that a portion of the Indian subcontinent was thrust beneath Tibet a distance of perhaps 400 kilometers. If so, the added crustal thickness would account for the lofty landscape of southern Tibet, which has an average elevation higher than Mount Whitney, the highest point in the contiguous United States.

The collision with Asia slowed but did not stop the northward migration of India, which has since penetrated at least 2000 kilometers (1200 miles) into the mainland of Asia. Crustal shortening accommodated some of this motion. Much of the remaining penetration into Asia caused lateral displacement of large blocks of the Asian crust by a mechanism described as *continental escape*. As shown in **FIGURE 6.42**, when India continued its northward trek, parts of Asia were "squeezed" eastward out of the collision zone. These displaced crustal blocks include much of present-day Indochina and sections of mainland China.

A similar but much older collision is believed to have taken place when the European continent collided with the Asian continent to produce the Ural Mountains, which extend in a north-south direction through Russia. Prior to the discovery of plate tectonics, geologists had difficulty explaining the existence of mountain ranges such as the Urals, which are located deep within continental interiors. How could thousands of meters of marine sediment be deposited and then become highly deformed while situated in the middle of a large stable landmass?

Other mountain ranges showing evidence of continental collisions are the Alps and the Appalachians. The Appalachians resulted from collisions among North America, Europe, and northern Africa. Although they have since separated, these landmasses were juxtaposed as part of the supercontinent of Pangaea less than 200 million years ago. Detailed studies in the southern Appalachians indicate that the formation of this mountain belt was more complex than once thought. Rather than forming during a single continental collision, the Appalachians resulted from several distinct episodes of mountain building occurring over a period of nearly 300 million years.

with Asia were immense and caused the more deformable materials located on the seaward edges of these landmasses to become highly folded and faulted (**FIGURE 6.41B**). The shortening and thickening of the crust elevated great quantities of crustal material, thereby generating the spectacular Himalayan mountains (see Figure 6.35).

In addition to uplift, crustal shortening caused rocks at the "bottom of the pile" to become deeply buried—an environment where they experienced elevated temperatures and pressures (Figure 6.41B). Partial melting within

DID YOU KNOW?

During the assembly of Pangaea, the landmasses of Europe and Siberia collided to produce the Ural Mountains. Long before the discovery of plate tectonics, this extensively eroded mountain chain was regarded as the boundary between Europe and Asia.

FIGURE 6.41 Illustration showing the collision of India with the Eurasian plate producing the spectacular Himalayas.

FIGURE 6.42 The collision between India and Asia that generated the Himalayas and Tibetan Plateau also severely deformed much of Southeast Asia. **A.** Map view of some of the major structural features of Southeast Asia thought to be related to this episode of mountain building. **B.** Recreation of the deformation of Asia, with a rigid block representing India pushed into a mass of deformable modeling clay.

THE CHAPTER IN REVIEW

- *Earthquakes* are vibrations produced by the rapid release of energy from rocks that rupture when subjected to stresses beyond their limit. The movements that produce earthquakes occur along large fractures, called *faults*, which are often associated with plate boundaries.

- Two main groups of *seismic waves* are generated during an earthquake: (1) *surface waves*, which travel along the outer layer of Earth; and (2) *body waves*, which travel through Earth's interior. Body waves are further divided into *primary waves* (P waves), which push (compress) and pull (expand) rocks in the direction the wave is traveling, and *secondary waves* (S waves), which "shake" the particles in rock at right angles to their direction of travel. The P waves can travel through solids, liquids, and gases; the S waves travel only through solids. In any solid material, P waves travel about 1.7 times faster than S waves.

- The location on Earth's surface directly above the focus of an earthquake is the *epicenter*. An epicenter is determined using the difference in velocities of P and S waves.

- *There is a close correlation between earthquake epicenters and plate boundaries.* The principal earthquake epicenter zones are along the margin of the Pacific Ocean, known as the *circum-Pacific belt,* and through the world's oceans along the *oceanic ridge system.*

- Seismologists use two fundamentally different measures to describe the size of an earthquake—intensity and magnitude. *Intensity* is a measure of the degree of ground shaking at a given locale based on the amount of damage. The *Modified Mercalli Intensity Scale* uses damages to buildings in California to estimate the intensity of ground shaking for a local earthquake. *Magnitude* is calculated from seismic records and estimates the amount of energy released at the source of an earthquake. Using the *Richter scale,* the magnitude of an earthquake is estimated by measuring the *amplitude* (maximum displacement) of the largest seismic wave recorded. A logarithmic scale is used to express magnitude, in which a tenfold increase in ground shaking corresponds to an increase of 1 on the magnitude scale. *Moment magnitude* is currently used to estimate the size of moderate and large earthquakes. It is calculated using the average displacement of the fault, the area of the fault surface, and the sheer strength of the faulted rock.

- The most obvious factors that determine the amount of destruction accompanying an earthquake are the *magnitude* of the earthquake and the *proximity* of the quake to a populated area. *Structural damage* attributable to earthquake vibrations depends on several factors, including (1) *intensity,* (2) *duration* of the vibrations, (3) *nature of the material* upon which the structure rests, and (4) the *design* of the structure. Secondary effects of earthquakes include *tsunamis, landslides, ground subsidence,* and *fire.*

- As indicated by the behavior of P and S waves as they travel through Earth, the four major zones of Earth's interior are (1) *crust* (the very thin outer layer, 5 to 40 kilometers); (2) *mantle* (a rocky layer located below the crust with a thickness of 2900 kilometers); (3) *outer core* (a layer about 2270 kilometers thick, which exhibits the characteristics of a mobile liquid); and (4) *inner core* (a solid metallic sphere with a radius of about 1216 kilometers).

- *Deformation* refers to changes in the shape and/or volume of a rock body. Rocks deform differently depending on the environment (temperature and confining pressure), the composition of the rock, and the length of time stress is maintained. Rocks first respond by deforming *elastically* and will return to their original shape when the stress is removed. Once their elastic limit (strength) is surpassed, rocks either deform by ductile flow or fracture. *Ductile deformation* is a solid-state flow that results in a change in size and shape of rocks without fracturing. Ductile deformation occurs in a high-temperature/high-pressure environment. In a near-surface environment, most rocks deform by *brittle failure.*

- Among the most basic geologic structures associated with rock deformation are *folds* (flat-lying sedimentary and volcanic rocks bent into a series of wavelike undulations). The two most common types of folds are *anticlines,* formed by the upfolding, or arching, of rock layers, and *synclines,* which are downfolds. Most folds are the result of horizontal *compressional stresses. Domes* (upwarped structures) and *basins* (downwarped structures) are circular or somewhat elongated folds formed by vertical displacements of strata.

- *Faults* are fractures in the crust along which appreciable displacement has occurred. Faults in which the movement is primarily vertical are called *dip-slip faults.* Dip-slip faults include both *normal* and *reverse faults.* Low-angle reverse faults are called *thrust faults.* Normal faults indicate *tensional stresses* that pull the crust apart. Along spreading centers, divergence can cause a central block called a *graben,* bounded by normal faults, to drop as the plates separate.

- Subduction of oceanic lithosphere under a continental block gives rise to an *Andean-type plate margin* that is characterized by a continental volcanic arc and associated igneous plutons. In addition, sediment derived from the land, as well as material scraped from the subducting plate, becomes plastered against the landward side of the trench, forming an *accretionary wedge.* An excellent example of an inactive Andean-type mountain belt is found in the western United States and includes the Sierra Nevada and the Coast Range in California.

- Mountain belts can develop as a result of the collision and merger of an island arc, oceanic plateau, or some other small crustal fragment to a continental block. Many of the mountain belts of the North American Cordillera were generated in this manner.

- Continued subduction of oceanic lithosphere beneath an Andean-type continental margin will eventually close an ocean basin. The result will be a *continental collision* and the development of compressional mountains that are characterized by shortened and thickened crust as exhibited by the Himalayas. The development of a major mountain belt is often complex, involving two or more distinct episodes of mountain building. Continental collisions have generated many mountain belts, including the Alps, Urals, and Appalachians.

KEY TERMS

accretionary wedge (p. 198)

active continental margin (p. 197)

aftershock (p. 174)

anticline (p. 192)

asthenosphere (p. 189)

basin (p. 192)

body wave (p. 176)

brittle failure or brittle deformation (p. 191)

core (p. 190)

crust (p. 189)

deformation (p. 191)

dip-slip fault (p. 193)

dome (p. 192)

ductile deformation (p. 191)

earthquake (p. 172)

elastic rebound (p. 173)

epicenter (p. 172)

fault (p. 172, 192)

fault-block mountains (p. 193)

fault scarp (p. 193)

focus (p. 172)

fold (p. 192)

footwall block (p. 193)

foreshock (p. 175)

graben (p. 193)

hanging wall block (p. 193)

horst (p. 193)

inner core (p. 190)

intensity (p. 179)

liquefaction (p. 184)

lithosphere (p. 189)

lower mantle (p. 190)

magnitude (p. 179)

mantle (p. 189)

Modified Mercalli Intensity Scale (p. 180)

moment magnitude (p. 182)

normal fault (p. 193)

orogenesis (p. 196)

outer core (p. 190)

passive continental margin (p. 197)

primary (P) wave (p. 176)

reverse fault (p. 194)

Richter scale (p. 180)

secondary (S) wave (p. 176)

seismic waves (p. 172)

seismogram (p. 176)

seismograph (p. 176)

seismology (p. 176)

strike-slip fault (p. 194)

surface wave (p. 176)

syncline (p. 192)

terrane (p. 199)

thrust fault (p. 194)

transform fault (p. 195)

tsunami (p. 186)

QUESTIONS FOR REVIEW

1. What is an earthquake? Under what circumstances do earthquakes occur?

2. How are faults, foci, and epicenters related?

3. Who was first to explain the actual mechanism by which earthquakes are generated?

4. Explain what is meant by elastic rebound.

5. Faults that are experiencing no active creep may be considered "safe." Rebut or defend this statement.

6. Describe the principle of a seismograph.

7. List the major differences between P and S waves.

8. Most strong earthquakes occur in a zone on the globe known as the_____.

9. An earthquake measuring 7 on the Richter scale releases about_____times more energy than an earthquake with a magnitude of 6.

10. In addition to the destruction created directly by seismic vibrations, list three other types of destruction associated with earthquakes.

11. What is a tsunami? How is one generated?

12. Contrast the physical makeup of the asthenosphere and the lithosphere.

13. What is rock deformation?

14. How is brittle deformation different from ductile deformation?

15. Distinguish between anticlines and synclines, domes and basins, anticlines and domes.

16. Contrast the movements that occur along normal and reverse faults. What type of force is indicated by each fault?

17. Refer to Figure 6.31 p. 193. Which side of the fault shown here is the *hanging wall block* and which side is the *footwall block*? Is this a normal fault or a reverse fault?

18. How are reverse faults different from thrust faults? In what way are they the same?

19. The San Andreas Fault is an excellent example of a_____ fault.

20. Refer to the two photos in Figure 6.4 p. 174. Identify each as either a *right-lateral* or a *left-lateral* strike slip fault.

21. In the plate tectonics model, which type of plate boundary is most directly associated with mountain building?

22. What is an accretionary wedge? Briefly describe its formation.

23. What is a passive continental margin? Give an example. Give an example of an active continental margin.

24. How does the plate tectonics theory help explain the existence of fossil marine life in rocks atop the Ural Mountains?

COMPANION WEBSITE

The Foundations of Earth Science Website uses the resources and flexibility of the Internet to aid in your study of the topics in this chapter. Written and developed by the authors and other Earth science instructors, this site will help improve your understanding of Earth science. Visit **www.mygeoscienceplace.com** in order to

- **Review** key chapter concepts.
- **Read** with links to the ebook and to chapter-specific web resources

- **Visualize** and comprehend challenging topics using learning activities in *GEODe: Earth Science*.
- **Test** yourself with online quizzes.

GEODe: EARTH SCIENCE

GEODe: Earth Science is a valuable and easy to use learning aid that can be accessed from your book's Companion Website: **www.mygeoscienceplace.com**. It is a dynamic instructional tool that promotes understanding and reinforces important concepts by using tutorials, animations, and exercises that actively engage the student.

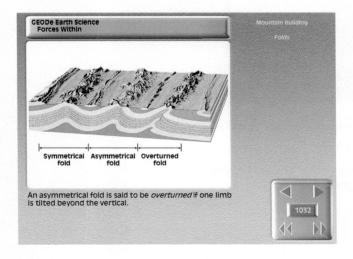

An asymmetrical fold is said to be *overturned* if one limb is tilted beyond the vertical.

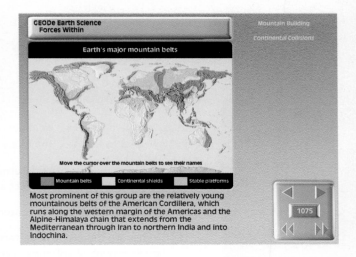

Most prominent of this group are the relatively young mountainous belts of the American Cordillera, which runs along the western margin of the Americas and the Alpine-Himalaya chain that extends from the Mediterranean through Iran to northern India and into Indochina.

FIRES WITHIN
IGNEOUS ACTIVITY

FOCUS ON LEARNING

To assist you in learning the important concepts in this chapter, you will find it helpful to focus on the following questions:

1. What primary factors determine the nature of volcanic eruptions? How do these factors affect a magma's viscosity?

2. What materials are associated with a volcanic eruption?

3. What are the eruptive patterns and characteristic shapes of the three groups of volcanoes generally recognized by volcanologists?

4. What are some other Earth features formed by volcanic activity?

5. What criteria are used to classify intrusive igneous bodies? What are some of these features?

6. What is the relation between volcanic activity and plate tectonics?

A recent eruption of Italy's Mount Etna.
(Photo by Mario Cipollini/Aurora Photos)

On Sunday, May 18, 1980, the most destructive volcanic eruption to occur in North America in historic times transformed a picturesque volcano into a decapitated remnant (**FIGURE 7.1**). On this date in southwestern Washington State, Mount St. Helens erupted with tremendous force. The blast blew out the entire north flank of the volcano, leaving a gaping hole. In one brief moment, a prominent volcano whose summit had been more than 2900 meters (9500 feet) above sea level was lowered by more than 400 meters (1350 feet).

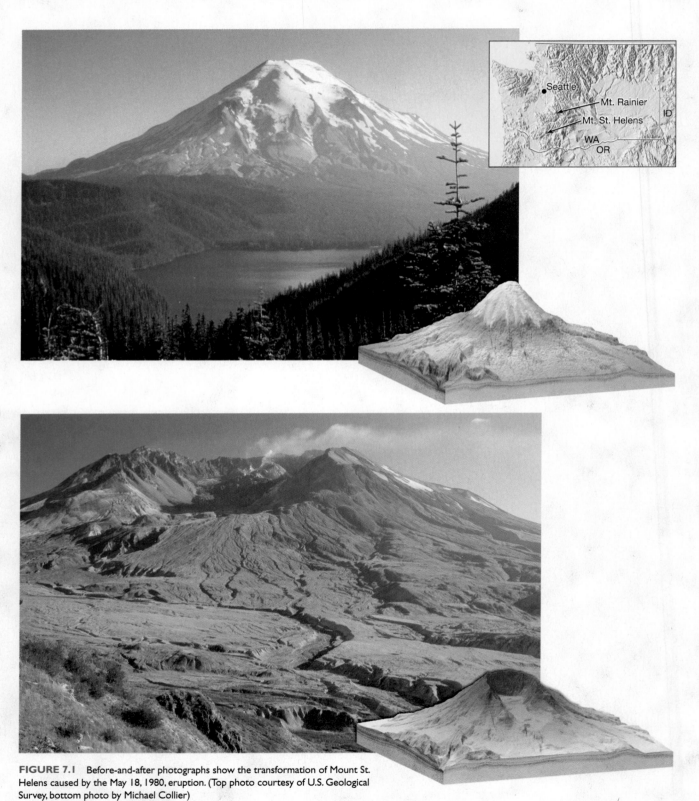

FIGURE 7.1 Before-and-after photographs show the transformation of Mount St. Helens caused by the May 18, 1980, eruption. (Top photo courtesy of U.S. Geological Survey, bottom photo by Michael Collier)

The event devastated a wide swath of timber-rich land on the north side of the mountain (**FIGURE 7.2**). Trees within a 400-square-kilometer area lay flattened and intertwined, stripped of their branches, looking like toothpicks strewn about. The accompanying mudflows carried ash, trees, and water-saturated rock debris 29 kilometers (18 miles) down the Toutle River. The eruption claimed 59 lives, some dying from the intense heat and the suffocating cloud of ash and gases, others from being hurled by the blast, and still others from entrapment in the mudflows.

The eruption ejected nearly a cubic kilometer of ash and rock debris. Following the explosion, Mount St. Helens continued to emit great quantities of hot gases and ash. The force of the blast was so strong that some ash was propelled more than 18,000 meters (over 11 miles) into the stratosphere. During the next few days, this very fine-grained material was carried around Earth by strong upper-air winds. Measurable deposits were reported in Oklahoma and Minnesota, with crop damage into central Montana. Meanwhile, ash fallout in the immediate vicinity exceeded 2 meters in depth. The air over Yakima, Washington (130 kilometers to the east), was so filled with ash that residents experienced midnight-like darkness at noon.

Not all volcanic eruptions are as violent as the 1980 Mount St. Helens event. Some volcanoes, such as Hawaii's Kilauea volcano, typically generate relatively quiet outpourings of fluid lavas. These "gentle" eruptions are not without some fiery displays; occasionally fountains of incandescent lava spray hundreds of meters into the air. During Kilauea's most recent active phase, which began in 1983, more than 180 homes and a national park visitor center have been destroyed.

Why do volcanoes like Mount St. Helens erupt explosively, whereas others like Kilauea are relatively quiet? Why do volcanoes occur in chains like the Aleutian Islands or the Cascade Range? Why do some volcanoes form on the ocean floor, whereas others occur on the continents? This chapter will deal with these and other questions as we explore the nature and movement of magma and lava.

THE NATURE OF VOLCANIC ERUPTIONS

Forces Within
▼ Igneous Activity

What determines whether a volcano extrudes magma violently or "gently"? The primary factors include the magma's *composition,* its *temperature,* and the amount of *dissolved gases* it contains. To varying degrees, these factors affect the magma's mobility, or **viscosity** (*viscos* = sticky). The more viscous the material, the greater its resistance to flow. For example, compare syrup to water—syrup is more viscous and thus, more resistant to flow, than water. Magma associated with an explosive eruption may be five times more viscous than magma that is extruded in a quiescent manner.

Factors Affecting Viscosity

The effect of temperature on viscosity is easily seen. Just as heating syrup makes it more fluid (less viscous), the mobility of lava is strongly influenced by temperature. As lava cools and begins to congeal, its mobility decreases and eventually the flow halts.

A more significant factor influencing volcanic behavior is the chemical composition of the magma. Recall that a major difference among various igneous rocks is their silica (SiO_2) content (Table 7.1). Magmas that produce basaltic rocks contain about 50 percent silica, whereas granitic magmas contain more than 70 percent silica. Intermediate rock types—andesite and diorite—contain about 60 percent silica.

A magma's viscosity is directly related to its silica content—*the more silica in magma, the greater its viscosity.* Silica impedes the flow of magma because silicate structures start to link together into long chains early in the crystallization process. Consequently, silica-rich granitic magmas are very viscous and when they erupt, tend to form comparatively short, thick lava flows. By contrast, basaltic lavas that contain less silica are relatively fluid and have been known to travel 150 kilometers (90 miles) or more before congealing.

The amount of **volatiles** (the gaseous components of magma, mainly water) contained in magma also affects its mobility. Other factors being equal, water dissolved in the

FIGURE 7.2 Douglas fir trees were snapped off or uprooted by the lateral blast of Mount St. Helens on May 18, 1980. (Large photo by Lyn Topinka/AP Photo/U.S. Geological Survey; Inset photo by John M. Burnley/Photo Researchers, Inc.)

Table 7.1   Magmas' different compositions cause properties to vary

Composition	Silica Content	Viscosity	Gas Content	Tendency to Form Pyroclastics	Volcanic Landform
Basaltic (Mafic)	Least (~50%)	Least	Least (1–2%)	Least	Shield Volcanoes Basalt Plateaus Cinder Cones
Andesitic (Intermediate)	Intermediate (~60%)	Intermediate	Intermediate (3–4%)	Intermediate	Composite Cones
Granitic (Felsic)	Most (~70%)	Greatest	Most (4–6%)	Greatest	Pyroclastic Flows Volcanic Domes

magma tends to increase fluidity because it impedes the formation of long silicate chains by breaking silicon–oxygen bonds. It follows, therefore, that the loss of gases renders magma or lava more viscous.

Why Do Volcanoes Erupt?

Most magma is generated by partial melting of the rock peridotite in the upper mantle to form magma with a basaltic composition. Once formed, the buoyant molten rock will rise toward the surface. Because the density of crustal rocks tends to decrease toward the surface, ascending basaltic magma may reach a level where the rocks above are less dense. Should this occur, the molten material begins to collect or pond, forming a magma chamber. As the magma body cools, minerals having high melting temperatures crystallize first, leaving the remaining molten material enriched in silica and other less dense components. Some of this highly evolved material may be buoyant enough to ascend to the surface to produce a volcanic eruption. In most settings, only a fraction of magma generated at depth ever reaches the surface.

Triggering Hawaiian-Type Eruptions

Eruptions that involve very fluid basaltic magmas are often triggered by the arrival of a new batch of magma into a near-surface magma reservoir. This can be detected because the summit of the volcano begins to inflate months, or even years, before an eruption begins. The injection of a fresh supply of molten rock causes the magma chamber to swell and fracture the rock above. This, in turn, mobilizes the magma, which quickly moves upward along the newly formed openings, often generating outpourings of lava for weeks, months, or even years.

DID YOU KNOW?

Chile, Peru, and Ecuador boast the highest volcanoes in the world. Dozens of cones exceed 6000 m (20,000 ft). Two volcanoes located in Ecuador, Chimborazo and Cotopaxi, were once considered the world's highest mountains. That distinction remained until the Himalayas were surveyed in the nineteenth century.

The Role of Volatiles in Eruptions

All magmas contain some water and other volatiles that are held in solution by the immense pressure of the overlying rock. When magma rises (or the rocks confining the magma fail) a reduction in pressure occurs and the dissolved gases begin to separate and form tiny bubbles. This is analogous to opening a warm soda and allowing the carbon dioxide bubbles to escape.

When fluid basaltic magmas erupt, the pressurized gases escape with relative ease. At temperatures of 1000°C and low near-surface pressures, these gases can quickly expand to occupy hundreds of times their original volumes. On some occasions, these expanding gases propel incandescent lava hundreds of meters into the air, producing lava fountains (**FIGURE 7.3**). Although spectacular, these fountains are mostly harmless and not generally associated with major explosive events that cause great loss of life and property.

At the other extreme, highly viscous, granitic magmas may produce explosive clouds of hot ash and gases that evolve into buoyant plumes called **eruption columns** that extend thousands of meters into the atmosphere (**FIGURE 7.4**). Because of the high viscosity of silica-rich magmas, a significant portion of the volatiles remain dissolved until the magma reaches a shallow depth—where tiny bubbles begin to form and grow in size. Bubbles grow by two processes, continued separation of gases from the melt and expansion of bubbles as the confining pressure drops. Should the pressure of the expanding magma body exceed the strength of the overlying rock, fracturing occurs. As magma moves up the fractures, a further drop in confining pressure causes more gas bubbles to form and grow. This chain reaction may generate an explosive event in which magma is literally blown into fragments (ash and pumice) that are carried to great heights by the hot gases. (As exemplified by the 1980 eruption of Mount St. Helens, the collapse of a volcano's flank can also trigger an energetic explosive eruption.)

When magma in the uppermost portion of the magma chamber is forcefully ejected by the escaping gases, the confining pressure on the molten rock directly below drops suddenly. Thus, rather than a single "bang," volcanic eruptions are really a series of explosions.

To summarize, the viscosity of magma, plus the quantity of dissolved gases and the ease with which they can escape, determines to a large extent the nature of a volcanic

FIGURE 7.3 Pyroclastic material and fluid basaltic lava erupting from Kilauea Volcano, Hawaii. (Photo by Douglas Peebles)

eruption. In general, hot basaltic magmas contain a smaller gaseous component and permit these gases to escape with relative ease as compared to more silica-rich granitic magmas. This explains the contrast between "gentle" outflows of fluid basaltic lavas in Hawaii and the explosive and sometimes catastrophic eruptions of viscous lavas from volcanoes such as Mount St. Helens (1980), Mount Pinatubo in the Philippines (1991), and Soufriere Hills on the island of Montserrat (1995).

MATERIALS EXTRUDED DURING AN ERUPTION

GEODe
EARTH SCIENCE
  Forces Within
  ▼ Igneous Activity

Volcanoes extrude lava, large volumes of gas, and pyroclastic materials (broken rock, lava "bombs," fine ash, and dust). In this section we will examine each of these materials.

Lava Flows

The vast majority of lava on Earth, more than 90 percent of the total volume, is estimated to be basaltic in composition. Hot basaltic lavas, which are usually very fluid, generally flow in thin, broad sheets or streamlike ribbons. On the island of Hawaii, these lavas have been clocked at 30 kilometers (19 miles) per hour down steep slopes. However, flow rates of 10 to 300 meters (30 to 1000 feet) per hour are more common. By contrast, the movement of silica-rich, rhyolitic lava may be too slow to perceive. Furthermore, most rhyolitic lavas seldom travel more than a few kilometers from their vents. As you might expect, andesitic lavas, which are intermediate in composition, exhibit characteristics that are between the extremes.

FIGURE 7.4 Steam and ash eruption column from Mount Ruapehu, Tongariro National Park, New Zealand. (Photo by ImageState/Alamy)

Aa and Pahoehoe Flows

Two types of lava flows are known by their Hawaiian names. The most common of these, **aa** (pronounced ah-ah) **flows**, have surfaces of rough jagged blocks with dangerously sharp edges and spiny projections (**FIGURE 7.5A**). Crossing an aa flow can be a trying and miserable experience. By contrast, **pahoehoe** (pronounced pah-hoy-hoy) **flows** exhibit smooth surfaces that often resemble the twisted braids of ropes (**FIGURE 7.5B**). Pahoehoe means "on which one can walk."

Aa and pahoehoe lavas can erupt from the same vent. However, pahoehoe lavas form at higher temperatures and are more fluid than aa flows. In addition, pahoehoe lavas can change into aa lavas during flow, although the reverse (aa to pahoehoe) does not occur.

One of the factors that facilitate the change from pahoehoe to aa is cooling that occurs as the flow moves away from the vent. Cooling, as stated previously, increases viscosity and also promotes bubble formation. Escaping gas bubbles produce numerous voids and sharp spines in the surface of the congealing lava. As the molten interior advances, the outer crust is broken further, transforming a relatively smooth surface into an advancing mass of rough, clinkery rubble.

Occasionally, basaltic lavas have been known to move at agonizingly slow rates. In 1990, near the Hawaiian village of Kalapana, the villagers had to watch for weeks as a pahoehoe flow crept toward their homes at only a few meters per hour. Although most residents were able to escape injury, they were unable to stop the flow and their houses were eventually incinerated.

Lava Tubes

Hardened basaltic flows commonly contain cavelike tunnels called **lava tubes** that were once conduits carrying lava from the volcanic vent to the flow's leading edge (**FIGURE 7.6**).

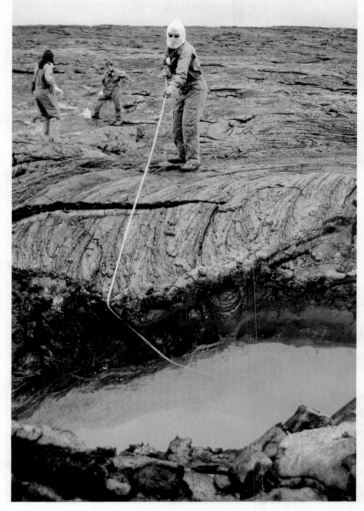

FIGURE 7.6 Lava flows often develop a solid crust while the molten lava below continues to advance in conduits called *lava tubes*. View of an active lava tube as seen through the collapsed roof. (Photo by Jeffrey Judd, U.S. Geological Survey)

A.

B.

FIGURE 7.5 Lava flows. **A.** A typical slow-moving basaltic aa flow. **B.** A typical fluid pahoehoe (ropy) lava. Both of these lava flows erupted from a rift on the flank of Hawaii's Kilauea Volcano. (Photo **A** by J. D. Griggs, U.S. Geological Survey and photo **B** by Philip Rosenberg/Pacific Stock)

These conduits develop in the interior of a flow where temperatures remain high long after the surface hardens. Lava tubes are important features because they serve as insulated pathways that facilitate the advance of lava great distances from their source.

Lava tubes are associated with volcanoes that emit fluid basaltic lava and are found in most parts of the world. Even the massive volcanoes on Mars have flows that contain numerous lava tubes. Some lava tubes exhibit extraordinary dimensions—one such structure, Kazumura Cave, located on the southeast slope of Hawaii's Mauna Loa volcano, extends for more than 60 kilometers (40 miles).

Gases

Magmas contain varying amounts of dissolved gases (*volatiles*) held in the molten rock by confining pressure, just as carbon dioxide is held in soft drinks. As with soft drinks, as soon as the pressure is reduced, the gases begin to escape. Obtaining gas samples from an erupting volcano is difficult and dangerous, so geologists usually must estimate the amount of gas originally contained within the magma.

The gaseous portion of most magmas makes up from 1 to 6 percent of the total weight, with most of this in the form of water vapor. Although the percentage may be small, the actual quantity of emitted gas can exceed thousands of tons per day. Occasionally, eruptions emit colossal amounts of volcanic gases that rise high into the atmosphere, where they may reside for several years.

The composition of volcanic gases is important because they contribute significantly to our planet's atmosphere. Analyses of samples taken during Hawaiian eruptions indicate that the gas component is about 70 percent water vapor, 15 percent carbon dioxide, 5 percent nitrogen, 5 percent sulfur dioxide, with lesser amounts of chlorine, hydrogen, and argon. (The relative proportion of each gas varies significantly from one volcanic region to another.) Sulfur compounds are easily recognized by their pungent odor. Volcanoes are also natural sources of air pollution—some emit large quantities of sulfur dioxide, which readily combines with atmospheric gases to form sulfuric acid and other sulfate compounds.

Pyroclastic Materials

When volcanoes erupt energetically they eject pulverized rock, lava, and glass fragments from the vent. These particles are referred to as **pyroclastic materials** (*pyro* = fire, *clast* = fragment). Fragments range in size from very fine dust and sand-sized volcanic ash (less than 2 millimeters) to pieces that weigh several tons.

Ash and *dust* particles are produced when gas-rich viscous magma erupts explosively (see Figure 7.4). As magma moves up in the vent, the gases rapidly expand, generating material that resembles the froth that flows from a bottle of champagne. As the hot gases expand explosively, the froth is blown into very fine glassy fragments (**FIGURE 7.7**). When the hot ash falls, the glassy shards often fuse to form a rock

FIGURE 7.7 Pyroclastic materials. **A.** *Volcanic ash* and small pumice fragments (*lapilli*) that erupted from Mount St. Helens in 1980. Inset photo is an image obtained using a scanning electron microscope (SEM). This vesicular ash particle exhibits a glassy texture and is roughly the diameter of a human hair. **B.** Volcanic block. Volcanic blocks are solid fragments that were ejected from a volcano during an explosive eruption. **C.** These basaltic bombs were erupted by Mauna Kea Volcano, Hawaii. Volcanic bombs are lava fragments that are ejected while still molten and often acquire rounded aerodynamic shapes as they travel through the air. (Photos courtesy of U.S. Geological Survey)

called *welded tuff.* Sheets of this material, as well as ash deposits that later consolidate, cover vast portions of the western United States.

Somewhat larger fragments that range in size from small beads to walnuts are known as *lapilli* ("little stones"). These ejecta are commonly called *cinders* (2–64 millimeters). Particles larger than 64 millimeters (2.5 inches) in diameter are called *blocks* when they are made of hardened lava and *bombs* when they are ejected as incandescent lava. Because bombs are semimolten upon ejection, they often take on a streamlined shape as they hurtle through the air (Figure 7.7C). Because of their size, bombs and blocks usually fall near the vent; however, they are occasionally propelled great distances.

VOLCANIC STRUCTURES AND ERUPTIVE STYLES

Forces Within
▼ Igneous Activity

The popular image of a volcano is that of a solitary, graceful, snowcapped cone, such as Mount Hood in Oregon or Japan's Fujiyama. These picturesque, conical mountains are produced by volcanic activity that occurred intermittently over thousands, or even hundreds of thousands, of years. However, many volcanoes do not fit this image. Cinder cones are quite small and form during a single eruptive phase that lasts a few days to a few years. Other volcanic landforms are not volcanoes at all. For example, Alaska's Valley of Ten Thousand Smokes is a flat-topped deposit consisting of 15 cubic kilometers of ash that erupted in less than 60 hours and blanketed a section of river valley to a depth of 200 meters (600 feet).

Volcanic landforms come in a wide variety of shapes and sizes, and each structure has a unique eruptive history. Nevertheless, volcanologists have been able to classify volcanic landforms and determine their eruptive patterns. In this section we will consider the general anatomy of a volcano and look at three major volcanic types: shield volcanoes, cinder cones, and composite cones.

Anatomy of a Volcano

Volcanic activity frequently begins when a fissure (crack) develops in the crust as magma moves forcefully toward the

FIGURE 7.9 Crater versus caldera. **A.** The crater of Mount Vesuvius, Italy, is about 0.5 kilometer in diameter. The city of Naples is located northwest of Vesuvius, whereas Pompeii, the Roman town that was buried by an eruption in A.D. 79, is located southeast of the volcano. **B.** The huge caldera—6 kilometers in diameter—formed when Tambora's peak was removed during an explosive eruption in 1815. (Photos courtesy of NASA)

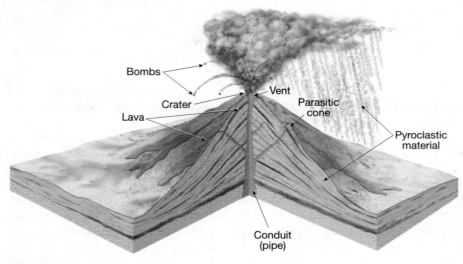

FIGURE 7.8 Anatomy of a "typical" composite cone (see also Figures 7.10 and 7.13 for a comparison with a shield and cinder cone, respectively).

surface. As the gas-rich magma moves up through a fissure, its path is usually localized into a circular **conduit**, or **pipe**, that terminates at a surface opening called a **vent** (**FIGURE 7.8**). Successive eruptions of lava, pyroclastic material, or frequently a combination of both often separated by long periods of inactivity eventually build the cone-shaped structure we call a **volcano**.

Located at the summit of most volcanoes is a somewhat funnel-shaped depression, called a **crater** (*crater* = a bowl). Volcanoes that are built primarily of pyroclastic materials typically have craters that form by gradual accumulation of volcanic debris on the surrounding rim. Other craters form during explosive eruptions as the rapidly ejected particles erode the crater walls (**FIGURE 7.9A**). Craters also form when the summit area of a volcano collapses following an eruption. Some volcanoes have very large circular depressions called *calderas* that have diameters greater than one kilometer and in rare cases can exceed 50 kilometers (**FIGURE 7.9B**). We will consider the formation of various types of calderas later in this chapter.

During early stages of growth most volcanic discharges come from a central summit vent. As a volcano matures, material also tends to be emitted from fissures that develop along the flanks or at the base of the volcano. Continued activity from a flank eruption may produce a small **parasitic cone** (*parasitus* = one who eats at the table of another). Italy's Mount Etna, for example, has more than 200 secondary vents, some of which have built parasitic cones. Many of these vents, however, emit only gases and are appropriately called **fumaroles** (*fumus* = smoke).

Shield Volcanoes

Shield volcanoes are produced by the accumulation of fluid basaltic lavas and exhibit the shape of a broad, slightly domed structure that resembles a warrior's shield (**FIGURE 7.10**). Most shield volcanoes begin on the ocean floor as seamounts, a few of which grow large enough to form volcanic islands. Examples include the Canary Islands, the Hawaiian Islands, the Galapagos, and Easter Island. In addition, some shield volcanoes form on continental crust.

Mauna Loa: A Classic Shield Volcano

Extensive study of the Hawaiian Islands confirms that they are constructed of a myriad of thin basaltic lava flows averaging a few meters thick intermixed with relatively

minor amounts of pyroclastic ejecta. Mauna Loa is one of five overlapping shield volcanoes that together comprise the Big Island of Hawaii (Figure 7.10). From its base on the floor of the Pacific Ocean to its summit, Mauna Loa is over 9 kilometers (6 miles) high, exceeding that of Mount Everest. This massive pile of basaltic rock has a volume of 80,000 cubic kilometers that was extruded over a span of more than one million years. The volume of material composing Mauna Loa is roughly 200 times greater than the amount composing a large composite cone such as Mount Rainier (**FIGURE 7.11**). Although the shield volcanoes that comprise islands are often quite large, some are more modest in size. In addition, an estimated one million basaltic submarine volcanoes (seamounts) of various sizes dot the ocean floor.

The flanks of Mauna Loa have gentle slopes of only a few degrees. The low-angle results because very hot, fluid lava travels "fast and far" from the vent. In addition, most of the lava (perhaps 80 percent) flows through a well-developed system of lava tubes (see Figure 7.6). This greatly increases the distance lava can travel before it solidifies. Thus, lava emitted near the summit often reaches the sea, thereby adding to the width of the cone at the expense of its height.

Another feature common to many active shield volcanoes is a large, steep-walled caldera that occupies the summit. Calderas on large shield volcanoes form when the roof above the magma chamber collapses. This usually occurs as the magma reservoir empties following a large eruption, or as magma migrates to the flank of a volcano to feed a fissure eruption.

In the final stage of growth, shield volcanoes are more sporadic and pyroclastic ejections are more common. Further, lavas increase in viscosity, resulting in thicker, shorter flows. These eruptions tend to steepen the slope of the summit area, which often becomes capped with clusters of cinder cones. This may explain why Mauna Kea, which is a more mature volcano that has not erupted in historic times, has a steeper summit than Mauna Loa, which erupted as recently as 1984. Astronomers are so certain that Mauna Kea is "over the hill" that they have built an elaborate observatory on its summit, housing some of the world's finest (and most expensive) telescopes.

FIGURE 7.10 Mauna Loa is one of five shield volcanoes that together make up the island of Hawaii. Shield volcanoes are built primarily of fluid basaltic lava flows and contain only a small percentage of pyroclastic materials. (Photo by Greg Vaughn/Alamy)

Kilauea, Hawaii: Eruption of a Shield Volcano

Kilauea, the most active and intensely studied shield volcano in the world, is located on the

FIGURE 7.11   Profiles comparing scales of different volcanoes. **A.** Profile of Mauna Loa, Hawaii, the largest shield volcano in the Hawaiian chain. Note size comparison with Mount Rainier, Washington, a large composite cone. **B.** Profile of Mount Rainier, Washington. Note how it dwarfs a typical cinder cone. **C.** Profile of Sunset, Arizona, a typical steep-sided cinder cone.

island of Hawaii in the shadow of Mauna Loa. More than 50 eruptions have been witnessed here since record keeping began in 1823. Several months before each eruptive phase, Kilauea inflates as magma gradually migrates upward and accumulates in a central reservoir located a few kilometers below the summit. For up to 24 hours in advance of an eruption, swarms of small earthquakes warn of the impending activity.

Most of the recent activity on Kilauea has occurred along the flanks of the volcano in a region called the East Rift Zone. A rift eruption here in 1960 engulfed the coastal village of Kapoho, located nearly 30 kilometers (20 miles) from the source. The longest and largest rift eruption ever recorded on Kilauea began in 1983 and continues to this day, with no signs of abating.

The first discharge began along a 6-kilometer (4-mile) fissure where a 100-meter (300-foot) high "curtain of fire" formed as red-hot lava was ejected skyward (**FIGURE 7.12**). When the activity became localized, a cinder and spatter cone given the Hawaiian name *Puu Oo* was built. Over the next 3 years the general eruptive pattern consisted of short periods (hours to days) when fountains of gas-rich lava sprayed skyward. Each event was followed by nearly a month of inactivity.

By the summer of 1986 a new vent opened 3 kilometers downrift. Here smooth-surfaced pahoehoe lava formed a lava lake. Occasionally the lake overflowed, but more often lava escaped through tunnels to feed flows that moved down the southeastern flank of the volcano toward the sea. These flows destroyed nearly a hundred rural homes, covered a major roadway, and eventually reached the sea. Lava has been intermittently pouring into the ocean ever since, adding new land to the island of Hawaii.

DID YOU KNOW?

According to legend, Pele, the Hawaiian goddess of volcanoes, makes her home at the summit of Kilauea volcano. Evidence for her existence is "Pele's hair"—thin, delicate strands of glass, which are soft and flexible and have a golden-brown color. This threadlike volcanic glass forms when blobs of hot lava are spattered and shredded by escaping gases.

Situated just 32 kilometers (20 miles) off the southern coast of Kilauea, a submarine volcano, Loihi, is also active. It, however, has another 930 meters (3100 feet) to go before it breaks the surface of the Pacific Ocean.

Cinder Cones

As the name suggests, **cinder cones** (also called **scoria cones**) are built from ejected lava fragments that take on the appearance of cinders or clinkers as they begin to harden in flight (**FIGURE 7.13**). These pyroclastic fragments range in size from fine ash to bombs that may exceed a meter in diameter. However, most of the volume of a cinder cone consists of pea- to walnut-sized lapilli that are markedly vesicular and have a black to reddish-brown color. (These vesicular rock fragments are called *scoria*.) Although cinder cones are composed mostly of loose pyroclastic material, they sometimes extrude lava. On such occasions the discharges most often come from vents located at or near the base rather than from the summit crater.

Cinder cones have very simple, distinctive shapes determined by the slope that loose pyroclastic material maintains as it comes to rest (**FIGURE 7.14**). Because cinders have a high angle of repose (the steepest angle at which material

FIGURE 7.12   Lava "curtain" extruded along the East Rift Zone, Kilauea, Hawaii. (Photo by Greg Vaughn/Alamy)

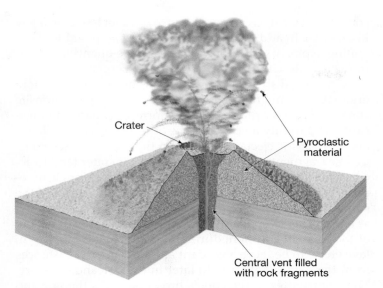

FIGURE 7.13   Cinder cones are built from ejected lava fragments (mostly cinders and bombs) and are usually less than 300 meters (1000 feet) in height.

Crater

Pyroclastic material

Central vent filled with rock fragments

Lava flow

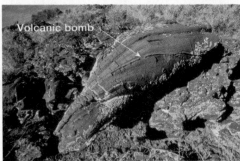

Volcanic bomb

FIGURE 7.14   SP Crater, a cinder cone located in the San Francisco Peaks volcanic field north of Flagstaff, Arizona. The lava flow in the upper part of the image originated from the base of the cinder cone. Inset photo shows a large bomb on the slopes of SP Crater. (Photos by Michael Collier)

remains stable), cinder cones are steep-sided, having slopes between 30 and 40 degrees. In addition, cinder cones have large, deep craters in relation to the overall size of the structure. Although relatively symmetrical, many cinder cones are elongated, and higher on the side that was downwind during the eruptions.

Most cinder cones are produced by a single, short-lived eruptive event. One study found that half of all cinder cones examined were constructed in less than one month, and that 95 percent formed in less than one year. However, in some cases, they remain active for several years. Parícutin, shown in FIGURE 7.15, had an eruptive cycle that spanned 9 years. Once the event ceases, the magma in the "plumbing" connecting the vent to the magma source solidifies and the volcano usually does not erupt again. (One exception is Cerro Negro, a cinder cone in Nicaragua, which has erupted more than 20 time since it formed in 1850.) As a consequence of this short life span, cinder cones are small, usually between 30 meters (100 feet) and 300 meters (1000 feet). A few rare examples exceed 700 meters (2100 feet) in height.

Cinder cones number in the thousands around the globe. Some occur in volcanic fields such as the one near Flagstaff, Arizona, which consists of about 600 cones. Others are parasitic cones that are found on the flanks of larger volcanoes.

Parícutin: Life of a Garden-Variety Cinder Cone

One of the few volcanoes studied by geologists from its very beginning is the cinder cone called Parícutin, located west of Mexico City. In 1943 its eruptive phase began in a cornfield owned by Dionisio Pulido, who witnessed the event as he prepared the field for planting.

For two weeks prior to the first eruption, numerous Earth tremors caused apprehension in the nearby village of Parícutin. Then on February 20 sulfurous gases began billowing from a small depression that had been in the cornfield for as long as people could remember. During the night, hot, glowing rock fragments were ejected from the vent, producing

FIGURE 7.15   The village of San Juan Parangaricutiro engulfed by aa lava from Parícutin, shown erupting in the background. Only the church towers remain. (Photo by Tad Nichols)

a spectacular fireworks display. Explosive discharges continued, throwing hot fragments and ash occasionally as high as 6000 meters (20,000 feet) into the air. Larger fragments fell near the crater, some remaining incandescent as they rolled down the slope. These built an aesthetically pleasing cone, while finer ash fell over a much larger area, burning and eventually covering the village of Parícutin. In the first day the cone grew to 40 meters (130 feet), and by the fifth day it was more than 100 meters (330 feet) high.

The first lava flow came from a fissure that opened just north of the cone, but after a few months flows began to emerge from the base of the cone itself. In June 1944 a clinkery aa flow 10 meters (30 feet) thick moved over much of the village of San Juan Parangaricutiro, leaving only the church steeple exposed (Figure 7.15). After 9 years of intermittent pyroclastic explosions and nearly continuous discharge of lava from vents at its base, the activity ceased almost as quickly as it had begun. Today, Parícutin is just another one of the scores of cinder cones dotting the landscape in this region of Mexico. Like the others, it will not erupt again.

Composite Cones

Earth's most picturesque yet potentially dangerous volcanoes are **composite cones** or **stratovolcanoes**. Most are located in a relatively narrow zone that rims the Pacific Ocean, appropriately called the *Ring of Fire* (see Figure 7.29). This active zone consists of a chain of continental volcanoes that are distributed along the west coast of the Americas, including the large cones of the Andes in South America and the Cascade Range of the western United States and Canada. The latter group includes Mount St. Helens, Mount Shasta, and Mount Garibaldi. The most active regions in the Ring of Fire are located along curved belts of volcanic cones situated adjacent to the deep-ocean trenches of the northern and western Pacific. This nearly continuous chain of volcanoes stretches from the Aleutian Islands to Japan and the Philippines and to the North Island of New Zealand. These impressive volcanic structures are manifestations of processes that occur in the mantle in association with *subduction zones*.

The classic composite cone is a large, nearly symmetrical structure consisting of alternating layers of explosively erupted cinders and ash interbedded with lava flows. A few composite cones, notably Italy's Etna and Stromboli, display very persistent eruption activity, and molten lava has been observed in their summit craters for decades. Stromboli is so well known for eruptions that eject incandescent blobs of lava that it has been referred to as the "Lighthouse of the Mediterranean." Mount Etna, on the other hand, has erupted, on average, once every two years since 1979 (see Chapter Opening photo).

Just as shield volcanoes owe their shape to fluid basaltic lavas, composite cones reflect the viscous nature of the material from which they are made. In general, composite cones are the product of gas-rich magma having an andesitic composition. However, many composite cones also emit various amounts of fluid basaltic lava and, occasionally, pyroclastic material having rhyolitic composition. Relative to shields, the silica-rich magmas typical of composite cones generate thick viscous lavas that travel less than a few kilometers. In addition, composite cones are noted for generating explosive eruptions that eject huge quantities of pyroclastic material.

A conical shape, with a steep summit area and more gradually sloping flanks, is typical of many large composite cones. This classic profile, which adorns calendars and postcards, is partially a consequence of the way viscous lavas and pyroclastic ejecta contribute to the growth of the cone. Coarse fragments ejected from the summit crater tend to accumulate near their source. Because of their high angle of repose, coarse materials contribute to the steep slopes of the summit area. Finer ejecta, on the other hand, are deposited as a thin layer over a large area. This acts to flatten the flank of the cone. In addition, during the early stages of growth, lavas tend to be more abundant and flow greater distances from the vent than lavas do later in the volcano's history. This contributes to the cone's broad base. As the volcano matures, the shorter flows that come from the central vent serve to armor and strengthen the summit area. Consequently, steep slopes exceeding 40 degrees are sometimes possible. Two of the most perfect cones—Mount Mayon in the Philippines and Fujiyama in Japan—exhibit the classic form we expect of a composite cone, with its steep summit and gently sloping flanks (**FIGURE 7.16**).

Despite the symmetrical forms of many composite cones, most have complex histories. Huge mounds of volcanic debris surrounding these structures provide evidence that large sections of these volcanoes slid down slope as massive landslides. Others develop horseshoe-shaped depressions at their summits as a result of explosive lateral eruptions—as occurred during the 1980 eruption of Mount St. Helens. Often, so much rebuilding has occurred since these eruptions that no trace of the amphitheater-shaped scars remain.

LIVING IN THE SHADOW OF A COMPOSITE CONE

More than 50 volcanoes have erupted in the United States in the past 200 years. Fortunately, the most explosive of these eruptions occurred in sparsely inhabited regions of Alaska. On a global scale many destructive eruptions have occurred during the past few thousand years, a few of which may have influenced the course of human civilization.

Nuée Ardente: A Deadly Pyroclastic Flow

One of the most destructive forces of nature are **pyroclastic flows**, which consist of hot gases infused with incandescent ash and larger lava fragments. Also referred to as **nuée ardentes** (*glowing avalanches*), these fiery flows are capable of racing down steep volcanic slopes at speeds that can exceed 200 kilometers (125 miles) per hour (**FIGURE 7.17**). Nuée ardentes are composed of two parts—a low-density cloud of hot expanding gases containing fine ash particles, and a ground-hugging portion that contains most of the material in the flow.

Driven by gravity, pyroclastic flows tend to move in a manner similar to snow avalanches. They are mobilized by

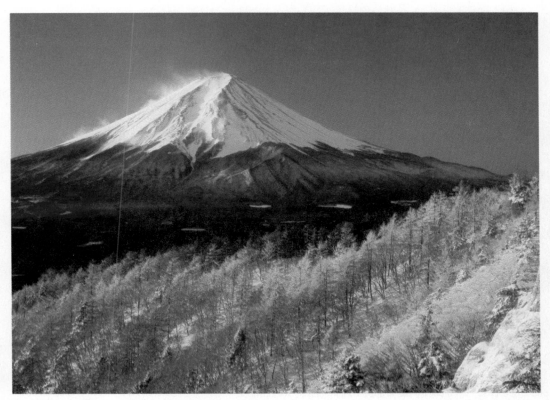

FIGURE 7.16   Japan's Fujiyama exhibits the classic form of a composite cone—steep summit and gently sloping flanks. (Photo by Koji Nakano/Getty Images/Sebun)

FIGURE 7.17   Pyroclastic flows. **A.** Illustration of a fiery ash and pumice flow racing down the slope of a volcano. **B.** Pyroclastic flow moving rapidly down the forested slopes of Mt. Unzen toward a Japanese village. (Photo by AP World Wide)

Prevailing wind

Eruption column

Ash fall

Bombs

Pyroclastic flow

A.

B.

volcanic gases released from the lava fragments and by the expansion of heated air that is overtaken and trapped in the moving front. These gases reduce friction between the fragments and the ground. This helps explain why some nuée ardente deposits are found more than 100 kilometers (60 miles) from their source.

Sometimes powerful hot blasts that carry small amounts of ash separate from the main body of a pyroclastic flow. These low-density clouds, called *surges*, can be deadly, but seldom have sufficient force to destroy buildings in their paths. Nevertheless, on June 3, 1991, a hot ash cloud from Japan's Unzen Volcano engulfed and burned hundreds of homes and moved cars as much as 80 meters (250 feet).

Pyroclastic flows may originate in a variety of volcanic settings. Some occur when a powerful eruption blasts pyroclastic material out of the side of a volcano—the lateral eruption of Mount St. Helens in 1980, for example. More frequently, however, nuée ardentes are generated by the collapse of tall eruption columns during an explosive event. When gravity eventually overcomes the initial upward thrust provided by the escaping gases, the ejecta begin to fall, sending massive amounts of incandescent blocks, ash, and pumice cascading downslope.

In summary, pyroclastic flows are a mixture of hot gases and pyroclastic materials moving along the ground, driven primarily by gravity. In general, flows that are fast and highly turbulent can transport fine particles for distances of 100 kilometers or more.

The Destruction of St. Pierre

In 1902 an infamous nuée ardente and associated surge from Mount Pelée, a small volcano on the Caribbean island of Martinique, destroyed the port town

FIGURE 7.18   St. Pierre as it appeared shortly after the eruption of Mount Pelée, 1902. (Reproduced from the collection of the Library of Congress) Inset photo shows St. Pierre before the eruption. Many vessels are offshore, as was the case on the day of the eruption. (Photo courtesy of The Granger Collection, New York)

of St. Pierre. Although the main pyroclastic flow was largely confined to the valley of Riviere Blanche, the fiery surge spread south of the river and quickly engulfed the entire city. The destruction happened in moments and was so devastating that almost all of St. Pierre's 28,000 inhabitants were killed. Only one person on the outskirts of town—a prisoner protected in a dungeon—and a few people on ships in the harbor were spared (**FIGURE 7.18**).

Within days of this calamitous eruption, scientists arrived on the scene. Although St. Pierre was mantled by only a thin layer of volcanic debris, they discovered that masonry walls nearly a meter thick were knocked over like dominoes; large trees were uprooted and cannons were torn from their mounts. A further reminder of the destructive force of this nuée ardente is preserved in the ruins of the mental hospital. One of the immense steel chairs that had been used to confine alcoholic patients can be seen today, contorted, as though it were made of plastic.

Lahars: Mudflows on Active and Inactive Cones

In addition to violent eruptions, large composite cones may generate a type of very fluid mudflow referred to by its Indonesian name **lahar**. These destructive flows occur when volcanic debris becomes saturated with water and rapidly moves down steep volcanic slopes, generally following gullies and stream valleys. Some lahars may be triggered when magma is emplaced near the surface, causing large volumes of ice and snow to melt. Others are generated when heavy rains saturate weathered volcanic deposits. Thus, lahars may occur even when a volcano is *not* erupting.

When Mount St. Helens erupted in 1980, several lahars were generated. These flows and accompanying flood waters raced down nearby river valleys at speeds exceeding 30 kilometers per hour. These raging rivers of mud destroyed or severely damaged nearly all the homes and bridges along their paths. Fortunately, the area was not densely populated (**FIGURE 7.19**).

FIGURE 7.19   Lahars are mudflows that originate on volcanic slopes. This lahar raced down the Muddy River located southeast of Mount St. Helens following the May 18, 1980, eruption. Notice the former height of this fluid mudflow as recorded by the mudflow line on the tree trunks. Note person (circled) for scale. (Photo by Lyn Topinka/U.S. Geological Survey)

In 1985 deadly lahars were produced during a small eruption of Nevado del Ruiz, a 5300-meter (17,400-foot) volcano in the Andes Mountains of Colombia. Hot pyroclastic material melted ice and snow that capped the mountain (*nevado* means *snow* in Spanish) and sent torrents of ash and debris down three major river valleys that flank the volcano. Reaching speeds of 100 kilometers (60 miles) per hour, these mudflows tragically took 25,000 lives.

Mount Rainier, Washington, is considered by many to be America's most dangerous volcano because, like Nevado del Ruiz, it has a thick year-round mantle of snow and glacial ice. Adding to the risk is the fact that more than 100,000 people live in the valleys around Rainier, and many homes are built on deposits left by lahars that flowed down the volcano hundreds or thousands of years ago. A future eruption, or perhaps just a period of extraordinary rainfall, may produce lahars that could take similar paths.

Eruption of Mount Mazama

Partially emptied magma chamber

Collapse of Mount Mazama

Formation of Crater Lake and Wizard Island

FIGURE 7.20 Sequence of events that formed Crater Lake, Oregon. About 7000 years ago a violent eruption partly emptied the magma chamber, causing the summit of former Mount Mazama to collapse. Rainfall and groundwater contributed to form Crater Lake, the deepest lake in the United States. Subsequent eruptions produced the cinder cone called Wizard Island. (After H. Williams, *The Ancient Volcanoes of Oregon.* Photo courtesy of the U.S. Geological Survey)

OTHER VOLCANIC LANDFORMS

The most obvious volcanic structure is a cone. But other distinctive and important landforms are also associated with volcanic activity.

Calderas

Calderas (*caldaria* = a cooking pot) are large depressions with diameters that exceed one kilometer and have a somewhat circular form. (Those less than a kilometer across are called *collapse pits* or *craters.*) Most calderas are formed by one of the following processes: (1) the collapse of the summit of a large composite volcano following an explosive eruption of silica-rich pumice and ash fragments (*Crater Lake-type calderas*); (2) the collapse of the top of a shield volcano caused by subterranean drainage from a central magma chamber (*Hawaiian-type calderas*); and (3) the collapse of a large area, caused by the discharge of colossal volumes of silica-rich pumice and ash along ring fractures (*Yellowstone-type calderas*).

Crater Lake–Type Calderas

Crater Lake, Oregon, is located in a caldera that has a maximum diameter of 10 kilometers (6 miles) and is 1175 meters (more than 3800 feet) deep. This caldera formed about 7000 years ago when a composite cone, later named Mount Mazama, violently extruded 50 to 70 cubic kilometers of pyroclastic material (**FIGURE 7.20**). With the loss of support,

1500 meters (nearly a mile) of the summit of this once prominent cone collapsed. After the collapse, rainwater filled the caldera (Figure 7.20). Later volcanic activity built a small cinder cone in the caldera. Today this cone, called Wizard Island, provides a mute reminder of past activity.

Hawaiian-Type Calderas

Although some calderas are produced by *collapse following an explosive eruption,* many are not. For example, Hawaii's active shield volcanoes, Mauna Loa and Kilauea, both have large calderas at their summits. Kilauea's measures 3.3 by 4.4 kilometers (about 2 by 3 miles) and is 150 meters (500 feet) deep. The walls of this caldera are almost vertical, and as a result, it looks like a vast, nearly flat-bottomed pit. Kilauea's caldera formed by gradual subsidence as magma slowly drained laterally from the underlying magma chamber to the East Rift Zone, leaving the summit unsupported.

Yellowstone-Type Calderas

Historic and destructive eruptions such as Mount St. Helens pale in comparison to what happened 630,000 years ago in the region now occupied by Yellowstone National Park, when approximately 1000 cubic kilometers of pyroclastic material erupted. This super-eruption sent showers of ash as far away as the Gulf of Mexico and resulted in the eventual development of a caldera 70 kilometers (43 miles) across and gave rise to the Lava Creek Tuff, a hardened ash deposit that is 400 meters (more than 1200 feet) thick in some places. Vestiges of this event are the many hot springs and geysers in the Yellowstone region.

Based on the extraordinary volume of erupted material, researchers have determined that the magma chambers associated with Yellowstone-type calderas must also be similarly monstrous. As more and more magma accumulates, the pressure within the magma chamber begins to exceed the pressure exerted by the weight of the overlying rocks. An eruption occurs when the gas-rich magma raises the overlying strata enough to create vertical fractures that extend to the surface. Magma surges upward along these cracks forming a ring-shaped eruption. With a loss of support, the roof of the magma chamber collapses forcing even more gas-rich magma toward the surface.

Caldera-forming eruptions are of colossal proportions, ejecting huge volumes of pyroclastic materials, mainly in the form of ash and pumice fragments. Typically, these materials form pyroclastic flows that sweep across the landscape, destroying most living things in their paths. Upon coming to rest, the hot fragments of ash and pumice fuse together, forming a welded tuff that closely resembles a solidified lava flow. Despite the immense size of these calderas, their eruptions are brief, lasting hours to perhaps a few days.

Unlike calderas associated with shield volcanoes or composite cones, these depressions are so large and poorly defined that many remained undetected until high-quality aerial or satellite images became available. Other examples of large calderas located in the United States are California's Long Valley Caldera, La Garita Caldera, located in

the San Juan Mountains of southern Colorado, and the Valles Caldera west of Los Alamos, New Mexico. These and similar calderas found around the globe are the largest volcanic structures on Earth. Volcanologists have compared their destructive force with that of the impact of a small asteroid. Fortunately, no eruption of this type has occurred in historic times.

Fissure Eruptions and Basalt Plateaus

The greatest volume of volcanic material is extruded from fractures in the crust called **fissures** (*fissura* = to split). Rather than building a cone, these long, narrow cracks tend to emit low-viscosity basaltic lavas that blanket a wide area (**FIGURE 7.21**).

FIGURE 7.21 Basaltic fissure eruption. **A.** Lava fountaining from a fissure and formation of fluid lava flows called *flood basalts.* **B.** Photo of basalt flows near Idaho Falls. (Photo by John S. Shelton)

In 1783, a deadly fissure eruption took place in Iceland along a 24-km (15-mi) rift. The eruption extruded 12 cu km (3 cu mi) of fluid basaltic lava. In addition, sulfurous gases and ash were emitted that destroyed grasslands, killing most of Iceland's livestock. The eruption and ensuing famine killed 10,000 Icelanders—roughly one in five. Recently, a volcanologist who is an expert on this event concluded that a similar eruption today would disrupt commercial aviation in the Northern Hemisphere for several months.

The Columbia Plateau in the northwestern United States is the product of this type of activity (**FIGURE 7.22**). Numerous **fissure eruptions** have buried the landscape creating a lava plateau nearly a mile thick. Some of the lava remained molten long enough to flow 150 kilometers

(90 miles) from its source. The term **flood basalts** appropriately describes these deposits.

Massive accumulations of basaltic lava, similar to those of the Columbia Plateau, occur elsewhere in the world. One of the largest examples is the Deccan Traps, a thick sequence of flat-lying basalt flows covering nearly 500,000 square kilometers (195,000 square miles) of west central India. When the Deccan Traps formed about 66 million years ago, nearly 2 million cubic kilometers of lava were extruded in less than 1 million years. Several other huge areas of flood basalts, including the Ontong Java Plateau, are found on the floor of the ocean.

Volcanic Pipes and Necks

Most volcanoes are fed magma through short conduits, called *pipes* that connect a magma chamber to the surface. One rare type of pipe, called a *diatreme* extends to depths that exceed 200 kilometers (125 miles). Magmas that migrate upward through these pipes travel rapidly enough that they undergo very little alteration during their ascent. Geologists consider these unusually deep pipes to be "windows" into Earth that allow us to view rock normally found only at great depths.

The best-known volcanic pipes are the diamond-bearing structures of South Africa. The rocks filling these pipes originated at depths of at least 150 kilometers (90 miles), where pressure is high enough to generate diamonds and other high-pressure minerals. The task of transporting essentially unaltered magma (along with diamond inclusions) through 150 kilometers of solid rock is exceptional. This fact accounts for the scarcity of natural diamonds.

Volcanoes on land are continually being lowered by weathering and erosion. Cinder cones are easily eroded because they are composed of unconsolidated materials. However, all volcanoes will eventually succumb to erosion. As erosion progresses, the rock occupying a volcanic pipe is often more resistant and may remain standing above the surrounding terrain long after most of the cone has vanished. Shiprock, New Mexico, is a classic example of this structure, which geologists call a **volcanic neck** (**FIGURE 7.23**). Higher than many skyscrapers, Shiprock is but one

FIGURE 7.22 Volcanic areas that comprise the Columbia Plateau in the Pacific Northwest. **A.** The Columbia River basalts cover an area of nearly 200,000 square kilometers (80,000 square miles). Activity here began about 17 million years ago as lava began to pour out of large fissures, eventually producing a basalt plateau with an average thickness of more than 1 kilometer. **B.** Basalt flows exposed along Dry Falls in eastern Washington state. (Photo by E.J. Tarbuck)

FIGURE 7.23   Shiprock, New Mexico, is a volcanic neck. This structure, which stands over 420 meters (1380 feet) high, consists of igneous rock that crystallized in the vent of a volcano that has long since been eroded away. (Photo by Dennis Tasa)

Intrusions are known to occur in a great variety of sizes and shapes. Some of the most common types are illustrated in **FIGURE** 7.24. Notice that some plutons have a tabular (table-top) shape, whereas others are best described as massive. Also, observe that some of these bodies cut across existing structures, such as sedimentary strata; whereas others form when magma is injected between sedimentary layers. Because of these differences, intrusive igneous bodies are generally classified according to their shape as either **tabular** (*tabula* = table) or **massive** and by their orientation with respect to the host rock. Igneous bodies are said to be **discordant** (*discordare* = to disagree) if they cut across existing structures and **concordant** (*concordare* = to agree) if they form parallel to features such as sedimentary strata.

of many such landforms that protrude conspicuously from the red desert landscapes of the American Southwest.

INTRUSIVE IGNEOUS ACTIVITY

Forces Within
▼ Igneous Activity

Although volcanic eruptions can be violent and spectacular events, most magma is emplaced and crystallizes at depth, without fanfare. Therefore, understanding the igneous processes that occur deep underground is as important to geologists as the study of volcanic events.

When magma rises though the crust it forcefully displaces preexisting crustal rocks referred to as *host* or *country rock*. Invariably some of the magma will not reach the surface, but instead crystallize or "freeze" at depth where it becomes an intrusive igneous rock. Much of what is known about intrusive igneous activity has come from the study of old, now solid, magma bodies exhumed by erosion.

Nature of Intrusive Bodies

The structures that result from the emplacement of magma into preexisting rocks are called **intrusions** or **plutons**. Because all intrusions form out of view beneath Earth's surface, they are studied primarily after uplifting and erosion have exposed them. The challenge lies in reconstructing the events that generated these structures millions or even hundreds of millions of years ago.

Tabular Intrusive Bodies: Dikes and Sills

Tabular intrusive bodies are produced when magma is forcibly injected into a fracture or zone of weakness, such as a bedding surface (Figure 7.24). **Dikes** are discordant bodies that cut across bedding surfaces or other structures in the host rock. By contrast, **sills** are nearly horizontal, concordant bodies that form when magma exploits weaknesses between sedimentary beds or other structures (**FIGURE** 7.25). In general, dikes serve as tabular conduits that transport magma, whereas sills store magma.

Dikes and sills are typically shallow features, occurring where the host rocks are sufficiently brittle to fracture. Although they can range in thickness from less than a millimeter, to over a kilometer, most are in the 1- to 20-meter range. Because dikes and sills are relatively uniform in thickness and can extend for many kilometers, they are assumed to be the product of very fluid, and therefore, mobile magmas.

Dikes and sills can occur as solitary bodies, but dikes in particular tend to form in roughly parallel groups called *dike swarms*. These multiple structures are thought to reflect the tendency for fractures to form in sets when tensional forces stretch brittle country rock. Dikes can also occur radiating from an eroded volcanic neck, like spokes on a wheel. In these situations the active ascent of magma is thought to have generated fissures in the volcanic cone out of which lava flowed.

Dikes frequently weather more slowly than the surrounding rock. When exposed by erosion, dikes tend to have a wall-like appearance, as shown in Figure 7.23.

FIGURE 7.24 Illustration showing basic igneous structures. **A.** This block diagram shows the relationship between volcanism and intrusive igneous activity. **B.** This view illustrates the basic intrusive igneous structures, some of which have been exposed by erosion long after their formation. **C.** After millions of years of uplifting and erosion, a batholith is exposed at the surface.

In many respects, sills closely resemble buried lava flows. Both are tabular and can have a wide aerial extent and both may exhibit columnar jointing (**FIGURE 7.26**). **Columnar joints** form as igneous rocks cool and develop shrinkage fractures that produce elongated, pillarlike columns. Further, because sills generally form in near-surface environments and may be only a few meters thick, the emplaced magma often cools quickly enough to generate a fine-grained texture. (Recall that most intrusive igneous bodies have a coarse-grained texture.)

FIGURE 7.25   Salt River Canyon, Arizona. The dark, essentially horizontal band is a sill of basaltic composition that intruded horizontal layers of sedimentary rock. (Photo by E. J. Tarbuck)

to 100 kilometers wide; The Sierra Nevada batholith, for example, is a continuous granitic structure that forms much of the Sierra Nevada in California (**FIGURE 7.27**). An even larger batholith extends for over 1800 kilometers (1100 miles) along the Coast Mountains of western Canada and into southern Alaska. Although batholiths can cover a large area, recent gravitational studies indicate that most are less than 10 kilometers (6 miles) thick. Some are even thinner. The Coastal batholith of Peru, for example, is essentially a flat slab with an average thickness of only 2 to 3 kilometers (1 to 2 miles).

Batholiths are almost always made up of felsic and intermediate rock types and are often referred to as "granite batholiths." Large granite batholiths consist of hundreds of plutons that intimately crowd against or penetrate one another. These bulbous masses were emplaced over spans of millions of years. The intrusive activity that created the Sierra Nevada batholith, for example, occurred nearly continuously over a 130-million-year period that ended about 80 million years ago.

By definition, a plutonic body must have a surface exposure greater than 100 square kilometers (40 square miles) to be considered a batholith. Smaller plutons of this type are termed **stocks**. However, many stocks appear to be portions of much larger intrusive bodies that would be called batholiths if they were fully exposed.

A nineteenth-century study by G. K. Gilbert of the U.S. Geological Survey in the Henry Mountains of Utah produced the first clear evidence that igneous intrusions can lift the sedimentary strata they penetrate. Gilbert named the igneous intrusions he observed **laccoliths**, which he envisioned as igneous rock forcibly injected between sedimentary strata, so as to arch the beds above, while leaving those below relatively flat. It is now known that the five major peaks of the Henry Mountains are not laccoliths, but stocks. However, these central magma bodies are the source material for branching offshoots that are true laccoliths, as Gilbert defined them (**FIGURE 7.28**).

FIGURE 7.26   Columnar jointing in basalt. Giants Causeway National Park, Northern Ireland. These five-to seven-sided columns are produced by contraction and fracturing that results as a lava flow or sill gradually cools. (Photo by John Lawrence/Getty Images)

Massive Intrusive Bodies: Batholiths, Stocks, and Laccoliths

By far the largest intrusive igneous bodies are **batholiths** (*bathos* = depth, *lithos* = stone). Batholiths occur as mammoth linear structures several hundreds of kilometers long and up

FIGURE 7.27 An aerial view showing a portion of the Sierra Nevada batholith. Uplift and erosion has exposed this huge intrusive feature. (Photo by Diane Miller/photolibrary.com)

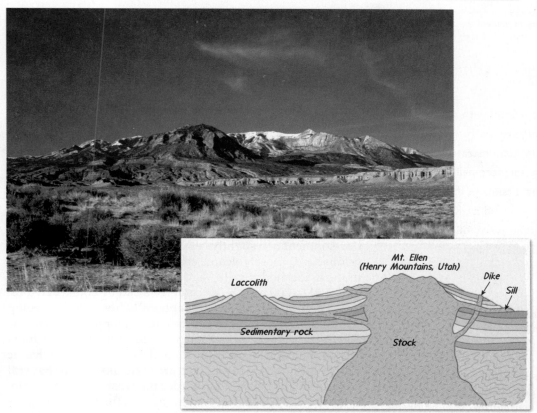

Geologist's Sketch

FIGURE 7.28 Mount Ellen, the northernmost of five peaks that make up Utah's Henry Mountains. Although the main intrusions in the Henry Mountains are stocks, numerous laccoliths formed as offshoots of these structures. (Photo by Michael DeFreitas North America/Alamy)

the circum-Pacific belt known as the *Ring of Fire* (**FIGURE 7.29**). These volcanoes consist mainly of composite cones that emit volatile-rich magma having an intermediate (andesitic) composition and that occasionally produce awe-inspiring eruptions.

A second group includes the basaltic shields that emit very fluid lavas. These volcanic structures comprise most of the islands of the deep ocean basins, including the Hawaiian Islands, the Galapagos, and Easter Island. In addition, this group includes many active submarine volcanoes that dot the ocean floor; particularly notable are the innumerable small seamounts that lay along the axis of the mid-ocean ridge. At these depths, the pressures are so great that the gases that are emitted quickly dissolve in the seawater and never reach the surface. Thus, firsthand knowledge of these eruptions is limited, coming mainly from deep-diving submersibles.

A third group includes volcanic structures that appear to be somewhat randomly distributed in the interiors of the continents. None are found in Australia nor in the eastern two-thirds of North and South America. Africa is notable because it has many potentially active volcanoes including Mount Kilimanjaro, the highest point on the continent (5895 meters, 19,454 feet). Volcanism on continents is the most diverse, ranging from eruptions of very fluid basaltic lavas, such as those that generated the Columbia Plateau, to explosive eruptions of silica-rich rhyolitic magma, as occurred in Yellowstone.

Until the late 1960s, geologists had no explanation for the apparently haphazard distribution of continental volcanoes, nor were they able to account for the almost continuous chain of volcanoes that circles the margin of the Pacific basin. With the development of the theory of plate tectonics, the picture was greatly clarified. Recall that most primary (unaltered) magma originates in the upper mantle and that

PLATE TECTONICS AND IGNEOUS ACTIVITY

Geologists have known for decades that the global distribution of volcanism is not random. Most active volcanoes are located along the margins of the ocean basins—most notably within

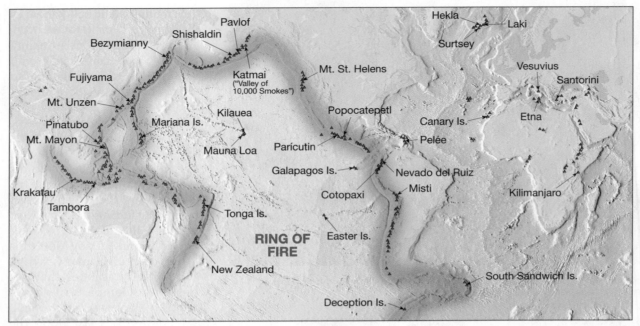

FIGURE 7.29 Locations of some of Earth's major volcanoes.

the mantle is essentially solid, *not molten* rock. The basic connection between plate tectonics and volcanism is that *plate motions provide the mechanisms by which mantle rocks melt to generate magma.*

We will examine three zones of igneous activity and their relationship to plate boundaries. These active areas are located (1) *along convergent plate boundaries,* where plates move toward each other and one sinks beneath the other; (2) *along divergent plate boundaries*, where plates move away from each other and new seafloor is created; and (3) *areas within plates* that are not associated with any plate boundary. These three volcanic settings are depicted in **FIGURE 7.30.**

Volcanism at Convergent Plate Boundaries

Recall that at convergent plate boundaries slabs of oceanic crust are bent as they descend into the mantle, generating an oceanic trench. As a slab sinks deeper into the mantle, the increase in temperature and pressure drives volatiles (mostly water) from the oceanic crust. These mobile fluids migrate upward into the wedge-shaped piece of mantle located between the subducting slab and overriding plate (Figure 7.30A). Once the sinking slab reaches a depth of about 100 kilometers, these water-rich fluids reduce the melting point of hot mantle rock sufficiently to trigger some melting. The partial melting of mantle rock (peridotite) generates magma with a basaltic composition. After a sufficient quantity of magma has accumulated, it slowly migrates upward.

Volcanism at a convergent plate margin results in the development of a slightly curved chain of volcanoes called a *volcanic arc*. These volcanic chains develop roughly parallel to the associated trench—at distances of 200 to 300 kilometers (100 to 200 miles). Volcanic arcs can be constructed on oceanic or continental lithosphere. Those that develop within the ocean and grow large enough for their tops to rise above the surface are labeled *island archipelagos* in most atlases. Geologists prefer the more descriptive term **volcanic island arcs**, or simply **island arcs** (**FIGURE 7.30A**). Several young volcanic island arcs border the western Pacific basin, including the Aleutians, the Tongas, and the Marianas.

Volcanism associated with convergent plate boundaries may also develop where slabs of oceanic lithosphere are subducted under continental lithosphere to produce a **continental volcanic arc** (**FIGURE 7.30E**). The mechanisms that generate these mantle-derived magmas are essentially the same as those operating at island arcs. The major difference is that continental crust is much thicker and is composed of rocks having a higher silica content than oceanic crust. Hence through the assimilation of silica-rich crustal rocks, plus extensive magmatic differentiation, a mantle-derived magma may become highly evolved as it rises through continental crust. Stated another way, the primary magmas generated in the mantle may change from a comparatively dry, fluid basaltic magma to a viscous andesitic or rhyolitic magma having a high concentration of volatiles as it moves up through the continental crust. The volcanic chain of the Andes Mountains along the western margin of South America is perhaps the best example of a mature continental volcanic arc.

Volcanism at Divergent Plate Boundaries

The greatest volume of magma (perhaps 60 percent of Earth's total yearly output) is produced along the oceanic ridge system in association with seafloor spreading (**FIGURE 7.30B**). Below the ridge axis where lithospheric plates are continually being pulled apart, the solid yet mobile mantle responds to the decrease in overburden and rises to fill the rift. As rock rises, it experiences a decrease in confining pressure and undergoes melting without the addition of heat. This process, called *decompression melting,* is the most common process by which mantle rocks melt.

Partial melting of mantle rock at divergent boundaries produces basaltic magma. Because this newly formed magma is less dense than the mantle rock from which it is derived, it rises and collects in reservoirs located just beneath the ridge crest. About 10 percent of the molten rock eventually migrates upward along fissures to erupt as lava flows on the ocean floor. This activity continuously adds new basaltic rock to plate margins, temporarily welding them together, only to break again as seafloor spreading continues. Along some ridges, outpourings of bulbous pillow lavas build numerous small seamounts.

Although divergent boundaries are most often located along the axis of an oceanic ridge, some are not. In particular, the East African Rift is a site where continental lithosphere is being pulled apart (**FIGURE 7.30F**). In this setting, magma is generated by decompression melting in the same manner as along the oceanic ridge system. Vast outpourings of fluid lavas as well as basaltic shield volcanoes are common in this region.

Intraplate Volcanism

We know why igneous activity is initiated along plate boundaries, but why do eruptions occur in the interiors of plates? Hawaii's Kilauea is considered the world's most active volcano, yet it is situated thousands of kilometers from the nearest plate boundary in the middle of the vast Pacific plate (**FIGURE 7.30C**). Other sites of **intraplate volcanism** (meaning "within the plate") include the Canary Islands, Yellowstone, and several volcanic centers that you may be surprised to learn are located in the Sahara Desert of Africa.

Geologists now recognize that most intraplate volcanism occurs where a mass of hotter than normal mantle material called a **mantle plume** ascends toward the surface (**FIGURE 7.30C**). Although the depth at which mantle plumes originate is still hotly debated, some appear to form deep within Earth at the core-mantle boundary. These plumes of solid yet mobile mantle rock rise toward the surface in a manner similar to the blobs that form within a lava lamp. (These are the trendy lamps that contain two immiscible liquids in a glass container. As the base of the lamp is heated, the denser liquid at the bottom becomes buoyant and forms blobs that rise to the top.) Like the blobs in a lava lamp, a mantle plume has a bulbous head that draws out a narrow stalk beneath it as it rises. Once the plume head nears the top of the mantle, decompression melting generates basaltic magma that may eventually trigger volcanism at the surface.

The result is a localized volcanic region a few hundred kilometers across called a **hot spot** (**FIGURE 7.30C**). More than 40 hot spots have been identified, and most have persisted for millions of years. The land surface surrounding a hot spot is often elevated, because it is buoyed up by the rising plume of warm low-density material. Furthermore, by measuring the heat flow in these regions, geologists have determined that the mantle beneath hot spots must be 100 to 150°C hotter than normal mantle material.

Mantle plumes are responsible for the vast outpourings of basaltic lava that created the large basalt plateaus including the Siberian Traps in Russia, India's Deccan Plateau, and the Ontong Java Plateau on the floor of the western Pacific. The most widely accepted explanation for these eruptions, which emit extremely large volumes of basaltic lava over relatively short time intervals, involves a plume with a monstrous head. Upon reaching the base of the lithosphere, the unusually hot, massive head begins to melt. Melting progresses rapidly, causing the burst of volcanism that emits voluminous outpourings of lava to form a huge basalt plateau in a matter of a million or so years.

LIVING WITH VOLCANOES

About 10 percent of Earth's population lives in the vicinity of an active volcano. In fact, several major cities including Seattle, Washington; Mexico City, Mexico; Tokyo, Japan; Naples, Italy; and Quito, Ecuador, are located on or near a volcano (**FIGURE 7.31**).

A. Convergent plate volcanism
(Island arc)

Volcanic island arc

Trench

Oceanic crust

Marginal sea

Continental crust

Mantle rock melts

Water driven from plate

Subducting oceanic lithosphere

Asthenosphere

Mount Augustine, Alaska (USGS)

C. Intraplate volcanism
(Oceanic)

Oceanic crust

Hot spot

Hawaii

Decompression melting

Rising mantle plume

North America

Hawaii

South America

Kilauea, Hawaii
(J. D. Griggs/USGS)

Continental volcanic arc

Trench

Oceanic crust

Continental crust

Subducting oceanic lithosphere

Mantle rock melts

Water driven from plate

E. Convergent plate volcanism
(Continental volcanic arc)

FIGURE 7.30 Three zones of volcanism. Two of the zones are associated with plate boundaries. The third zone includes those volcanic structures that are irregularly distributed in the interiors of plates.

B. Divergent plate volcanism
(Oceanic ridge)

Oceanic crust

Magma chamber

Decompression melting

Asthenosphere

Iceland (Wedigo Ferchland)

Mid-Atlantic Ridge

Deccan Plateau

Africa

East Africa Rift Valley

D. Intraplate volcanism
(Continental)

Flood basalts

Hot spot

Continental crust

Decompression melting

Rising mantle plume

Rift valley

Continental crust

Decompression melting

Mount Kilimanjaro, Africa
(Daryl Balfour)

F. Divergent plate volcanism
(Continental rifting)

231

FIGURE 7.31 Seattle, Washington, with Mount Rainier in the background. (Photo by Ken Straiton/Corbis)

Volcanic Hazards

Volcanoes produce a wide variety of potential hazards that can kill people and wildlife, as well as destroy property (**FIGURE 7.32**). Perhaps the greatest threats to life are pyroclastic flows. These hot mixtures of gas, ash, and pumice that sometimes exceed 800°C race down the flanks of volcanoes, giving people little chance to escape.

Lahars, which can occur even when a volcano is quiet, are perhaps the next most dangerous volcanic hazard (**FIGURE 7.33**). These mixtures of volcanic debris and water can flow for tens of kilometers down steep volcanic slopes at speeds that may exceed 100 kilometers (60 miles) per hour. Lahars pose a potential threat to many communities downstream from glacier-clad volcanoes such as Mount Rainier. Other potentially destructive mass-wasting events include the rapid collapse of the volcano's summit or flank.

Other obvious hazards include explosive eruptions that can endanger people and property hundreds of miles from a

Until recently the dominant view of Western societies was that humans possess the wherewithal to subdue volcanoes and other types of catastrophic natural hazards. Today it is apparent that volcanoes are not only very destructive but unpredictable as well. With this awareness, a new attitude is developing—"How do we live with volcanoes?"

FIGURE 7.32 Simplified drawing showing a wide variety of natural hazards associated with volcanoes. (After U.S. Geological Survey)

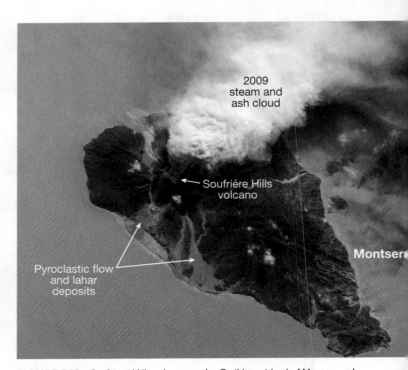

FIGURE 7.33 Soufriere Hills volcano on the Caribbean island of Montserrat has been active since 1995. A pyroclastic flow destroyed the airport and the capital city, Plymouth. About two thirds of the population have left the island. (NASA Photo)

volcano. During the past 15 years at least 80 commercial jets have been damaged by inadvertently flying into clouds of volcanic ash (Figure 7.33). One of these was a near crash that occurred in 1989 when a Boeing 747, with more than 300 passengers aboard, encountered an ash cloud from Alaska's Redoubt volcano. All four engines stalled after they became clogged with ash. Fortunately, the engines were restarted at the last minute and the aircraft managed to land safely in Anchorage.

Monitoring Volcanic Activity

Today a number of volcano-monitoring techniques are employed, with most of them aimed at detecting the movement of magma from a subterranean reservoir (typically several kilometers deep) toward the surface. The four most noticeable changes in a volcanic landscape caused by the migration of magma are (1) changes in the pattern of volcanic earthquakes; (2) expansion of a near-surface magma chamber, which leads to inflation of the volcano; (3) changes in the amount and/or composition of the gases that are released from a volcano; and (4) an increase in ground temperature caused by the emplacement of new magma.

Almost a third of all volcanoes that have erupted in historic times are now monitored using seismographs, instruments that detect earthquake tremors. In general, a sharp increase in seismic unrest followed by a period of relative quiet has been shown to be a precursor for many volcanic eruptions. However, some large volcanic structures have exhibited lengthy periods of seismic unrest. For example, Rabaul Caldera in New Guinea recorded a strong increase in seismicity in 1981. This activity lasted 13 years and finally culminated with an eruption in 1994. Occasionally, a large earthquake triggers a volcanic eruption, or at least disturbs the volcano's plumbing. Kilauea, for example, began to erupt after the Kalapana earthquake of 1977.

The roof of a volcano may rise as new magma accumulates in its interior—a phenomena that precedes many volcanic eruptions. Because the accessibility of many volcanoes is limited, remote sensing devices, including lasers, Doppler radar, and Earth orbiting satellites, are often used to determine whether or not a volcano is swelling. The recent discovery of ground doming at Three Sisters volcanoes in Oregon was first detected using radar images obtained from satellites (**FIGURE 7.34**).

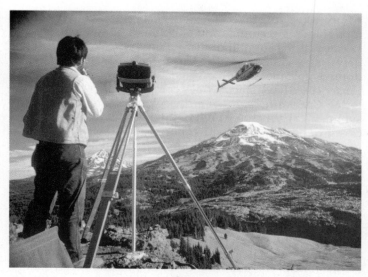

FIGURE 7.34   Monitoring South Sister Volcano, Cascade Range, Oregon. This geologist is measuring the degree of inflation of the volcano's surface for potential eruptive activity.

Volcanologists also frequently monitor the gases that are released from volcanoes in an effort to detect even minor changes in their amount and/or composition. Some volcanoes show an increase in sulfur dioxide (SO_2) emissions months or years prior to an eruption. On the other hand, a few days prior to the 1991 eruption of Mount Pinatubo, emissions of carbon dioxide (CO_2) dropped dramatically.

The development of remote sensing devices has greatly increased our ability to monitor volcanoes. These instruments and techniques are particularly useful for monitoring eruptions in progress. Photographic images and infrared (heat) sensors can detect lava flows and volcanic columns rising from a volcano. Furthermore, satellites can detect ground deformation as well as monitor SO_2 emissions.

The overriding goal of all monitoring is to discover precursors that may warn of an imminent eruption. This is accomplished by first diagnosing the current condition of a volcano and then using this baseline data to predict its future behavior. Stated another way, a volcano must be observed over an extended period to recognize significant changes from its "resting state."

THE CHAPTER IN REVIEW

• The primary factors that determine the nature of volcanic eruptions include the magma's *temperature*, its *composition*, and the *amount of dissolved gases* it contains. As lava cools, it begins to congeal; and as *viscosity* increases, its mobility decreases. *The viscosity of magma is directly related to its silica content.* Rhyolitic lava, with its high silica content, is very viscous and forms short, thick flows. *Basaltic* lava, with a lower silica content, is more fluid and may travel a long distance before

congealing. Dissolved gases provide the force that propels molten rock from the vent of a volcano.

• The materials associated with a volcanic eruption include *lava flows* (*pahoehoe* and *aa* flows for basaltic lavas); *gases* (primarily in the form of *water vapor*); and *pyroclastic material* (pulverized rock and lava fragments blown from the volcano's vent, which include *ash, pumice, lapilli, cinders, blocks,* and *bombs*).

• Successive eruptions of lava from a central vent result in a mountainous accumulation of material known as a *volcano*. Located at the summit of many volcanoes is a steep-walled depression called a *crater*. *Shield cones* are broad, slightly domed volcanoes built primarily of fluid, basaltic lava. *Cinder cones* have steep slopes composed of pyroclastic material. *Composite cones*, or *stratovolcanoes*, are large, nearly symmetrical structures built of interbedded lavas and pyroclastic deposits. Composite cones produce some of the most violent volcanic activity. Often associated with a violent eruption is a *nuée ardente*, a fiery cloud of hot gases infused with incandescent ash that races down steep volcanic slopes. Large composite cones may also generate a type of mudflow known as a *lahar*.

• Most volcanoes are fed by *conduits* or *pipes*. As erosion progresses, the rock occupying the pipe is often more resistant and may remain standing above the surrounding terrain as a *volcanic neck*. The summits of some volcanoes have large, nearly circular depressions called *calderas* that result from collapse following an explosive eruption. Calderas also form on shield volcanoes by subterranean drainage from a central magma chamber, and the largest calderas form by the discharge of colossal volumes of silica-rich pumice along ring fractures. Although volcanic eruptions from a central vent are the most familiar, by far the largest amounts of volcanic material are extruded from cracks in the crust called *fissures*. The term *flood basalt* describes the fluid, waterlike, basaltic lava flows that cover an extensive region in the northwestern

United States known as the Columbia Plateau. When silica-rich magma is extruded, *pyroclastic flows* consisting largely of ash and pumice fragments usually result.

• Intrusive igneous bodies are classified according to their *shape* and by their *orientation with respect to the host rock*, generally sedimentary rock. The two general shapes are *tabular* (tablelike) and *massive*. Intrusive igneous bodies that cut across existing sedimentary beds are said to be *discordant*, whereas those that form parallel to existing sedimentary beds are *concordant*.

• *Dikes* are tabular, discordant igneous bodies produced when magma is injected into fractures that cut across rock layers. Tabular, concordant bodies called *sills* form when magma is injected along the bedding surfaces of sedimentary rocks. *Laccoliths* are similar to sills but form from less-fluid magma that collects as a lens-shaped mass that arches the overlying strata upward. *Batholiths*, the largest intrusive igneous bodies with surface exposures of more than 100 square kilometers (40 square miles), frequently make up the cores of mountains.

• *Most active volcanoes are associated with plate boundaries.* Active areas of volcanism are found along oceanic ridges where seafloor spreading is occurring (*divergent plate boundaries*), in the vicinity of ocean trenches where one plate is being subducted beneath another (*convergent plate boundaries*), and in the interiors of plates themselves (*intraplate volcanism*). Rising plumes of hot mantle rock are the source of most intraplate volcanism.

KEY TERMS

aa flow (p. 212)	discordant (p. 224)	lahar (p. 220)	scoria cone (p. 216)
batholith (p. 226)	eruption columns (p. 210)	lava tube (p. 212)	shield volcano (p. 215)
caldera (p. 221)	fissure (p. 222)	mantle plume (p. 229)	sill (p. 224)
cinder cone (p. 216)	fissure eruption (p. 223)	massive (p. 224)	stocks (p. 226)
columnar joint (p. 225)	flood basalt (p. 223)	nuée ardente (p. 218)	stratovolcano (p. 218)
composite cone (p. 218)	fumarole (p. 215)	pahoehoe flow (p. 212)	tabular (p. 224)
concordant (p. 224)	hot spot (p. 229)	parasitic cone (p. 215)	vent (p. 214)
conduit (p. 214)	intraplate volcanism (p. 229)	pipe (p. 214)	viscosity (p. 209)
continental volcanic arc (p. 228)	intrusions (p. 224)	pluton (p. 224)	volatiles (p. 209)
crater (p. 214)	island arc (p. 228)	pyroclastic flow (p. 218)	volcanic island arc (p. 228)
dike (p. 224)	laccolith (p. 226)	pyroclastic materials (p. 213)	volcanic neck (p. 223)
			volcano (p. 214)

QUESTIONS FOR REVIEW

1. What is the difference between *magma* and *lava*?
2. List the three factors that determine the nature of a volcanic eruption. What role does each play?
3. Why is a volcano fed by highly viscous magma likely to be a greater threat than a volcano supplied with very fluid magma?
4. Describe *pahoehoe* and *aa* lava.

5. List the main gases released during a volcanic eruption. What role do gases play in volcanic eruptions?
6. Analysis of samples taken during Hawaiian eruptions on the island of Hawaii indicate that _____ was the most abundant gas released.
7. How do volcanic bombs differ from blocks of pyroclastic debris?

8. Compare a volcanic *crater* to a *caldera*.

9. Compare and contrast the three main types of volcanoes (size, shape, eruptive style, and so forth).

10. Name a prominent example of each of the three types of volcanoes.

11. Compare the formation of Hawaii with that of Parícutin.

12. Describe the formation of Crater Lake. Compare it to the caldera formed during the eruption of Kilauea.

13. What is Shiprock, New Mexico, and how did it form?

14. How do the eruptions that created the Columbia Plateau differ from eruptions that create large composite cones?

15. Describe each of the five intrusive igneous features discussed in the text (*dike, sill, laccolith, stock,* and *batholith*).

16. Why might a laccolith be detected at Earth's surface before being exposed by erosion?

17. What is the largest of all intrusive igneous bodies? Is it tabular or massive? Concordant or discordant?

18. Volcanism at divergent plate boundaries is associated with which rock type? What causes rocks to melt in these regions?

19. What is the Ring of Fire?

20. What type of plate boundary is associated with the Ring of Fire?

21. Are volcanic eruptions in the Ring of Fire generally quiet or violent? Name a volcano that would support your answer.

22. How is magma generated at convergent plate boundaries?

23. The Hawaiian Islands and Yellowstone National Park are thought to be associated with which of the three zones of volcanism?

24. What is the source of magma for the zone referred to in the previous questions.

25. Volcanic islands in the deep ocean are composed primarily of which igneous rock type?

26. What are the four changes in a volcanic area that are monitored in order to detect the movement of magma?

27. List at least two reasons why an eruption of Mount Rainier similar to the one that occurred at Mount St. Helens in 1980 would be considerably more destructive.

28. Describe four natural hazards associated with volcanoes.

COMPANION WEBSITE

The *Foundations of Earth Science* Website uses the resources and flexibility of the Internet to aid in your study of the topics in this chapter. Written and developed by the authors and other Earth science instructors, this site will help improve your understanding of Earth science. Visit **www.mygeoscienceplace.com** in order to:

• **Review** key chapter concepts.

• **Read** with links to the ebook and to chapter-specific web resources.

• **Visualize** and comprehend challenging topics using learning activities in *GEODe: Earth Science.*

• **Test** yourself with online quizzes.

GEODe: EARTH SCIENCE

GEODe: Earth Science is a valuable and easy to use learning aid that can be accessed from your book's Companion Website: **www.mygeoscienceplace.com**. It is a dynamic instructional tool that promotes understanding and reinforces important concepts by using tutorials, animations, and exercises that actively engage the student.

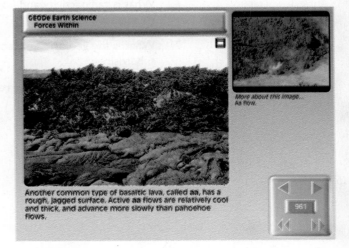

GEOLOGIC TIME

FOCUS ON LEARNING

To assist you in learning the important concepts in this chapter, you will find it helpful to focus on the following questions:

1. What is the doctrine of uniformitarianism? How does it differ from catastrophism?

2. What are the two types of dates used by geologists when they interpret Earth history?

3. What are the basic laws, principles, and techniques used to establish relative dates?

4. What are fossils? What conditions favor the preservation of organisms as fossils?

5. How are fossils used to correlate rocks of similar ages that are in different places?

6. What is radioactivity, and how are radioactive isotopes used in radiometric dating?

7. What is the geologic time scale, and what are its principal subdivisions?

8. Why is it difficult to assign reliable numerical dates to samples of sedimentary rock?

Paleontologists excavating the remains of an Ice Age mammoth near Hot Springs in the Black Hills of South Dakota. These animals were prehistoric relatives of modern elephants. Fossils are important tools in deciphering Earth history.

(Photo by Richard T. Nowitz/Photo Researchers, Inc.)

In the eighteenth century, James Hutton recognized the immensity of Earth history and the importance of time as a component in all geologic processes. In the nineteenth century, others effectively demonstrated that Earth had experienced many episodes of mountain building and erosion, which must have required great spans of geologic time. Although these pioneering scientists understood that Earth was very old, they had no way of knowing its true age. Was it tens of millions, hundreds of millions, or even billions of years old? Rather, a geologic time scale was developed that showed the sequence of events based on relative dating principles. What were these principles? What part did fossils play? With the discovery of radioactivity and the development of radiometric dating techniques, geologists can now assign fairly accurate dates to many of the events in Earth history. What is radioactivity? Why is it a good "clock" for dating the geologic past? This chapter will answer these questions.

GEOLOGY NEEDS A TIME SCALE

In 1869, John Wesley Powell, who was later to head the U.S. Geological Survey, led a pioneering expedition down the Colorado River and through the Grand Canyon (**FIGURE 8.1**)*. Writing about the strata that were exposed by the downcutting of the river, Powell observed that "the canyons of this region would be a Book of Revelations in the rock-leaved Bible of geology." He was undoubtedly impressed with the millions of years of Earth history exposed along the walls of the Grand Canyon (**FIGURE 8.2**).

Powell realized that the evidence for an ancient Earth is concealed in its rocks. Like the pages in a long and complicated history book, rocks record the geologic events and changing life forms of the past. The book, however, is not complete. Many pages, especially in the early chapters, are missing. Others are tattered, torn, or smudged. Yet, enough of the book remains to allow much of the story to be deciphered.

Interpreting Earth history is an important goal of geology. Like a modern-day sleuth, the geologist must interpret clues found preserved in the rocks. By studying rocks, especially sedimentary rocks, and the features they contain, geologists can unravel the complexities of the past.

Geologic events by themselves, however, have little meaning until they are put into a time perspective. Studying

A.

FIGURE 8.1 **A.** Start of the expedition from Green River station. A drawing from Powell's 1875 book. **B.** Major John Wesley Powell, pioneering geologist and the second director of the U.S. Geological Survey. (Courtesy of the U.S. Geological Survey, Denver)

Down the Great Unknown, a book by Edward Dolnick (HarperCollins, 2001), is a fascinating account of the journey.

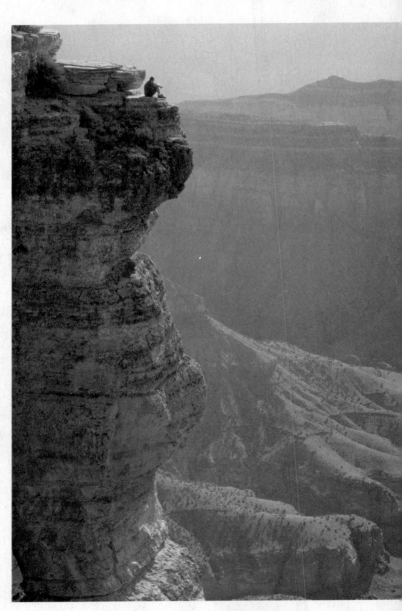

FIGURE 8.2 This hiker is resting atop the Kaibab Formation, the uppermost layer in the Grand Canyon. Hundreds of millions of years of Earth history is contained in the strata that lay beneath him. This is a view of Cape Royal on the Grand Canyon's North Rim. (Photo by Michael Collier)

history, whether it be the Civil War or the Age of Dinosaurs, requires a calendar. Among geology's major contributions is a calendar called the *geologic time scale* and the discovery that Earth history is exceedingly long.

The geologists who developed the geologic time scale revolutionized the way people think about time and perceive our planet. They learned that Earth is much older than anyone had previously imagined and that its surface and interior have been changed over and over again by the same geologic processes that operate today.

SOME HISTORICAL NOTES ABOUT GEOLOGY

The nature of our Earth—its materials and processes—has been a focus of study for centuries. However, the late 1700s is generally regarded as the beginning of modern geology. It was during this time that James Hutton published his important work, *Theory of the Earth*. Prior to this time, a great many explanations about Earth history relied on supernatural events.

Catastrophism

In the mid-1600s, James Ussher, Anglican Archbishop of Armagh, Primate of All Ireland, published a work that had immediate and profound influence. A respected scholar of the Bible, Ussher constructed a chronology of human and Earth history in which he determined that Earth was only a few thousand years old, having been created in 4004 B.C. Ussher's treatise earned widespread acceptance among Europe's scientific and religious leaders, and his chronology was soon printed in the margins of the Bible itself.

During the 1600s and 1700s, the doctrine of **catastrophism** strongly influenced people's thinking about Earth. Briefly stated, catastrophists believed that Earth's varied landscapes had been fashioned primarily by great catastrophes. Features such as mountains and canyons, which today we know take great periods of time to form, were explained as having been produced by sudden and often worldwide disasters of unknowable causes that no longer operate. This philosophy was an attempt to fit the rate of Earth's processes to the prevailing ideas on Earth's age.

The Birth of Modern Geology

When James Hutton, a Scottish physician and gentleman farmer, published his *Theory of the Earth* in the late 1700s, he put forth a principle that is a pillar of geology today, **uniformitarianism**. It states that *the physical, chemical, and biological laws that operate today have also operated in the geologic past.* This means that the forces and processes that we observe presently shaping our planet have been at work for a very long time. Thus, to understand ancient rocks, we must first understand present-day processes and their results. This idea is commonly expressed by saying, "The present is the key to the past."

Prior to Hutton's *Theory of the Earth*, no one had effectively demonstrated that geologic processes occur over extremely long periods of time. However, Hutton persuasively argued that processes that appear weak and slow acting could, over long spans of time, produce effects that were just as great as those resulting from sudden catastrophic events. Unlike his predecessors, Hutton cited verifiable observations to support his ideas.

For example, when he argued that mountains are sculpted and ultimately destroyed by weathering and the work of running water, and that their wastes are carried to the oceans by processes that can be observed, Hutton said, "We have a chain of facts which clearly demonstrates that the materials of the wasted mountains have traveled through the rivers"; and further, "There is not one step in all this progress that is not to be actually perceived." He then went on to summarize these thoughts by asking a question and immediately providing the answer: "What more can we require? Nothing but time."

Geology Today

The basic tenets of uniformitarianism are just as viable today as in Hutton's day. We realize more strongly than ever that the present gives us insight into the past and that the physical, chemical, and biological laws that govern geologic processes remain unchanging through time. However, we also understand that the doctrine should not be taken too literally. To say that geologic processes in the past were the same as those occurring today is not to suggest that they always had the same relative importance or that they operated at precisely the same rate. Moreover, some important geologic processes are not currently observable, but evidence that they occur is well established. For example, we know that Earth has experienced impacts from large meteorites even though we have no human witnesses. Such events altered Earth's crust, modified its climate, and strongly influenced life on the planet.

The acceptance of the concept of uniformitarianism, however, meant the acceptance of a very long history for Earth. Although Earth's processes vary in their intensity, they still take a long time to create or destroy major landscape features. For example, geologists have established that mountains once existed in portions of present-day Minnesota, Wisconsin, Michigan, and Manitoba. Today, the region consists of low hills and plains. Erosion (processes that wear land away) gradually destroyed these peaks. Estimates indicate that the North American continent is being lowered at a rate of about 3 centimeters (1 inch) per 1000 years. At this rate, it would take 100 million years for water, wind, and ice to lower mountains that were 3000 meters (10,000 feet) high.

But even this time span is relatively short on the time scale of Earth history, because the rock record shows that Earth has experienced *many cycles* of mountain building and erosion. Concerning the ever-changing nature of Earth through great expanses of geologic time, Hutton made a statement that was to become his most famous. In concluding his classic 1788 paper published in the *Transactions of the Royal Society of Edinburgh*, he stated, "The results, therefore, of our present enquiry is, that we find no vestige of a beginning—no prospect of an end."

It is important to remember that although many features of our physical landscape may seem to be unchanging over the decades we might observe them, they are nevertheless changing, but on time scales of hundreds, thousands, or even many millions of years.

RELATIVE DATING—KEY PRINCIPLES

Deciphering Earth History
▼ Relative Dating

The geologists who developed the geologic time scale revolutionized the way people think about time and perceive our planet. They learned that Earth is much older than anyone had previously imagined and that its surface and interior have been changed over and over again by the same geologic processes that operate today.

During the late 1800s and early 1900s, various attempts were made to determine Earth's age. Although some of the methods appeared promising at the time, none proved to be reliable. What these scientists were seeking was a **numerical date**. Such dates specify the actual number of years that have passed since an event occurred. Today, our understanding of radioactivity allows us to accurately determine numerical dates for many rocks that represent important events in Earth's distant past. We will study radioactivity later in this chapter. Prior to the discovery of radioactivity, geologists had no accurate and dependable method of numerical dating and had to rely solely on relative dating.

Relative dating means that rocks are placed in their proper *sequence of formation*—which formed first, second, third, and so on. Relative dating cannot tell us how long ago something took place, only that it followed one event and preceded another. The relative dating techniques that were developed are valuable and still widely used. Numerical dating methods did not replace these techniques; they simply supplemented them. To establish a relative time scale, a few simple principles or rules had to be discovered and applied. Although they may seem obvious to us today, they were major breakthroughs in thinking at the time, and their discovery and acceptance were important scientific achievements.

Law of Superposition

Nicolaus Steno (1638–1686), a Danish anatomist, geologist, and priest, is credited with being the first to recognize a sequence of historical events in an outcrop of sedimentary rock layers. Working in the mountains of western Italy, Steno applied a very simple rule that became the most basic principle of relative dating—the **law of superposition**. The law simply states that in an undeformed sequence of sedimentary rocks, each bed is older than the one above it and younger than the one below. Although it may seem obvious that a rock layer could not be deposited unless it had something older beneath it for support, it was not until 1669 that Steno clearly stated the principle.

This rule also applies to other surface-deposited materials such as lava flows and beds of ash from volcanic eruptions. Applying the law of superposition to the beds exposed in the upper portion of the Grand Canyon (**FIGURE 8.3**), you can

Youngest ↑

Oldest

Kaibab Limestone—shallow marine limestone that rims much of the canyon

Toroweap Formation—shallow marine, thin-to-medium bedded sandy limestone

Coconino Sandstone—cliff-forming cross-bedded sandstone

Hermit Shale—red, slope-forming thinly-bedded shales and siltstones

Supai Group—alternating layers of sandstone, siltstone and shale

Geologist's Sketch

FIGURE 8.3 Applying the law of superposition to these layers exposed in the upper portion of the Grand Canyon, the Supai Group is oldest and the Kaibab Limestone is youngest. (Photo by E. J. Tarbuck)

easily place the layers in their proper order. Among those that are shown, the sedimentary rocks in the Supai Group must be the oldest, followed in order by the Hermit Shale, Coconino Sandstone, Toroweap Formation, and Kaibab Limestone.

Principle of Original Horizontality

Steno is also credited with recognizing the **principle of original horizontality**. This principle simply states that most layers of sediment are deposited in a horizontal position. Thus, if we observe rock layers that are flat, it means they have not been disturbed and still have their *original* horizontality. The layers in the Grand Canyon illustrate this in Figure 8.2 and Figure 8.3. But if they are folded or inclined at a steep angle, they must have been moved into that position by crustal disturbances sometime *after* their deposition (**FIGURE 8.4**).

Principle of Cross-Cutting Relationships

When a fault cuts through other rocks, or when magma intrudes and crystallizes, we can assume that the fault or intrusion is younger than the rocks affected. For example, in **FIGURE 8.5**, the faults and dikes clearly must have occurred *after* the sedimentary layers were deposited.

This is the **principle of cross-cutting relationships**. By applying the cross-cutting principle, you can see that fault A occurred *after* the sandstone layer was deposited, because it "broke" the layer. However, fault A occurred *before* the conglomerate was laid down, because that layer is unbroken.

We can also state that dike B and its associated sill are older than dike A, because dike A cuts the sill. In the same manner, we know that the batholith was emplaced after movement occurred along fault B, but before dike B was formed. This is true because the batholith cuts across fault B, and dike B cuts across the batholith.

Inclusions

Sometimes inclusions can aid the relative dating process. **Inclusions** are fragments of one rock unit that have been enclosed within another. The basic principle is logical and straightforward. The rock mass adjacent to the one containing the inclusions must have been there first in order to provide the rock fragments. Therefore, the rock mass containing inclusions is the younger of the two. **FIGURE 8.6** provides an example. In part A, we know that the intrusive igneous rock is younger because it contains inclusions of the surrounding rock. In part C, the inclusions of intrusive igneous rock in the adjacent sedimentary layer (above

FIGURE 8.4 Most layers of sediment are deposited in a nearly horizontal position. Thus, when we see rock layers that are folded or tilted, we can assume that they must have been moved into that position by crustal disturbances *after* their deposition. These folded strata are at Agio Pavlos on the Mediterranean island of Crete. (Photo by Marco Simoni/Robert Harding)

FIGURE 8.5 Cross-cutting relationships are an important principle used in relative dating. An intrusive rock body is younger than the rocks it intrudes. A fault is younger than the rock layers it cuts.

A. Intrusive igneous rock

B. Exposure and weathering of intrusive igneous rock

C. Deposition of sedimentary layers

FIGURE 8.6 These diagrams illustrate two ways that inclusions can form, as well as a type of unconformity termed a *nonconformity*. In part **A**, the inclusions in the igneous mass represent unmelted remnants of the surrounding host rock that were broken off and incorporated at the time the magma was intruded. In part **C**, the igneous rock must be older than the overlying sedimentary beds because the sedimentary beds contain inclusions of the igneous rock. When older intrusive igneous rocks are overlain by younger sedimentary layers, a *nonconformity* is said to exist. The inset shows a close-up of an inclusion of igneous rock in a younger host rock.

representing certain spans of geologic time. However, no place on Earth has a complete set of conformable strata.

Throughout Earth history, the deposition of sediment has been interrupted again and again. All such breaks in the rock record are termed *unconformities*. An **unconformity** represents a long period during which deposition ceased, erosion removed previously formed rocks, and then deposition resumed. In each case, Earth's crust has undergone uplift and erosion, followed by subsidence and renewed sedimentation. Unconformities are important features because they represent significant geologic events in Earth history. Moreover, their recognition helps us identify which intervals of time are not represented by strata and are missing from the geologic record.

The rocks exposed in the Grand Canyon of the Colorado River represent a tremendous span of geologic history. It is a wonderful place to take a trip through time. The canyon's colorful strata record a long history of sedimentation in a variety of environments—advancing seas, rivers and deltas, tidal flats, and sand dunes. But the record is not continuous. Unconformities represent vast amounts of time that are not accounted for in the canyon's layers. **FIGURE 8.7** is a geologic cross section of the Grand Canyon. Refer to it as you read about three basic types of unconformities: angular unconformities, disconformities, and nonconformities.

the line labeled "nonconformity") indicate that the sedimentary layer was deposited on top of an eroded igneous mass rather than being intruded from below by a mass of magma that later crystallized.

Unconformities

When we observe layers of rock that have been deposited essentially without interruption, we call them **conformable**. Many areas exhibit conformable beds

Angular Unconformity

The most easily recognized unconformity is **angular unconformity**. It consists of tilted or folded sedimentary rocks that are overlain by younger, more flat-lying strata. An angular unconformity indicates that during the pause in deposition, a period of deformation (folding or tilting) as well as erosion occurred. The steps in **FIGURE 8.8** illustrate this process.

When James Hutton studied an angular unconformity in Scotland more than 200 years ago, it was clear to him that it

FIGURE 8.7   This cross section through the Grand Canyon illustrates the three basic types of unconformities. An angular unconformity can be seen between the tilted Precambrian Unkar Group and the Cambrian Tapeats Sandstone. Two disconformities are marked, above and below the Redwall Limestone. A nonconformity occurs between the igneous and metamorphic rocks exposed in the inner gorge and the sedimentary strata of the Unkar Group. A nonconformity, highlighted by a photo, also occurs between the rocks of the inner gorge and the Tapeats Sandstone.

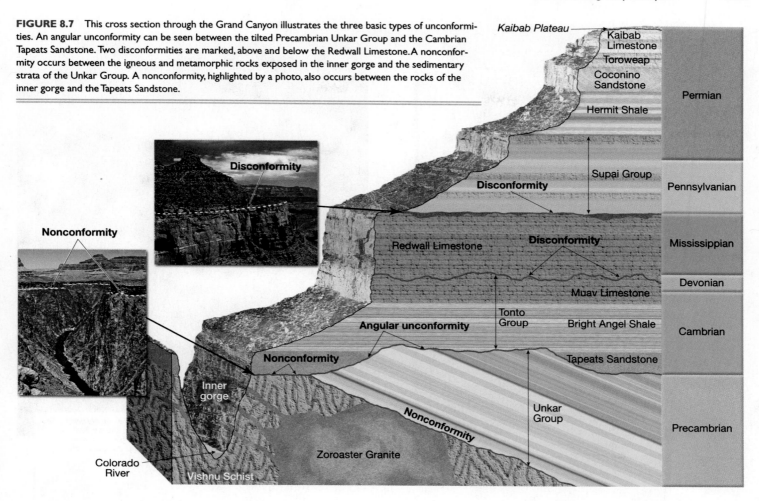

represented a major episode of geologic activity (**FIGURE 8.9**). He also appreciated the immense time span implied by such relationships. Later, when a companion wrote of their visit to the site, he stated that, "The mind seemed to grow giddy by looking so far into the abyss of time."

Disconformity

When contrasted with angular unconformities, **disconformities** are more common but usually far less conspicuous because the strata on either side are essentially parallel. Many disconformities are difficult to identify because the rocks above and below are similar and there is little evidence of erosion. Such a break often resembles an ordinary bedding plane. Other disconformities are easier to identify because the ancient erosion surface is cut deeply into the older rocks below. Two disconformities are labeled on the geological cross section of the Grand Canyon in Figure 8.7.

Nonconformity

The third basic type of unconformity is **nonconformity**. Here, the break separates older metamorphic or intrusive

igneous rocks from younger sedimentary strata (see Figure 8.6). Just as angular unconformities and disconformities imply crustal movements, so, too, do nonconformities. Intrusive igneous masses and metamorphic rocks originate far below the surface. For a nonconformity to develop, a period of uplift and the erosion of overlying rocks must occur. Once exposed at the surface, the igneous or metamorphic rocks are subjected to weathering and erosion prior to subsidence and the renewal of sedimentation.

Applying Relative Dating Principles

By applying the principles of relative dating to the hypothetical geologic cross section shown in **FIGURE 8.10**, the rocks and the events in Earth history they represent can be placed into their proper sequence. The statements within the figure summarize the logic used to interpret the cross section. In this example, we establish a relative time scale for the rocks and events in the area of the cross section. Remember, we do not know how many years of Earth history are represented, nor do we know how this area compares to any other.

A. Deposition

B. Uplifting and folding

Uplift

C. Erosion

6 (Angular unconformity)

Sea level

D. Subsidence and renewed deposition

TIME

FIGURE 8.8 Formation of an angular unconformity. An angular unconformity represents a period during which deformation and erosion occurred.

CORRELATION OF ROCK LAYERS

To develop a geologic time scale that applies to the entire Earth, rocks of similar age in different regions must be matched up. Such a task is referred to as **correlation**. Within a limited area, correlating the rocks of one locality with those of another may be done simply by walking along the outcropping edges. However, this may not be possible when a bed is not continuously exposed. Correlation over short distances is often achieved by noting the position of a rock layer in a sequence of strata. Or, a layer may be identified in another location if it consists of very distinctive or uncommon minerals.

By correlating the rocks from one place to another, a more comprehensive view of the geologic history of a region is possible. **FIGURE 8.11** shows the correlation of strata at three sites on the Colorado Plateau in southern Utah and northern Arizona. No single locale exhibits the entire sequence, but correlation reveals a more complete picture of the sedimentary rock record.

Many geologic studies involve relatively small areas. Such studies are important in their own right, but their full

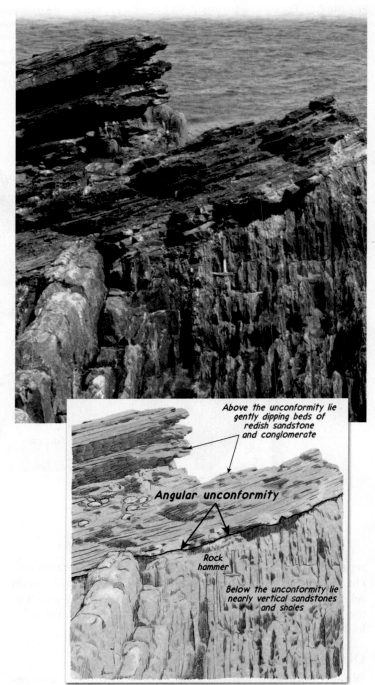

Above the unconformity lie gently dipping beds of redish sandstone and conglomerate

Angular unconformity

Rock hammer

Below the unconformity lie nearly vertical sandstones and shales

Geologist's Sketch

FIGURE 8.9 This angular unconformity at Siccar Point, Scotland, was first described by James Hutton more than 200 years ago. (Photo by Marli Miller)

DID YOU KNOW?

The *word fossil* comes from the Latin *fossilium*, which means "dug up from the ground." As originally used by medieval writers, a fossil was *any* stone, ore, or gem that came from an underground source. In fact, many early books on mineralogy are called books of fossils. The current meaning of fossil came about during the 1700s.

FIGURE 8.10 Applying relative dating principles to a geologic cross section of a hypothetical region.

value is realized only when the rocks are correlated with those of other regions. Although the methods just described are sufficient to trace a rock formation over relatively short distances, they are not adequate for matching rocks that are separated by great distances. When correlation between widely separated areas or between continents is the objective, geologists must rely on fossils.

FOSSILS: EVIDENCE OF PAST LIFE

Fossils, the remains or traces of prehistoric life, are important inclusions in sediment and sedimentary rocks. They are important basic tools for interpreting the geologic past. The scientific study of fossils is called **paleontology**. It is an

interdisciplinary science that blends geology and biology in an attempt to understand all aspects of the succession of life over the vast expanse of geologic time. Knowing the nature of

DID YOU KNOW?

People frequently confuse paleontology and archaeology. Paleontologists study fossils and are concerned with *all* life forms in the geologic past. By contrast, archaeologists focus on the material remains of past human life. These remains include both the objects used by people long ago, called *artifacts*, and the buildings and other structures associated with where people lived, called *sites*.

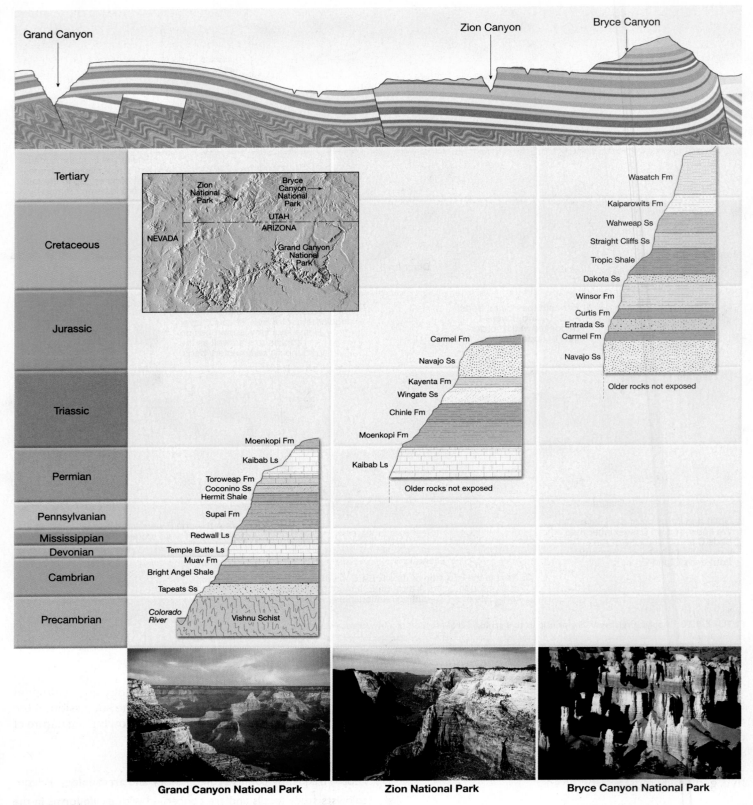

Grand Canyon National Park

Zion National Park

Bryce Canyon National Park

FIGURE 8.11 Correlation of strata at three locations on the Colorado Plateau allows for a more complete view of the extent of sedimentary rocks in the region. (After U.S. Geological Survey. Insert photos E. J. Tarbuck) the life forms that existed at a particular time helps researchers understand past environmental conditions. Further, fossils are important time indicators and play a key role in correlating rocks of similar ages that are from different places.

Types of Fossils

Fossils are of many types. The remains of relatively recent organisms may not have been altered at all. Such objects as teeth, bones, and shells are common examples. Far less common are entire animals, flesh included, that have been preserved because of rather unusual circumstances. Remains of prehistoric elephants called mammoths that were frozen in the Arctic tundra of Siberia and Alaska are examples, as are the mummified remains of sloths preserved in a dry cave in Nevada.

Given enough time, the remains of an organism are likely to be modified. Fossils often become *petrified* (literally, "turned into stone"), meaning that the small internal cavities and pores of the original structure are filled with precipitated mineral matter (**FIGURE 8.12A**). In other instances *replacement* may occur. The cell walls and other solid material are removed and replaced with mineral matter. The microscopic details of the replaced structure are sometimes faithfully retained.

Molds and casts constitute another common class of fossils. When a shell or other structure is buried in sediment and then dissolved by underground water, a *mold* is created. The mold faithfully reflects only the shape and surface marking of the organism; it does not reveal any information concerning its internal structure. If these hollow spaces are subsequently filled with mineral matter, *casts* are created (**FIGURE 8.12B**).

A type of fossilization called *carbonization* is particularly effective in preserving leaves and delicate animal forms. It occurs when fine sediment encases the remains of an organism. As time passes, pressure squeezes out the liquid and gaseous components and leaves behind a thin residue of carbon (**FIGURE 8.12C**). Black shales deposited as organic-rich mud in oxygen-poor environments often contain abundant carbonized remains. If the film of carbon is lost from a fossil preserved in fine-grained sediment, a replica of the surface, called an *impression*, may still show considerable detail (**FIGURE 8.12D**).

FIGURE 8.12 There are many types of fossilization. Six examples are shown here. **A.** Petrified wood in Petrified Forest National Park, Arizona. **B.** This trilobite photo illustrates mold and cast. **C.** A fossil bee preserved as a thin carbon film. **D.** Impressions are common fossils and often show considerable detail. **E.** Insect in amber. **F.** Coprolite or fossil dung. (Photo A by Bernhard Edmaier/Photo Researchers, Inc.; Photos B, D, and F by E. J. Tarbuck; Photo C courtesy of Florissant Fossil Beds National Monument; Photo E by Colin Keates/Dorling Kindersly Media Library)

Delicate organisms, such as insects, are difficult to preserve, and consequently they are relatively rare in the fossil record. They must not only be protected from decay, but also not be subjected to any pressure that would crush them. One way in which some insects have been preserved is in *amber,* the hardened resin of ancient trees. The fly in **FIGURE 8.12E** was preserved after being trapped in a drop of sticky resin. Resin sealed off the insect from the atmosphere and protected the remains from damage by water and air. As the resin hardened, a protective pressure-resistant case formed.

In addition to the fossils already mentioned, there are numerous other types, many of them only traces of prehistoric life. Examples of such indirect evidence include the following:

1. Tracks—animal footprints made in soft sediment that was later lithified.
2. Burrows—tubes in sediment, wood, or rock made by an animal. These holes may later become filled with mineral matter and preserved. Some of the oldest-known fossils are believed to be worm burrows.
3. Coprolites—fossil dung and stomach contents that can provide useful information pertaining to food habits of organisms (**FIGURE 8.12F**).
4. Gastroliths—highly polished stomach stones that were used in the grinding of food by some extinct reptiles.

Conditions Favoring Preservation

Only a tiny fraction of the organisms that have lived during the geologic past have been preserved as fossils. The remains of an animal or plant are normally destroyed. Under what circumstances are they preserved? Two special conditions appear to be necessary: rapid burial and the possession of hard parts.

When an organism perishes, its soft parts are usually quickly eaten by scavengers or decomposed by bacteria. Occasionally, however, the remains are buried by sediment. When this occurs, the remains are protected from the environment where destructive processes operate. Rapid burial, therefore, is an important condition favoring preservation.

In addition, animals and plants have a much better chance of being preserved as part of the fossil record if they have hard parts. Although traces and imprints of soft-bodied animals such as jellyfish, worms, and insects exist, they are not common. Flesh usually decays so rapidly that preservation is exceedingly unlikely. Hard parts such as shells, bones, and teeth predominate in the record of past life.

DID YOU KNOW?

Even when organisms die and their tissues decay, the organic compounds (hydrocarbons) of which they were made may survive in sediments. These are called *chemical fossils.* These hydrocarbons form oil and gas, but some residues can persist in the rock record and be analyzed to determine the kinds of organisms they are derived from.

Because preservation is contingent on special conditions, the record of life in the geologic past is biased. The fossil record of those organisms with hard parts that lived in areas of sedimentation is quite abundant. However, we get only an occasional glimpse of the vast array of other life forms that did not meet the special conditions favoring preservation.

Fossils and Correlation

The existence of fossils had been known for centuries, yet it was not until the late 1700s and early 1800s that their significance as geologic tools was made evident. During this period, an English engineer and canal builder, William Smith, discovered that each rock formation in the canals he worked on contained fossils unlike those in the beds either above or below. Further, he noted that sedimentary strata in widely separated areas could be identified—and correlated—by their distinctive fossil content.

Based on Smith's classic observations and the findings of many geologists who followed, one of the most important and basic principles in historical geology was formulated: *Fossil organisms succeed one another in a definite and determinable order, and, therefore, any time period can be recognized by its fossil content.* This has come to be known as the **principle of fossil succession**. In other words, when fossils are arranged according to their age by applying the law of superposition to the rocks in which they are found, they do not present a random or haphazard picture. To the contrary, fossils document the evolution of life through time.

For example, an Age of Trilobites is recognized quite early in the fossil record. Then, in succession, paleontologists recognize an Age of Fishes, an Age of Coal Swamps, an Age of Reptiles, and an Age of Mammals. These "ages" pertain to groups that were especially plentiful and characteristic during particular time periods. Within each of the ages, subdivisions are based on certain species of trilobites, and certain types of fish, reptiles, and so on. This same succession of dominant organisms, never out of order, is found on every major landmass.

Once fossils were recognized as time indicators, they became the most useful means of correlating rocks of similar ages in different regions. Geologists pay particular attention to certain fossils called **index fossils**. These fossils are widespread geographically and are limited to a short span of geologic time, so their presence provides an important method of matching rocks of the same age. Rock formations, however, do not always contain a specific index fossil. In such situations, groups of fossils, called *fossil assemblages,* are used to establish the age of the bed. **FIGURE 8.13** illustrates how an assemblage of fossils can be used to date rocks more precisely than could be accomplished by the use of only one of the fossils.

In addition to being important and often essential tools for correlation, fossils are important environmental indicators. Although much can be deduced about past environments by studying the nature and characteristics of sedimentary rocks, a close examination of the fossils present can usually provide a great deal more information.

For example, when the remains of certain clam shells are found in limestone, the geologist can assume that the region

Age ranges of some fossil groups

Rock unit A

Age of rock unit A

Rock unit B

Age of rock unit B

Younger

TIME

Older

FIGURE 8.13　Overlapping ranges of fossils help date rocks more exactly than using a single fossil.

was once covered by a shallow sea, because that is where clams live today. Also, by using what we know of living organisms, we can conclude that fossil animals with thick shells capable of withstanding pounding and surging waves must have inhabited shorelines. On the other hand, animals with thin, delicate shells probably indicate deep, calm offshore waters. Hence, by looking closely at the types of fossils, the approximate position of an ancient shoreline may be identified.

Further, fossils can indicate the former temperature of the water. Certain present-day corals require warm and shallow tropical seas like those around Florida and the Bahamas. When similar corals are found in ancient limestones, they indicate that a Florida-like marine environment must have existed when they were alive. These are just a few examples of how fossils can help unravel the complex story of Earth history.

DATING WITH RADIOACTIVITY

GEODe
EARTH
SCIENCE
Deciphering Earth History
▼ Radiometric Dating

In addition to establishing relative dates by using the principles described in the preceding sections, it is also possible to obtain reliable numerical dates for events in the geologic

past. We know that Earth is about 4.6 billion years old and that the dinosaurs became extinct about 65.5 million years ago. Dates that are expressed in millions and billions of years truly stretch our imagination because our personal calendars involve time measured in hours, weeks, and years. Nevertheless, the vast expanse of geologic time is a reality, and it is radiometric dating that allows us to measure it accurately. In this section, you will learn about radioactivity and its application in radiometric dating.

Reviewing Basic Atomic Structure

Recall from Chapter 1 that each atom has a *nucleus* containing protons and neutrons and that the nucleus is orbited by electrons. *Electrons* have a negative electrical charge, and *protons* have a positive charge. A *neutron* is actually a proton and an electron combined, so it has no charge (it is neutral).

The *atomic number* (the element's identifying number) is the number of protons in the nucleus. Every element has a different number of protons in the nucleus and thus a different atomic number (hydrogen = 1, oxygen = 8, uranium = 92, etc.). Atoms of the same element always have the same number of protons, so the atomic number is constant.

Practically all (99.9 percent) of an atom's mass is found in the nucleus, indicating that electrons have practically no mass at all. By adding together the number of protons and neutrons in the nucleus, the *mass number* of the atom is determined. The number of neutrons in the nucleus can vary. These variants, called *isotopes,* have different mass numbers.

To summarize with an example, uranium's nucleus always has 92 protons, so its atomic number always is 92. But its neutron population varies, so uranium has three isotopes: uranium-234 (number of protons + neutrons = 234), uranium-235, and uranium-238. All three isotopes are mixed in nature. They look the same and behave the same in chemical reactions.

Radioactivity

The forces that bind protons and neutrons together in the nucleus are usually strong. However, in some isotopes, the nuclei are unstable because the forces binding protons and neutrons together are not strong enough. As a result, the nuclei spontaneously break apart (decay), a process called **radioactivity**. What happens when unstable nuclei break apart?

Three common types of radioactive decay are illustrated in **FIGURE 8.14** and are summarized as follows:

1. *Alpha particles* (α particles) may be emitted from the nucleus. An alpha particle consists of 2 protons and 2 neutrons. Consequently, the emission of an alpha particle means (a) the mass number of the isotope is reduced by 4, and (b) the atomic number is decreased by 2.

2. When a *beta particle* (β particle), or electron, is given off from a nucleus, the mass number remains unchanged, because electrons have practically no mass. However, because the electron has come from a neutron (remember, a neutron is a combination of a proton and an electron), the nucleus contains one more proton than before. Therefore, the atomic number increases by 1.

3. Sometimes an electron is captured by the nucleus. The electron combines with a proton and forms an additional neutron. As in the last example, the mass number remains unchanged. However, because the nucleus now contains one less proton, the atomic number decreases by 1.

An unstable (radioactive) isotope is referred to as the *parent*. The isotopes resulting from the decay of the parent

FIGURE 8.15 The most common isotope of uranium (U-238) is an example of a radioactive decay series. Before the stable end product (Pb-206) is reached, many different isotopes are produced as intermediate steps.

are the *daughter products*. **FIGURE 8.15** provides an example of radioactive decay. When the radioactive parent, uranium-238 (atomic number 92, mass number 238), decays, it follows a number of steps, emitting eight alpha particles and six beta particles before finally becoming the stable daughter product lead-206 (atomic number 82, mass number 206).

Certainly among the most important results of the discovery of radioactivity is that it provides a reliable method of calculating the ages of rocks and minerals that contain particular radioactive isotopes. The procedure is called **radiometric dating**. Why is radiometric dating reliable? The rates of decay for many isotopes have been precisely measured and do not vary under the physical conditions that exist in Earth's outer layers. Therefore, each radioactive isotope used for dating has been decaying at a fixed rate ever since the formation of the rocks in which it occurs, and the products of decay have been accumulating at a corresponding rate. For example, when uranium is incorporated into a mineral that crystallizes from magma, there is no lead (the stable daughter product) from previous decay. The radiometric "clock" starts at this point. As the uranium in this newly formed mineral disintegrates, atoms of the daughter product are trapped and measurable amounts of lead eventually accumulate.

Half-Life

The time required for one half of the nuclei in a sample to decay is called the **half-life** of the isotope. Half-life is a common way of expressing the rate of radioactive disintegration. **FIGURE 8.16** illustrates what occurs when a radioactive parent decays directly into its stable daughter product. When the

A. Alpha Emission

Unstable parent nucleus → Daughter nucleus   Atomic number: 2 fewer   Atomic mass: 4 fewer   Alpha particle emission

Proton, Neutron

B. Beta Emission

Unstable parent nucleus → Daughter nucleus   Atomic number: 1 more   Atomic mass: no change   Beta (electron) emission (−)

Neutron, Proton

C. Electron Capture

Unstable parent nucleus → Daughter nucleus   Atomic number: 1 fewer   Atomic mass: no change

Electron (−), Proton, Neutron

FIGURE 8.14 Common types of radioactive decay. Notice that in each case, the number of protons (atomic number) in the nucleus changes, thus producing a different element.

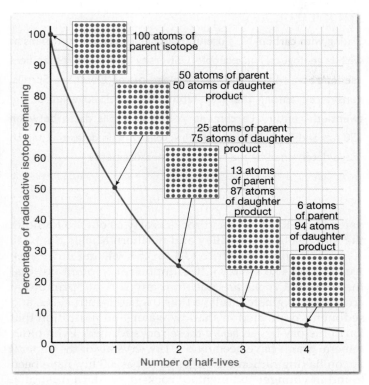

FIGURE 8.16 The radioactive decay curve shows change that is exponential. Half of the radioactive parent remains after one half-life. After a second half-life, one-quarter of the parent remains, and so forth.

Table 8.1 Radioactive isotopes frequently used in radiometric dating

Radioactive Parent	Stable Daughter Product	Currently Accepted Half-Life Values
Uranium-238	Lead-206	4.5 billion years
Uranium-235	Lead-207	713 million years
Thorium-232	Lead-208	14.1 billion years
Rubidium-87	Strontium-87	47.0 billion years
Potassium-40	Argon-40	1.3 billion years

quantities of parent and daughter are equal (ratio 1:1), we know that one half-life has transpired. When one-quarter of the original parent atoms remain and three-quarters have decayed to the daughter product, the parent/daughter ratio is 1:3, and we know that two half-lives have passed. After three half-lives, the ratio of parent atoms to daughter atoms is 1:7 (one parent atom for every seven daughter atoms).

If the half-life of a radioactive isotope is known and the parent–daughter ratio can be determined, the age of the sample can be calculated. For example, assume that the half-life of a hypothetical unstable isotope is 1 million years and the parent–daughter ratio in a sample is 1:15. Such a ratio indicates that four half-lives have passed and that the sample must be 4 million years old.

Radiometric Dating

Notice that the *percentage* of radioactive atoms that decay during one half-life is always the same: 50 percent. However, the *actual number* of atoms that decay with the passing of each half-life continually decreases. As the percentage of radioactive parent atoms declines, the proportion of stable daughter atoms rises, with the increase in daughter atoms just matching the drop in parent atoms. This fact is the key to radiometric dating.

Of the many radioactive isotopes that exist in nature, five have proved particularly important in providing radiometric ages for ancient rocks (Table 8.1). Rubidium-87, uranium-238, and uranium-235 are used for dating rocks that are millions of

years old, but potassium-40 is more versatile. Although the half-life of potassium-40 is 1.3 billion years, analytical techniques make possible the detection of tiny amounts of its stable daughter product, argon-40, in some rocks that are younger than 100,000 years. Another important reason for its frequent use is that potassium is abundant in many common minerals, particularly micas and feldspars.

It is important to realize that an accurate radiometric date can be obtained only if the mineral remained a closed system during the entire period since its formation. A correct date is not possible unless there was neither the addition nor loss of parent or daughter isotopes. This is not always the case. In fact, an important limitation of the potassium-argon method arises from the fact that argon is a gas, and it may leak from minerals, throwing off measurements.

Remember that although the basic principle of radiometric dating is simple, the actual procedure is quite complex. The analysis that determines the quantities of parent and daughter must be painstakingly precise. In addition, some radioactive materials do not decay directly into the stable daughter product. As you saw in Figure 8.15 uranium-238 produces 13 intermediate unstable daughter products before the fourteenth and final daughter product, the stable isotope lead-206, is produced.

Dating with Carbon-14

To date very recent events, carbon-14 is used. Carbon-14 is the radioactive isotope of carbon. The process is often called **radiocarbon dating**. Because the half-life of carbon-14 is only 5,730 years, it can be used for dating events from the historic past as well as those from very recent geologic history. In some cases, carbon-14 can be used to date events as far back as 75,000 years.

DID YOU KNOW?

One common precaution against sources of error in radiometric dating is the use of cross checks. This simply involves subjecting a sample to two different methods. If the two dates agree, the likelihood is high that the date is reliable. If an appreciable difference is found, other cross checks must be employed to determine which, if either, is correct.

Carbon-14 is continuously produced in the upper atmosphere as a consequence of cosmic-ray bombardment. Cosmic rays, which are high-energy particles, shatter the nuclei of gas atoms, releasing neutrons. Some of the neutrons are absorbed by nitrogen atoms (atomic number 7), causing their nuclei to emit a proton. As a result, the atomic number decreases by 1 (to 6), and a different element, carbon-14, is created (**FIGURE 8.17A**). This isotope of carbon quickly becomes incorporated into carbon dioxide, which circulates in the atmosphere and is absorbed by living matter. As a result, all organisms contain a small amount of carbon-14, including yourself.

While an organism is alive, the decaying radiocarbon is continually replaced, and the proportions of carbon-14 and carbon-12 remain constant. Carbon-12 is the stable and most common isotope of carbon. However, when any plant or animal dies, the amount of carbon-14 gradually decreases as it decays to nitrogen-14 by beta emission (**FIGURE 8.17B**). By comparing the proportions of carbon-14 and carbon-12 in a sample, radiocarbon dates can be determined.

Although carbon-14 is useful in dating only the last small fraction of geologic time, it has become a valuable tool for anthropologists, archaeologists, and historians, as well as for geologists who study very recent Earth history. In fact, the development of radiocarbon dating was considered so important that the chemist who discovered this application, Willard F. Libby, received a Nobel prize.

Importance of Radiometric Dating

Radiometric dating methods have produced literally thousands of dates for events in Earth history. Rocks exceeding 3.5 billion years in age are found on all of the continents. Earth's oldest rocks (so far) are gneisses from northern Canada near Great Slave Lake that have been dated at 4.03 billion years (b.y.). Rocks from western Greenland have been

dated at 3.7 to 3.8 b.y., and rocks nearly as old are found in the Minnesota River Valley and northern Michigan (3.5 to 3.7 b.y.), in southern Africa (3.4 to 3.5 b.y.), and in western Australia (3.4 to 3.6 b.y.). It is important to point out that these ancient rocks are not from any sort of "primordial crust" but originated as lava flows, igneous intrusions, and sediments deposited in shallow water—an indication that Earth history began *before* these rocks formed. Even older mineral grains have been dated. Tiny crystals of the mineral zircon having radiometric ages as old as 4.3 b.y. have been found in younger sedimentary rocks in western Australia. The source rocks for these tiny durable grains either no longer exist or have not yet been found.

Radiometric dating has vindicated the ideas of Hutton, Charles Darwin, and others who inferred that geologic time must be immense. Indeed, modern dating methods have proved that there has been enough time for the processes we observe to have accomplished tremendous tasks.

THE GEOLOGIC TIME SCALE

Deciphering Earth History
▼ Geologic Time Scale

Geologists have divided the whole of geologic history into units of varying magnitude. Together, they comprise the **geologic time scale** of Earth history (**FIGURE 8.18**). The major units of the time scale were delineated during the nineteenth century, principally by scientists in Western Europe and Great Britain. Because radiometric dating was unavailable at that time, the entire time scale was created using methods of relative dating. It was only in the twentieth century that radiometric dating permitted numerical dates to be added.

Structure of the Time Scale

The geologic time scale divides the 4.6-billion-year history of Earth into many different units and provides a meaningful time frame within which the events of the geologic past are arranged. As shown in Figure 8.18, **eons** represent the greatest expanses of time. The eon that began about 542 million years ago is the **Phanerozoic**, a term derived from Greek words meaning "visible life." It is an appropriate description because the rocks and deposits of the Phanerozoic eon contain abundant fossils that document major evolutionary trends.

FIGURE 8.17 **A.** Production and **B.** decay of carbon-14. These sketches represent the nuclei of the respective atoms.

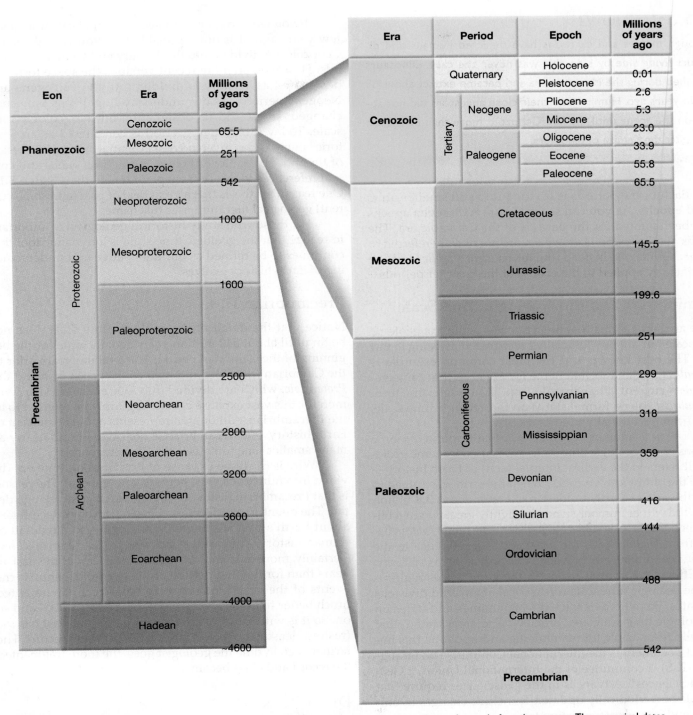

FIGURE 8.18 The geologic time scale. Numbers on the time scale represent time in millions of years before the present. The numerical dates were added long after the time scale had been established using relative dating techniques. The Precambrian accounts for more than 88 percent of geologic time. The time scale is a dynamic tool. Advances in the geosciences require that updates be made from time to time. This version was updated in July 2009.

Another glance at the time scale shows that eons are divided into **eras**. The three eras within the Phanerozoic are the **Paleozoic** ("ancient life"), the **Mesozoic** ("middle life"), and the **Cenozoic** ("recent life"). As the names imply, these eras are bounded by profound worldwide changes in life forms.

Each era of the Phanerozoic eon is divided into units known as **periods**. The Paleozoic has seven and the Mesozoic and Cenozoic each have three. Each of these periods is characterized by a somewhat less profound change in life forms as compared with the eras.

Each of the periods is divided into still smaller units called **epochs**. As you can see in Figure 8.18, seven epochs have been named for the periods of the Cenozoic era. The epochs of other periods, however, are not usually referred to by specific names. Instead, the terms *early, middle,* and *late* are generally applied to the epochs of these earlier periods.

Terminology and the Geologic Time Scale

There are some terms that are associated with the geologic time scale but are not "officially" recognized as being a part of it. The best known and the most common example is *Precambrian*—the informal name for the eons that came before the current Phanerozoic eon. Although the term *Precambrian* has no formal status on the geologic time scale, it has been traditionally used as though it did.

Hadean is another informal term that is found on some versions of the geologic time scale and is used by some geologists. It refers to the earliest interval (eon) of Earth history—before the oldest known rocks. When the term was coined in 1972, the age of Earth's oldest rocks was about 3.8 billion years. Today that number stands at slightly greater than 4 billion, and, of course, is subject to revision. The name *Hadean* derives from *Hades* Greek for *underworld*—a reference to the "hellish" conditions that prevailed on Earth early in its history.

Effective communication in the geosciences requires that the geologic time scale consist of standardized divisions and dates. So, who determines which names and dates on the geologic time scale are "official"? The organization that is largely responsible for maintaining and updating this important document is the International Committee on Stratigraphy (ICS), a committee of the International Union of Geological Sciences*. Advances in the geosciences require that the scale be periodically updated to include changes in unit names and boundary age estimates.

For example, the geologic time scale shown in Figure 8.18 was updated as recently as July 2009. After considerable dialogue among geologists who focus on very recent Earth history, the ICS changed the date for the start of the Quaternary period and the Pleistocene epoch from 1.8 million to 2.6 million years ago. Who knows, perhaps by the time you read this, other changes will have been made.

*To view the current version of the ICS time scale, go to http://www.stratigraphy.org. *Stratigraphy* is the branch of geology that studies rock layers (strata) and layering (stratification), thus its primary focus is sedimentary and layered volcanic rocks.

If you were to examine a geologic time scale from just a few years ago, it is quite possible that you would see the Cenozoic era divided into the Tertiary and Quaternary periods. However, on more recent versions the space formerly designated as Tertiary is divided into the Paleogene and Neogene periods. As our understanding of this time span changed, so too did its designation on the geologic time scale. Today the Tertiary period is considered as an "historic" name and is given no official status on the ICS version of the time scale. Nevertheless, many time scales still contain references to the Tertiary period, including Figure 8.18. One reason for this is that a great deal of past (and some current) geological literature uses this name.

For those who study historical geology, it is important to realize that the geologic time scale is a dynamic tool that continues to be refined as our knowledge and understanding of Earth history evolves.

Precambrian Time

Notice that the detail of the geologic time scale does not begin until about 542 million years ago, the date for the beginning of the Cambrian period. The 4 billion years prior to the Cambrian is divided into two eons, the *Archean* and the *Proterozoic*, which are divided into four eras. It is also common for this vast expanse of time to simply be referred to as the **Precambrian**. Although it represents about 88 percent of Earth history, the Precambrian is not divided into nearly as many smaller time units as is the Phanerozoic eon.

Why is the huge expanse of Precambrian time not divided into numerous eras, periods, and epochs? The reason is that Precambrian history is not known in great enough detail. The quantity of information geologists have deciphered about Earth's past is somewhat analogous to the detail of human history. The farther back we go, the less we know. Certainly, more data and information exist about the past 10 years than for the first decade of the twentieth century; the events of the nineteenth century have been documented much better than the events of the first century A.D., and so on. So it is with Earth history. The more recent past has the freshest, least disturbed, and most observable record. The farther back in time the geologist goes, the more fragmented the record and clues become.

DIFFICULTIES IN DATING THE GEOLOGIC TIME SCALE

Although reasonably accurate numerical dates have been worked out for the periods of the geologic time scale (see Figure 8.18), the task is not without difficulty. The primary problem in assigning numerical dates is the fact that not all rocks can be dated by radiometric methods. For a radiometric date to be useful, all minerals in the rock must have formed at about the same time. For this reason, radioactive isotopes can be used to determine when minerals in an igneous rock crystallized and when pressure and heat created new minerals in a metamorphic rock.

However, samples of sedimentary rock can only rarely be dated directly by radiometric means. A sedimentary rock may include particles that contain radioactive isotopes, but the rock's age cannot be accurately determined because the grains that make up the rock are not the same age as the rock in which they occur. Rather, the sediments have been weathered from rocks of diverse ages (**FIGURE 8.19**).

Radiometric dates obtained from metamorphic rocks may also be difficult to interpret, because the age of a particular mineral in a metamorphic rock does not necessarily represent the time when the rock initially formed. Instead, the date may indicate any one of a number of subsequent metamorphic phases.

If samples of sedimentary rocks rarely yield reliable radiometric ages, how can numerical dates be assigned to sedimentary layers? Usually the geologist must relate them to datable igneous masses, as in **FIGURE 8.20**. In this example, radiometric dating has determined the ages of the volcanic ash bed within the Morrison Formation and the dike cutting the Mancos Shale and Mesaverde Formation. The sedimentary beds below the ash are obviously older than the ash, and all the layers above the ash are younger (principle of superposition). The dike is younger than the Mancos Shale and the Mesaverde Formation but older than the Wasatch Formation because the dike does not intrude the Tertiary rocks (cross-cutting relationships).

From this kind of evidence, geologists estimate that a part of the Morrison Formation was deposited about 160 million years ago, as indicated by the ash bed. Further, they conclude that the Tertiary period began after the intrusion of the dike, 66 million years ago. This is one example of literally thousands that illustrates how datable materials are used to "bracket" the various episodes in Earth history within specific time periods. It shows the necessity of combining laboratory dating methods with field observations of rocks.

FIGURE 8.19 A useful numerical date for this conglomerate is not possible because the gravel that composes it was derived from rocks of diverse ages. (Photo by E. J. Tarbuck)

FIGURE 8.20 Numerical dates for sedimentary layers are usually determined by examining their relationship to igneous rocks. (After U.S. Geological Survey)

THE CHAPTER IN REVIEW

• During the seventeenth and eighteenth centuries, *catastrophism* influenced the formulation of explanations about Earth. Catastrophism states that Earth's landscapes have been developed primarily by great catastrophes. By contrast, *uniformitarianism*, one of the fundamental principles of modern geology advanced by *James Hutton* in the late 1700s, states that the physical, chemical, and biological laws that operate today have also operated in the geologic past. The idea is often summarized as "the present is the key to the past." Hutton argued that processes that appear to be slow acting could, over long spans of time, produce effects that were just as great as those resulting from sudden catastrophic events.

• The two types of dates used by geologists to interpret Earth history are (1) *relative dates,* which put events in their *proper sequence of formation,* and (2) *numerical dates,* which pinpoint the *time in years* when an event took place.

• Relative dates can be established using the *law of superposition, principle of original horizontality, principle of cross-cutting relationships, inclusions,* and *unconformities.*

• *Correlation,* matching up two or more geologic phenomena of similar ages in different areas, is used to develop a geologic time scale that applies to the entire Earth.

• *Fossils* are the remains or traces of prehistoric life. The special conditions that favor preservation are *rapid burial* and the possession of *hard parts* such as shells, bones, or teeth.

• Fossils are used to *correlate* sedimentary rocks that are widely separated by using the rocks' distinctive fossil content and applying the *principle of fossil succession.* The principle of fossil succession states that fossil organisms succeed one another in a definite and determinable order, and, therefore, any time period can be recognized by its fossil content.

• Each atom has a nucleus containing *protons* (positively charged particles) and *neutrons* (neutral particles). Orbiting the nucleus are negatively charged *electrons.* The *atomic number* of an atom is the number of protons in the nucleus. The *mass number* is the number of protons plus the number of neutrons in an atom's nucleus. *Isotopes* are variants of the same atom, but with a different number of neutrons and hence a different mass number.

• *Radioactivity* is the spontaneous breaking apart (decay) of certain unstable atomic nuclei. Three common forms of radioactive decay are (1) emission of an alpha particle from the nucleus, (2) emission of a beta particle (or electron) from the nucleus, and (3) capture of an electron by the nucleus.

• An unstable *radioactive isotope,* called the *parent,* will decay and form *daughter products.* The length of time for one-half of the nuclei of a radioactive isotope to decay is called the *half-life* of the isotope. If the half-life of the isotope is known, and the parent–daughter ratio can be measured, the age of a sample can be calculated.

• The *geologic time scale* divides Earth history into units of varying magnitude. It is commonly presented in chart form, with the oldest time and event at the bottom and the youngest at the top. The principal subdivisions of the geologic time scale, called *eons,* include the *Archean* and *Proterozoic* (together, these two eons are commonly referred to as the *Precambrian*), and, beginning about 542 million years ago, the *Phanerozoic.* The Phanerozoic (meaning "visible life") eon is divided into the following eras: *Paleozoic* ("ancient life"), *Mesozoic* ("middle life"), and *Cenozoic* ("recent life").

• A significant problem in assigning numerical dates to units of time is that *not all rocks can be dated radiometrically.* A sedimentary rock may contain particles of many ages that have been weathered from different rocks that formed at various times. One way geologists assign numerical dates to sedimentary rocks is to relate them to datable igneous masses, such as dikes and volcanic ash beds.

KEY TERMS

angular unconformity (p. 242)	epoch (p. 254)	Mesozoic era (p. 253)	Precambrian (p. 254)
catastrophism (p. 239)	era (p. 253)	nonconformity (p. 243)	radioactivity (p. 249)
Cenozoic era (p. 253)	fossil (p. 245)	numerical date (p. 240)	radiocarbon dating (p. 251)
conformable (p. 242)	fossil succession, principle of (p. 248)	original horizontality, principle of (p. 241)	radiometric dating (p. 250)
correlation (p. 244)	geologic time scale (p. 252)	paleontology (p. 245)	relative dating (p. 240)
cross-cutting relationships, principle of (p. 241)	half-life (p. 250)	Paleozoic era (p. 253)	superposition, law of (p. 240)
disconformity (p. 243)	inclusions (p. 241)	period (p. 253)	unconformity (p. 242)
eon (p. 252)	index fossil (p. 248)	Phanerozoic eon (p. 252)	uniformitarianism (p. 239)

QUESTIONS FOR REVIEW

1. Contrast the philosophies of *catastrophism* and *uniformitarianism.* How did the proponents of each perceive the age of Earth?

2. Distinguish between numerical dates and relative dates.

3. What is the law of superposition? How are cross-cutting relationships used in relative dating?

4. When you observe an outcrop of steeply inclined sedimentary layers, what principle allows you to assume that the beds became tilted *after* they were deposited?

5. Refer to Figure 8.5 (p. 241) and answer the following questions:
   a. Is fault A older or younger than the sandstone layer?
   b. Is dike A older or younger than the sandstone layer?
   c. Was the conglomerate deposited before or after fault A?
   d. Was the conglomerate deposited before or after fault B?
   e. Which fault is older, A or B?
   f. Is dike A older or younger than the batholith?

6. A mass of granite is in contact with a layer of sandstone. Using a principle described in this chapter, explain how you might determine whether the sandstone was deposited on top of the granite or the granite was intruded into the sandstone after the sandstone was deposited.

7. Distinguish among angular unconformity, disconformity, and nonconformity.

8. What is meant by the term *correlation*?

9. List and briefly describe at least five different types of fossils.

10. List two conditions that improve an organism's chances of being preserved as a fossil.

11. Why are fossils such useful tools in correlation?

12. If a radioactive isotope of thorium (atomic number 90, mass number 232) emits six alpha particles and four beta particles during the course of radioactive decay, what are the atomic number and mass number of the stable daughter product?

13. Why is radiometric dating the most reliable method of dating the geologic past?

14. Assume that a hypothetical radioactive isotope has a half-life of 10,000 years. If the ratio of radioactive parent to stable daughter product is 1:3, how old is the rock containing the radioactive material?

15. To make calculations easier, let us round the age of Earth to 5 billion years.

    a. What fraction of geologic time is represented by recorded history (assume 5000 years for the length of recorded history)?

    b. The first abundant fossil evidence does not appear until the beginning of the Cambrian period (542 million years ago). What percentage of geologic time is represented by abundant fossil evidence?

16. What subdivisions make up the geologic time scale? What is the primary basis for differentiating the eras?

17. Briefly describe the difficulties in assigning numerical dates to layers of sedimentary rock.

COMPANION WEBSITE

The *Foundations of Earth Science* Website uses the resources and flexibility of the Internet to aid in your study of the topics in this chapter. Written and developed by the authors and other Earth science instructors, this site will help improve your understanding of Earth science. Visit **www.mygeoscienceplace.com** in order to:

• **Review** key chapter concepts.

• **Read** with links to the ebook and to chapter-specific web resources.

• **Visualize** and comprehend challenging topics using learning activities in *GEODe: Earth Science*.

• **Test** yourself with online quizzes.

GEODe: EARTH SCIENCE

GEODe: Earth Science is a valuable and easy to use learning aid that can be accessed from your book's Companion Website: **www.mygeoscienceplace.com**. It is a dynamic instructional tool that promotes understanding and reinforces important concepts by using tutorials, animations, and exercises that actively engage the student.

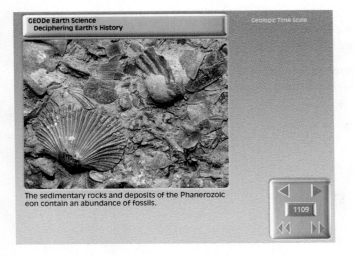

The sedimentary rocks and deposits of the Phanerozoic eon contain an abundance of fossils.

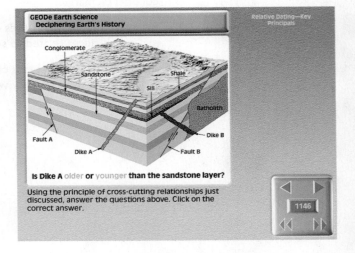

Using the principle of cross-cutting relationships just discussed, answer the questions above. Click on the correct answer.

OCEANS:
THE LAST FRONTIER

To assist you in learning the important concepts in this chapter, you will find it helpful to focus on the following questions:

1. What is oceanography?

2. What is the extent and distribution of the world's oceans?

3. What are the principal elements that contribute to the ocean's salinity? What are the sources for these elements?

4. How do temperature, salinity, and density change with depth in the open ocean?

5. What techniques are used to map the ocean floor?

6. How does a passive continental margin differ from an active continental margin?

7. What are the major features of the deep ocean basin? How are mid-ocean ridges related to seafloor spreading?

8. What are the various types of seafloor sediments? How can these sediments be used to study worldwide climate changes?

Sea ice in the Arctic Ocean. Sea ice is frozen seawater. The area covered by Arctic sea ice at the end of the summer melt period has been declining. This decline is linked to global warming. See Figure 9.5 for more information about this. (Photo by Sue Flood/Getty Images)

CHAPTER
9

259

Calling Earth the "water planet" is certainly appropriate, because nearly 71 percent of its surface is covered by the global ocean. Although the ocean comprises a much greater percentage of Earth's surface than do the continents, it was only in the relatively recent past that the ocean became an important focus of study. Recently there has been a virtual explosion of data about the oceans, and with it, oceanography has grown dramatically. **Oceanography** is a composite science that draws on the methods and knowledge of biology, chemistry, physics, and geology to study all aspects of the world ocean.

THE VAST WORLD OCEAN

A glance at a globe or a view of Earth from space reveals a planet dominated by the world ocean (**FIGURE 9.1**). It is for this reason that Earth is often referred to as the *blue planet*.

Geography of the Oceans

The area of Earth is about 510 million square kilometers (197 million square miles). Of this total, approximately 360 million square kilometers (140 million square miles), or 71 percent, is represented by oceans and marginal seas (seas around the ocean's margin, such as the Mediterranean Sea and the Caribbean Sea). Continents and islands comprise the remaining 29 percent, or 150 million square kilometers (58 million square miles).

By studying a globe or world map, it is readily apparent that the continents and oceans are not evenly divided between the Northern and Southern hemispheres (Figure 9.1). When we compute the percentages of land and water in the Northern Hemisphere, we find that nearly 61 percent of the surface is water, and about 39 percent is land. In the Southern Hemisphere, on the other hand, almost 81 percent of the surface is water, and only 19 percent is land. It is no wonder then that the Northern Hemisphere is called the *land hemisphere*, and the Southern Hemisphere the *water hemisphere*.

FIGURE 9.2A shows the distribution of land and water in the Northern and Southern hemispheres by way of a graph. Between latitudes 45 degrees north and 70 degrees north, there is actually more land than water, whereas between 40 degrees south and 65 degrees south there is almost no land to interrupt the oceanic and atmospheric circulation.

The world ocean can be divided into four main ocean basins (**FIGURE 9.2B**):

1. The *Pacific Ocean*, which is the largest ocean (and the largest single geographic feature on the planet), covers more than half of the ocean surface area on Earth. In fact, the Pacific Ocean is so large that all of the continents could fit into the space occupied by it—with room left over! It is also the world's deepest ocean, with an average depth of 3940 meters (12,927 feet).

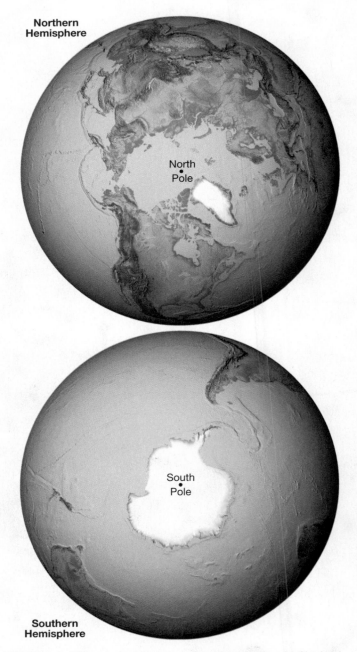

FIGURE 9.1 These views of Earth show the uneven distribution of land and water between the Northern and Southern hemispheres. Almost 81 percent of the Southern Hemisphere is covered by the oceans—20 percent more than the Northern Hemisphere.

2. The *Atlantic Ocean* is about half the size of the Pacific Ocean but is not quite as deep. It is a relatively narrow ocean as compared to the Pacific and is bounded by almost parallel continental margins.

3. The *Indian Ocean* is slightly smaller than the Atlantic Ocean but has about the same average depth. Unlike the Pacific and Atlantic oceans, it is largely a Southern Hemisphere water body.

4. The *Arctic Ocean* is about 7 percent of the size of the Pacific Ocean and is only a little more than one-quarter as deep as the rest of the oceans.

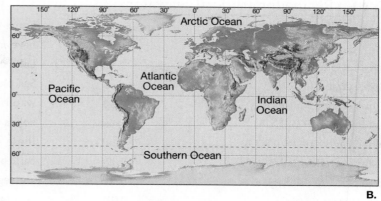

FIGURE 9.2 Distribution of land and water. **A.** The graph shows the amount of land and water in each 5-degree latitude belt. **B.** The world map provides a more familiar view.

DID YOU KNOW?

The Bering Sea is the most northerly marginal sea of the Pacific Ocean and connects to the Arctic Ocean through the Bering Straits. This water body is effectively cut off from the Pacific basin by the Aleutian Islands, which were created by volcanic activity associated with northward subduction of the Pacific plate.

Comparing the Oceans to the Continents

A major difference between continents and the ocean basins is their relative levels. The average elevation of the continents above sea level is about 840 meters (2756 feet), whereas the average depth of the oceans is nearly four and a half times this amount—3729 meters (12,234 feet). The volume of ocean water is so large that if Earth's solid mass were perfectly smooth (level) and spherical, the oceans would cover Earth's entire surface to a uniform depth of more than 2000 meters (1.2 miles)!

COMPOSITION OF SEAWATER

What is the difference between pure water and seawater? One of the most obvious differences is that seawater contains dissolved substances that give it a distinctly salty taste. These dissolved substances are not simply sodium chloride (common table salt)—they include various other salts, metals, and even dissolved gases. In fact, every known naturally occurring element is found dissolved in at least trace amounts in seawater. Unfortunately, the salt content of seawater makes it unsuitable for drinking or for irrigating most crops and causes it to be highly corrosive to many materials. Yet, many parts of the ocean are teeming with life that is superbly adapted to the marine environment.

Salinity

Seawater consists of about 3.5 percent (by weight) dissolved mineral substances that are collectively termed *salts*.

Although the percentage of dissolved components may seem small, the actual quantity is huge because the ocean is so vast.

Salinity is the total amount of solid material dissolved in water. More specifically, it is the ratio of the mass of dissolved substances to the mass of the water sample. Many common quantities are expressed in percent (%), which is really *parts per hundred*. Because the proportion of dissolved substances in seawater is such a small number, oceanographers typically express salinity *in parts per thousand* (‰). Thus, the average salinity of seawater is 3.5% or 35‰.

FIGURE 9.3 shows the principal elements that contribute to the ocean's salinity. Artificial seawater could be approximated by following the recipe in Table 9.1. This table shows that most of the salt in seawater is sodium chloride—common table salt. Sodium chloride together with the next four most abundant salts comprise more than 99 percent of all dissolved substances in the sea. Although

FIGURE 9.3 Relative proportions of water and dissolved components in seawater. Components shown by chemical symbol are chlorine (Cl^-), sodium (Na^+), sulfate (SO_4^{2-}), magnesium (Mg^{2+}), calcium (Ca^{2+}), potassium (K^+), strontium (Sr^{2+}), bromine (Br^-), and carbon (C).

Table 9.1   Recipe for artificial seawater

To make seawater, combine:	Amount (grams)
Sodium chloride (NaCl)	23.48
Magnesium chloride (MgCl$_2$)	4.98
Sodium sulfate (Na$_2$SO$_4$)	3.92
Calcium chloride (CaCl$_2$)	1.10
Potassium chloride (KCl)	0.66
Sodium bicarbonate (NaHCO$_3$)	0.192
Potassium bromide (KBr)	0.096
Hydrogen borate (H$_3$BO$_3$)	0.026
Strontium chloride (SrCl$_2$)	0.024
Sodium fluoride (NaF)	0.003
Then add:	
Pure water (H$_2$O) to form 1000 grams of solution.	

only eight elements make up these five most abundant salts, seawater contains all of Earth's other naturally occurring elements. Despite their presence in minute quantities, many of these elements are very important in maintaining the necessary chemical environment for life in the sea.

Sources of Sea Salts

What are the primary sources for the vast quantities of dissolved substances in the ocean? Chemical weathering of rocks on the continents is one source. These dissolved materials are delivered to the oceans by streams at an estimated rate of more than 2.5 billion tons annually. The second major source of elements found in ocean water is Earth's interior. Through volcanic eruptions, large quantities of water and dissolved gases have been emitted during much of geologic time. This process, called *outgassing*, is the principal source of water in the oceans and in the atmosphere. Certain elements—notably chlorine, bromine, sulfur, and boron—were outgassed along with water and exist in the ocean in much greater abundance than could be explained by weathering of rocks alone.

Although rivers and volcanic activity continually contribute salts to the oceans, the salinity of seawater is not increasing. In fact, evidence suggests that the composition of seawater has been relatively stable for millions of years. Why doesn't the sea get saltier? The answer is that material is being removed just as rapidly as it is added. For example, some dissolved components are withdrawn from seawater by plants and animals as they build hard parts. Other components are removed when they chemically precipitate from the water as sediment. Still others are exchanged at oceanic ridges by hydrothermal activity. The net effect is that the overall makeup of seawater remains relatively constant through time.

Processes Affecting Seawater Salinity

Because the ocean is well mixed, the relative abundances of the major components in seawater are essentially constant,

DID YOU KNOW?

Some of saltiest water in the world is found in arid regions that have inland lakes, which are often called "seas." The Great Salt Lake in Utah, for example, has a salinity of 280‰, and the Dead Sea on the border of Israel and Jordan has a salinity of 330‰. The water in the Dead Sea, therefore, contains 33 percent dissolved solids and is almost *10 times saltier than seawater*. As a result, these waters have such high density and are so buoyant that you can easily float while lying down in the water—with your arms and legs sticking up above water level (see Figure 9.7)!

no matter where the ocean is sampled. Variations in salinity, therefore, are primarily a consequence of changes in the water content of the solution.

Various surface processes alter the amount of water in seawater, thereby affecting salinity. Processes that add large amounts of fresh water to seawater—and thereby decrease salinity—include precipitation, runoff from land, icebergs melting, and sea ice melting. Processes that remove large amounts of fresh water from seawater—and thereby increase seawater salinity—include evaporation and the formation of sea ice. High salinities, for example, are found where evaporation rates are high, as is the case in the dry subtropical regions (roughly between 25 and 35 degrees north or south latitude). Conversely, where large amounts of precipitation dilute ocean waters, as in the midlatitudes (between 35 and 60 degrees north or south latitude) and near the equator, lower salinities prevail (**FIGURE 9.4**).

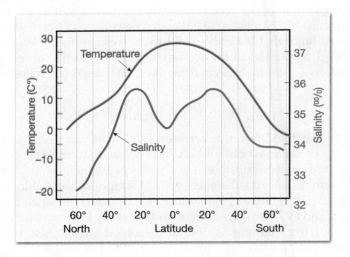

FIGURE 9.4   This graph shows variations in the ocean's surface temperature (top curve) and surface salinity (lower curve) with latitude. As you might expect, average temperatures are highest near the equator and get colder moving poleward. Important factors influencing differences in surface salinity are variations in rainfall and rates of evaporation. For example, in the dry subtropics in the vicinity of the Tropics of Cancer and Capricorn, high evaporation rates remove more water than is replaced by the meager rainfall, resulting in high surface salinities. In the wet equatorial region, abundant rainfall reduces surface salinities.

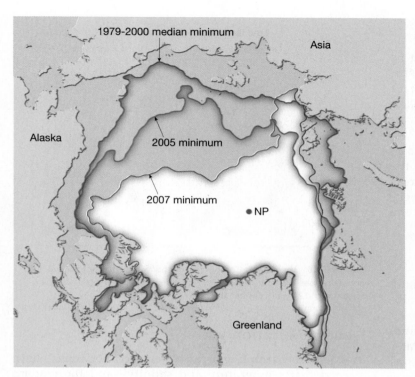

FIGURE 9.5   Sea ice is frozen seawater. In winter the Arctic Ocean is completely ice covered. In summer some of the sea ice melts. This map shows the extent of sea ice at the *end* of the summer melting period in 2005 and 2007 compared to the average for the 1979–2000 period. The extent of sea ice in September 2007 was 39 percent below the long-term average for 1979–2000. This trend is likely an impact of global warming (see Chapter 11).

Surface salinity in polar regions varies seasonally due to the formation and melting of sea ice. When seawater freezes in winter, sea salts do not become part of the ice. Therefore, the salinity of the remaining seawater increases. In summer when sea ice melts, the addition of the relatively fresh water dilutes the solution and salinity decreases (**FIGURE 9.5**).

Surface salinity variation in the open ocean normally ranges from 33‰ to 38‰. Some marginal seas, however, demonstrate extraordinary extremes. For example, in the restricted waters of the Middle East's Persian Gulf and Red Sea—where evaporation far exceeds precipitation—salinity may exceed 42‰. Conversely, very low salinities occur where large quantities of fresh water are supplied by rivers and precipitation. Such is the case for northern Europe's Baltic Sea, where salinity is often below 10‰.

OCEAN TEMPERATURE VARIATIONS WITH DEPTH

If a thermometer were lowered from the surface of the ocean into deeper water, what temperature pattern would be found? Surface waters are warmed by the Sun, so they generally have higher temperatures than deeper waters.

However, the observed temperature pattern depends on the latitude.

FIGURE 9.6 shows two graphs of temperature versus depth: one for high-latitude regions and one for low-latitude regions. The low-latitude curve begins at the surface with high temperature, but the temperature decreases rapidly with depth because of the inability of the Sun's rays to penetrate very far into the ocean. At a depth of about 1000 meters (3300 feet), the temperature remains just a few degrees above freezing and is relatively constant from this level down to the ocean floor. The layer of ocean water between about 300 meters (980 feet) and 1000 meters (3300 feet), where there is a rapid change of temperature with depth, is called the **thermocline** (*thermo* = heat, *cline* = slope). The thermocline is a very important zone in the ocean because it creates a vertical barrier to many types of marine life.

The high-latitude curve in Figure 9.6 displays a pattern quite different from the low-latitude curve. Surface water temperatures in high latitudes are much cooler than in low latitudes, so the curve begins at the surface with low temperature. Deeper in the ocean, the temperature of the water is similar to that at the surface (just a few degrees above freezing), so the curve remains vertical and there is no rapid change of temperature with depth. A thermocline is not present in high latitudes; instead, the water column is *isothermal* (*iso* = same, *thermal* = heat).

Some high-latitude waters can experience minor warming during the summer months. Thus, certain high-latitude regions experience an extremely weak seasonal thermocline. Midlatitude waters, on the other hand, experience a more dramatic seasonal thermocline and exhibit characteristics intermediate between high- and low-latitude regions.

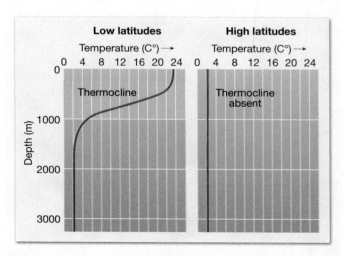

FIGURE 9.6   Variations in ocean water temperature with depth for low- and high-latitude regions. The layer of rapidly changing temperature, called the *thermocline*, is not present in the high latitudes.

OCEAN DENSITY VARIATION

Density is defined as mass per unit volume but can be thought of as a measure of *how heavy something is for its size.* For instance, an object that has low density is lightweight for its size, such as a dry sponge, foam packing, or a surfboard. Conversely, an object that has high density is heavy for its size, such as cement and many metals.

Density is an important property of ocean water because it determines the water's vertical position in the ocean. Furthermore, density differences cause large areas of ocean water to sink or float. For example, when high-density seawater is added to low-density fresh water, the denser seawater sinks below the fresh water.

Factors Affecting Seawater Density

Seawater density is influenced by two main factors: *salinity* and *temperature.* An increase in salinity adds dissolved substances and results in an increase in seawater density (**FIGURE 9.7**). An increase in temperature, on the other hand, causes water to expand and results in a decrease in seawater density. Such a relationship, where one variable decreases as a result of another variable's increase, is known as an *inverse relationship,* where one variable is *inversely proportional* with the other.

Temperature has the greatest influence on surface seawater density because variations in surface seawater temperature are greater than salinity variations. In fact, only in the extreme polar areas of the ocean, where temperatures are low and remain relatively constant, does salinity significantly affect density. Cold water that also has high salinity is some of the highest-density water in the world.

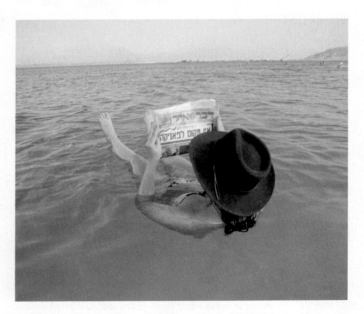

FIGURE 9.7 The Dead Sea, which has a salinity of 330‰ (almost 10 times the average salinity of seawater), has high density. As a result, it also has high buoyancy that allows swimmers to float easily. (Photo by Peter Guttman/Corbis/Bettmann)

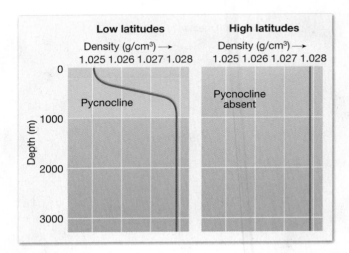

FIGURE 9.8 Variations in ocean water density with depth for low- and high-latitude regions. The layer of rapidly changing density, called the *pycnocline*, is present in the low latitudes but absent in the high latitudes.

Density Variation with Depth

By extensively sampling ocean waters, oceanographers have learned that temperature and salinity—and the water's resulting density—vary with depth. **FIGURE 9.8** shows two graphs of density versus depth: one for high-latitude regions and one for low-latitude regions.

The low-latitude curve in Figure 9.8 begins at the surface with low density (related to high surface water temperatures). However, density increases rapidly with depth because the water temperature is getting colder. At a depth of about 1000 meters (3300 feet), seawater density reaches a maximum value related to the water's low temperature. From this depth to the ocean floor, density remains constant and high. The layer of ocean water between about 300 meters (980 feet) and 1000 meters (3300 feet), where there is a rapid change of density with depth, is called the **pycnocline** (*pycno* = density, *cline* = slope). A pycnocline has a high gravitational stability and presents a significant barrier to mixing between low-density water above and high-density water below.

The high-latitude curve in Figure 9.8 is also related to the temperature curve for high latitudes shown in Figure 9.6. Figure 9.8 shows that in high latitudes, there is high-density (cold) water at the surface and high-density (cold) water below. Thus, the high-latitude density curve remains vertical, and there is no rapid change of density with depth. A pycnocline is not present in high latitudes, instead, the water column is *isopycnal* (*iso* = same, *pycno* = density).

Ocean Layering

The ocean, like Earth's interior, is layered according to density. Low-density water exists near the surface, and higher-density water occurs below. Except for some shallow inland seas with a high rate of evaporation, the highest-density water is found at the greatest ocean depths. Oceanographers generally recognize a three-layered structure in most parts of the open ocean: a shallow surface mixed zone, a transition zone, and a deep zone (**FIGURE 9.9**).

Transition zone (18%)

Deep zone (80%)

Ocean floor

60°N   40°   20°   0°   20°   40°   60°S

Latitude

FIGURE 9.9 Oceanographers recognize three main layers in the ocean based on water density, which varies with temperature and salinity. The warm *surface mixed layer* accounts for only 2 percent of ocean water; the *transition zone* includes the thermocline and pycnocline and accounts for 18 percent of ocean water; the *deep zone* contains cold, high-density water that accounts for 80 percent of ocean water.

Because solar energy is received at the ocean surface, it is here that water temperatures are warmest. The mixing of these waters by waves as well as the turbulence from currents and tides creates a rapid vertical heat transfer. Hence, this *surface mixed zone* has nearly uniform temperatures. The thickness and temperature of this layer vary, depending on latitude and season. The zone usually extends to about 300 meters (980 feet) but may attain a thickness of 450 meters (1500 feet). The surface mixed zone accounts for only about 2 percent of ocean water.

Below the sun-warmed zone of mixing, the temperature falls abruptly with depth (see Figure 9.6). Here, a distinct layer called the *transition zone* exists between the warm surface layer above and the deep zone of cold water below. The transition zone includes a prominent thermocline and associated pycnocline and accounts for about 18 percent of ocean water.

Below the transition zone is the *deep zone*, where sunlight never reaches and water temperatures are just a few degrees above freezing. As a result, water density remains constant and high. Remarkably, the deep zone includes

about 80 percent of ocean water, indicating the immense depth of the ocean (the average depth of the ocean is more than 3700 meters or 12,200 feet).

In high latitudes, the three-layer structure does not exist because the water column is isothermal and isopycnal, which means that there is no rapid change in temperature or density with depth. Consequently, good vertical mixing between surface and deep waters can occur in high-latitude regions. Here, cold high-density water forms at the surface, sinks, and initiates deep-ocean currents, which are discussed in Chapter 10.

AN EMERGING PICTURE OF THE OCEAN FLOOR

The Global Ocean
▼ Floor of the Ocean

If all the water were removed from the ocean basins, a great variety of features would be seen, including broad volcanic peaks, deep trenches, extensive plains, linear mountain chains, and large plateaus. In fact, the scenery would be nearly as diverse as that on the continents.

Mapping the Seafloor

The complex nature of ocean-floor topography did not begin to unfold until the historic three-and-a-half-year voyage of the HMS *Challenger* (**FIGURE 9.10**). From December 1872 to

FIGURE 9.10 The first systematic bathymetric measurements of the ocean were made aboard the HMS *Challenger*, which departed England in December 1872 and returned in May 1876. (From C.W. Thompson and Sir John Murray. *Report on the Scientific Results of the Voyage of the HMS* Challenger, Vol. 1, Great Britain: Challenger Office, 1895, Plate 1. Library of Congress.)

May 1876, the *Challenger* expedition made the first comprehensive study of the global ocean ever attempted. During the 127,500-kilometer (79,200-mile) voyage, the ship and its crew of scientists traveled to every ocean except the Arctic. Throughout the voyage, they sampled a multitude of ocean properties, including water depth, which was accomplished by laboriously lowering long weighted lines overboard. The knowledge gained by the *Challenger* of the ocean's great depths and varied topography expanded with the laying of transatlantic telegraph cables. A far better understanding of the seafloor emerged with the development of modern instruments that measure ocean depths. **Bathymetry** (*bathos* = depth, *metry* = measurement) is the measurement of ocean depths and the charting of the shape or topography of the ocean floor.

Modern Bathymetric Techniques

Today, sound energy is used to measure water depths. The basic approach employs **sonar**, an acronym for *so*und *na*vigation and *ranging*. The first devices that used sound to measure water depth, called **echo sounders**, were developed early in the twentieth century. Echo sounders work by transmitting a sound wave (called a *ping*) into the water in order to produce an echo when it bounces off any object, such as a large marine organism or the ocean floor (**FIGURE 9.11A**). A sensitive receiver intercepts the echo reflected from the bottom, and a clock precisely measures the travel time to fractions of a second. By knowing the speed of sound waves in water—about 1500 meters (4900 feet) per second—and the time required for the energy pulse to reach the ocean floor and return, depth can be calculated. Depths determined from continuous monitoring of these echoes are plotted to create a profile of the ocean floor. By laboriously combining profiles from several adjacent traverses, a chart of the seafloor was produced.

Following World War II, the U.S. Navy developed *sidescan sonar* to look for explosive devices that had been deployed in shipping lanes. These torpedo-shaped instruments can be towed behind a ship where they send out a fan

of sound extending to either side of the ship's track. By combining swaths of sidescan sonar data, researchers produced the first photograph-like images of the seafloor. Although sidescan sonar provides valuable views of the seafloor, it does not provide bathymetric (water depth) data.

This drawback was resolved in the 1990s with the development of *high-resolution multibeam* instruments. These systems use hull-mounted sound sources that send out a fan of sound and then record reflections from the seafloor through a set of narrowly focused receivers aimed at different angles. Rather than obtaining the depth of a single point every few seconds, this technique makes it possible for a survey ship to map the features of the ocean floor along a strip tens of kilometers wide (**FIGURE 9.11B**). These systems can collect bathymetric data of such high resolution that they can distinguish depths that differ by less than a meter. When multibeam sonar is used to make a map of a section of seafloor, the ship travels through the area in a regularly spaced back-and-forth pattern known as "mowing the lawn."

Despite their greater efficiency and enhanced detail, research vessels equipped with multibeam sonar travel at a mere 10 to 20 kilometers (6 to 12 miles) per hour. It would take at least 100 vessels outfitted with this equipment hundreds of years to map the entire seafloor. This explains why only about 5 percent of the seafloor has been mapped in detail—and why large areas of the seafloor have not yet been mapped with sonar at all.

Seismic Reflection Profiles

Marine geologists are also interested in viewing the rock structure beneath the sediments that blanket much of the seafloor. This can be accomplished by making a **seismic reflection profile**. To construct such a profile, strong low-frequency sounds are produced by explosions (depth charges) or air guns. These sound waves penetrate beneath the seafloor and reflect off

FIGURE 9.11 Various types of sonar. **A.** An echo sounder determines the water depth by measuring the time interval required for an acoustic wave to travel from a ship to the seafloor and back. The speed of sound in water is 1500 m/sec. Therefore, depth = ½ (1500 m/sec × echo travel time). **B.** Modern multibeam sonar and sidescan sonar obtain an "image" of a narrow swath of seafloor every few seconds.

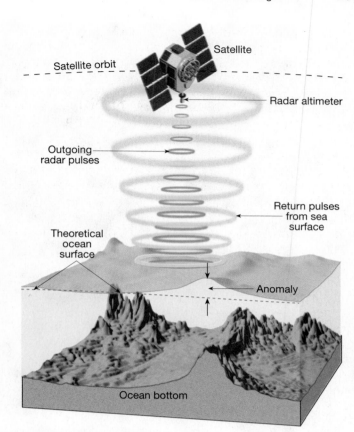

FIGURE 9.12 Seismic cross section and matching sketch across a portion of the Madeira Abyssal Plain in the eastern Atlantic, showing the irregular oceanic crust buried by sediments. (Data courtesy of Charles Hollister, Woods Hole Oceanographic Institution)

FIGURE 9.13 A satellite altimeter measures the variation in sea surface elevation, which is caused by gravitational attraction and mimics the shape of the seafloor. The sea surface anomaly is the difference between the measured and theoretical ocean surface.

the contacts between rock layers and fault zones. **FIGURE 9.12** shows a seismic profile of a portion of the Madeira Abyssal Plain in the eastern Atlantic. Although the seafloor here is flat, notice the irregular ocean crust buried by a thick accumulation of sediments.

Viewing the Ocean Floor from Space

Another technological breakthrough that has led to an enhanced understanding of the seafloor involves measuring the shape of the ocean surface from space. After compensating for waves, tides, currents, and atmospheric effects, it was discovered that the ocean surface is not perfectly flat because gravity attracts water toward regions where massive seafloor features occur. Therefore, mountains and ridges produce elevated areas on the ocean surface, and, conversely, canyons and trenches cause slight depressions. Satellites equipped with *radar altimeters* are able to measure these subtle differences by bouncing microwaves off the sea surface (**FIGURE 9.13**). These devices can measure variations as small as a few centimeters. Such data have added greatly to the knowledge of ocean-floor topography. Combined with traditional sonar depth measurements, the data are used to produce detailed ocean-floor maps, such as the one shown in **FIGURE 9.14**.

Provinces of the Ocean Floor

Oceanographers studying the topography of the ocean floor have delineated three major units: *continental margins,* the *deep-ocean basin,* and the *oceanic (mid-ocean) ridge.* The map in **FIGURE 9.15** outlines these provinces for the North Atlantic

Ocean, and the profile at the bottom of the illustration shows the varied topography. Such profiles usually have their vertical dimension exaggerated many times—40 times in this case—to make topographic features more conspicuous. Vertical exaggeration, however, makes slopes shown in seafloor profiles appear to be *much* steeper than they actually are.

CONTINENTAL MARGINS

 The Global Ocean
▼ Floor of the Ocean

Two types of **continental margins** have been identified—passive and active. Passive margins are found along most of the coastal areas that surround the Atlantic Ocean, including the east coasts of North and South America, as well as the coastal areas of western Africa and Europe. Passive margins are *not* associated with plate boundaries and, therefore, experience little volcanism and few earthquakes. Here, weathered materials eroded from the adjacent landmass accumulate to form a thick, broad wedge of relatively undisturbed sediments.

By contrast, active continental margins occur where oceanic lithosphere is being subducted beneath the edge of a continent. The result is a relatively narrow margin, consisting of highly deformed sediments that were scraped from

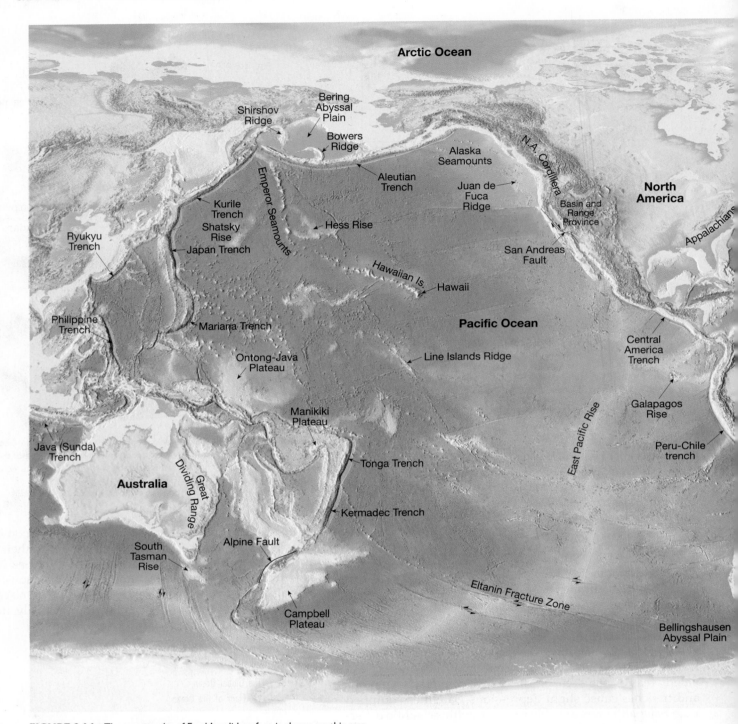

FIGURE 9.14 The topography of Earth's solid surface is shown on this map.

the descending lithospheric slab and plastered against the margin of the overriding continent. Active continental margins are common around the Pacific Rim, where they parallel deep oceanic trenches.

Passive Continental Margins

The features comprising a **passive continental margin** include the continental shelf, the continental slope, and the continental rise (**FIGURE 9.16**).

Continental Shelf

The **continental shelf** is a gently sloping submerged surface extending from the shoreline toward the deep-ocean basin. Because it is underlain by continental crust, it is clearly a flooded extension of the continents. The continental shelf varies greatly in width. Although almost nonexistent along some continents, the shelf may extend seaward as far as 1500 kilometers (930 miles) along others. On the average, the continental shelf is about 80 kilometers (50 miles) wide and

130 meters (423 feet) deep at its seaward edge. The average inclination of the continental shelf is only about one-tenth of 1 degree, a drop of only about 2 meters per kilometer (10 feet per mile). The slope is so slight that it would appear to an observer to be a horizontal surface.

Continental shelves represent only 7.5 percent of the total ocean area, but they have economic and political significance because they contain important mineral deposits, including large reservoirs of petroleum and natural gas, as well as huge sand and gravel deposits. The waters of the continental shelf also contain many important fishing grounds that are significant sources of food.

The continental shelf tends to be relatively featureless; however, some areas are mantled by extensive glacial deposits and thus are quite rugged. In addition, some continental shelves are dissected by large valleys running from the coastline into deeper waters. Many of these *shelf valleys* are the seaward extensions of river valleys on the adjacent landmass. They were excavated during the Pleistocene epoch (Ice Age) when enormous quantities of water were

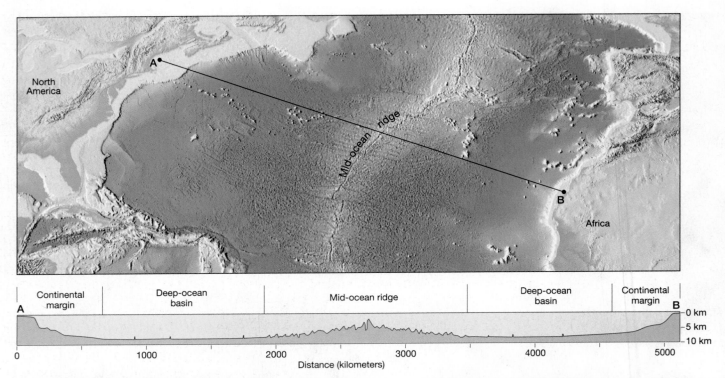

FIGURE 9.15 Map view *(top)* and corresponding profile view *(bottom)* showing the major topographic divisions of the North Atlantic Ocean. On the profile, the vertical scale has been exaggerated to make topographic features more conspicuous.

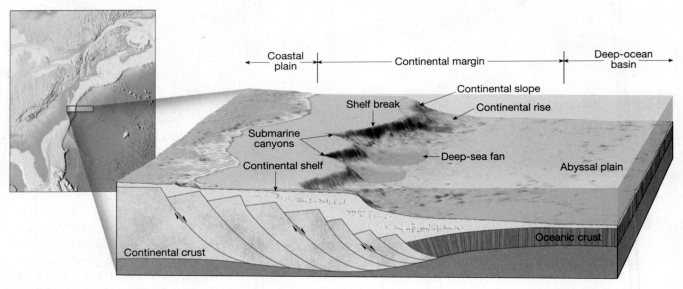

FIGURE 9.16 Schematic view showing the major features of a passive continental margin. Note that the slopes shown for the continental shelf and continental slope are greatly exaggerated. The continental shelf has an average slope of one-tenth of 1 degree, whereas the continental slope has an average slope of about 5 degrees.

stored in vast ice sheets on the continents. This caused sea level to drop by 100 meters (330 feet) or more, exposing large areas of the continental shelves (see Figure 4.19, p. 125). Because of this drop in sea level, rivers extended their courses, and land-dwelling plants and animals inhabited the newly exposed portions of the continents.

Most continental shelves associated with passive margins, such as those along the East Coast of the United States, consist of thick accumulations of shallow-water sediments. These sediments are frequently several kilometers thick and are interbedded with limestones that formed during earlier periods of coral reef building, a process that occurs only in shallow water. Such evidence led researchers to conclude that these thick accumulations of sediment are produced along a gradually subsiding continental margin.

Continental Slope

Marking the seaward edge of the continental shelf is the **continental slope**, a relatively steep zone (as compared with the shelf) that marks the boundary between continental crust and oceanic crust (Figure 9.16). Although the inclination of the continental slope varies greatly from place to place, it averages about 5 degrees and may exceed 25 degrees. Further, the continental slope is a relatively narrow feature, averaging only about 20 kilometers (12 miles) wide.

Continental Rise

In regions where trenches do not exist, the steep continental slope merges into a more gradual incline known as the **continental rise**. Here, the slope drops to about one-third degree, or about 6 meters per kilometer (30 feet per mile). Whereas the width of the continental slope averages about 20 kilometers (12 miles), the continental rise may extend for hundreds of kilometers into the deep-ocean basin.

The continental rise consists of a thick accumulation of sediment that moved downslope from the continental shelf to the deep-ocean floor. Most sediments are delivered to the base of the continental slope by *turbidity currents* that follow submarine canyons. (We will discuss these shortly.) When

these dense, muddy currents emerge from the mouth of a canyon onto the relatively flat ocean floor, they deposit sediment that forms a **deep-sea fan** (Figure 9.16). As fans from adjacent submarine canyons grow, they merge with one another to produce the continuous apron of sediment at the base of the continental slope that we call the continental rise.

Submarine Canyons and Turbidity Currents

Deep, steep-sided valleys known as **submarine canyons** are cut into the continental slope and may extend across the entire continental rise to the deep-ocean basin (**FIGURE 9.17**). Although some of these canyons appear to be the seaward extensions of river valleys, many others do not line up in this manner. Furthermore, submarine canyons extend to depths far below the maximum lowering of sea level during the Ice Age, so we cannot attribute their formation to stream erosion.

These submarine canyons have probably been excavated by turbidity currents. **Turbidity currents** are down slope movements of dense, sediment-laden water. They are created when sand and mud on the continental shelf and slope are dislodged and thrown into suspension. Because the mud-choked water is denser than normal seawater, it flows downslope as a mass, eroding and accumulating more sediment as it goes. The erosional work repeatedly carried on by these muddy torrents is thought to be the major force in the excavation of most submarine canyons.

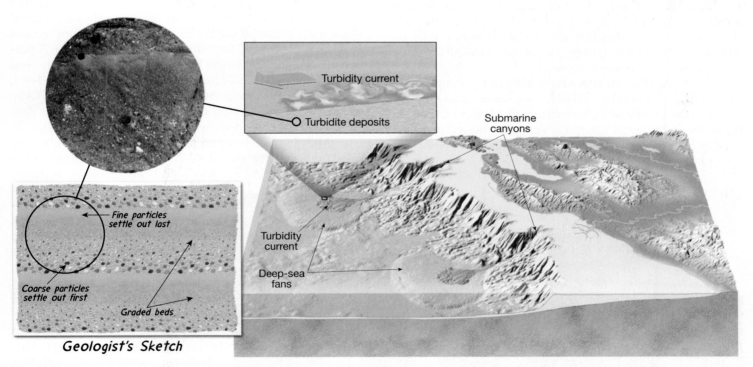

FIGURE 9.17 Turbidity currents are downslope movements of dense, sediment-laden water. They are created when sand and mud on the continental shelf and slope are dislodged and thrown into suspension. Because this mud-choked water is denser than normal seawater, it flows downslope, eroding and accumulating more sediment. Turbidity currents are an important process in the formation of submarine canyons. Beds deposited by these currents are called *turbidites*. Each event produces a single bed characterized by a decrease in sediment size from bottom to top, a feature known as a *graded bed*. (Photo by Marli Miller)

Turbidity currents usually originate along the continental slope and continue across the continental rise, still cutting channels. Eventually, they lose momentum and come to rest along the floor of the deep-ocean basin. As these currents slow, suspended sediments begin to settle out. First, the coarser sand is dropped, followed by successively finer accumulations of silt and then clay. These deposits, called *turbidites,* display a decrease in sediment grain size from bottom to top, a phenomenon known as *graded bedding.*

Turbidity currents are an important mechanism of sediment transport in the ocean. By the action of turbidity currents, submarine canyons are excavated and sediments are carried to the deep-ocean floor.

Active Continental Margins

Along active continental margins the continental shelf is very narrow, if it exists at all, and the continental slope descends abruptly into a deep-ocean trench. In this situation, the landward wall of the trench and the continental slope are essentially the same feature.

Active continental margins are located primarily around the margins of the Pacific Ocean where oceanic lithosphere is being subducted beneath the leading edge of a continent (**FIGURE 9.18**). In such settings, sediments from the ocean floor and pieces of oceanic crust are scraped from the descending oceanic plate and plastered against the edge of the overriding continent. This chaotic accumulation of deformed sediment and scraps of oceanic crust is called an *accretionary wedge.* Prolonged plate subduction, along with the accretion of sediments on the landward side of the trench, can produce massive accumulations of sediment along active continental margins.

Some subduction zones have little or no accumulation of sediments, indicating that ocean sediments are being carried into the mantle with the subducting plate. In these locations, the continental margin is very narrow, as the trench may lie a mere 50 kilometers (30 miles) offshore.

DEEP-OCEAN BASIN

The Global Ocean
▼ Floor of the Ocean

Between the continental margin and the oceanic ridge lies the **deep-ocean basin** (see Figure 9.15 p. 270). The size of this region—almost 30 percent of Earth's surface—is roughly comparable to the percentage of the surface that presently projects above sea level as land. This region includes *deep-ocean trenches,* which are extremely deep linear depressions in the ocean floor; remarkably flat regions, known as *abyssal plains;* tall volcanic peaks, called *seamounts;* and extensive areas of lava flows piled one atop the other, called *oceanic plateaus.*

Deep-Ocean Trenches

Deep-ocean trenches are long, relatively narrow troughs that are the deepest parts of the ocean. Most trenches are located along the margins of the Pacific Ocean, where many exceed 10,000 meters (33,000 feet) in depth (see Figure 9.14). A portion of one—the Challenger Deep in the Mariana Trench—has been measured at 11,022 meters (36,163 feet) below sea level, making it the deepest known part of the world ocean. Only two trenches are located in the Atlantic—the Puerto Rico Trench and the South Sandwich Trench (see Figure 9.14).

Although deep-ocean trenches represent only a very small portion of the area of the ocean floor, they are nevertheless significant geologic features. Trenches are sites of plate convergence where slabs of oceanic lithosphere subduct and plunge back into the mantle. In addition to earthquakes being created as one plate "scrapes" beneath another, volcanic activity is also associated with these regions. Thus, trenches are often paralleled by an arc-shaped row of active volcanoes called a **volcanic island arc.** Furthermore, **continental volcanic arcs,** such as those making up portions of the Andes and Cascades, are located parallel to trenches that lie adjacent to continental margins (see Figure 9.18). The volcanic

FIGURE 9.18   Active continental margin. Sediments from the ocean floor are scraped from the descending plate and added to the continental crust as an accretionary wedge.

activity associated with the trenches that surround the Pacific Ocean explains why the region is called the *Ring of Fire.*

Abyssal Plains

Abyssal plains are deep and incredibly flat features; in fact, these regions are likely the most level places on Earth. The abyssal plain found off the coast of Argentina, for example, has less than 3 meters (10 feet) of relief over a distance exceeding 1300 kilometers (800 miles). The monotonous topography of abyssal plains is occasionally interrupted by the protruding summit of a buried volcanic peak.

Using seismic profilers, instruments whose signals penetrate far below the ocean floor, researchers have determined that abyssal plains consist of thick accumulations of sediment that have buried an otherwise rugged ocean floor (see Figure 9.12). The nature of the sediment indicates that these plains consist primarily of sediments transported far out to sea by turbidity currents.

Abyssal plains occur in all of the oceans. However, because the Atlantic Ocean has fewer trenches to act as traps for the sediments carried down the continental slope, it has more extensive abyssal plains than does the Pacific.

Seamounts, Guyots, and Oceanic Plateaus

Dotting the ocean floor are submarine volcanoes called **seamounts**, which may rise hundreds of meters above the surrounding topography. It is estimated that more than a million exist. Some grow large enough to become oceanic islands, but most do not have a sufficiently long eruptive history to build a structure above sea level. Although seamounts are found on the floors of all the oceans, they are most common in the Pacific.

Some, like the Hawaiian Island-Emperor Seamount chain, which stretches from the Hawaiian Islands to the Aleutian trench, form over volcanic hot spots in association with mantle plumes (see Figure 5.22, p. 161). Others are born near oceanic ridges. If the volcano is large enough before it is carried from the magma source by plate movement, the structure may emerge as an island. Examples in the Atlantic include the Azores, Ascension, Tristan da Cunha, and St. Helena.

During the time they exist as islands, some of these volcanic structures are lowered to near sea level by the forces of weathering and erosion. In addition, islands gradually sink and disappear below the water surface as the moving plate slowly carries them away from the elevated oceanic ridge or hot spot where they originated. Submerged, flat-topped seamounts that formed in this manner are called **guyots** or **tablemounts**.*

The ocean floor also contains several massive **oceanic plateaus,** which resemble flood basalt provinces on the continents. Oceanic plateaus, which in some cases are more than 30 kilometers thick, were generated from vast outpourings of fluid basaltic lavas. Some oceanic plateaus appear to have formed quickly in geologic terms. Examples include the Ontong Java Plateau, which formed in less than 3 million years, and the Kerguelen Plateau, which formed in 4.5 million years.

THE OCEANIC RIDGE

GEODe
EARTH SCIENCE
The Global Ocean
▼ Floor of the Ocean

Along well-developed divergent plate boundaries, the seafloor is elevated, forming a broad linear swell called the **oceanic ridge**, or **mid-ocean ridge**. Our knowledge of the oceanic ridge system comes from soundings of the ocean floor, core samples from deep-sea drilling, visual inspection using deep-diving submersibles, and even firsthand study of slices of ocean floor that have been thrust onto dry land during continental collisions. At oceanic ridges we find extensive faulting, earthquakes, high heat flow, and volcanism.

Anatomy of the Oceanic Ridge

The oceanic ridge system winds through all major oceans in a manner similar to the seam on a baseball and is the longest topographic feature on Earth, exceeding 70,000 kilometers (43,000 miles) in length (**FIGURE 9.19**). The crest of the ridge typically stands 2 to 3 kilometers above the adjacent deep-ocean basins and marks the plate boundary where new oceanic crust is created.

Notice in Figure 9.19 that large sections of the oceanic ridge system have been named based on their locations within the various ocean basins. Some ridges run through the middle of ocean basins, where they are appropriately called *mid-ocean* ridges. The Mid-Atlantic Ridge and the Mid-Indian Ridge are examples. By contrast, the East Pacific Rise is *not* a "mid-ocean" feature. Rather, as its name implies, it is located in the eastern Pacific, far from the center of the ocean.

The term *ridge* is somewhat misleading, because these features are not narrow and steep as the term implies, but have widths of from 1000 to 4000 kilometers (about 620 to 2500 miles) and the appearance of broad, elongated swells that exhibit varying degrees of ruggedness. Furthermore, the ridge system is broken into segments that range from a few tens to hundreds of kilometers in length. Each segment is offset from an adjacent segment by a transform fault.

Oceanic ridges are as high as some mountains on the continents; but the similarities end there. Whereas most mountain ranges on land form when the compressional forces associated with continental collisions fold and metamorphose thick sequences of sedimentary rocks, oceanic ridges form where upwelling from the mantle generates new oceanic crust. Oceanic ridges consist of layers and piles of newly formed basaltic rocks that are buoyantly uplifted by the hot mantle rocks from which they formed.

---

*The term *guyot* is named after Princeton University's first geology professor. It is pronounced "GEE-oh" with a hard g as in "give."

FIGURE 9.19   Distribution of the oceanic ridge system. The map shows ridge segments that exhibit slow, intermediate, and fast spreading rates.

Along the axis of some segments of the oceanic ridge system are deep, down-faulted structures called **rift valleys** because of their striking similarity to the continental rift valleys found in East Africa (**FIGURE 9.20**). Some rift valleys, including those along the rugged Mid-Atlantic Ridge, are typically 30 to 50 kilometers wide and have walls that tower 500 to 2500 meters (1640 to 8200 feet) above the valley floor. This makes them comparable to the deepest and widest part of Arizona's Grand Canyon.

Why Is the Oceanic Ridge Elevated?

The primary reason for the elevated position of the ridge system is that newly created oceanic lithosphere is hot and therefore less dense than cooler rocks of the deep-ocean basin. As the newly formed basaltic crust travels away from the ridge crest, it is cooled from above as seawater circulates through the pore spaces and fractures in the rock. In addition, it cools because it gets farther and farther from the zone of hot mantle upwelling. As a result, the lithosphere gradually cools, contracts, and becomes denser. This thermal contraction accounts for the greater ocean depths that occur away from the ridge. It takes almost 80 million years of cooling and contraction for rock that was once part of an elevated ocean-ridge system to relocate to the deep-ocean basin.

FIGURE 9.20   The axes of some segments of the oceanic ridge system contain deep, down-faulted structures called *rift valleys*. Some may exceed 50 kilometers (31 miles) in width and 2000 meters (6600 feet) in depth.

SEAFLOOR SEDIMENTS

Except for steep areas of the continental slope and areas near the crest of the mid-ocean ridge, the ocean floor is covered with sediment. Part of this material has been deposited by turbidity currents, and the rest has slowly settled to the seafloor from above. The thickness of this carpet of debris varies greatly. In some trenches, which act as traps for sediments originating on the continental margin, accumulations may approach 10 kilometers (6 miles). In general, however, sediment accumulations are considerably less. In the Pacific Ocean, for example, uncompacted sediment measures about 600 meters (2000 feet) or less, whereas on the floor of the Atlantic, the thickness varies from 500 to 1000 meters (1600 to 3300 feet).

Types of Seafloor Sediments

Seafloor sediments can be classified according to their origin into three broad categories: (1) **terrigenous** ("derived from land"), (2) **biogenous** ("derived from organisms"), and (3) **hydrogenous** ("derived from water"). Although each category is discussed separately, remember that all seafloor sediments are mixtures. No body of sediment comes entirely from a single source.

Terrigenous Sediment

Terrigenous sediment consists primarily of mineral grains that were weathered from continental rocks and transported to the ocean. Larger particles (sand and gravel) usually settle rapidly near shore, whereas the very smallest particles take years to settle to the ocean floor and may be carried thousands of kilometers by ocean currents. As a consequence, virtually every area of the ocean receives some terrigenous sediment. The rate at which this sediment accumulates on the deep-ocean floor, though, is very slow. To form a 1-centimeter (0.4-inch) abyssal clay layer, for example, requires as much as 50,000 years. Conversely, on the continental margins near the mouths of large rivers, terrigenous sediment accumulates rapidly and forms thick deposits.

Biogenous Sediment

Biogenous sediment consists of shells and skeletons of marine animals and algae (**FIGURE 9.21**). This debris is produced mostly by microscopic organisms living in the sunlit waters near the ocean surface. Once these organisms die, their hard *tests (testa* = shell) continually "rain" down and accumulate on the seafloor.

The most common biogenous sediment is *calcareous* ($CaCO_3$) *ooze*, which, as the name implies, has the consistency of thick mud. This sediment is produced from the tests

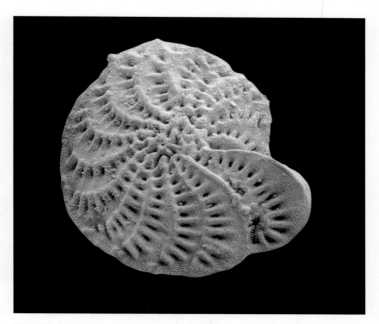

FIGURE 9.21 Image from a scanning electron microscope of the shell (test) of foraminifera, an example of biogenous sediment. These tiny, single-celled organisms are sensitive to even small fluctuations in temperature. Seafloor sediments containing fossils such as this are useful recorders of climate change. (Photo by Andrew Syred/Photo Researchers, Inc.)

of organisms that inhabit warm surface waters. When calcareous hard parts slowly sink through a cool layer of water, they begin to dissolve. This results because the deeper cold seawater is richer in carbon dioxide and is thus more acidic than warm water. In seawater deeper than about 4500 meters (15,000 feet), calcareous tests will completely dissolve before they reach bottom. Consequently, calcareous ooze does not accumulate at these greater depths.

Other biogenous sediments include *siliceous* ($SiO2$) *ooze* and phosphate-rich material. The former is composed primarily of tests of diatoms (single-celled algae) and radiolaria (single-celled animals), whereas the latter is derived from the bones, teeth, and scales of fish and other marine organisms.

Hydrogenous Sediment

Hydrogenous sediment consists of minerals that crystallize directly from seawater through various chemical reactions. For example, some limestones are formed when calcium carbonate precipitates directly from the water; however, most limestone is composed of biogenous sediment.

Some of the most common types of hydrogenous sediment include the following:

- *Manganese nodules* are rounded, hard lumps of manganese, iron, and other metals that precipitate in concentric layers around a central object (such as a volcanic pebble or a grain of sand). The nodules can be up to 20 centimeters (8 inches) in diameter and are often littered across large areas of the deep seafloor (**FIGURE 9.22A**).

- *Calcium carbonates* form by precipitation directly form seawater in warm climates. If this material is buried and hardened, it forms limestone. Most limestone, however, is composed of biogenous sediment.

A.   **B.**

FIGURE 9.22   Examples of hydrogenous sediment. **A.** Manganese nodules. (Photo by Charles A Winters/Photo Researchers, Inc.) **B.** View from the submersible *Alvin* of a black smoker spewing hot, mineral-rich water along the East Pacific Rise. When heated solutions meet cold seawater, metal sulfides precipitate and form mounds of minerals around these hydrothermal vents. (Photo by Dudley Foster © Woods Hole Oceanographic Institution)

- *Metal sulfides* are usually precipitated as coatings on rocks near black smokers associated with the crest of the mid-ocean ridge (**FIGURE 9.22B**). These deposits contain iron, nickel, copper, zinc, silver, and other metals in varying proportions.
- *Evaporites* form where evaporation rates are high and there is restricted open-ocean circulation. As water evaporates from such areas, the remaining seawater becomes saturated with dissolved minerals, which then begin to precipitate. Heavier than seawater, they sink to the bottom or form a characteristic white crust of evaporite minerals around the edges of these areas. Collectively termed *salts,* some evaporite minerals taste salty, such as *halite* (common table salt, NaCl), and some do not, such as the calcium sulfate minerals *anhydrite* ($CaSO_4$) and *gypsum* ($CaSO_4 \cdot 2H_2O$).

Seafloor Sediment—A Storehouse of Climate Data

Reliable climate records go back only a couple of hundred years, at best. How do scientists learn about climates and climate change prior to that time? The answer is that they must reconstruct past climates from *indirect evidence;* that is, they

DID YOU KNOW?

Communities of organisms reside around hydrothermal vents (black smokers) in dark, hot sulfur-rich environments where photosynthesis cannot occur (see Figure 9.22B). The base of the food web is provided by bacterialike organisms that use a process called *chemosynthesis* and heat from the vents to produce sugars and other foods that allow them and many other organisms to live in this extreme environment.

must analyze phenomena that respond to and reflect changing atmospheric conditions. An interesting and important technique for analyzing Earth's climate history is the study of seafloor sediments.

We know that the parts of the Earth system are linked so that a change in one part can produce changes in any or all of the other parts. In this example you will see how changes in atmospheric and oceanic temperatures are reflected in the nature of life in the sea.

Most seafloor sediments contain the remains of organisms that once lived near the sea surface (the ocean–atmosphere interface). When such near-surface organisms die, their shells slowly settle to the floor of the ocean, where they become part of the sedimentary record (**FIGURE 9.23**). These seafloor sediments are useful recorders of worldwide climate change because the numbers and types of organisms living near the sea surface change with the climate:

> We would expect that in any area of the ocean/atmosphere interface the average annual temperature of the surface water of the ocean would approximate that of the contiguous atmosphere. The temperature equilibrium established between surface seawater and the air above it should mean that. . . . changes in climate should be reflected in changes in organisms living near the surface of the deep sea. . . . When we recall that the seafloor sediments in vast areas of the ocean consist mainly of shells of pelagic foraminifers, and that these animals are sensitive to variations in water temperature, the connection between such sediments and climate change becomes obvious.*

---

*Richard F. Flint, *Glacial and Quaternary Geology* (New York: John Wiley and Sons, 1971), p. 718.

FIGURE 9.23 Laboratory work is an important part of what many geologists do. These scientists are working with a core of seafloor sediments. Such cores often contain useful data about the geologic past and Earth's climate history. (Photo by Science Source/Photo Resarchers, Inc.)

Thus, in seeking to understand climate change as well as other environmental transformations, scientists are tapping the huge reservoir of data in seafloor sediments. The sediment cores gathered by drilling ships and other research vessels have provided invaluable data that have significantly expanded our knowledge and understanding of past climates (**FIGURE 9.24**).

One notable example of the importance of seafloor sediments to our understanding of climate change relates to unraveling the fluctuating atmospheric conditions of the Ice Age. The records of temperature changes contained in cores of sediment from the ocean floor have proven critical to our present understanding of this recent span of Earth history.

FIGURE 9.24 The *Chikyu* (meaning "Planet Earth" in Japanese) is the world's most advanced scientific drilling vessel. It is capable of staying at one site for an extended period and drilling deep into the seabed. It is part of the Integrated Ocean Drilling Program (IODP). (AP Photo/Itsuo Inouye)

THE CHAPTER IN REVIEW

• *Oceanography* is an interdisciplinary science that draws on the methods and knowledge of biology, chemistry, physics, and geology to study all aspects of the world ocean.

• *Earth is a planet dominated by oceans.* Seventy-one percent of Earth's surface area is oceans and marginal seas. In the Southern Hemisphere, often called the *water hemisphere,* about 81 percent of the surface is water. Of the three major oceans, Pacific, Atlantic, and Indian, the *Pacific Ocean* is the *largest,* contains slightly *more than half of the water* in the world ocean, and has the *greatest average depth*—3940 meters (12,927 feet).

• *Salinity* is the proportion of dissolved salts to pure water, usually expressed in parts per thousand (‰). The average salinity in the open ocean ranges from 35‰ to 37‰. The principal elements that contribute to the ocean's salinity are *chlorine* (55%) and *sodium* (31%). The primary *sources for the elements in sea salt* are *chemical weathering* of rocks on the continents and volcanic *outgassing.*

• *Variations in seawater salinity* are primarily caused by changing the *water content.* Natural processes that add large amounts of fresh water to seawater and *decrease salinity* include *precipitation, runoff from land, icebergs melting,* and *sea ice melting.* Processes that remove large amounts of fresh water from seawater and *increase salinity* include the *formation of sea ice* and *evaporation.* Seawater salinity in the open ocean *ranges from 33‰ to 38‰,* with some marginal seas experiencing considerably more variation.

• The ocean's *surface temperature* is related to the amount of solar energy received and *varies as a function of latitude.* Low-latitude regions have relatively warm surface water and distinctly colder water at depth, creating a *thermocline,* which is a layer of rapidly changing temperature. No thermocline exists in high-latitude regions, because there is little temperature difference between the top and bottom of the water column. The water column is *isothermal.*

• Seawater *density is mostly affected by water temperature* but also by salinity. Low-latitude regions have distinctly denser (colder) water at depth as compared to the surface, creating a *pycnocline,* which is a layer of rapidly changing density. No pycnocline exists in high-latitude regions because the water column is *isopycnal.*

• Most open-ocean regions exhibit a *three-layered structure based on water density*. The shallow *surface mixed zone* has warm and nearly uniform temperatures. The *transition zone* includes a prominent thermocline and associated pycnocline. The *deep zone* is continually dark and cold and accounts for 80 percent of the water in the ocean. In high latitudes, the three-layered structure does not exist.

• *Ocean bathymetry is determined using echo sounders and multibeam sonars*, which bounce sonic signals off the ocean floor. Ship-based receivers record the reflected echoes and accurately measure the time interval of the signals. With this information, ocean depths are calculated and plotted to produce maps of ocean-floor topography. Recently, *satellite measurements* of the shape of the ocean surface have added data for mapping ocean-floor features.

• The zones that collectively make up *a passive continental margin* include the *continental shelf* (a gently sloping, submerged surface extending from the shoreline toward the deep-ocean basin), *continental slope* (the true edge of the continent, which has a steep slope that leads from the continental shelf into deep water), and in regions where trenches do not exist, the steep continental slope merges into a gradual incline known as the *continental rise*. The continental rise consists of sediments that have moved downslope from the continental shelf to the deep-ocean floor.

• *Submarine canyons* are deep, steep-sided valleys that originate on the continental slope and may extend to the deep-ocean basin. Many submarine canyons have been excavated by *turbidity currents* (downslope movements of dense, sediment-laden water).

• *Active continental margins* are located primarily around the margin of the Pacific Ocean in areas where the leading edge of a continent is over-running oceanic lithosphere. Here, sediment scraped from the descending oceanic plate is plastered against the continent to form a collection of sediments called an *accretionary wedge*. An active continental margin generally has a narrow continental shelf, which grades into a deep-ocean trench.

• The *deep-ocean basin* lies between the continental margin and the mid-ocean ridge system. The features of the deep-ocean basin include *deep-ocean trenches* (the deepest parts of the ocean, where moving crustal plates descend into the mantle), *abyssal plains* (very level regions consisting of thick accumulations of sediments that were deposited atop the low, rough portions of the ocean floor by turbidity currents), *seamounts* (isolated volcanic peaks on the ocean floor that originate near mid-ocean ridges or in association with volcanic hot spots), and *oceanic plateaus* (vast accumulations of basaltic lava flows).

• The *oceanic (mid-ocean) ridge* winds through the middle of most ocean basins. Seafloor spreading occurs near the center of this broad feature, which is characterized by an elevated position, extensive faulting, and volcanic structures that have developed on newly formed oceanic crust. Most of the geologic activity associated with ridges occurs along a narrow region on the ridge crest, called the *rift valley*, where magma moves upward to create new slivers of oceanic crust.

• *There are three broad categories of seafloor sediments*. *Terrigenous sediment* consists primarily of mineral grains that were weathered from continental rocks and transported to the ocean; *biogenous sediment* consists of shells and skeletons of marine animals and plants; and *hydrogenous sediment* includes minerals that crystallize directly from seawater through various chemical reactions.

• *Seafloor sediments are helpful when studying worldwide climate changes* because they often contain the remains of organisms that once lived near the sea surface. The numbers and types of these organisms change as the climate changes, and their remains in seafloor sediments record these changes.

KEY TERMS

abyssal plain (p. 273)

active continental margin (p. 272)

bathymetry (p. 266)

biogenous sediment (p. 275)

continental margin (p. 267)

continental rise (p. 271)

continental shelf (p. 268)

continental slope (p. 271)

continental volcanic arc (p. 272)

deep-ocean basin (p. 272)

deep-ocean trench (p. 272)

deep-sea fan (p. 271)

density (p. 264)

echo sounder (p. 266)

guyot (p. 273)

hydrogenous sediment (p. 275)

oceanic plateau (p. 273)

oceanic (mid-ocean) ridge (p. 273)

oceanography (p. 260)

passive continental margin (p. 268)

pycnocline(p. 264)

rift valley (p. 274)

salinity (p. 261)

seamount (p. 273)

seismic reflection profile (p. 266)

sonar (p. 266)

submarine canyon (p. 271)

tablemount (p. 273)

terrigenous sediment (p. 275)

thermocline (p. 263)

turbidity current (p. 271)

volcanic island arc (p. 272)

QUESTIONS FOR REVIEW

1. How does the area of Earth's surface covered by the oceans compare with the area of the continents? Describe the distribution of land and water on Earth.

2. Name the four main ocean basins. Of the four:
   a. Which one is the largest in area? Which one is smallest?

   b. Which one is the deepest? Which one is shallowest?

   c. Which one is almost entirely within the Southern Hemisphere?

   d. Which one is exclusively in the Northern Hemisphere?

3. How does the average depth of the ocean compare to the average elevation of the continents?

4. What is meant by *salinity*? What is the average salinity of the ocean?

5. What are the six most abundant components (elements) dissolved in seawater? What is produced when the two most abundant elements are combined?

6. What are the two primary sources for the materials that comprise the dissolved components in seawater?

7. Describe the processes that affect seawater salinity. For each process, indicate whether water is added or removed and if it decreases or increases salinity. What physical conditions create high-salinity water in the Red Sea and low-salinity water in the Baltic Sea?

8. Describe ocean temperature change with depth in both the high and low latitudes. Why do high-latitude waters usually lack a thermocline?

9. Describe density variation with depth in both the high and low latitudes. Why do high-latitude waters generally lack a pycnocline?

10. Describe the ocean's layered structure. Why does the three-layer structure not exist in high latitudes?

11. Assuming that the average speed of sound waves in water is 1500 meters per second, determine the water depth if the signal sent out by an echo sounder requires 6 seconds to strike bottom and return to the recorder (see Figure 9.11, p. 266).

12. Describe how satellites orbiting Earth can determine features on the seafloor without being able to directly observe them beneath several kilometers of seawater.

13. List the three subdivisions of a passive continental margin. Which subdivision is considered a flooded extension of the continent? Which has the steepest slope?

14. Describe the differences between active and passive continental margins. Be sure to include how various features relate to plate tectonics and give a geographic example of each type of margin.

15. Defend or rebut the statement "Most submarine canyons found on the continental slope and rise were formed during the Ice Age when rivers extended their valleys seaward."

16. Why are abyssal plains more extensive on the floor of the Atlantic than on the floor of the Pacific?

17. How are mid-ocean ridges and deep-ocean trenches related to plate tectonics?

18. Distinguish among the three basic types of seafloor sediment.

19. Why are seafloor sediments useful in studying climates of the past?

COMPANION WEBSITE

The *Foundations of Earth Science* Website uses the resources and flexibility of the Internet to aid in your study of the topics in this chapter. Written and developed by the authors and other Earth science instructors, this site will help improve your understanding of Earth science. Visit **www.mygeoscienceplace.com** in order to:

- **Review** key chapter concepts.
- **Read** with links to the ebook and to chapter-specific web resources.

- **Visualize** and comprehend challenging topics using learning activities in *GEODe: Earth Science*.
- **Test** yourself with online quizzes.

GEODe: EARTH SCIENCE

GEODe: Earth Science is a valuable and easy to use learning aid that can be accessed from your book's Companion Website: **www.mygeoscienceplace.com.** It is a dynamic instructional tool that promotes understanding and reinforces important concepts by using tutorials, animations, and exercises that actively engage the student.

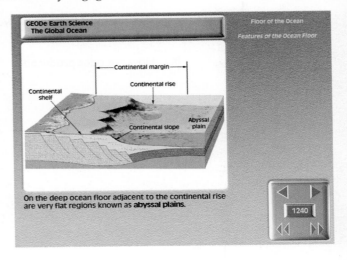

The floor of the ocean is divided into three broad zones. These zones can be identified on this map and profile of the North Atlantic.

On the deep ocean floor adjacent to the continental rise are very flat regions known as **abyssal plains.**

THE RESTLESS OCEAN

To assist you in learning the important concepts in this chapter, you will find it helpful to focus on the following questions:

1. What forces create and influence surface ocean currents?

2. What is the basic pattern of surface ocean currents in each major ocean basin?

3. How do ocean currents influence climate?

4. What two factors are most significant in creating a dense mass of ocean water?

5. What factors determine the height, length, and period of a wave?

6. What are some typical shoreline features produced by wave erosion and from sediment deposited by beach drift and longshore currents?

7. What is the difference between a submergent and an emergent coast?

8. How are tides produced?

Hatteras Island, North Carolina, is a barrier
island. When storm waves strike this beach,
these homes are obviously vulnerable.
(Photo by Michael Collier)

The restless waters of the ocean are constantly in motion, powered by many different forces. Winds, for example, generate surface currents, which influence coastal climate and provide nutrients that affect the abundance of algae and other marine life in surface waters. Winds also produce waves that carry energy from storms to distant shores, where their impact erodes the land (**FIGURE 10.1**). In some areas, density differences create deep-ocean circulation, which is important for ocean mixing and nutrient recycling. In addition, the Moon and the Sun produce tides, which periodically raise and lower sea level. This chapter will examine these movements of ocean waters and their effects upon coastal regions.

THE OCEAN'S SURFACE CIRCULATION

Ocean currents are masses of ocean water that flow from one place to another. The amount of water can be large or small, currents can be at the surface or deep below, and the phenomena that create them can be simple or complex. In all cases, however, the currents that are generated involve water masses in motion.

Surface currents develop from friction between the ocean and the wind that blows across its surface. Some of these currents are short-lived and affect only small areas. Such water movements are responses to local or seasonal influences. Other surface currents are relatively permanent phenomena that extend over large portions of the oceans. These major horizontal movements of surface waters are closely related to the global pattern of prevailing winds.* As an example, **FIGURE 10.2** shows how the wind belts known as the *Trade Winds* and the *Westerlies* create large, circular-moving loops of water in the Atlantic Ocean. The same wind belts influence the other oceans as well, so that a similar pattern of currents can also be seen in the Pacific and Indian oceans. Essentially, the pattern of surface ocean circulation closely matches the pattern of global winds, but is also strongly influenced by the distribution of major landmasses. Other factors that affect surface current patterns include gravity, friction, and the Coriolis effect.

The Pattern of Ocean Currents

Huge circular-moving current systems dominate the surfaces of the oceans. These large whirls of water within an ocean basin are called **gyres** (*gyros* = a circle). **FIGURE 10.3**

*Details about the global pattern of winds appear in Chapter 13, The Atmosphere in Motion.

FIGURE 10.1   When waves break against the shore, the force of the water can be powerful. These storm waves are breaking along the coast of Wales. Wind is responsible for creating waves and also is the force that drives the ocean's surface circulation. (Photo by Photolibrary Wales/Alamy)

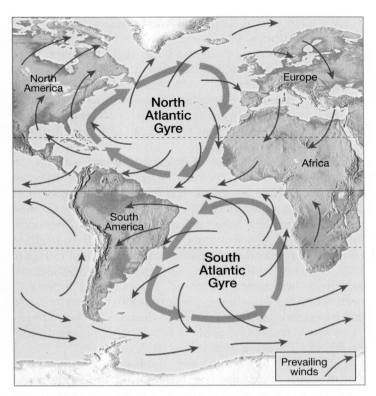

FIGURE 10.2 Idealized surface circulation pattern for the Atlantic Ocean. The prevailing winds create circular-moving loops of water (known as gyres) at the surface in both parts of the Atlantic Ocean basin.

shows the world's five main gyres: the *North Pacific Gyre*, the *South Pacific Gyre*, the *North Atlantic Gyre*, the *South Atlantic Gyre*, and the *Indian Ocean Gyre* (which exists mostly within the Southern Hemisphere). The center of each gyre coincides with the subtropics at about 30 degrees north or south latitude, so they are often called *subtropical gyres*.

As shown in Figure 10.3, subtropical gyres rotate clockwise in the Northern Hemisphere and counterclockwise in the Southern Hemisphere. Why do the gyres flow in different directions in the two hemispheres? Although wind is the force that generates surface currents, other factors also influence the movement of ocean waters. The most significant of these is the **Coriolis effect**. Because of Earth's rotation, currents are deflected to the *right* in the Northern Hemisphere and to the *left* in the Southern Hemisphere. (The Coriolis effect is more fully explained in Chapter 13.) As a consequence, gyres flow in opposite directions in the two different hemispheres.

Four main currents generally exist within each gyre (Figure 10.3). The North Pacific Gyre, for example, consists of the North Equatorial Current, the Kuroshio Current, the North Pacific Current, and the California Current. The tracking of floating objects that are released into the ocean intentionally or accidentally reveals that it takes about six years for the objects to go all the way around the loop.

The North Atlantic Ocean has four main currents, too (Figure 10.3). Beginning near the equator, the North Equatorial Current is deflected northward through the Caribbean, where it becomes the Gulf Stream. As the Gulf Stream moves

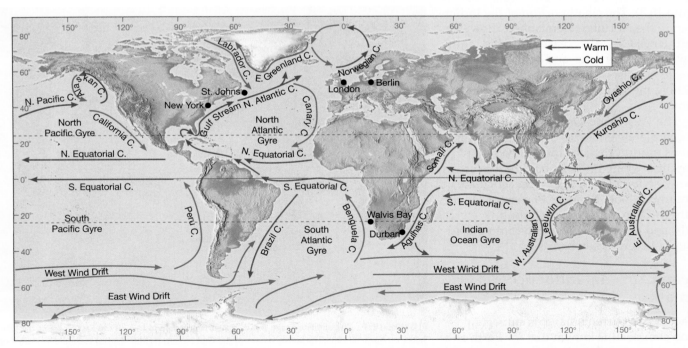

FIGURE 10.3 Average ocean surface currents in February–March. The ocean's circulation is organized into five major current gyres (large circular-moving loops), which exist in the North Pacific, South Pacific, North Atlantic, South Atlantic, and Indian Oceans. Poleward-moving currents are warm and equatorward-moving currents are cold. Surface ocean currents are driven by global winds and play an important role in redistributing heat around the globe. Note that cities mentioned in the text discussion are shown on the map.

along the East Coast of the United States, it is strengthened by the prevailing westerly winds and is deflected to the east (to the right) offshore of North Carolina into the North Atlantic. As it continues northeastward, it gradually widens and slows until it becomes a vast, slowly moving current known as the North Atlantic Current, which because of its sluggish nature, is also known as the North Atlantic Drift.

As the North Atlantic Current approaches Western Europe, it splits, part of it moving northward past Great Britain, Norway, and Iceland, carrying heat to these otherwise chilly areas. The other part is deflected southward as the cool Canary Current. As the Canary Current moves southward, it eventually merges into the North Equatorial Current, completing the gyre. Because the North Atlantic Ocean basin is about half the size of the North Pacific, it takes floating objects about three years to go completely around this gyre.

The circular motion of gyres leaves a large central area that has no well-defined currents. In the North Atlantic, this zone of calmer waters is known as the Sargasso Sea, named for the large quantities of *Sargassum*, a type of floating seaweed encountered there.

The ocean basins in the Southern Hemisphere exhibit a similar pattern of flow as the Northern Hemisphere basins, with surface currents that are influenced by wind belts, the position of continents, and the Coriolis effect. In the South Atlantic and South Pacific, for example, surface ocean circulation is very much the same as in their Northern Hemisphere counterparts except that the direction of flow is counterclockwise (Figure 10.3).

The Indian Ocean exists mostly in the Southern Hemisphere, so it follows a surface circulation pattern similar to other Southern Hemisphere ocean basins (Figure 10.3). The small portion of the Indian Ocean in the Northern Hemisphere, however, is influenced by the seasonal wind shifts known as the summer and winter *monsoons* (*mausim* = season). When the winds change direction, the surface currents also reverse direction.

The West Wind Drift is the only current that completely encircles Earth (Figure 10.3). It flows around the ice-covered continent of Antarctica, where no large landmasses are in the way, so its cold surface waters circulate in a continuous loop. It moves in response to the Southern Hemisphere's prevailing westerly winds, and portions of it split off into the adjoining southern ocean basins.

Ocean Currents Influence Climate

Surface ocean currents have an important effect on climate. It is known that for Earth as a whole, the gains in solar energy equal the losses to space of heat radiated from the surface. When most latitudes are considered individually, however, this is not the case.

There is a net gain of energy in lower latitudes and a net loss at higher latitudes. Because the tropics are not becoming progressively warmer, nor the polar regions colder, there must be a large-scale transfer of heat from areas of excess to areas of deficit. This is indeed the case. *The transfer of heat by winds and ocean currents equalizes these latitudinal energy imbalances.* Ocean water movements account for about a quarter of this total heat transport, and winds the remaining three-quarters (**FIGURE 10.4**).

The moderating effect of poleward-moving warm ocean currents is well known. The North Atlantic Drift, an extension of the warm Gulf Stream, keeps wintertime temperatures in Great Britain and much of Western Europe warmer than would be expected for their latitudes. London is farther north than St. John's, Newfoundland, yet is not nearly so frigid in winter. (Cities mentioned in this section are shown in Figure 10.3). Because of the prevailing westerly winds, the moderating effects are carried far inland. For example, Berlin (52° north latitude) has a mean January temperature similar to that experienced at New York City, which lies 12° latitude farther south. The January mean at London (51° north latitude) is 4.5°C (8.1°F) higher than at New York City.

In contrast to warm ocean currents like the Gulf Stream, the effects of which are felt most during the winter, cold currents exert their greatest influence in the tropics or during the summer months in the middle latitudes. For example, the cool Benguela Current off the western coast of southern Africa moderates the tropical heat along this coast. Walvis Bay (23° south latitude), a town adjacent to the Benguela Current, is 5°C (9°F) cooler in summer than Durban, which is 6° latitude

FIGURE 10.4 This satellite image shows sea-surface temperatures off the East Coast of the United States on April 18, 2005. The warm waters of the Gulf Stream (lighter shades) extend diagonally from bottom left to top right. The current transports heat from the tropics far into the North Atlantic. This image shows several deep bends in the path of the Gulf Stream. In fact, the northernmost of the two deep bends actually loops back on itself, creating a closed-off eddy. On the northern side of the current, cold waters (blue) dip southward into the Gulf Stream's warmth. Gray areas indicate clouds. (NASA)

farther poleward but on the eastern side of South Africa, away from the influence of the cold current. The east and west coasts of South America provide another example. **FIGURE 10.5** shows monthly mean temperatures for Rio de Janeiro, Brazil, which is influenced by the warm Brazil Current and Arica, Chile, which is adjacent to the cold Peru Current. Closer to home, because of the cold California Current, summer temperatures in subtropical coastal southern California are lower by 6°C (10.8°F) or more compared to East Coast stations.

In addition to influencing temperatures of adjacent land areas, cold currents have other climatic influences. For example, where tropical deserts exist along the west coasts of continents, cold ocean currents have a dramatic impact. The principal west coast deserts are the Atacama in Peru and Chile and the Namib in southwestern Africa. The aridity along these coasts is intensified because the lower atmosphere is chilled by cold offshore waters. When this occurs, the air becomes very stable and resists the upward movement necessary to create precipitation-producing clouds. In addition, the presence of cold currents causes temperatures to approach and often reach the dew point, the temperature at which water vapor condenses. As a result, these areas are characterized by high relative humidities and much fog. Thus, not all tropical deserts are

FIGURE 10.5 Monthly mean temperatures for Rio de Janeiro, Brazil, and Arica, Chile. Both are coastal cities near sea level. Even though Arica is closer to the equator, its temperatures are cooler than at Rio de Janeiro. Arica is influenced by the cold Peru Current whereas Rio de Janeiro is adjacent to the warm Brazil Current.

hot with low humidities and clear skies. Rather, the presence of cold currents transforms some tropical deserts into relatively cool, damp places that are often shrouded in fog.

Upwelling

In addition to producing surface currents, winds can also cause *vertical* water movements. **Upwelling**, the rising of cold water from deeper layers to replace warmer surface water, is a common wind-induced vertical movement. One type of upwelling, called *coastal upwelling*, is most characteristic along the west coasts of continents, most notably along California, western South America, and West Africa.

Coastal upwelling occurs in these areas when winds blow toward the equator and parallel to the coast (**FIGURE 10.6**). Coastal winds combined with the Coriolis effect cause surface water to move away from shore. As the surface layer moves away from the coast, it is replaced by water that "upwells" from below the surface. This slow upward movement of water from depths of 50 to 300 meters (165 to 1000 feet) brings water that is cooler than the original surface water and results in lower surface water temperatures near the shore.

For swimmers who are accustomed to the warm waters along the mid-Atlantic shore of the United States, a swim in the Pacific off the coast of central California can be a chilling surprise. In August, when temperatures in the Atlantic are 21°C (70°F) or higher, central California's surf is only about 15°C (60°F).

Upwelling brings greater concentrations of dissolved nutrients, such as nitrates and phosphates, to the ocean surface. These nutrient-enriched waters from below promote the growth of microscopic plankton, which in turn support extensive populations of fish and other marine organisms. Figure 10.6 is a satellite image that shows high productivity due to coastal upwelling off the southwest coast of Africa.

DEEP-OCEAN CIRCULATION

In contrast to the largely horizontal movements of surface currents, deep-ocean circulation has a significant vertical component and accounts for the thorough mixing of deep-water masses. This component of ocean circulation is a response to density differences among water masses that cause denser water to sink and slowly spread out beneath the surface. Because the density variations that cause deep-ocean circulation are caused by differences in temperature

Chlorophyll a Concentration
mg/m3

FIGURE 10.6   Coastal upwelling occurs along the west coasts of continents where winds blow toward the equator and parallel to the coast. The Coriolis effect (deflection to the left in the Southern Hemisphere) causes surface water to move away from the shore, which brings cold, nutrient-rich water to the surface. This image from the SeaStar satellite shows chlorophyll concentration along the southwest coast of Africa (February 21, 2001). An instrument aboard the satellite detects changes in seawater color caused by changing concentrations of chlorophyll. High chlorophyll concentrations indicate high amounts of photosynthesis, which is linked to the upwelling nutrients. Red indicates high concentrations and blue low concentrations. (Provided by the SeaWiFS Project, NASA/Goddard Space Flight Center and ORBIMAGE)

and salinity, deep-ocean circulation is also referred to as **thermohaline** (*thermo* = heat, *haline* = salt) **circulation**.

An increase in seawater density can be caused by either a decrease in temperature or an increase in salinity. Density changes due to salinity variations are important in very high latitudes, where water temperature remains low and relatively constant.

Most water involved in deep-ocean currents (thermohaline circulation) begins in high latitudes at the surface. In these regions, where surface waters are cold, salinity increases when sea ice forms (**FIGURE 10.7**). Recall from Chapter 9

FIGURE 10.7   Sea ice in the waters surrounding Antarctica. When seawater freezes, sea salts do not become part of the ice. Consequently, the salt content of the remaining seawater becomes more concentrated, which makes it denser and prone to sink. (Photo by John Higdon/agefotostock)

that when seawater freezes to form sea ice, salts do not become part of the ice. As a result, the salinity (and therefore the density) of the remaining seawater increases. When this surface water becomes dense enough, it sinks, initiating deep-ocean currents. Once this water sinks, it is removed from the physical processes that increased its density in the first place, and so its temperature and salinity remain largely unchanged for the duration of the time it spends in the deep ocean.

Near Antarctica, surface conditions create the highest density water in the world. This cold saline brine slowly sinks to the seafloor, where it moves throughout the ocean basins in sluggish currents. After sinking from the surface of the ocean, deep waters will not reappear at the surface for an average of 500 to 2000 years.

A simplified model of ocean circulation is similar to a conveyor belt that travels from the Atlantic Ocean through the Indian and Pacific oceans and back again (**FIGURE 10.8**). In this model, warm water in the ocean's upper layers flows poleward, converts to dense water, and returns toward the equator as cold deep water that eventually upwells to complete the circuit. As this "conveyor belt" moves around the globe, it influences global climate by converting warm water to cold and liberating heat to the atmosphere.

THE SHORELINE: A DYNAMIC INTERFACE

Shorelines are dynamic environments. Their topography, geologic makeup, and climate vary greatly from place to place. Continental and oceanic processes converge along coasts to create landscapes that frequently undergo rapid change. When it comes to the deposition of sediment, they are transition zones between marine and continental environments.

Nowhere is the restless nature of the ocean's water more noticeable than along the shore—the dynamic interface among air, land, and sea. An *interface* is a common boundary where different parts of a system interact. This is certainly an appropriate designation for the coastal zone, where we can see the rhythmic rise and fall of tides and observe waves rolling in and breaking. Sometimes, the waves are low and gentle. At other times, they pound the shore with awesome fury.

Although it may not be obvious, the shoreline is constantly being modified by waves. Crashing surf can erode the adjacent land. Wave activity also moves sediment toward and away from the shore, as well as along it. Such activity sometimes produces narrow sandbars that frequently change size and shape as storm waves come and go.

The nature of present-day shorelines is not just the result of the relentless attack of the land by the sea. Indeed, the shore has a complex character that results from multiple geologic processes. For example, practically all coastal areas were affected by the worldwide rise in sea level that accompanied the melting of glaciers at the close of the Pleistocene epoch. As the sea encroached landward, the shoreline retreated, becoming superimposed upon existing landscapes that had resulted from such diverse processes as stream erosion, glaciation, volcanic activity, and the forces of mountain building.

Today, the coastal zone is experiencing intensive human activity. Unfortunately, people often treat the shoreline as if it were a stable platform on which structures can safely be built. This attitude inevitably leads to conflicts between people and nature. As you will see, many coastal landforms, especially beaches and barrier islands, are relatively fragile, short-lived features that are frequently inappropriate sites for development (**FIGURE 10.9**).

WAVES

The Global Ocean
▼ Coastal Processes

Ocean waves are energy traveling along the interface between ocean and atmosphere, often transferring energy from a storm far out at sea over distances of several thousand kilometers. That's why even on calm days the ocean still has waves that travel across its surface. When observing waves, always remember that you are watching *energy* travel through a medium (water). If you make waves by tossing a pebble into a pond, or by splashing in a pool, or by blowing across the surface of a cup of coffee, you are imparting *energy* to the water, and the waves you see are just the visible evidence of the energy passing through.

Wind-generated waves provide most of the energy that shapes and modifies shorelines. Where the land and sea meet, waves that may have traveled unimpeded for hundreds or thousands of kilometers suddenly encounter a barrier that will not allow them to advance farther and must absorb their energy. Stated another way, the shore is the location where a practically irresistible force confronts an almost immovable object. The conflict that results is never ending and sometimes dramatic.

Wave Characteristics

Most ocean waves derive their energy and motion from the wind. When a breeze is less than 3 kilometers (2 miles) per hour, only small wavelets appear. At greater wind speeds, more stable waves gradually form and advance with the wind.

Characteristics of ocean waves are illustrated in **FIGURE 10.10**, which shows a simple, nonbreaking waveform. The tops of the waves are the *crests*, which are separated by *troughs*. Halfway between the crests and troughs is the *still water level*, which is the level that the water would occupy if there were no waves. The vertical distance between trough and crest is called the **wave height**, and the horizontal distance between successive crests (or troughs) is the **wavelength**. The time it takes one full wave—one wavelength—to pass a fixed position is the **wave period**.

The height, length, and period that are eventually achieved by a wave depend on three factors: (1) wind speed; (2) length of time the wind has blown; and (3) **fetch**, the distance that wind has traveled across open water. As the quantity of energy transferred from the wind to the water increases, both the height and steepness of the waves increase. Eventually, a critical point is reached where waves grow so tall that they topple over, forming ocean breakers called *whitecaps*.

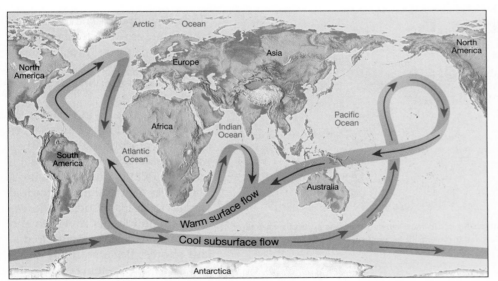

FIGURE 10.8 Schematic map showing the conveyor-belt circulation of the world ocean. Source areas for dense water masses exist in high-latitude regions. Here cold, high-salinity water sinks and flows into all of the oceans. This water slowly ascends throughout the oceans and completes the conveyor by returning to the source areas as warm surface currents.

FIGURE 10.9 Crystal Beach, Texas, on September 16, 2008, three days after Hurricane Ike came ashore. At landfall the storm had sustained winds of 165 kilometers (105 miles) per hour. The extraordinary storm surge caused much of the damage pictured here. (Photo by Earl Nottingham/Associated Press)

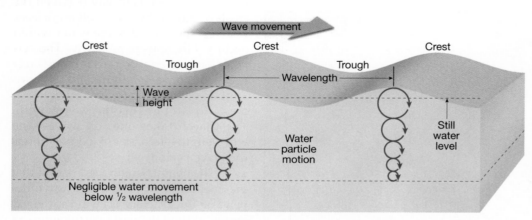

FIGURE 10.10 Diagrammatic view of an idealized nonbreaking ocean wave showing the basic parts of a wave as well as the movement of water particles at depth. Negligible water movement occurs below a depth equal to one-half the wavelength (*lower dashed line*).

"fully developed." The reason that waves can grow no further is that they are losing as much energy through the breaking of whitecaps as they are receiving from the wind.

When the wind stops or changes direction, or the waves leave the storm area where they were created, they continue on without relation to local winds. The waves also undergo a gradual change to *swells*, which are lower in height and longer in length and may carry a storm's energy to distant shores. Because many independent wave systems exist at the same time, the sea surface acquires a complex and irregular pattern, sometimes producing very large waves. The sea waves that are seen from shore are usually a mixture of swells from faraway storms and waves created by local winds.

For a particular wind speed, there is a maximum fetch and duration of wind beyond which waves will no longer increase in size. When the maximum fetch and duration are reached for a given wind velocity, the waves are said to be

Circular Orbital Motion

Waves can travel great distances across ocean basins. In one study, waves generated near Antarctica were tracked as they traveled through the Pacific Ocean basin. After more than 10,000 kilometers (over 6000 miles), the waves finally expended their energy a week later along the shoreline of the Aleutian Islands of Alaska. The water itself does not travel the entire distance, but the waveform does. As the wave travels, the water passes the energy along by moving in a circle. This movement is called *circular orbital motion.*

Observation of an object floating in waves reveals that it moves not only up and down but also slightly forward and backward with each successive wave. **FIGURE 10.11** shows that a floating object moves up and backward as the crest approaches, up and forward as the crest passes, down and forward after the crest, down and backward as the trough approaches, and then it rises and moves backward again as the next crest advances. When the movement of the toy boat shown in Figure 10.11 is traced as a wave passes, it can be seen that the boat moves in a circle and it returns to

FIGURE 10.11   The movements of the toy boat show that the wave form advances, but the water does not advance appreciably from its original position. In this sequence, the wave moves from left to right as the boat (and the water in which it is floating) rotates in an imaginary circle.

essentially the same place. Circular orbital motion allows a waveform (the wave's shape) to move forward *through the water* while the individual water particles that transmit the wave move around in a circle. Wind moving across a field of wheat causes a similar phenomenon: The wheat itself does not travel across the field, but the waves do.

The energy contributed by the wind to the water is transmitted not only along the surface of the sea but also downward. However, beneath the surface the circular motion rapidly diminishes until, at a depth equal to one-half the wavelength measured from still water level, the movement of water particles becomes negligible. This depth is known as the *wave base.* The dramatic decrease of wave energy with depth is shown by the rapidly diminishing diameters of water-particle orbits in Figure 10.10.

Waves in the Surf Zone

As long as a wave is in deep water, it is unaffected by water depth (**FIGURE 10.12** *left).* However, when a wave approaches the shore, the water becomes shallower and influences wave behavior. The wave begins to "feel bottom" at a water depth equal to its wave base. Such depths interfere with water movement at the base of the wave and slow its advance (Figure 10.12 *center).*

As a wave advances toward the shore, the slightly faster waves farther out to sea catch up, decreasing the wavelength. As the speed and length of the wave diminish, the wave steadily grows higher. Finally, a critical point is reached when the wave is too steep to support itself and the wave front collapses, or *breaks* (Figure 10.12, *right),* causing water to advance up the shore.

The turbulent water created by breaking waves is called **surf**. On the landward margin of the surf zone, the turbulent sheet of water from collapsing breakers, called *swash,* moves up the slope of the beach. When the energy of the swash has been expended, the water flows back down the beach toward the surf zone as *backwash.*

BEACHES AND SHORELINE PROCESSES

 The Global Ocean
▼ Coastal Processes

For many, a beach is a sandy area where people lie in the sun and walk along the water's edge. Technically, a **beach** is an accumulation of sediment found along the landward margins

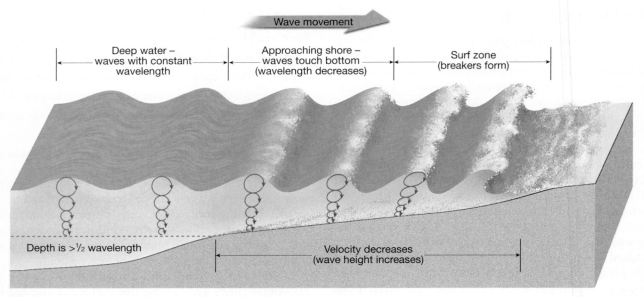

FIGURE 10.12   Changes that occur when a wave moves onto shore. The waves touch bottom as they encounter water depths less than half a wavelength. The wave speed decreases, and the waves stack up against the shore, causing the wavelength to decrease. This results in an increase in wave height to the point where the waves pitch forward and break in the surf zone.

of the ocean or a lake. Along straight coasts, beaches may extend for tens or hundreds of kilometers. Where coasts are irregular, beach formation may be confined to the relatively quiet waters of bays.

Beaches are composed of whatever material is locally abundant. The sediment for some beaches is derived from the erosion of adjacent cliffs or nearby coastal mountains. Other beaches are built from sediment delivered to the coast by rivers. Although the mineral makeup of many beaches is dominated by durable quartz grains, other minerals may be dominant. For example, in areas such as southern Florida most beaches are composed largely of shell fragments. Some beaches on volcanic islands are composed of weathered grains of the basaltic lava that comprise the islands or of coarse debris eroded from coral reefs that develop around many tropical islands (**FIGURE 10.13**).

Regardless of the composition, the material that comprises the beach does not stay in one place. Instead, the waves that crash along the shoreline are constantly moving it. Thus, beaches can be thought of as material in transit along the shoreline.

Wave Erosion

During calm weather, wave action is minimal. During storms, however, waves can cause much erosion. The impact of large, high-energy waves against the shore can be awesome in its violence. Each breaking wave may hurl thousands of tons of water against the land, sometimes causing the ground literally to tremble. The pressures exerted by Atlantic waves in winter, for example, average nearly 10,000 kilograms per square meter (more than 2000 pounds per square foot). The force during storms is even greater.

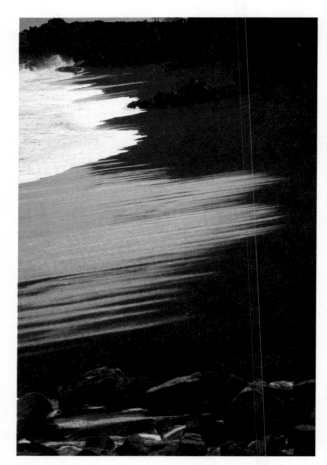

FIGURE 10.13   Beaches are composed of whatever material is locally abundant. The black sand at this Hawaiian beach is derived from dark volcanic rock. To see other beaches look at the chapter-opening photo, Figure 10.14A, and Figure 10.23. (Photo by E.J. Tarbuck)

It is no wonder that cracks and crevices are quickly opened in cliffs, coastal structures, and anything else that is subjected to these enormous shocks (see Figure 10.1, p. 282). Water is forced into every opening, causing air in the cracks to become highly compressed by the thrust of crashing waves. When the wave subsides, the air expands rapidly, dislodging rock fragments and enlarging and extending fractures.

In addition to the erosion caused by wave impact and pressure, **abrasion**, the sawing and grinding action of the water armed with rock fragments, is also important. In fact, abrasion is probably more intense in the surf zone than in any other environment. Smooth rounded stones and pebbles along the shore are obvious reminders of the relentless grinding action of rock against rock in the surf zone (**FIGURE 10.14A**). Rock fragments are also used as "tools" by the waves as they cut horizontally into the land (**FIGURE 10.14B**).

Sand Movement on the Beach

Beaches are sometimes called "rivers of sand." The reason is that the energy from breaking waves often causes large quantities of sand to move along the beach face and in the surf zone roughly parallel to the shoreline. Wave energy also causes sand to move perpendicular to (toward and away from) the shoreline.

Movement Perpendicular to the Shoreline

If you stand ankle-deep in water at the beach, you will see that swash and backwash move sand toward and away from the shoreline. Whether there is a net loss or addition of sand depends on the level of wave activity. When wave activity is relatively light (less energetic waves), much of the swash soaks into the beach, which reduces the backwash. Consequently, the swash dominates and causes a net movement of sand up the beach face.

When high-energy waves prevail, the beach is saturated from previous waves, so much less of the swash soaks in. As a result, the beach erodes because backwash is strong and causes a net movement of sand toward open water.

Along many beaches, light wave activity is the rule during the summer. Therefore, a wide sandy beach gradually develops. During winter, when storms are frequent and more powerful, strong wave activity erodes and narrows the beach. A wide beach that may have taken months to build can be dramatically narrowed in just a few hours by the high-energy waves created by a strong winter storm.

Wave Refraction

The bending of waves, called **wave refraction**, plays an important part in shoreline processes (**FIGURE 10.15**). It affects the distribution of energy along the shore and thus strongly influences where and to what degree erosion, sediment transport, and deposition will take place.

A.   **B.**

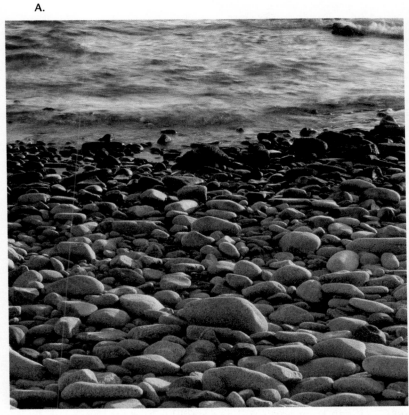

FIGURE 10.14   A. Abrasion can be intense in the surf zone. Smooth rounded stones along the shore are an obvious reminder of this fact. (Photo by Michael Collier)
B. Sandstone cliff undercut by wave erosion at Gabriola Island, British Columbia, Canada. (Photo by Fletcher and Baylis/Photo Researchers, Inc.)

FIGURE 10.15 As waves first touch bottom in the shallows along an irregular coast, they are slowed, causing them to bend (refract) and align nearly parallel to the shoreline. **A.** In this diagram, waves approach nearly straight on. Refraction causes wave energy to be concentrated at headlands (resulting in erosion) and dispersed in bays (resulting in deposition). **B.** Wave refraction at Rincon Point, California. (Photo by Woody Woodworth/Creation Captured)

Waves travel at original speed in deep water

Surf zone

Waves "feel bottom" and slow down in surf zone

Shoreline

Land

Result: waves bend so that they strike the shore more directly

Surf zone

B.

Beach deposits

Headland

A.

Waves seldom approach the shore straight on. Rather, most waves move toward the shore at a slight angle. However, when they reach the shallow water of a smoothly sloping bottom, the wave crests are refracted (bent) and tend to become parallel to the shore. Such bending occurs because the part of the wave nearest the shore touches bottom and slows first, whereas the part of the wave that is still in deep water continues forward at its full speed. The net result is a wave that approaches nearly parallel to the shore regardless of its original orientation.

Because of refraction, wave energy is concentrated against the sides and ends of headlands that project into the water, whereas wave attack is weakened in bays. This differential wave attack along irregular coastlines is illustrated in Figure 10.15. Because the waves reach the shallow water in front of the headland sooner than they do in adjacent bays, they are bent more nearly parallel to the protruding land and strike it from all three sides. By contrast, refraction in

the bays causes waves to diverge and expend less energy. In these zones of weakened wave activity, sediments can accumulate and form sandy beaches. Over a long period, erosion of the headlands and deposition in the bays will straighten an irregular shoreline.

Longshore Transport

Although waves are refracted, most still reach the shore at a slight angle. Consequently, the uprush of water from each breaking wave (the swash) is at an oblique angle to the shoreline. However, the backwash is straight down the slope of the beach. The effect of this pattern of water movement is to transport sediment in a zigzag pattern along the beach face (**FIGURE 10.16**). This movement is called **beach drift**, and it can transport sand and pebbles hundreds or even thousands of meters daily. However, a more typical rate is 5 to 10 meters (16 to 33 feet) per day.

A.

B.

FIGURE 10.16 **A.** Beach drift and longshore currents are created by obliquely breaking waves. Beach drift occurs as incoming surf carries sand obliquely up the beach, while the water from spent waves carries it directly down the slope of the beach. Similar movements occur offshore in the surf zone to create the longshore current. These processes transport large quantities of material along the beach and in the surf zone. **B.** Waves approaching the beach at a slight angle near Oceanside, California, produce a longshore current moving from left to right. (Photo by John S. Shelton)

Waves that approach the shore at an angle also produce currents within the surf zone that flow parallel to the shore and move substantially more sediment than beach drift (Figure 10.16). Because the water here is turbulent, these **longshore currents** easily move the fine suspended sand and roll larger sand and gravel along the bottom. When the sediment transported by longshore currents is added to the quantity moved by beach drift, the total amount can be very large. At Sandy Hook, New Jersey, for example, the quantity of sand transported along the shore over a 48-year period averaged almost 680,000 metric tons (750,000 short tons) annually. For a 10-year period at Oxnard, California, more than 1.4 million metric tons (1.5 million short tons) of sediment moved along the shore each year.

Both rivers and coastal zones move water and sediment from one area (*upstream*) to another (*downstream*). As a result, the beach is often characterized as a "river of sand." Beach drift and longshore currents, however, move in a zigzag pattern, whereas rivers flow mostly in a turbulent, swirling fashion. Additionally, the direction of flow of longshore currents along a shoreline can change, whereas rivers flow in the same direction (downhill). Longshore currents change direction because waves approach the beach in different directions each season. Nevertheless, longshore currents generally flow southward along both the Atlantic and Pacific shores of the United States.

SHORELINE FEATURES

The Global Ocean
▼ Coastal Processes

A fascinating assortment of shoreline features can be observed along the world's coastal regions. These shoreline features vary depending on the type of rocks exposed along the shore, the intensity of waves, and the nature of coastal currents, as well as whether the coast is stable, sinking, or rising. Features that owe their origin primarily to the work of erosion are called *erosional features,* whereas deposits of sediment produce *depositional features.*

Erosional Features

Many coastal landforms owe their origin to erosional processes. Such erosional features are common along the rugged and irregular New England coast and along the steep shorelines of the West Coast of the United States.

Wave-Cut Cliffs, Wave-Cut Platforms, and Marine Terraces

Wave-cut cliffs, as the name implies, originate by the cutting action of the surf against the base of coastal land. As erosion progresses, rocks overhanging the notch at the base of the cliff crumble into the surf and the cliff retreats. A relatively flat, benchlike surface, called a **wave-cut platform,** is left behind by the receding cliff (**FIGURE 10.17** *left*). The platform broadens as wave attack continues. Some debris produced by the breaking waves remains along the water's edge as sediment on the beach, and the remainder is transported farther seaward. If a wave-cut platform is uplifted above sea level by tectonic forces, it becomes a **marine terrace** (Figure 10.17, *right*). Marine terraces are easily recognized by their gentle seaward-sloping shape and are often perceived as desirable sites for coastal development.

Sea Arches and Sea Stacks

Headlands that extend into the sea are vigorously attacked by waves because of refraction. The surf erodes the rock selectively, wearing away the softer or more highly fractured rock at the fastest rate. At first, sea caves may form. When two caves on opposite sides of a headland unite, a **sea arch** results (**FIGURE 10.18**). Eventually, the arch falls in, leaving an isolated remnant, or **sea stack**, on the wave-cut platform (Figure 10.18). In time, it, too, will be consumed by the action of the waves.

DID YOU KNOW?

Along shorelines composed of unconsolidated material rather than hard rock, the rate of erosion by breaking waves can be extraordinary. In parts of Britain, where waves have the easy task of eroding glacial deposits of sand, gravel, and clay, the coast has been worn back 3 to 5 km (2 to 3 mi) since Roman times (2000 years ago), sweeping away many villages and ancient landmarks.

FIGURE 10.17   Wave-cut platform and marine terrace. A wave-cut platform is exposed at low tide along the California coast at Bolinas Point near San Francisco. To the right, uplift has produced an elevated wave-cut platform, called a marine terrace. (Photo by John S. Shelton)

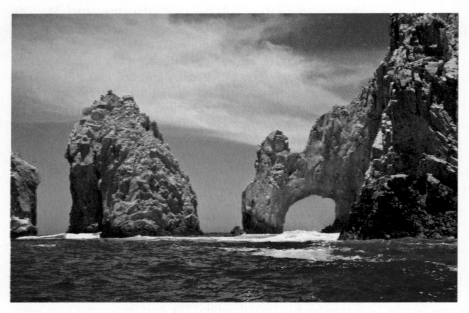

FIGURE 10.18   Sea arch and sea stack at the tip of Mexico's Baja Peninsula. (Photo by Lew Robertson/Getty Images)

Depositional Features

Sediment eroded from the beach is transported along the shore and deposited in areas where wave energy is low. Such processes produce a variety of depositional features.

Spits, Bars, and Tombolos

Where beach drift and longshore currents are active, several features related to the movement of sediment along the shore may develop. A **spit** is an elongated ridge of sand that projects from the land into the mouth of an adjacent bay. Often the end in the water hooks landward in response to the dominant direction of the longshore current. Both images in **FIGURE 10.19** show spits. The term **baymouth bar** is applied to a sandbar that completely crosses a bay, sealing it off from the open ocean. Such a feature tends to form across bays where currents are weak, allowing a spit to extend to the other side (Figure 10.19A). A **tombolo**, a ridge of sand that connects an island to the mainland or to another island, forms in much the same manner as a spit.

Barrier Islands

The Atlantic and Gulf coastal plains are relatively flat and slope gently seaward. The shore zone is characterized by **barrier islands**. These low ridges of sand parallel the coast at distances from 3 to 30 kilometers (1.9 to 19 miles) offshore. From Cape Cod, Massachusetts, to Padre Island, Texas, nearly 300 barrier islands rim the coast (**FIGURE 10.20**).

Most barrier islands are from 1 to 5 kilometers (0.6 to 3 miles) wide and between 15 and 30 kilometers (9 to 19 miles) long. The tallest features are sand dunes, which usually reach heights of 5 to 10 meters (16 to 33 feet). The lagoons that separate these narrow islands from the shore are zones of relatively quiet water that allow small craft traveling between New York and northern Florida to avoid the rough waters of the North Atlantic.

Barrier islands probably formed in several ways. Some originated as spits that were subsequently severed from the mainland by wave erosion or by the general rise in sea level following the last episode of glaciation. Others were created when turbulent waters in the line of breakers heaped up sand that had been scoured from the bottom. Finally, some barrier islands may be former sand-dune ridges that originated along the shore during the last glacial period, when sea level was lower. As the ice sheets melted, sea level rose and flooded the area behind the beach–dune complex.

such as spits and baymouth bars. At the same time, rivers fill the bays with sediment. Ultimately, a smooth coast results.

STABILIZING THE SHORE

The Global Ocean
▼ Coastal Processes

The coastal zone teems with human activity. Unfortunately, people often treat the shoreline as if it were a stable platform on which structures can be built safely. This approach jeopardizes both people and the shoreline because many coastal landforms are relatively fragile, short-lived features that are easily damaged by development. As anyone who has endured a strong coastal storm knows, the shoreline is not always a safe place to live. The chapter-opening photo and Figure 10.9 remind us of that fact.

Compared with other natural hazards, such as earthquakes, volcanic eruptions, and landslides, shoreline erosion appears to be a more continuous and predictable process that causes relatively modest damage to limited areas. In reality, the shoreline is one of Earth's most dynamic places that changes rapidly in response to natural forces. Exceptional storms are capable of eroding beaches and cliffs at rates that far exceed the long-term average. Such bursts of accelerated erosion not only have a significant impact on the natural evolution of a coast but can also have a profound impact on people who reside in the coastal zone. Erosion along the coast causes significant property damage. Huge sums are spent annually not only to repair damage but also to prevent or control erosion. Already a problem at many sites, shoreline erosion is certain to become increasingly serious as extensive coastal development continues.

Although the same processes cause change along every coast, not all coasts respond in the same way. Interactions among different processes and the relative importance of each process depend on local factors. The factors include (1) the proximity of a coast to sediment-laden rivers, (2) the degree of tectonic activity, (3) the topography and composition of the land, (4) prevailing winds and weather patterns, and (5) the configuration of the coastline and near-shore areas.

During the past 100 years, growing affluence and increasing demands for recreation have brought unprecedented development to many coastal areas. As both the number and the value of buildings have increased, so, too, have efforts to protect property from storm waves by stabilizing the shore. Also, controlling the natural migration of sand is an ongoing struggle in many coastal areas. Such interference can result in unwanted changes that are difficult and expensive to correct.

Hard Stabilization

Structures built to protect a coast from erosion or to prevent the movement of sand along a beach are known as **hard stabilization**. Hard stabilization can take many forms and often results in predictable yet unwanted outcomes. Hard stabilization includes groins, breakwaters, and seawalls.

FIGURE 10.19   A. High-altitude image of a well-developed spit and baymouth bar along the coast of Martha's Vineyard, Massachusetts. (Image courtesy of USDA-ASCS) **B.** This photograph, taken from the International Space Station, shows Provincetown Spit located at the tip of Cape Cod. (NASA image)

The Evolving Shore

A shoreline continually undergoes modification regardless of its initial configuration. At first, most coastlines are irregular, although the degree of and reason for the irregularity may differ considerably from place to place. Along a coastline that is characterized by varied geology, the pounding surf may initially increase its irregularity because the waves will erode the weaker rocks more easily than the stronger ones. However, if a shoreline remains stable, marine erosion and deposition will eventually produce a straighter, more regular coast.

FIGURE 10.21 illustrates the evolution of an initially irregular coast that remains relatively stable and shows many of the coastal features discussed in the previous section. As headlands are eroded and erosional features such as wave-cut cliffs and wave-cut platforms are created, sediment is produced that is carried along the shore by beach drift and longshore currents. Some material is deposited in the bays, whereas other debris is formed into depositional features

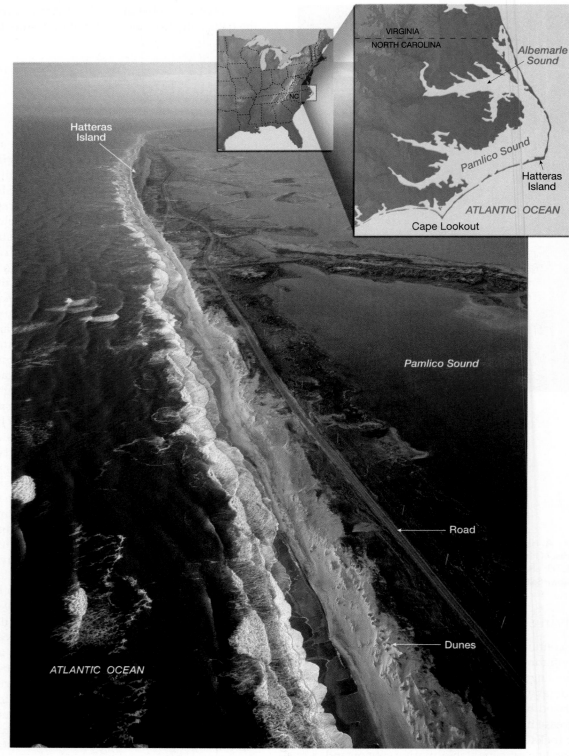

FIGURE 10.20   Nearly 300 barrier islands rim the Gulf and Atlantic coasts. The islands along the coast of North Carolina are excellent examples. (Photo by Michael Collier)

Groins

To maintain or widen beaches that are losing sand, groins are sometimes constructed. A **groin** is a barrier built at a right angle to the beach to trap sand that is moving parallel to the shore. Groins are usually constructed of large rocks but may also be composed of wood. These structures often do their job so effectively that the longshore current beyond the groin becomes sand-starved. As a result, the current erodes sand from the beach on the downstream side of the groin.

FIGURE 10.21   These diagrams illustrate the changes that can take place through time along an initially irregular coastline that remains relatively stable. The coastline shown in part **A** gradually evolves to **B** and then **C**. The diagrams also serve to illustrate many of the features described in the section on shoreline features. (Photos A and C by E. J. Tarbuck; Photo B by Michael Collier)

To offset this effect, property owners downstream from the structure may erect a groin on their property. In this manner, the number of groins multiplies, resulting in a *groin field* (**FIGURE 10.22**). An example of such proliferation is the shoreline of New Jersey, where hundreds of these structures have been built. Because it has been shown that groins often do not provide a satisfactory solution, they are no longer the preferred method of keeping beach erosion in check.

Breakwaters and Seawalls

Hard stabilization can also be built parallel to the shoreline. One such structure is a **breakwater**, which is designed to

protect boats from the force of large breaking waves by creating a quiet water zone near the shore. However, when this is done, the reduced wave activity along the shore behind the structure may allow sand to accumulate. If this happens, the boat anchorage will eventually fill with sand while the downstream beach erodes and retreats. At Santa Monica, California, where the building of a breakwater created such a problem, the city uses a dredge to remove sand from the protected quiet water zone and deposit it farther downstream where longshore currents continue to move the sand down the coast (**FIGURE 10.23**).

Another type of hard stabilization built parallel to the shore is a **seawall**, which is designed to armor the coast and

FIGURE 10.22   A series of groins along the shoreline near Chichester, Sussex, England. (Photo by Sandy Stockwell/London Aerial Photo Library/CORBIS)

FIGURE 10.23   Aerial view of a breakwater at Santa Monica, California. The breakwater appears as a faint line in the water behind which many boats are anchored. The construction of the breakwater disrupted longshore transport and caused the seaward growth of the beach. (Photo by John S. Shelton)

defend property from the force of breaking waves. Waves expend much of their energy as they move across an open beach. Seawalls cut this process short by reflecting the force of unspent waves seaward. As a consequence, the beach to the seaward side of the seawall experiences significant erosion and may, in some instances, be eliminated entirely. Once the width of the beach is reduced, the seawall is subjected to even greater pounding by the waves. Eventually,

this battering takes its toll on the seawall such that the seawall will fail and a larger, more expensive structure must be built to take its place.

The wisdom of building temporary protective structures along shorelines is increasingly questioned. The opinion of many coastal scientists and engineers is expressed in the following excerpt from a position paper that was developed as a result of a conference on America's eroding shoreline:

> It is now clear that halting the receding shoreline with protective structures benefits only a few and seriously degrades or destroys the natural beach and the value it holds for the majority. Protective structures divert the ocean's energy temporarily from private properties, but usually refocus the energy on the adjacent natural beaches. Many interrupt the natural sand flow in coastal currents, robbing many beaches of vital sand replacement.*

Alternatives to Hard Stabilization

Armoring the coast with hard stabilization has several potential drawbacks, including the cost of the structure and the loss of sand on the beach. Alternatives to hard stabilization include beach nourishment and relocation.

Beach Nourishment

Beach nourishment represents an approach to stabilizing shoreline sands without hard stabilization. As the term implies, this practice simply involves the addition of large quantities of sand to the beach system (**FIGURE 10.24**). By building the beaches seaward, beach quality and storm protection are both improved. Beach nourishment, however, is not a permanent solution to the problem of shrinking beaches because the same processes that removed the sand in the first place will eventually remove the replacement sand as well. In addition, it can be very expensive because huge volumes of sand must be transported to the beach from offshore areas, nearby rivers, or other source areas. Orrin Pilkey, a respected coastal scientist, described the situation this way:

> Nourishment has been carried out on beaches on both sides of the continent, but by far the greatest effort in dollars and sand volume has been expended on the East Coast barrier islands between the southern shore of Long Island, N.Y., and southern Florida. Over this shoreline reach, communities have added a total of 500 million cubic yards of sand on 195 beaches in 680 separate instances. Some beaches have been renourished more than 20 times each since 1965. Virginia Beach has been renourished more than 50 times. Nourished beaches typically cost between $2 million and $10 million per mile.**

*"Strategy for Beach Preservation Proposed," *Geotimes* 3 (No. 12, December 1985): 15.

**"Beaches Awash with Politics," *Geotimes,* July 2005, pp. 38–39.

A.   **B.**

FIGURE 10.24   Miami Beach. **A.** Before beach nourishment. **B.** After beach nourishment. (Courtesy of the U.S. Army Corps of Engineers, Vicksburg District)

Such proposals, of course, are controversial. People with significant shoreline investments shudder at the thought of not rebuilding and defending coastal developments from the erosional wrath of the sea. Others, however, argue that with sea level rising, the impact of coastal storms will only get worse in the decades to come. This group advocates that oft-damaged structures be relocated or abandoned to improve personal safety and to reduce costs. Such ideas will no doubt be the focus of much study and debate as states and communities evaluate and revise coastal land-use policies.

In some instances, beach nourishment can lead to unwanted environmental effects. Beach replenishment at Waikiki Beach, Hawaii, involved replacing the natural coarse calcareous beach sand with softer, muddier sand. Destruction of the softer sand by breaking waves increased the water's turbidity and killed offshore coral reefs. Similar damage to local coral communities occurred after beach replenishment at Miami Beach.

Beach nourishment appears to be an economically viable long-range solution to the beach-preservation problem only in areas with dense development, large supplies of sand, relatively low wave energy, and reconcilable environmental issues. Unfortunately, few areas possess all these attributes.

Relocation

Instead of building structures such as groins and seawalls to hold the shoreline in place or adding sand to replenish eroding beaches, another option is also available. Many coastal scientists and planners are calling for a policy shift from defending and rebuilding beaches and coastal property in high hazard areas to *relocating* storm-damaged or at-risk buildings and letting nature reclaim the beach. This approach is similar to the one adopted by the federal government for river floodplains following the devastating 1993 Mississippi River floods, in which vulnerable structures were abandoned and relocated on higher, safer ground.

DID YOU KNOW?

A significant impact of human-induced global warming is a rise in sea level. As this occurs, coastal cities, wetlands, and low-lying islands could be threatened with more frequent flooding, increased shoreline erosion, and saltwater encroachment into coastal rivers and aquifers. There's more about global warming in Chapter 11.

Erosion Problems along U.S. Coasts

The shoreline along the Pacific Coast of the United States is strikingly different from that characterizing the Atlantic and Gulf Coast regions. Some of the differences are related to plate tectonics. The West Coast represents the leading edge of the North American plate; therefore, it experiences active uplift and deformation. By contrast, the East Coast is a tectonically quiet region that is far from any active plate margin. Because of this basic geological difference, the nature of shoreline erosion problems along America's opposite coasts is different.

Atlantic and Gulf Coasts

Much of the coastal development along the Atlantic and Gulf coasts has occurred on barrier islands. Typically, barrier islands consist of a wide beach that is backed by dunes and separated from the mainland by marshy lagoons. The broad expanses of sand and exposure to the ocean have made barrier islands exceedingly attractive sites for development. Unfortunately, development has taken place more rapidly than has our understanding of barrier island dynamics.

Because barrier islands face the open ocean, they receive the full force of major storms that strike the coast. When a storm occurs, the barriers absorb the energy of the waves primarily through the movement of sand. This process and the dilemma that results have been described as follows:

> Waves may move sand from the beach to offshore areas or, conversely, into the dunes; they may erode the dunes, depositing sand onto the beach or carrying it out to sea; or they may carry sand from the beach and the dunes into the marshes behind the barrier, a process known as *overwash*. The common factor is movement. Just as a flexible reed may survive a wind that destroys an oak tree, so the barriers survive hurricanes and

nor'easters not through unyielding strength but by giving before the storm.

This picture changes when a barrier is developed for homes or a resort. Storm waves that previously rushed harmlessly through gaps between the dunes now encounter buildings and roadways. Moreover, since the dynamic nature of the barriers is readily perceived only during storms, homeowners tend to attribute damage to a particular storm, rather than to the basic mobility of coastal barriers. With their homes or investments at stake, local residents are more likely to seek to hold the sand in place and the waves at bay than to admit that development was improperly placed to begin with.*

Pacific Coast

In contrast to the broad, gently sloping coastal plains of the Atlantic and Gulf Coasts, much of the Pacific Coast is characterized by relatively narrow beaches that are backed by steep cliffs and mountain ranges. Recall that America's western margin is a more rugged and tectonically active region than the eastern margin. Because uplift continues, the rise in sea level in the West is not so readily apparent. Nevertheless, like the shoreline erosion problems facing the East's barrier islands, West Coast difficulties also stem largely from the alteration of natural systems by people.

A major problem facing the Pacific shoreline—particularly along southern California—is a significant narrowing of many beaches. The bulk of the sand on many of these beaches is supplied by rivers that transport it from the mountainous regions to the coast. Over the years, this natural flow of material to the coast has been interrupted by dams built for irrigation and flood control. The reservoirs effectively trap the sand that would otherwise nourish the beach environment. When the beaches were wider, they served to protect the cliffs behind them from the force of storm waves. Now, however, the waves move across the narrowed beaches without losing much energy and cause more rapid erosion of the sea cliffs.

Although the retreat of the cliffs provides material to replace some of the sand impounded behind dams, it also endangers homes and roads built on the bluffs. In addition, development atop the cliffs aggravates the problem. Urbanization increases runoff, which, if not carefully controlled, can result in serious bluff erosion. Watering lawns and gardens adds significant quantities of water to the slope. This water percolates downward toward the base of the cliff, where it may emerge in small seeps. This action reduces the slope's stability and facilitates mass wasting.

Shoreline erosion along the Pacific Coast varies considerably from one year to the next, largely because of the sporadic occurrence of storms. As a consequence, when the infrequent but serious episodes of erosion occur, the damage

is often blamed on the unusual storms and not on coastal development or the sediment-trapping dams that may be great distances away. If, as predicted, sea level experiences a significant rise in the years to come because of global warming, increased shoreline erosion and seacliff retreat should be expected along many parts of the Pacific Coast.

COASTAL CLASSIFICATION

The great variety of shorelines demonstrates their complexity. Indeed, to understand any particular coastal area, many factors must be considered, including rock types, size and direction of waves, frequency of storms, tidal range, and offshore topography. In addition, practically all coastal areas were affected by the worldwide rise in sea level that accompanied the melting of Ice Age glaciers at the close of the Pleistocene epoch. Finally, tectonic events that uplift or downdrop the land or change the volume of ocean basins must be taken into account. The large number of factors that influence coastal areas makes shoreline classification difficult.

Many geologists classify coasts based on changes that have occurred with respect to sea level. This commonly used classification system divides coasts into two general categories: emergent and submergent. **Emergent coasts** develop either because an area experiences uplift or as a result of a drop in sea level. Conversely, **submergent coasts** are created when sea level rises or the land adjacent to the sea subsides.

Emergent Coasts

In some areas, the coast is clearly emergent because rising land or falling water levels expose wave-cut cliffs and marine terraces above sea level. Excellent examples include portions of coastal California where uplift has occurred in the recent geologic past. The elevated marine terrace in Figure 10.17 (p. 294) illustrates this situation. In the case of the Palos Verdes Hills, south of Los Angeles, California, seven different terrace levels exist, indicating at least seven episodes of uplift. The ever persistent sea is now cutting a new platform at the base of the cliff. If uplift follows, it, too, will become an elevated marine terrace.

Other examples of emergent shores include regions that were once buried beneath great ice sheets. When glaciers were present, their weight depressed the crust, and when the ice melted, the crust began gradually to spring back. Consequently, prehistoric shoreline features today are found high above sea level. The Hudson Bay region of Canada is one such area, portions of which are still rising at a rate of more than 1 centimeter (0.4 inch) annually.

Submergent Coasts

Other coastal areas show definite signs of submergence. Shorelines that have been submerged in the relatively recent past are often highly irregular because the sea typically floods the lower reaches of river valleys flowing into the

*Frank Lowenstein, "Benches or Bedrooms—The Choice as Sea Level Rises," *Oceanus* 28 (No. 3, Fall 1985): 22.

ocean. The ridges separating the valleys, however, remain above sea level and project into the sea as headlands. These drowned river mouths, which are called **estuaries**, characterize many coasts today. Along the Atlantic coastline, Chesapeake and Delaware bays are examples of estuaries created by submergence (**FIGURE 10.25**). The picturesque coast of Maine, particularly in the vicinity of Acadia National Park, is another excellent example of an area that was flooded by the postglacial rise in sea level and transformed into a highly irregular submerged coastline.

Keep in mind, however, that most coasts have a complicated geologic history. With respect to sea level, many coasts have at various times emerged and then submerged again. Each time, they retain some of the features created during the previous event.

FIGURE 10.25 Major estuaries along the East Coast of the United States. The lower portions of many river valleys were flooded by the rise in sea level that followed the end of the last Ice Age, creating large estuaries such as Chesapeake and Delaware bays.

TIDES

Tides are daily changes in the elevation of the ocean surface. Their rhythmic rise and fall along coastlines have been known since antiquity. Other than waves, they are the easiest ocean movements to observe (**FIGURE 10.26**).

Although known for centuries, tides were not explained satisfactorily until Sir Isaac Newton applied the law of gravitation to them. Newton showed that there is a mutual attractive force between two bodies, as between Earth and the Moon. Because both the atmosphere and the ocean are fluids and are free to move, both are deformed by this force. Hence, ocean tides result from the gravitational attraction exerted upon Earth by the Moon and, to a lesser extent, by the Sun.

Causes of Tides

To illustrate how tides are produced, consider Earth as a rotating sphere covered to a uniform depth with water (**FIGURE 10.27**). (Ignore the effect of the Sun for now.) It is easy to see how the Moon's gravitational force can cause the water to bulge on the side of Earth nearest the Moon. In addition, however, an equally large tidal bulge is produced on the *opposite* side of Earth.

Both tidal bulges are caused, as Newton discovered, by the pull of gravity. Gravity is inversely proportional to the square of the distance between two objects, meaning simply that it quickly weakens with distance. In this case, the two objects are the Moon and Earth. Because the force of gravity decreases with distance, the Moon's gravitational pull on Earth is slightly greater on the near side of Earth than on the far side. The result of this differential pulling is to stretch (elongate) the "solid" Earth very slightly. In contrast, the world ocean, which is mobile, is deformed quite dramatically by this effect to produce the two opposing tidal bulges.

Because the position of the Moon changes only moderately in a single day, the tidal bulges remain in place while Earth rotates "through" them. If you stand on the seashore for 24 hours, Earth will rotate you through alternating areas of higher and lower water. As you are carried into each tidal bulge, the tide rises, and as you are carried into the intervening troughs between the tidal bulges, the tide falls. Therefore, most places on Earth experience two high tides and two low tides each day.

DID YOU KNOW?

Tides can be used to generate electrical power by constructing a dam across the mouth of a bay or estuary in a coastal area having a large tidal range. The narrow opening between the bay and the open ocean magnifies the variations in water level as tides rise and fall and the strong in-and-out flow is used to drive turbines. The largest plant yet constructed is along the coast of France.

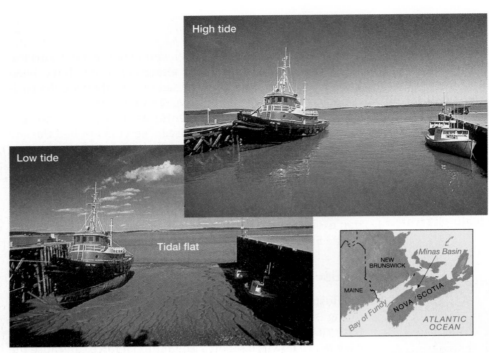

FIGURE 10.26 High tide and low tide on Nova Scotia's Minas Basin in the Bay of Fundy. The areas exposed during low tide and flooded during high tide are called *tidal flats*. Tidal flats here are extensive. (Courtesy Nova Scotia Department of Tourism and Culture)

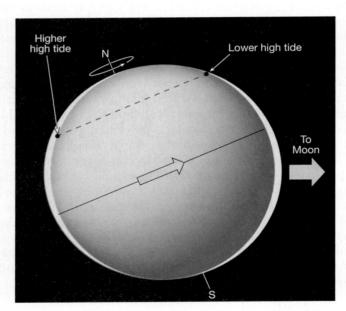

FIGURE 10.27 Idealized tidal bulges on Earth caused by the Moon. If Earth were covered to a uniform depth with water, there would be two tidal bulges: one on the side of Earth facing the Moon (*right*) and the other on the opposite side of Earth (*left*). Depending on the Moon's position, tidal bulges may be inclined relative to Earth's equator. In this situation, Earth's rotation causes two unequal high tides during a day.

In addition, the tidal bulges migrate as the Moon revolves around Earth about every 29½ days. As a result, the tides—like the time of moonrise—shift about 50 minutes later each day. In essence, the tidal bulges exist in fixed positions relative to the Moon, which is slowly moving eastward.

Many locations may show an inequality between the high tides during a given day. Depending on the Moon's position, the tidal bulges may be inclined to the equator as in Figure 10.27. This figure illustrates that one high tide experienced by an observer in the Northern Hemisphere is considerably higher than the high tide half a day later. In contrast, a Southern Hemisphere observer would experience the opposite effect.

Monthly Tidal Cycle

The primary body that influences the tides is the Moon, which makes one complete revolution around Earth every 29½ days. The Sun, however, also influences the tides. It is far larger than the Moon, but because it is much farther away, its effect is considerably less. In fact, the Sun's tide-generating effect is only about 46 percent that of the Moon's.

Near the times of new and full moons, the Sun and Moon are aligned and their forces are added together (**FIGURE 10.28A**). Accordingly, the combined gravity of these two tide-producing bodies causes larger tidal bulges (higher high tides) and larger tidal troughs (lower low tides), producing a large tidal range. These are called the **spring tides**, which have no connection with the spring season but occur twice a month during the times when the Earth–Moon–Sun system is aligned. Conversely, at about the time of the first and third quarters of the Moon, the gravitational forces of the Moon and Sun act on Earth at right angles, and each partially offsets the influence of the other (**FIGURE 10.28B**). As a result, the daily tidal range is less. These are called **neap tides**, which also occur twice each month. Each month, then, there are two spring tides and two neap tides, each about one week apart.

Tidal Patterns

So far, the basic causes and types of tides have been explained. Keep in mind, however, that these theoretical considerations cannot be used to predict either the height or the time of actual tides at a particular place. Many factors—including the shape of the coastline, the configuration of ocean basins, and water depth—greatly influence the tides. Consequently, tides at various locations respond differently to the tide-producing forces. Thus, the nature of the tide at any coastal location can be determined most accurately by actual observation. The predictions in tidal tables and tidal data on nautical charts are based on such observations.

FIGURE 10.28 Earth–Moon–Sun positions and the tides. **A.** When the Moon is in the full or new position, the tidal bulges created by the Sun and Moon are aligned. There is a large tidal range on Earth, and spring tides are experienced. **B.** When the Moon is in the first- or third-quarter position, the tidal bulges produced by the Moon are at right angles to the bulges created by the Sun. Tidal ranges are smaller, and neap tides are experienced.

DID YOU KNOW?

The world's largest tidal range (difference between successive high and low tides) is found in the northern end of Nova Scotia's Bay of Fundy. Here, the maximum spring tidal range is about 17 m (56 ft). This leaves boats "high and dry" during low tide (see Figure 10.26, p. 302).

Three main tidal patterns exist worldwide. A **diurnal** (*diurnal* = daily) **tidal pattern** is characterized by a single high tide and a single low tide each tidal day (**FIGURE 10.29**). Tides of this type occur along the northern shore of the Gulf of Mexico, among other locations. A **semidiurnal** (*semi* = twice, *diurnal* = daily) **tidal pattern** exhibits two high tides and two low tides each tidal day, with the two highs about the same height and the two lows about the same height (Figure 10.29). This type of tidal pattern is common along the Atlantic Coast of the United States. A **mixed tidal pattern** is similar to a semidiurnal pattern except that it is characterized by a large inequality in high-water heights, low-water heights, or both (Figure 10.29). In this case, there are usually two high and two low tides each day, with high tides of different heights and low tide of different heights. Such tides are prevalent along the Pacific Coast of the United States and in many other parts of the world.

Tidal Currents

Tidal current is the term used to describe the *horizontal* flow of water accompanying the rise and fall of the tides. These water movements induced by tidal forces can be important in some coastal areas. Tidal currents that advance into the

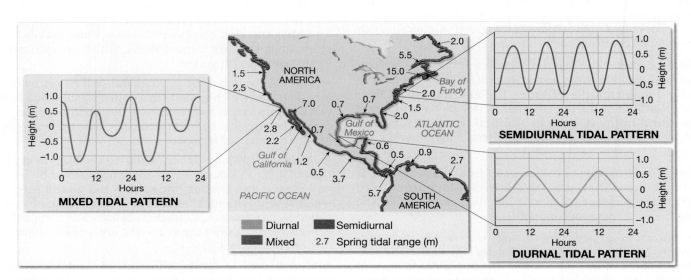

FIGURE 10.29 Tidal patterns and their occurrence along North and Central American coasts. A diurnal tidal pattern *(lower right)* shows one high and low tide each tidal day. A semidiurnal pattern *(upper right)* shows two highs and lows of approximately equal heights during each tidal day. A mixed tidal pattern *(left)* shows two highs and lows of unequal heights during each tidal day.

coastal zone as the tide rises are called *flood currents*. As the tide falls, seaward-moving water generates *ebb currents*. Periods of little or no current, called *slack water*, separate flood and ebb. The areas affected by these alternating tidal currents are called **tidal flats** (see Figure 10.26, p. 302). Depending on the nature of the coastal zone, tidal flats vary from narrow strips seaward of the beach to zones that may extend for several kilometers.

   Although tidal currents are not important in the open sea, they can be rapid in bays, river estuaries, straits, and other narrow places. Off the coast of Brittany in France, for example, tidal currents that accompany a high tide of 12 meters (40 feet) may attain a speed of 20 kilometers (12 miles) per hour. Tidal currents are not generally considered to be major agents of erosion and sediment transport. Notable exceptions occur where tides move through narrow inlets, where they scour the narrow entrances to many harbors that would otherwise be blocked.

   Sometimes deposits called **tidal deltas** are created by tidal currents (**FIGURE 10.30**). They may develop either as *flood deltas* landward of an inlet or as *ebb deltas* on the seaward side of an inlet. Because wave activity and longshore currents are reduced on the sheltered landward side, flood deltas are more common and actually more prominent (see

FIGURE 10.30   As a rapidly moving tidal current moves through a barrier island's inlet into the quiet waters of a lagoon, the current slows and deposits sediment, creating a tidal delta. Because this tidal delta has developed on the landward side of the inlet, it is called *a flood delta*. Such a tidal delta is also shown and labeled on Figure 10.19A.

Figure 10.19A, p 295). They form after the tidal current moves rapidly through an inlet. As the current emerges into more open waters from the narrow passage, it slows and deposits its load of sediment.

THE CHAPTER IN REVIEW

• *The ocean's surface currents follow the general pattern of the world's major wind belts.* Surface currents are parts of huge, slowly moving loops of water called *gyres* that are centered in the subtropics of each ocean basin. *The positions of the continents* and the *Coriolis effect* also influence the movement of ocean water within gyres. Because of the Coriolis effect, subtropical gyres move *clockwise in the Northern Hemisphere* and *counterclockwise in the Southern Hemisphere.* Generally, *four main currents* comprise each subtropical gyre.

• *Ocean currents* can have a significant *effect on climate.* Poleward–moving *warm ocean currents moderate winter temperatures* in the middle latitudes. Cold currents exert their greatest influence during summer in middle latitudes and year-round in the tropics. In addition to cooler temperatures, *cold currents are associated with greater fog frequency and drought.*

• *Upwelling,* the rising of colder water from deeper layers, is a wind-induced movement that brings cold, nutrient-rich water to the surface *Coastal upwelling* is most characteristic along the west coasts of continents.

• In contrast to surface currents, *deep-ocean circulation* is governed by *gravity* and driven by *density differences.* The two factors that are most significant in creating a dense mass of water are *temperature* and *salinity,* so the movement of deep-ocean water is often termed *thermohaline circulation.* Most water involved in thermohaline circulation begins in high

latitudes at the surface when the salinity of the cold water increases as a result of sea ice formation. This dense water sinks, initiating deep-ocean currents.

• *Waves are moving energy* and *most ocean waves are initiated by the wind.* The three factors that influence the *height, wavelength,* and *period* of a wave are (1) *wind speed;* (2) *length of time the wind has blown;* and (3) *fetch,* the distance that the wind has traveled across open water. Once waves leave a storm area, they are termed *swells,* which are symmetrical, longer-wavelength waves.

• As waves travel, *water particles transmit energy by circular orbital motion,* which extends to a depth equal to one-half the wavelength. When a wave travels into shallow water, it experiences physical changes that can cause the wave to collapse, or *break,* and form *surf.*

• *Beaches are composed of any locally derived material* that is in transit along the shore. Wave erosion is caused by *wave impact pressure* and *abrasion* (the sawing and grinding action of water armed with rock fragments). The bending of waves is called *wave refraction.* Refraction causes wave impact to be concentrated against the sides and ends of headlands and dispersed in bays.

• Most waves reach the shore at an angle. The uprush (swash) and backwash of water from each breaking wave move the sediment in a zigzag pattern along the beach. This movement is called *beach drift.* Oblique waves also produce *longshore currents* within the surf zone that flow parallel to the shore and transport more sediment than does beach drift.

• *Erosional features* include *wave-cut cliffs* (which originate from the cutting action of the surf against the base of coastal land), *wave-cut platforms* (relatively flat, benchlike surfaces left behind by receding cliffs), and *marine terraces* (uplifted wave-cut platforms). Erosional features also include *sea arches* (formed when a headland is eroded and two sea caves from opposite sides unite), and *sea stacks* (formed when the roof of a sea arch collapses).

• Some of the *depositional features* that form when sediment is moved by beach drift and longshore currents are *spits* (elongated ridges of sand that project from the land into the mouth of an adjacent bay), *baymouth bars* (sandbars that completely cross a bay), and *tombolos* (ridges of sand that connect an island to the mainland or to another island). Along the Atlantic and Gulf coastal plains, the coastal region is characterized by offshore *barrier islands*, which are low ridges of sand that parallel the coast.

• Local *factors that influence shoreline erosion* are (1) the proximity of a coast to sediment-laden rivers, (2) the degree of tectonic activity, (3) the topography and composition of the land, (4) prevailing winds and weather patterns, and (5) the configuration of the coastline and near-shore areas.

• *Hard stabilization* involves building hard, massive structures in an attempt to protect a coast from erosion or prevent the movement of sand along the beach. Hard stabilization includes *groins* (short walls constructed at a right angle to the shore to trap moving sand), *breakwaters* (structures built parallel to the shore to protect it from the force of large breaking waves), and *seawalls* (armoring the coast to prevent waves from reaching the area behind the wall). *Alternatives* to *hard stabilization* include *beach nourishment*, which involves the addition of sand to replenish eroding beaches, and *relocation* of damaged or threatened buildings.

• Because of basic geologic differences, the *nature of shoreline erosion problems along America's Pacific and Atlantic/Gulf coasts is very different*. Much of the development along the Atlantic and Gulf coasts has occurred on barrier islands, which receive the full force of major storms. Much of the Pacific Coast is characterized by narrow beaches backed by steep cliffs and mountain ranges. A major problem facing the Pacific shoreline is the narrowing of beaches caused by dams that interrupt the natural flow of sand to the coast.

• One commonly used classification of coasts is based on changes that have occurred with respect to sea level. *Emergent coasts* often exhibit wave-cut cliffs and marine terraces and develop because an area experiences either uplift or a drop in sea level. Conversely, *submergent coasts* commonly display drowned river mouths called *estuaries* and are created when sea level rises or the land adjacent to the sea subsides.

• *Tides,* the daily rise and fall in the elevation of the ocean surface at a specific location, are caused by the *gravitational attraction* of the Moon and, to a lesser extent, the Sun. The Moon and the Sun each produce a pair *of tidal bulges* on Earth. These tidal bulges remain in fixed positions relative to the generating bodies as Earth rotates through them, resulting in alternating high and low tides. *Spring tides* occur near the times of new and full moons when the Sun and Moon are aligned and their bulges are added together to produce especially high and low tides (*a large daily tidal range).* Conversely, *neap tides* occur at about the times of the first and third quarters of the Moon when the bulges of the Moon and Sun are at right angles, producing a *smaller daily tidal range.*

• *Three main tidal patterns exist worldwide.* A *diurnal tidal pattern* exhibits one high and low tide daily; a *semidiurnal tidal pattern* exhibits two high and low tides daily of about the same height; and a *mixed tidal pattern* usually has two high and low tides of different heights daily.

• *Tidal currents* are horizontal movements of water that accompany the rise and fall of the tides. *Tidal flats* are the areas that are affected by the advancing and retreating tidal currents. When tidal currents slow after emerging from narrow inlets, they deposit sediment that may eventually create *tidal deltas.*

KEY TERMS

abrasion (p. 291)

barrier island (p. 294)

baymouth bar (p. 294)

beach (p 289)

beach drift (p. 292)

beach nourishment (p. 298)

breakwater (p. 297)

Coriolis effect (p. 283)

diurnal tidal pattern
   (p. 303)

emergent coast (p. 300)

estuary (p. 301)

fetch (p. 287)

groin (p. 296)

gyre (p. 282)

hard stabilization (p. 295)

longshore current (p. 293)

marine terrace (p. 293)

mixed tidal pattern (p. 303)

neap tide (p. 302)

sea arch (p. 294)

sea stack (p. 294)

seawall (p. 297)

semidiurnal tidal pattern
   (p. 303)

spit (p. 294)

spring tide (p. 302)

submergent coast (p. 300)

surf (p. 289)

thermohaline circulation
   (p. 286)

tidal current (p. 303)

tidal delta (p. 304)

tidal flat (p. 304)

tide (p. 301)

tombolo (p. 294)

upwelling (p. 285)

wave-cut cliff (p. 293)

wave-cut platform
   (p. 293)

wave height (p. 287)

wavelength (p. 287)

wave period (p. 287)

wave refraction (p. 291)

QUESTIONS FOR REVIEW

1. What is the primary driving force of surface ocean currents? How do the distribution of continents on Earth and the Coriolis effect influence these currents?

2. What is a *gyre*? How many currents exist within each gyre? Name the five subtropical gyres, and identify the primary surface currents that comprise each gyre.

3. How do ocean currents influence climate? Give at least one example.

4. Describe the process of coastal upwelling. Why is an abundance of marine life associated with these areas?

5. What is the driving force of deep-ocean circulation? Why is the movement of deep currents often termed *thermohaline circulation*?

6. List three factors that determine the height, length, and period of a wave.

7. Describe the motion of a floating object as a wave passes (see Figure 10.11, p. 289).

8. Describe the physical changes that occur to a wave's speed, wavelength, and height as a wave moves into shallow water and breaks on the shore.

9. How do waves cause erosion?

10. What is wave refraction? What is the effect of this process along irregular coastlines?

11. What is beach drift, and how is it related to a longshore current? Why are beaches often called "rivers of sand"?

12. Describe the formation of the following shoreline features: wave-cut cliff, wave-cut platform, marine terrace, sea stack, spit, baymouth bar, and tombolo.

13. List three ways that barrier islands may form.

14. List the types of hard stabilization and describe what each is intended to do. What effect does each one have on the distribution of sand on the beach?

15. In what direction is longshore transport occurring in Figure 10.22 (p. 298)? Is it toward the top left or toward the bottom right of the photo?

16. List two alternatives to hard stabilization, indicating potential problems with each one.

17. Relate the damming of rivers to the shrinking of beaches at some locations along the West Coast of the United States.

18. What observable features would lead you to classify a coastal area as emergent?

19. Are estuaries associated with submergent or emergent coasts? Explain.

20. Discuss the origin of ocean tides. Explain why the Sun's influence on Earth's tides is less than half that of the Moon's, even though the Sun is so much more massive than the Moon.

21. Explain how an observer can experience two unequal high tides during a day (see Figure 10.27, p. 302).

22. How do diurnal, semidiurnal, and mixed tidal patterns differ?

23. Distinguish between a flood current and an ebb current. Of flood current, ebb current, high slack water, and low slack water, when is the best time to navigate a boat in a shallow, rocky harbor?

COMPANION WEBSITE

The *Foundations of Earth Science* Website uses the resources and flexibility of the Internet to aid in your study of the topics in this chapter. Written and developed by the authors and other Earth science instructors, this site will help improve your understanding of Earth science. Visit **www.mygeoscienceplace.com** in order to:

• **Review** key chapter concepts.

• **Read** with links to the ebook and to chapter-specific web resources.

• **Visualize** and comprehend challenging topics using learning activities in *GEODe: Earth Science*.

• **Test** yourself with online quizzes.

GEODe: EARTH SCIENCE

GEODe: Earth Science is a valuable and easy to use learning aid that can be accessed from your book's Companion Website: **www.mygeoscienceplace.com**. It is a dynamic instructional tool that promotes understanding and reinforces important concepts by using tutorials, animations, and exercises that actively engage the student.

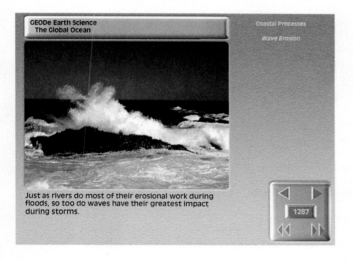

Just as rivers do most of their erosional work during floods, so too do waves have their greatest impact during storms.

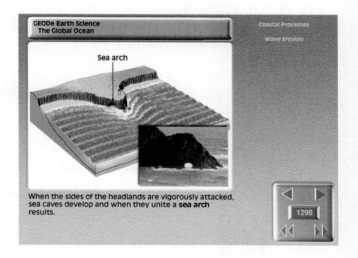

When the sides of the headlands are vigorously attacked, sea caves develop and when they unite a **sea arch** results.

HEATING THE ATMOSPHERE

FOCUS ON LEARNING

To assist you in learning the important concepts in this chapter, you will find it helpful to focus on the following questions:

1. What is weather? How is it different from climate?

2. What are the basic elements of weather and climate?

3. What are the major components of clean, dry air?

4. What is ozone and why is it important to life on Earth? In what atmospheric layer is it concentrated?

5. How do pressure and temperature change from Earth's surface to the top of the atmosphere?

6. What causes the seasons?

7. How do the noon sun angle and the length of daylight change between an equinox and a solstice?

8. What paths does solar radiation take once it is intercepted by Earth?

9. How is the atmosphere heated?

10. How are humans influencing global climate?

11. What causes temperature to vary from place to place?

CHAPTER 11

Solar radiation provides practically all of the energy that heats Earth's surface and atmosphere. (Photo by Jaynes Gallery/www.DanitaDelimont.com)

Earth's atmosphere is unique. No other planet in our solar system has an atmosphere with the exact mixture of gases or the heat and moisture conditions necessary to sustain life as we know it. The gases that make up Earth's atmosphere and the controls to which they are subject are vital to our existence. In this chapter, we will begin our examination of the ocean of air in which we all must live. What is the composition of the atmosphere? Where does the atmosphere end and outer space begin? What causes the seasons? How is air heated? What factors control temperature variations over the globe?

Weather influences our everyday activities, our jobs, and our health and comfort. Many of us pay little attention to the weather unless we are inconvenienced by it or it adds to our enjoyment outdoors. Nevertheless, few other aspects of our physical environment affect our lives more than the phenomena we collectively call the weather.

The United States occupies an area that stretches from the tropics to the Arctic Circle. It has thousands of miles of coastline and extensive regions that are far from the influence of the ocean. Some landscapes are mountainous and others are dominated by plains. It is a place where Pacific storms strike the West Coast, and the East is sometimes influenced by events in the Atlantic and the Gulf of Mexico. For those in the center of the country, it is common to experience weather events triggered when frigid southward-bound Canadian air masses clash with northward-moving ones.

Stories about weather are a routine part of the daily news. Articles and items about the effects of heat, cold, floods, drought, fog, snow, ice, and strong winds are commonplace. Of course, storms of all kinds are frequently front-page news (**FIGURE 11.1**). Beyond its direct impact on the lives of individuals, the weather has a strong effect on the world economy by influencing agriculture, energy use, water resources, transportation, and industry.

Weather clearly influences our lives a great deal. Yet, it is also important to realize that people influence the atmosphere and its behavior as well (**FIGURE 11.2**). There are, and will continue to be, significant political and scientific decisions that must be made involving these impacts. Important examples are air pollution control and the effects of human activities on global climate and the atmosphere's protective ozone layer. So there is a need for increased awareness and understanding of our atmosphere and its behavior.

WEATHER AND CLIMATE

GEODe
EARTH SCIENCE
Earth's Dynamic Atmosphere
▼ Introduction to the Atmosphere

Acted on by the combined effects of Earth's motions and energy from the Sun, our planet's formless and invisible envelope of air reacts by producing an infinite variety of weather, which in turn creates the basic patterns of global climates. Although not identical, weather and climate have much in common.

Weather is constantly changing, sometimes from hour to hour and at other times from day to day. It is a term that refers to the state of the atmosphere at a given time and place.

Whereas changes in the weather are continuous and sometimes seemingly erratic, it is nevertheless possible to arrive at a generalization of these variations. Such a description of aggregate weather conditions is termed **climate**. It is based on observations that have been accumulated over many years. Climate is often defined simply as "average weather," but this is an inadequate definition. To more accurately portray the character of an area, variations and extremes must also be included, as well as the probabilities that such departures will take place. For example, it is not only necessary for farmers to know the average rainfall during the growing season, but also important to know the frequency of extremely wet and extremely dry years. Thus, climate is the sum of all statistical weather information that helps describe a place or region.

Suppose you were planning a vacation trip to an unfamiliar place. You would probably want to know what kind of weather to expect. Such information would help as you selected clothes to pack and could influence decisions regarding activities you might engage in during your stay. Unfortunately, weather forecasts that go beyond a few days are not very dependable. Instead, you might ask someone who is familiar with the area about what kind of weather to expect. "Are thunderstorms common?" "Does it get cold at night?" "Are the afternoons sunny?" What you are seeking is information about the climate, the conditions that are typical for that place. Another useful source of information is the great variety of climate tables, maps, and graphs that are available. For example, the graph in **FIGURE 11.3** shows average daily high and low temperatures for each month, as well as extremes for New York City.

Such information could no doubt help as you planned your trip. But it is important to realize that *climate data*

A.

B.

FIGURE 11.1   There are few aspects of our physical environment that influence our daily lives more than the weather. The United States experiences a great variety of weather. (Photo A by Tetra Images/Photolibrary; Photo B by Mark Newman/Superstock)

cannot predict the weather. Although the place may usually (climatically) be warm, sunny, and dry during the time of your planned vacation, you may actually experience cool, overcast, and rainy weather. There is a well-known saying that summarizes this idea: "Climate is what you expect, but weather is what you get."

The nature of both weather and climate is expressed in terms of the same basic **elements**—those quantities or properties that are measured regularly. The most important are (1) air temperature, (2) humidity, (3) type and amount of cloudiness, (4) type and amount of precipitation, (5) air pressure, and (6) the speed and direction of the wind. These elements are the major variables by which weather patterns and climate types are depicted. Although you will study

these elements separately at first, keep in mind that they are very much interrelated. A change in one of the elements often produces changes in the others.

COMPOSITION OF THE ATMOSPHERE

Earth's Dynamic Atmosphere
▼ Introduction to the Atmosphere

Air is *not* a unique element or compound. Rather, **air** is a *mixture* of many discrete gases, each with its own physical properties, in which varying quantities of tiny solid and liquid particles are suspended.

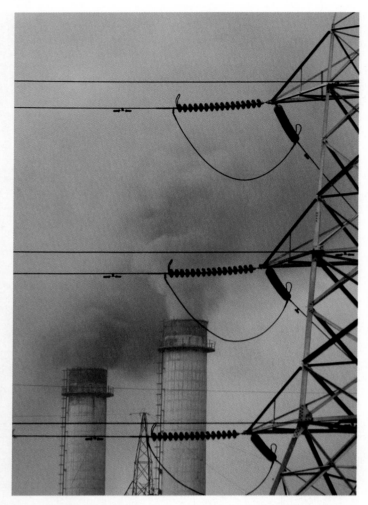

FIGURE 11.2 Smoke bellows from a coal-fired electrical generating plant in New Delhi, India, in June 2008. Humans have a significant influence on the atmosphere and its behavior. (AP Photo/Gurindes Osan)

FIGURE 11.3 Graph showing daily temperature data for New York City. In addition to the average daily maximum and minimum temperatures for each month, extremes are also shown. As this graph shows, there can be significant departures from average.

Major Components

The composition of air is not constant; it varies from time to time and from place to place. If the water vapor, dust, and other variable components were removed from the atmosphere, we would find that its makeup is very stable worldwide, up to an altitude of about 80 kilometers (50 miles).

As you can see in **FIGURE 11.4**, clean, dry air is composed almost entirely of two gases—78 percent nitrogen and 21 percent oxygen. Although these gases are the most plentiful components of air and are of great significance to life on Earth, they are of little or no importance in affecting weather phenomena. The remaining 1 percent of dry air is mostly the inert gas argon (0.93 percent) plus tiny quantities of a number of other gases. Carbon dioxide, although present in only minute amounts (0.038 percent), is nevertheless an important constituent of air, because it has the ability to absorb heat energy radiated by Earth and thus influences the heating of the atmosphere.

FIGURE 11.4 Proportional volume of gases comprising dry air. Nitrogen and oxygen clearly dominate.

Variable Components

Air includes many gases and particles that vary significantly from time to time and from place to place. Important examples include water vapor, dust particles, and ozone. Although usually present in small percentages, they can have significant effects on weather and climate.

Water Vapor

The amount of water vapor in the air varies considerably, from practically none at all up to about 4 percent by volume. Why is such a small fraction of the atmosphere so significant? Certainly, the fact that water vapor is the source of all clouds and precipitation would be enough to explain its importance. However, water vapor has other roles. Like carbon dioxide, it has the ability to absorb heat energy given off by Earth as well as some solar energy. It is therefore important when we examine the heating of the atmosphere.

When water changes from one state to another (see Figure 12.2, p. 343), it absorbs or releases heat. This energy is termed *latent heat,* which means "hidden" heat. As we will see in later chapters, water vapor in the atmosphere transports this latent heat from one region to another, and it is the energy source that helps drive many storms.

Aerosols

The movements of the atmosphere are sufficient to keep a large quantity of solid and liquid particles suspended within it. Although visible dust sometimes clouds the sky, these relatively large particles are too heavy to stay in the air for very long. Many other particles are microscopic and remain suspended for considerable periods of time. They may originate from many sources, both natural and human made, and include sea salts from breaking waves; fine soil blown into the air; smoke and soot from fires; pollen and microorganisms lifted by the wind, ash, and dust from volcanic eruptions; and more (**FIGURE 11.5A**). Collectively, these tiny solid and liquid particles are called **aerosols**.

From a meteorological standpoint, these tiny, often invisible particles can be significant. First, many act as surfaces on which water vapor can condense, an important function in the formation of clouds and fog. Second, aerosols can absorb or reflect incoming solar radiation. Thus, when an air pollution episode is occurring or when ash fills the sky following a volcanic eruption, the amount of sunlight reaching Earth's surface can be measurably reduced. Finally, aerosols contribute to an optical phenomenon we have all observed—the varied hues of red and orange at sunrise and sunset (**FIGURE 11.5B**).

A.

B.

FIGURE 11.5   A. This satellite image from November 11, 2002, shows two examples of aerosols. First, a large dust storm is blowing across northeastern China toward the Korean Peninsula. Second, a dense haze toward the south (bottom center) is human-generated air pollution. (NASA)
B. Dust in the air can cause sunsets to be especially colorful. (Photo by elwynn/Shutterstock)

Ozone

Another important component of the atmosphere is *ozone*. It is a form of oxygen that combines three oxygen atoms into each molecule (O_3). Ozone is not the same as the oxygen we breathe, which has two atoms per molecule (O_2). There is very little ozone in the atmosphere, and its distribution is not uniform. It is concentrated between 10 and 50 kilometers (6 and 31 miles) above the surface in a layer called the *stratosphere.*

In this altitude range, oxygen molecules (O_2) are split into single atoms of oxygen (O) when they absorb ultraviolet radiation emitted by the Sun. Ozone is then created when a single atom of oxygen (O) and a molecule of oxygen (O_2) collide. This must happen in the presence of a third, neutral molecule that acts as a *catalyst* by allowing the reaction to take place without itself being consumed in the process. Ozone is concentrated in the 10-to 50-kilometer height range because a crucial balance exists there: The ultraviolet radiation from the Sun is sufficient to produce single atoms of oxygen, and there are enough gas molecules to bring about the required collisions.

The presence of the ozone layer in our atmosphere is crucial to those of us who dwell on Earth. The reason is that ozone absorbs the potentially harmful ultraviolet (UV) radiation from the Sun. If ozone did not filter a great deal of the ultraviolet radiation, and if the Sun's UV rays reached the surface of Earth undiminished, our planet would be uninhabitable for most life as we know it. Thus, anything that reduces the amount of ozone in the atmosphere could affect the well-being of life on Earth. Just such a problem exists and is described in the next section.

Ozone Depletion—A Global Issue

Although stratospheric ozone is 10 to 50 kilometers up, it is vulnerable to human activities. Chemicals we produce are breaking up ozone molecules in the stratosphere, weakening our shield against UV rays. This loss of ozone is a serious global-scale environmental problem. Measurements over the past two decades confirm that ozone depletion is occurring worldwide and is especially pronounced above Earth's poles. You can see this effect over the South Pole in **FIGURE 11.6**.

Over the past half century, people have unintentionally placed the ozone layer in jeopardy by polluting the atmosphere. The most significant of the offending chemicals are known as *chlorofluorocarbons* (*CFCs* for short). Over the decades, many uses were developed for CFCs: coolants for air-conditioning and refrigeration equipment, cleaning solvents for electronic components, propellants for aerosol sprays, and the production of certain plastic foams.

Because CFCs are practically inert (that is, not chemically active) in the lower atmosphere, some of these gases gradually make their way to the ozone layer, where sunlight separates the chemicals into their constituent atoms. The chlorine atoms released this way break up some of the ozone molecules.

Because ozone filters out most of the UV radiation from the Sun, a decrease in its concentration permits more

Total ozone (Dobson Units)

110 220 330 440 550

FIGURE 11.6   This satellite image shows ozone distribution in the Southern Hemisphere on September 17, 2009. The area of greatest depletion is called the "ozone hole." Dark blue colors correspond to the region with the sparsest ozone. Average values are about 300 Dobson Units. Any area below 220 Dobson Units is considered part of the hole. The ozone hole forms over Antarctica during the Southern Hemisphere spring. At its greatest extent in 2009, it extended over about 24 million square kilometers (9.4 million square miles), an area roughly the size of North America. The largest ozone hole on record occurred in 2006. It was about 29 million square kilometers. (NASA)

of these harmful wavelengths to reach Earth's surface. The most serious threat to human health is an increased risk of skin cancer. An increase in damaging UV radiation also can impair the human immune system as well as promote cataracts, a clouding of the eye lens that reduces vision and may cause blindness if not treated.

In response to this problem, an international agreement known as the *Montreal Protocol* was developed under the sponsorship of the United Nations to eliminate the production and use of CFCs.

Although relatively strong action was taken, CFC levels in the atmosphere will not drop rapidly. Once in the atmosphere, CFC molecules can take many years to reach the ozone layer, and once there, they can remain active for decades. This does not promise a near-term reprieve for the ozone layer.

According to the U.S. Environmental Protection Agency, the ozone layer has not grown thinner since 1998 over most of the world. Between 2060 and 2075 the abundance of ozone-depleting gases is projected to fall to values that existed before the ozone hole began to form in the 1980s.

DID YOU KNOW?

Although naturally occurring ozone in the stratosphere is critical to life on Earth, it is regarded as a pollutant when produced at ground level because it can damage vegetation and be harmful to human health. Ozone is a major component in a noxious mixture of gases and particles called *photochemical smog*. It forms as a result of reactions triggered by sunlight that occur among pollutants emitted by motor vehicles and industrial sources.

VERTICAL STRUCTURE OF THE ATMOSPHERE

Earth's Dynamic Atmosphere
▼ Introduction to the Atmosphere

To say that the atmosphere begins at Earth's surface and extends upward is obvious. However, where does the atmosphere end and outer space begin? There is no sharp boundary; the atmosphere rapidly thins as you travel away from Earth, until there are too few gas molecules to detect.

Pressure Changes

To understand the vertical extent of the atmosphere, let us examine changes in atmospheric pressure with height. Atmospheric pressure is simply the weight of the air above. At sea level, the average pressure is slightly more than 1000 millibars (mb). This corresponds to a weight of slightly more than 1 kilogram per square centimeter (14.7 pounds per square inch). Obviously, the pressure at higher altitudes is less (**FIGURE 11.7**).

One-half of the atmosphere lies below an altitude of 5.6 kilometers (3.5 miles). At about 16 kilometers (10 miles), 90 percent of the atmosphere has been transversed, and above 100 kilometers (62 miles), only 0.00003 percent of all the gases making up the atmosphere remain. Even so, traces of our atmosphere extend far beyond this altitude, gradually merging with the emptiness of space.

Temperature Changes

By the early twentieth century, much had been learned about the lower atmosphere. The upper atmosphere was partly known from indirect methods. Data from balloons and kites showed that near Earth's surface air temperature drops with increasing height. This phenomenon is felt by anyone who has climbed a high mountain and is obvious in pictures of snowcapped mountaintops rising above snow-free lowlands (**FIGURE 11.8**). We divide the atmosphere vertically into four layers on the basis of temperature (**FIGURE 11.9**).

Troposphere

The bottom layer in which we live, where temperature decreases with an increase in altitude, is the **troposphere**. The term literally means the region where air "turns over," a

FIGURE 11.7 Atmospheric pressure variation with altitude. The rate of pressure decrease with an increase in altitude is not constant. Pressure decreases rapidly near Earth's surface and more gradually at greater heights. Put another way, the graph shows that the vast bulk of the gases making up the atmosphere is very near Earth's surface and that the gases gradually merge with the emptiness of space.

reference to the turbulent weather in this lowermost zone. The troposphere is the chief focus of meteorologists, because it is in this layer that essentially all important weather phenomena occur.

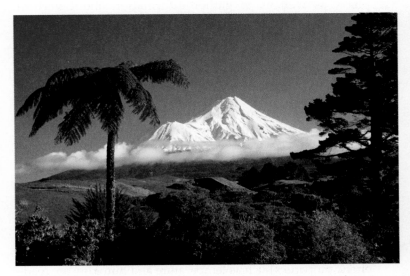

FIGURE 11.8 Temperatures drop with an increase in altitude in the troposphere. Therefore, it is possible to have snow on a mountaintop and warmer, snow-free lowlands below. (Photo by David Wall/www.DanitaDelimont.com)

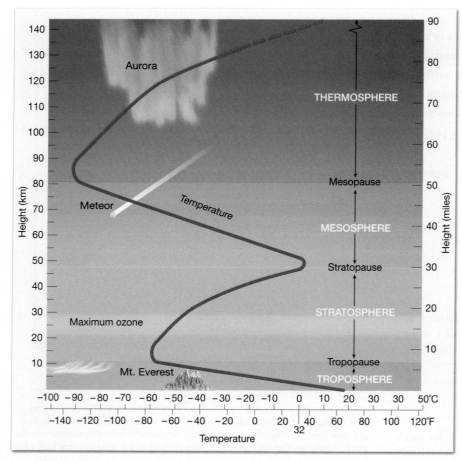

FIGURE 11.9 Thermal structure of the atmosphere.

The temperature decrease in the troposphere is called the **environmental lapse rate**. Although its average value is 6.5°C per kilometer (3.5°F per 1000 feet), a figure known as the *normal lapse rate,* its value is variable. To determine the actual environmental lapse rate for any particular time and place, as well as to gather information about vertical changes in pressure, wind, and humidity, radiosondes are used. The **radiosonde** is an instrument package that is attached to a balloon and transmits data by radio as it ascends through the atmosphere (**FIGURE 11.10**).

The thickness of the troposphere is not the same everywhere; it varies with latitude and the season. On the average, the temperature drop continues to a height of about 12 kilometers (7.4 miles). The outer boundary of the troposphere is the *tropopause.*

Stratosphere

Beyond the tropopause is the **stratosphere**. In the stratosphere, the temperature remains constant to a height of about 20 kilometers (12 miles) and then begins an increase that continues until the *stratopause,* at a height of about 50 kilometers (31 miles) above Earth's surface. Below the tropopause, atmospheric properties such as temperature and humidity are readily transferred by large-scale turbulence and mixing. Above the tropopause, in the stratosphere, they are not. The reason for the increased temperatures in the stratosphere is that the

atmosphere's ozone is concentrated in this layer. Recall that ozone absorbs ultraviolet radiation from the Sun. As a consequence, the stratosphere is heated.

Mesosphere

In the third layer, the **mesosphere**, temperatures again decrease with height until, at the *mesopause*—approximately 80 kilometers (50 miles) above the surface—the temperature approaches −90°C (−130°F). The coldest temperatures anywhere in the atmosphere occur at the mesopause. Because accessibility is difficult, the mesosphere is one of the least explored regions of the atmosphere. It cannot be reached by the highest research balloons nor is it accessible to the lowest orbiting satellites. Recent technical developments are just beginning to fill this knowledge gap.

Thermosphere

The fourth layer extends outward from the mesopause and has no well-defined upper limit. This is the **thermosphere**, a layer that contains only a tiny fraction of the atmosphere's mass. In the extremely rarefied air of this outermost layer, temperatures again increase owing to the absorption of shortwave high-energy solar radiation by atoms of oxygen and nitrogen.

Temperatures rise to extremely high values of more than 1000°C (1832°F) in the thermosphere. But such temperatures are not comparable to those experienced near Earth's surface. Temperature is defined in terms of the average speed at which molecules move. Because the gases of the thermosphere are moving at very high speeds, the temperature is very high. But the gases are so sparse that, collectively, they possess only an insignificant quantity of heat. For this reason, the temperature of a satellite orbiting Earth in the thermosphere is determined chiefly by the amount of solar radiation it absorbs and not by the high temperature of the almost nonexistent surrounding air. If an astronaut inside the satellite were to expose his or her hand, it would not feel hot.

EARTH–SUN RELATIONSHIPS

Earth's Dynamic Atmosphere
▼ Heating Earth's Surface and Atomosphere

Always remember that nearly all of the energy that drives Earth's variable weather and climate comes from the Sun. Earth intercepts only a minute percentage of the energy given off by the Sun—less than 1 two-billionth. This may seem to be an insignificant amount until we realize that it is several hundred thousand times the electrical-generating capacity of the United States.

Solar energy is not distributed evenly over Earth's land-sea surface. The amount of energy received varies with

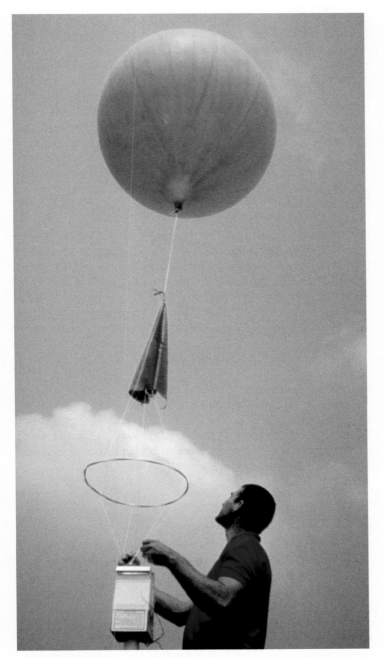

FIGURE 11.10 A lightweight package of instruments, the *radiosonde*, is carried aloft by a small weather balloon. Radiosondes supply data on vertical changes in temperature, pressure, and humidity. (Photo by NOAA/Seattle)

latitude, time of day, and season of the year. Contrasting images of polar bears on ice rafts and palm trees along a remote tropical beach serve to illustrate the extremes. It is the unequal heating of Earth that ultimately creates winds and drives ocean currents. These movements, in turn, transport heat from the tropics toward the poles in an unending attempt to balance energy inequalities. The consequences of these processes are the phenomena we call weather.

If the Sun were to be "turned off," global winds would quickly subside. Yet, as long as the Sun shines, the winds will blow and the phenomena we know as weather will

persist. So to understand how the atmosphere's dynamic weather machine works, we must first know why different latitudes receive varying quantities of solar energy and why the amount of solar energy changes to produce the seasons. As you will see, the variations in solar heating are caused by the motions of Earth relative to the Sun and by variations in Earth's land-sea surface.

Earth's Motions

Earth has two principal motions—rotation and revolution. **Rotation** is the spinning of Earth about its axis. The axis is an imaginary line running through the poles. Our planet rotates once every 24 hours, producing the daily cycle of daylight and darkness. At any moment, half of Earth is experiencing daylight, and the other half darkness. The line separating the dark half of Earth from the lighted half is called the **circle of illumination**.

Revolution refers to the movement of Earth in its orbit around the Sun. Hundreds of years ago, most people believed that Earth was stationary in space and that the Sun and stars revolved around our planet. We now know that Earth is traveling at more than 107,000 kilometers per hour (66,000 miles per hour) in its orbit about the Sun.

Seasons

We know that it is colder in winter than in summer. But why? Length of daylight certainly accounts for some of the difference. Long summer days expose us to more solar radiation, whereas short winter days expose us to less.

Furthermore, a gradual change in the angle of the noon Sun above the horizon is quite noticeable (**FIGURE 11.11**). At midsummer, the noon Sun is seen high above the horizon. But as summer gives way to autumn, the noon Sun appears lower in the sky and sunset occurs earlier each evening. What we observe here is the annual shifting of the solar angle or *altitude* of the Sun.

The seasonal variation in the altitude of the Sun affects the amount of energy received at Earth's surface in two ways. First, when the Sun is high in the sky, the solar rays are most concentrated (you can see this in **FIGURE 11.12A**). The lower the angle, the more spread out and less intense is the solar radiation that reaches the surface (**FIGURES 11.12B, C**). To illustrate this principle, hold a flashlight at a right angle to a surface and then change the angle.

Second, and of lesser importance, the angle of the Sun determines the thickness of the atmosphere the rays must penetrate (**FIGURE 11.13**). When the Sun is directly overhead, the rays pass through a thickness of only 1 atmosphere. But rays entering at a 30-degree angle travel through twice this amount, and 5-degree rays travel through a thickness roughly equal to 11 atmospheres. The longer the path, the greater the chances that sunlight will be absorbed, reflected, or scattered by the atmosphere, all of which reduce the intensity at the surface. These same effects account for the fact that we cannot look directly at the midday Sun, but we can enjoy gazing at a sunset.

It is important to remember that Earth has a spherical shape. On any given day, only places located at a particular

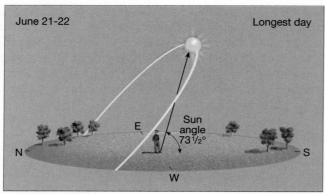

A. Summer solstice

June 21-22   Longest day

Sun angle 73½°

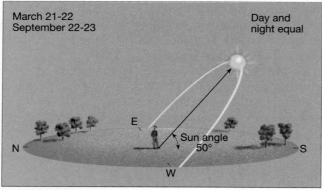

B. Spring or fall equinox

March 21-22
September 22-23   Day and night equal

Sun angle 50°

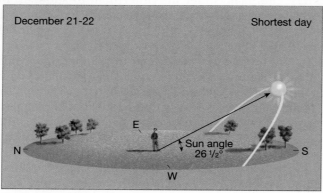

C. Winter solstice

December 21-22   Shortest day

Sun angle 26 ½°

FIGURE 11.11 Daily paths of the Sun for a place located at 40°N latitude for **A.** summer solstice, **B.** spring or fall equinox, and **C.** winter solstice. As we move from summer to winter, the angle of the noon Sun decreases from 73½, to 26½ degrees—a difference of 47 degrees. Notice also how the location of sunrise (east) and sunset (west) changes during a year.

latitude receive vertical (90-degree) rays from the Sun. As we move either north or south of this location, the Sun's rays strike at an ever decreasing angle. The nearer a place is to the latitude receiving vertical rays of the Sun, the higher will be its noon Sun and the more intense will be the radiation it receives (Figure 11.13).

Earth's Orientation

What causes yearly fluctuations in Sun angle and length of daylight? Variations occur because Earth's orientation to the Sun continually changes as it travels along its orbit. Earth's

axis (the imaginary line through the poles around which Earth rotates) is not perpendicular to the plane of its orbit around the Sun. Instead, it is tilted 23½ degrees from the perpendicular, as shown in Figure 11.13. This is termed the **inclination of the axis.** As you will see, if the axis were not inclined, we would have no seasonal changes. In addition, because the axis remains pointed in the same direction (toward the North Star) as Earth journeys around the Sun, the orientation of Earth's axis to the Sun's rays is constantly changing (**FIGURE 11.14**).

For example, on one day in June each year, Earth's position in orbit is such that the Northern Hemisphere is "leaning" 23½ degrees toward the Sun (Figure 11.14, left). Six months later, in December, when Earth has moved to the opposite side of its orbit, the Northern Hemisphere leans 23½ degrees away from the Sun (Figure 11.14, right). On days between these extremes, Earth's axis is leaning at amounts less than 23½ degrees to the rays of the Sun. This change in orientation causes the spot where the Sun's rays are vertical to make a yearly migration from 23½ degrees north of the equator to 23½ degrees south of the equator.

In turn, this migration causes the angle of the noon Sun to vary by as much as 47 degrees (23½ + 23½) during the year at places located poleward of latitude 23½ degrees. For example, a midlatitude city such as New York (about 40 degrees north latitude) has a maximum noon Sun angle of 73½ degrees when the Sun's vertical rays reach their farthest northward location in June and a minimum noon Sun angle of 26½ degrees six months later.

Solstices and Equinoxes

Historically, four days each year have been given special significance based on the annual migration of the direct rays of the Sun and its importance to the yearly weather cycle. On June 21 or 22, Earth is in a position such that the north end of its axis is tilted 23½ degrees *toward* the Sun (**FIGURE 11.15A**). At this time, the vertical rays of the Sun strike 23½ degrees north latitude (23½ degrees north of the equator), a latitude known as the **Tropic of Cancer.** For people in the Northern Hemisphere, June 21 or 22 is known as the **summer solstice,** the first "official" day of summer.

Six months later, on about December 21 or 22, Earth is in the opposite position, with the Sun's vertical rays striking at 23½ degrees south latitude (**FIGURE 11.15B**). This parallel is known as the **Tropic of Capricorn.** For those in the Northern

DID YOU KNOW?

The only state where the Sun is ever directly overhead is Hawaii because all other states are north of the Tropic of Cancer. Honolulu is about 21° north latitude and experiences a 90° Sun angle twice each year—once at noon on about May 27 and again at noon about July 20.

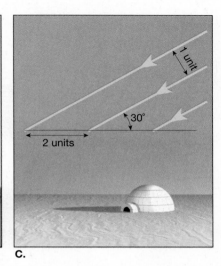

A.   **B.**   **C.**

FIGURE 11.12   Changes in the Sun's angle cause variations in the amount of solar energy reaching Earth's surface. The higher the angle, the more intense the solar radiation.

Hemisphere, December 21 and 22 is the **winter solstice**. However, at the same time in the Southern Hemisphere, people are experiencing just the opposite—the summer solstice.

Midway between the solstices are the equinoxes. September 22 or 23 is the date of the **autumnal equinox** in the Northern Hemisphere, and March 21 or 22 is the date of the **spring equinox**. On these dates, the vertical rays of the Sun strike the equator (0 degrees latitude) because Earth is in such a position in its orbit that the axis is tilted neither toward nor away from the Sun (**FIGURE 11.15C**).

The length of daylight versus darkness is also determined by Earth's position in orbit. The length of daylight on June 21, the summer solstice in the Northern Hemisphere, is greater than the length of night. This fact can be established from Figure 11.15A by comparing the fraction of a given

latitude that is on the "day" side of the circle of illumination with the fraction on the "night" side. The opposite is true for the winter solstice, when the nights are longer than the days. Again for comparison let us consider New York City, which has about 15 hours of daylight on June 21 and only about 9 hours on December 21 (you can see this in Figure 11.15 and Table 11.1). Also note from Table 11.1 that the farther north of the equator you are on June 21, the longer the period of daylight. When you reach the Arctic Circle (66½ degrees north latitude), the length of daylight is 24 hours. This is the land of the "midnight Sun," which does not set for about six months at the North Pole.

During an equinox (meaning "equal night"), the length of daylight is 12 hours *everywhere* on Earth, because the circle of illumination passes directly through the poles, dividing the latitudes in half (Figure 11.15C).

As a review of the characteristics of the summer solstice for the Northern Hemisphere, examine Figure 11.15A and Table 11.1 and consider the following facts:

1. The solstice occurs on June 21 or 22.
2. The vertical rays of the Sun are striking the Tropic of Cancer (23½ degrees north latitude).
3. Locations in the Northern Hemisphere are experiencing their greatest length of daylight (opposite for the Southern Hemisphere).
4. Locations north of the Tropic of Cancer are experiencing their highest noon Sun angles (opposite for places south of the Tropic of Capricorn).
5. The farther you are north of the equator, the longer the period of daylight, until the Arctic Circle is reached, where daylight lasts for 24 hours (opposite for the Southern Hemisphere).

The facts about the winter solstice are just the opposite. It should now be apparent why a midlatitude location is warmest in the summer, for it is then that days are longest and Sun's altitude is highest.

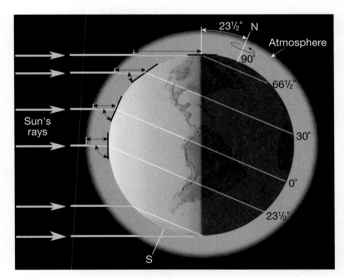

FIGURE 11.13   Rays striking Earth at a low angle (toward the poles) must travel through more of the atmosphere than rays striking at a high angle (around the equator) and thus are subject to greater depletion by reflection and absorption.

FIGURE 11.14 Earth-Sun relationships.

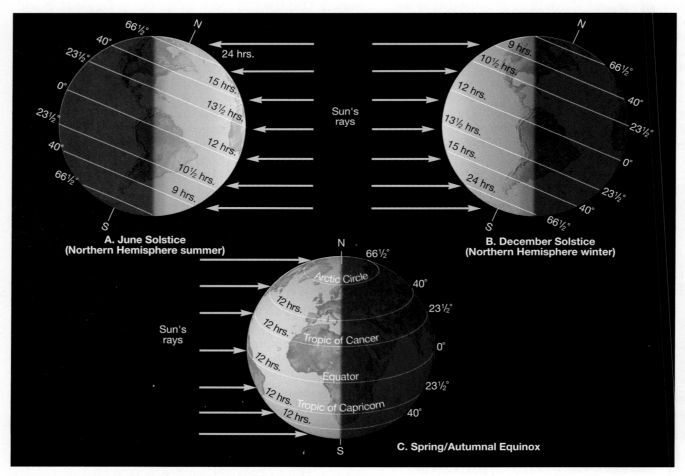

FIGURE 11.15 Characteristics of the solstices and equinoxes.

Table 11.1   Length of daylight

Latitude (degrees)	Summer Solstice	Winter Solstice	Equinoxes
0	12 h	12 h	12 h
10	12 h 35 min	11 h 25 min	12
20	13 h 12	10 h 48	12
30	13 h 56	10 h 04	12
40	14 h 52	9 h 08	12
50	16 h 18	7 h 42	12
60	18 h 27	5 h 33	12
70	24 h (for 2 mo)	0 00	12
80	24 h (for 4 mo)	0 00	12
90	24 h (for 6 mo)	0 00	12

In summary, seasonal variations in the amount of solar energy reaching places on Earth's surface are caused by the migrating vertical rays of the Sun and the resulting variations in Sun angle and length of daylight. These changes, in turn, cause the month-to-month variations in temperature observed at most locations outside the tropics. **FIGURE 11.16**

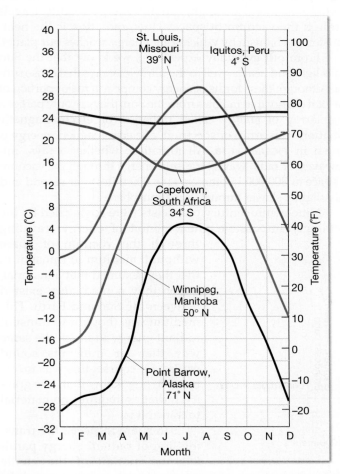

FIGURE 11.16   Mean monthly temperatures for five cities located at different latitudes. Note that Capetown, South Africa, experiences winter in June, July, and August.

shows mean monthly temperatures for selected cities at different latitudes. Notice that the cities located at more poleward latitudes experience larger temperature differences from summer to winter than do cities located nearer the equator. Also notice that temperature minimums for Southern Hemisphere locations occur in July, whereas they occur in January for most places in the Northern Hemisphere.

All places at the same latitude have identical Sun angles and lengths of daylight. If the Earth–Sun relationships just described were the only controls of temperature, we would expect these places to have identical temperatures as well. Obviously, this is not the case. Other factors that influence temperature are discussed later in the chapter.

ENERGY, HEAT, AND TEMPERATURE

The universe is made up of a combination of matter and energy. The concept of matter is easy to grasp because it is the "stuff" we can see, smell, and touch. Energy, on the other hand, is abstract and therefore more difficult to describe. For our purposes, we will define energy simply as *the capacity to do work.* We can think of work as being accomplished whenever matter is moved. You are likely familiar with some of the common forms of energy, such as thermal, chemical, nuclear, radiant (light), and gravitational energy. One type of energy is described as *kinetic energy,* which is energy of motion. Recall that matter is composed of atoms or molecules that are constantly in motion and therefore possesses kinetic energy.

Heat is a term that is commonly used synonymously with *thermal energy.* In this usage, heat is energy possessed by a material arising from the internal motions of its atoms or molecules. Whenever a substance is heated, its atoms move faster and faster, which leads to an increase in its heat content. **Temperature**, on the other hand, is related to the average kinetic energy of a material's atoms or molecules. Stated another way, the term *heat* generally refers to the quantity of energy present, whereas the word *temperature* refers to the intensity, that is, the degree of "hotness."

Heat and temperature are closely related concepts. Heat is the energy that flows because of temperature differences. In all situations, *heat is transferred from warmer to cooler objects.* Thus, if two objects of different temperature are in contact, the warmer object will become cooler and the cooler object will become warmer until they both reach the same temperature.

MECHANISMS OF HEAT TRANSFER

Earth's Dynamic Atmosphere
▼ Heating Earth's Surface and Atomosphere

The three mechanisms of heat transfer are conduction, convection, and radiation. Although we present them separately, all three processes go on simultaneously in the atmosphere. In addition, these mechanisms operate to transfer heat between Earth's surface (both land and water) and the atmosphere.

FIGURE 11.17 The three mechanisms of heat transfer: conduction, convection, and radiation.

Conduction

Conduction is familiar to all of us. Anyone who has touched a metal spoon that was left in a hot pan has discovered that heat was conducted through the spoon. **Conduction** *is the transfer of heat through matter by molecular activity.* The energy of molecules is transferred through collisions between one molecule and another, with the heat flowing from the higher temperature to the lower temperature.

The ability of substances to conduct heat varies considerably. Metals are good conductors, as those of us who have touched hot metal have quickly learned (**FIGURE 11.17**). Air, on the other hand, is a very poor conductor of heat. Consequently, conduction is important only between Earth's surface and the air directly in contact with the surface. As a means of heat transfer for the atmosphere as a whole, conduction is the least significant.

Convection

Much of the heat transport that occurs in the atmosphere is carried on by convection. **Convection** *is the transfer of heat by mass movement or circulation within a substance.* It takes place in fluids (for example, liquids like the ocean and gases like air) where the atoms and molecules are free to move about.

The pan of water in Figure 11.17 illustrates the nature of simple convective circulation. Radiation from the fire warms the bottom of the pan, which conducts heat to the water near the bottom of the container. As the water is heated, it expands and becomes less dense than the water above. Because of this new buoyancy, the warmer water rises. At the same time, cooler, denser water near the top of the pan sinks to the bottom, where it becomes heated. As long as the water is heated unequally—that is, from the bottom up—the water will continue to "turn over," producing a *convective circulation.* In a similar manner, most of the heat acquired in the lowest layer of the atmosphere by way of radiation and conduction is transferred by convective flow.

On a global scale, convection in the atmosphere creates a huge, worldwide circulation of air. This is responsible for the redistribution of heat between hot equatorial regions and the frigid poles. This important process is discussed in detail in Chapter 13.

Radiation

The third mechanism of heat transfer is **radiation**. As shown in Figure 11.17, radiation travels out in all directions from its source. Unlike conduction and convection, which need a medium to travel through, radiant energy readily travels through the vacuum of space. Thus, radiation is the heat-transfer mechanism by which solar energy reaches our planet.

From our everyday experience, we know that the Sun emits light and heat as well as the ultraviolet rays that cause suntan. Although these forms of energy comprise a major portion of the total energy that radiates from the Sun, they are only part of a large array of energy called radiation or **electromagnetic radiation**. This array, or spectrum, of electromagnetic energy is shown in **FIGURE 11.18**. All radiation, whether x-rays, microwaves, or radio waves, transmit energy through the vacuum of space at 300,000 kilometers (186,000 miles) per second and only slightly slower through our atmosphere.

Nineteenth-century physicists were so puzzled by the seemingly impossible phenomenon of energy traveling through the vacuum of space without a medium to transmit it, that they assumed that a material, which they named *ether,* existed between the Sun and Earth. This medium was thought to transmit radiant energy in much the same way that air transmits sound waves. Of course, this was incorrect. We now know that, like gravity, radiation requires no material to transmit it.

In some respects, the transmission of radiant energy parallels the motion of the gentle swells in the open ocean. Like ocean swells, electromagnetic waves come in various sizes. For

0.4 Violet	Blue	0.5 Green	Yellow	0.6 Orange	0.7 Red		

Visible light

Gamma rays | X rays | Ultraviolet | Infrared | Microwaves | Television, FM radio | Short-wave radio | Standard AM radio Broadcast band | Long radio waves

0.001 micrometer | 1 micrometer | 1000 micrometers | 1 meter | 1000 meters

Short-wave radiation   Long-wave radiation

FIGURE 11.18 The electromagnetic spectrum, illustrating the wavelengths and names of various types of radiation.

our purpose, the most important characteristic is their *wavelength,* or the distance from one crest to the next. Radio waves have the longest wavelengths, ranging to tens of kilometers, whereas gamma waves are the shortest, being less than one-billionth of a centimeter long.

Visible light, as the name implies, is the only portion of the spectrum we can see. We often refer to visible light as "white" light since it appears "white" in color. However, it is easy to show that white light is really a mixture of colors, each corresponding to a particular wavelength (**FIGURE 11.19**). Using a prism, we can divide white light into a color array rainbow. Figure 11.18 shows that violet has the shortest wavelength—0.4 micrometer—and red has the longest—0.7 micrometer.

Located adjacent to red and having a longer wavelength is **infrared** radiation, which we cannot see but which we can detect as heat. The closest invisible waves to violet are called **ultraviolet (UV)** rays and are responsible for sunburn after an intense exposure to the Sun. Although we divide radiant energy into groups based on our ability to perceive them, all forms of radiation are basically the same. When any form of radiant energy is absorbed by an object, the result is an increase in molecular motion, which causes a corresponding increase in temperature.

To better understand how the atmosphere is heated, it is useful to have a general understanding of the basic laws governing radiation:

1. *All objects, at whatever temperature, emit radiant energy.* Hence, not only hot objects such as the Sun but also Earth, including its polar ice caps, continually emit energy.

2. *Hotter objects radiate more total energy per unit area than do colder objects.*

3. *The hotter the radiating body, the shorter the wavelength of maximum radiation.* The Sun, with a surface temperature of about 5700°C, radiates maximum energy at 0.5 micrometer, which is in the visible range. The maximum radiation for Earth occurs at a wavelength of 10 micrometers, well within the infrared (heat) range. Because the maximum Earth radiation is roughly 20 times longer than the maximum solar radiation, Earth radiation is often called *long-wave radiation*, and solar radiation is called *short-wave radiation*.

4. *Objects that are good absorbers of radiation are good emitters as well.* Earth's surface and the Sun approach being perfect radiators because they absorb and radiate with nearly 100 percent efficiency for their respective temperatures. On the other hand, *gases are selective absorbers and radiators.* Thus, the atmosphere, which is nearly transparent (does not absorb) to certain wavelengths of radiation, is nearly opaque (a good absorber) to others. Our experience tells us that the atmosphere is transparent to visible light; hence, it readily reaches Earth's surface. This is not the case for the longer wavelength radiation emitted by Earth.

Figure 11.17 summarizes the various mechanisms of heat transfer. A portion of the radiant energy generated by the campfire is absorbed by the pan. This energy is readily transferred through the metal container by the process of conduction. Conduction also increases the temperature of the water at the bottom. Once warmed, this layer of water moves upward and is replaced by cool water descending from above. Thus, convection currents that redistribute the newly acquired energy throughout the pan are established. Meanwhile, the camper is warmed by radiation emitted by the fire and the pan. Furthermore, because metals are good conductors, the camper's hand is likely to be burned if he or she does not use a potholder. Like this example, the heating of Earth's atmosphere involves the processes of conduction, convection, and radiation, all of which occur simultaneously.

THE FATE OF INCOMING SOLAR RADIATION

Earth's Dynamic Atmosphere
▼ Heating Earth's Surface and Atmosphere

When radiation strikes an object, three different results usually occur. First, some of the energy is *absorbed* by the object. Recall that when radiant energy is absorbed, it is converted to heat, which causes an increase in temperature. Second, substances such as water and air are transparent to certain wavelengths of radiation. Such materials simply *transmit* this energy. Radiation that is transmitted does not contribute energy to the object. Third, some radiation may "bounce off" the object without being absorbed or transmitted. *Reflection* and *scattering* are responsible for redirecting incoming solar radiation. In summary, *radiation may be absorbed, transmitted, or redirected (reflected or scattered).*

FIGURE 11.20 shows the fate of incoming solar radiation averaged for the entire globe. Notice that the atmosphere is quite transparent to incoming solar radiation. On average,

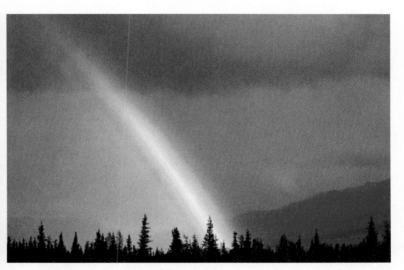

FIGURE 11.19 Visible light consists of an array of colors we commonly call the "colors of the rainbow." Rainbows are relatively common optical phenomena produced by the bending and reflection of light by drops of water. (Photo by Michael Giannechini/Photo Researchers, Inc.)

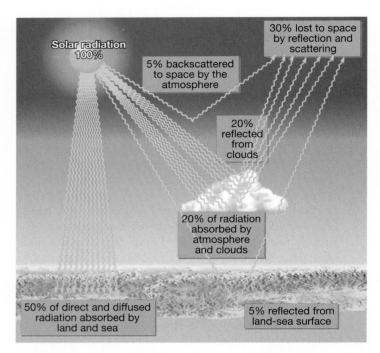

FIGURE 11.20 Average distribution of incoming solar radiation by percentage. More solar energy is absorbed by Earth's surface than by the atmosphere. Consequently, the air is not heated directly by the Sun but is heated indirectly from Earth's surface.

FIGURE 11.21 Reflection and scattering. **A.** Reflected light bounces back from a surface at the same angle at which it strikes that surface and with the same intensity. **B.** When a beam of light is scattered, it results in a larger number of weaker rays, traveling in all different directions. Usually more energy is scattered in the forward direction than is backscattered.

about 50 percent of the solar energy reaching the top of the atmosphere is absorbed at Earth's surface. Another 30 percent is reflected back to space by the atmosphere, clouds, and reflective surfaces. The remaining 20 percent is absorbed by clouds and the atmosphere's gases. What determines whether solar radiation will be transmitted to the surface, scattered, reflected outward, or absorbed by the atmosphere? As you will see, it depends greatly on the wavelength of the energy being transmitted, as well as on the nature of the intervening material.

Reflection and Scattering

Reflection is the process whereby light bounces back from an object at the same angle at which it encounters a surface and with the same intensity (**FIGURE 11.21A**). By contrast, **scattering** produces a larger number of weaker rays that travel in different directions. Although scattering disperses light both forward and backward (*backscattering*), more energy is dispersed in the forward direction (**FIGURE 11.21B**).

Reflection and Earth's Albedo

Energy is returned to space from Earth in two ways: reflection and emission of radiant energy. The portion of solar energy that is reflected back to space leaves in the same short wavelengths in which it came to Earth. About 30 percent of the solar energy reaching the outer atmosphere is reflected back to space. Included in this figure is the amount sent skyward by backscattering. This energy is lost to Earth and does not play a role in heating the atmosphere.

The fraction of the total radiation that is reflected by a surface is called its **albedo**. Thus, the albedo for Earth as a

whole (the *planetary albedo*) is 30 percent. However, the albedo from place to place as well as from time to time in the same locale varies considerably, depending on the amount of cloud cover and particulate matter in the air, as well as on the angle of the Sun's rays and the nature of the surface. A lower Sun angle means that more atmosphere must be penetrated, thus making the "obstacle course" longer and the loss of solar radiation greater (see Figure 11.13, p. 319). **FIGURE 11.22** gives the albedo for various surfaces. Note that the angle at which the Sun's rays strike a water surface greatly affects its albedo.

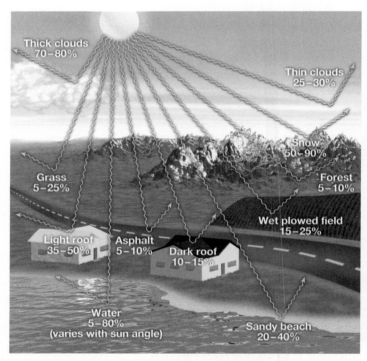

FIGURE 11.22 Albedo (reflectivity) of various surfaces. In general, light colored surfaces tend to be more reflective than dark-colored surfaces and thus have higher albedos.

Scattering

Although incoming solar radiation travels in a straight line, small dust particles and gas molecules in the atmosphere scatter some of this energy in all directions. The result, called **diffused light**, explains how light reaches into the area beneath a shade tree, and how a room is lit in the absence of direct sunlight. Further, scattering accounts for the brightness and even the blue color of the daytime sky. In contrast, bodies such as the Moon and Mercury, which are without atmospheres, have dark skies and "pitch-black" shadows, even during daylight hours. Overall, about half of the solar radiation that is absorbed at Earth's surface arrives as diffused (scattered) light.

Absorption

As stated earlier, gases are selective absorbers, meaning that they absorb strongly in some wavelengths, moderately in others, and only slightly in still others. When a gas molecule absorbs radiation, the energy is transformed into internal molecular motion, which is detectable as a rise in temperature.

Nitrogen, the most abundant constituent in the atmosphere, is a poor absorber of all types of incoming solar radiation. Oxygen and ozone are efficient absorbers of ultraviolet radiation. Oxygen removes most of the shorter ultraviolet radiation high in the atmosphere, and ozone absorbs most of the remaining UV rays in the stratosphere. The absorption of UV radiation in the stratosphere accounts for the high temperatures experienced there. The only other significant absorber of incoming solar radiation is water vapor, which, along with oxygen and ozone, accounts for most of the solar radiation absorbed directly by the atmosphere.

For the atmosphere as a whole, none of the gases are effective absorbers of visible radiation. This explains why most visible radiation reaches Earth's surface and why we say that the atmosphere is *transparent* to incoming solar radiation. Thus, the atmosphere does not acquire the bulk of its energy directly from the Sun. Rather, it is heated chiefly by energy that is first absorbed by Earth's surface and then reradiated to the sky.

HEATING THE ATMOSPHERE: THE GREENHOUSE EFFECT

Earth's Dynamic Atmosphere
▼ Heating Earth's Surface and Atmosphere

Approximately 50 percent of the solar energy that strikes the top of the atmosphere reaches Earth's surface and is absorbed. Most of this energy is then reradiated skyward. Because Earth has a much lower surface temperature than the Sun, the radiation that it emits has longer wavelengths than solar radiation.

The atmosphere as a whole is an efficient absorber of the longer wavelengths emitted by Earth (*terrestrial radiation*). Water vapor and carbon dioxide are the principal absorbing gases. Water vapor absorbs roughly five times more terrestrial radiation than do all of the other gases combined and accounts for the warm temperatures found in the lower troposphere, where it is most highly concentrated. Because the atmosphere is quite transparent to shorter-wavelength solar radiation and more readily absorbs longer-wavelength terrestrial radiation, the atmosphere is heated from the ground up rather than vice versa. This explains the general drop in temperature with increasing altitude experienced in the troposphere. The farther from the "radiator," the colder it becomes.

When the gases in the atmosphere absorb terrestrial radiation, they warm; but they eventually radiate this energy away. Some energy travels skyward, where it may be reabsorbed by other gas molecules, a possibility that is less likely with increasing height because the concentration of water vapor decreases with altitude. The remainder travels Earthward and is again absorbed by Earth. For this reason, Earth's surface is continually being supplied with heat from the atmosphere as well as from the Sun. Without these absorptive gases in our atmosphere, Earth would not be a suitable habitat for humans and numerous other life forms.

This very important phenomenon has been termed the **greenhouse effect** because it was once thought that greenhouses were heated in a similar manner (**FIGURE 11.23**). The gases of our atmosphere, especially water vapor and carbon dioxide, act very much like the glass in the greenhouse. They allow shorter-wavelength solar radiation to enter, where it is absorbed by the objects inside. These objects in turn radiate energy, but at longer wavelengths, to which glass is nearly opaque. The heat therefore is "trapped" in the greenhouse. However, a more important factor in keeping a greenhouse warm is the fact that the greenhouse itself prevents mixing of air inside with cooler air outside. Nevertheless, the term *greenhouse effect* is still used.

HUMAN IMPACT ON GLOBAL CLIMATE

Climate not only varies from place to place, but is naturally variable over time. During the great expanse of Earth history, and long before humans were roaming the planet, there were many shifts—from warm to cold and from wet to dry and back again. Today scientists understand that, in addition to the natural forces that cause variations in climate, humans are playing a significant role as well. One important example results from the addition of carbon dioxide and other trace gases to the atmosphere.

In the preceding section, you learned that carbon dioxide (CO_2) absorbs some of the radiation emitted by Earth and thus contributes to the greenhouse effect. Because CO_2 is an important heat absorber, it follows that a change in the atmosphere's CO_2 content could influence air temperature.

DID YOU KNOW?

If Earth's atmosphere had no greenhouse gases, its average surface temperature would be a frigid $-18°C$ ($-0.4°F$) instead of the relatively comfortable $14.5°C$ ($58°F$) that it is today.

Short-wave solar radiation passes through the atmosphere and is absorbed by Earth's surface.

Earth's surface emits longwave radiation which is absorbed by greenhouse gases.

Greenhouse gases reradiate some energy Earthward, thus trapping heat in the lower atmosphere.

H_2O

CO_2

FIGURE 11.23 The heating of the atmosphere. Most of the short-wavelength radiation from the Sun passes through the atmosphere and is absorbed by Earth's land-sea surface. This energy is then emitted from the surface as longer-wavelength radiation, much of which is absorbed by certain gases in the atmosphere. Some of the energy absorbed by the atmosphere will be radiated Earthward. This process, called the *greenhouse effect*, is responsible for keeping Earth's surface much warmer than it would otherwise be

CO_2 Levels Are Rising

Earth's tremendous industrialization of the past two centuries has been fueled—and still is fueled—by burning fossil fuels: coal, natural gas, and petroleum (**FIGURE 11.24**). Combustion of these fuels has added great quantities of carbon dioxide to the atmosphere.

The use of coal and other fuels is the most prominent means by which humans add CO_2 to the atmosphere, but it is not the only way. The clearing of forests also contributes substantially because CO_2 is released as vegetation is burned or decays. Deforestation is particularly pronounced in the tropics, where vast tracts are cleared for ranching and agriculture or subjected to inefficient commercial logging operations (**FIGURE 11.25**).

Some of the excess CO_2 is taken up by plants or is dissolved in the ocean. It is estimated that 45 to 50 percent remains in the atmosphere. **FIGURE 11.26** is a graphic record of changes in atmospheric CO_2 extending back 400,000 years. Over this long span, natural fluctuations varied from about 180 to 300 ppm. As a result of human activities, the present CO_2 level is about 30 percent higher than its highest level over at least the last 650,000 years. The rapid increase in CO_2 concentrations since the onset of industrialization is obvious. The annual rate at which atmospheric CO_2 concentrations are growing has been increasing over the last several decades (**FIGURE 11.27**).

The Atmosphere's Response

Given the increase in the atmosphere's carbon dioxide content, have global temperatures actually increased? The answer is yes. According to a 2007 report by the Intergovernmental

DID YOU KNOW?

Carbon dioxide is not the only gas contributing to global warming. Scientists have come to realize that industrial and agricultural activities are causing a buildup of several trace gases, including methane (CH_4) and nitrous oxide (N_2O), that also play a significant role. These gases absorb wavelengths of outgoing Earth radiation that would otherwise escape into space. Taken together, the effects of these gases may be nearly as great as that of CO_2 in warming Earth.

Petroleum 37%

Nuclear power 9%

Renewable energy 7%

Solar 1%

Natural Gas 24%

Coal 23%

Biomass 53%

Hydroelectric 34%

Wind 7%

Geothermal 5%

Total = 107 quadrillion btu

FIGURE 11.24 Paralleling the rapid growth of industrialization, beginning in the nineteenth century, has been the combustion of fossil fuels, which has added great quantities of carbon dioxide to the atmosphere. The graph shows energy consumption in the United States in 2008. The total was about 107 quadrillion Btu. A quadrillion is 10 raised to the 12th power, or a million million—a quadrillion Btu is a convenient unit for referring to U.S. energy use as a whole. (U.S. Department of Energy, Energy Information Administration)

A. **B.**

FIGURE 11.25 Clearing the tropical rain forest is a serious environmental issue. In addition to the loss of biodiversity, tropical deforestation is a significant source of carbon dioxide. According to U.N. estimates, about 25.1 million acres of tropical forest were permanently destroyed each year during the decade of the 1990s. Between the years 2000 and 2005, the average figure increased to 25.7 million acres per year. **A.** This August 2007 satellite image shows deforestation in the Amazon rain forest in western Brazil. Intact forest is dark green, whereas cleared areas are tan (bare ground) or light green (crops and pasture). (NASA) **B.** Fires are frequently used to clear the land. This scene is also in Brazil's Amazon Basin. (Photo by Pete Oxford/Nature Picture Library)

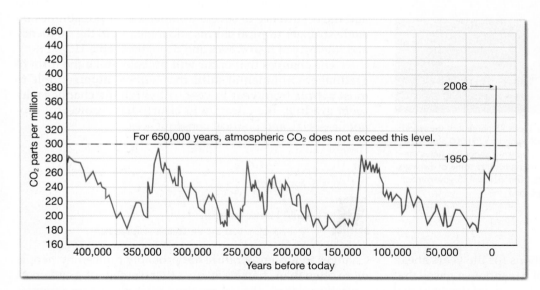

FIGURE 11.26 Carbon dioxide concentrations over the past 400,000 years. Most of the data comes from the analysis of air bubbles trapped in ice cores. The record since 1958 comes from direct measurements of atmosphere CO_2 taken at Mauna Loa Observatory, Hawaii. The rapid increase in CO_2 concentrations since the onset of the industrial revolution is obvious.

Panel on Climate Change (IPCC), "Warming of the climate system is unequivocal, as is now evident from observations of increases in global average air and ocean temperatures, widespread melting of snow and ice, and rising global sea level."* Most of the observed increase in global average temperatures since the mid-twentieth century is *very likely* due to the observed increase in human-generated greenhouse-gas concentrations. (As used by the IPCC, *very likely* indicates a probability of 90 to 99 percent.) Global warming since the mid-1970s is now about 0.6°C (1°F) and total warming in the past century is about 0.8°C (1.4°F). The upward trend in surface temperatures is shown in **FIGURE 11.28A**. The world map in **FIGURE 11.28B** compares surface temperatures for 2008 to the base period (1951–1980). You can see that the greatest warming has been in the Arctic and neighboring high-latitude regions. Here are some related facts:

- When we consider the time span for which there are instrumental records (since 1850), thirteen of the last fourteen years (1995–2008) rank among the fourteen warmest (**FIGURE 11.29**).
- Global mean temperature is now higher than at any time in at least the past 500 to 1000 years.
- The average temperature of the global ocean has increased to depths of at least 3000 meters (10,000 feet).

Are these temperature trends caused by human activities, or would they have occurred anyway? The scientific consensus of the IPCC is that human activities were *very likely* responsible for most of the temperature increase since 1950.

*IPCC, Summary for the Policy Makers. In *Climate Change 2007: The Physical Science Basis*, p. 4, Cambridge University Press, Cambridge, United Kingdom and New York, NY.

Annual CO₂ Contribution of an Average American

17,000 pounds of CO₂ by using 1,100 kilowatt-hours of electricity per month

8,800 pounds of CO₂ by using 6,300 cubic feet of natural gas per month

1,000 pounds of CO₂ by creating 4.5 pounds of trash per day

8,900 pounds of CO₂ by driving 160 miles per week

1,000 pounds of CO₂ by flying 1,900 miles per year

FIGURE 11.27 Americans are responsible for about 25 percent of the world's greenhouse-gas emissions. That amounts to 24,300 kilograms (54,000 pounds) of carbon dioxide each year for an average American, which is about five times the emissions of the average global citizen. This diagram represents some of the ways that people in the United States contribute. (Data from various U.S. government agencies; photo by Jerry Schad/Photo Researchers, Inc.)

What about the future? Projections for the years ahead depend in part on the quantities of greenhouse gases that are emitted. **FIGURE 11.30** shows the best estimates of global warming for several different scenarios. The 2007 IPCC report also states that if there is a doubling of the preindustrial level of carbon dioxide (280 ppm) to 560 ppm, the "likely temperature increase will be in the range of 2 to 4.5°C (3.5 to 8.1°F)." The increase is "very unlikely" (1 to 10 percent probability) to be less than 1.5°C (2.7°F) and values higher than 4.5°C (8.1°F) cannot be excluded.

Some Possible Consequences

What consequences can be expected if the carbon dioxide content of the atmosphere reaches a level that is twice what it was early in the twentieth century? Because the climate system is so complex, predicting the distribution of particular regional changes is speculative. It is not yet possible to pinpoint specifics, such as where or when it will become

drier or wetter. Nevertheless, plausible scenarios can be given for larger scales of space and time.

One important impact of human-induced global warming is a rise in sea level (**FIGURE 11.31**) Potential weather changes include shifts in the paths of large-scale storms, which in turn would affect the distribution of precipitation and the occurrence of severe weather. Other possibilities include stronger tropical storms and increases in the frequency and intensity of heat waves and droughts (Table 11.2)

The changes that occur will probably take the form of gradual environmental shifts that will be imperceptible to most people from year to year. Although the changes may seem gradual, the effects will clearly have powerful economic, social, and political consequences.

FOR THE RECORD: AIR TEMPERATURE DATA

Earth's Dynamic Atmosphere
▼ Temperature Data and the Controls of Temperature

Changes in air temperature are probably noticed by people more often than changes in any other element of weather. At a weather station, the temperature is monitored on a regular basis from instruments mounted in an instrument shelter (**FIGURE 11.32**). The shelter protects the instruments from direct sunlight and allows a free flow of air.

The daily maximum and minimum temperatures are the bases for much of the basic temperature data compiled by meteorologists:

1. By adding the maximum and minimum temperatures and then dividing by two, the *daily mean temperature* is calculated.

2. The *daily range* of temperature is computed by finding the difference between the maximum and minimum temperatures for a given day.

3. The *monthly mean* is calculated by adding together the daily means for each day of the month and dividing by the number of days in the month.

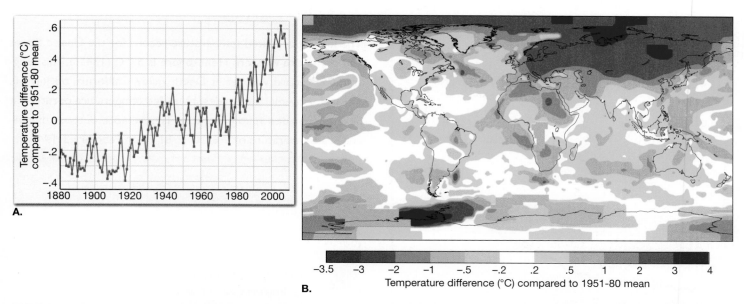

B.

FIGURE 11.28   A. The graph depicts global temperature change in °C since the year 1880. **B.** The world map shows how temperatures in 2008 deviated from the mean for the 1951–1980 base period. The high latitudes in the Northern Hemisphere clearly stand out. (After NASA/Goddard Institute for Space Studies)

FIGURE 11.29   Annual average global temperature variations for the period 1850 to 2008. The basis for comparison is the average for the 1961-1990 period (the 0.0 line on the graph). Each narrow bar on the graph represents the departure of the global mean temperature from the 1961–1990 average for a particular year. For example, the global mean temperature for 1862 was more than 0.5°C below the 1961–1990 average, whereas the global mean for 1998 was more than 0.5°C above.

line that connects points on a map that have the same temperature (*iso* = equal, *therm* = temperature). Therefore, all points through which an isotherm passes have identical temperatures for the time period indicated. Generally, isotherms representing 5° or 10° temperature differences are used, but any interval may be chosen. **FIGURE 11.33** illustrates how isotherms are drawn on a map. Notice that most isotherms do not pass directly through the observing stations, because the station readings may not coincide with the values chosen for the isotherms. Only an occasional station temperature will be exactly the same as the value of the isotherm, so it is usually necessary to draw the lines by estimating the proper position between stations.

4. The *annual mean* is an average of the 12 monthly means.
5. The *annual temperature range* is computed by finding the difference between the highest and lowest monthly means.

Mean temperatures are particularly useful for making comparisons, whether on a daily, monthly, or annual basis. It is quite common to hear a weather reporter state, "Last month was the hottest July on record," or "Today, Chicago was 10 degrees warmer than Miami." Temperature ranges are also useful statistics, because they give an indication of extremes.

To examine the distribution of air temperatures over large areas, isotherms are commonly used. An **isotherm** is a

Isothermal maps are valuable tools because they clearly make temperature distribution visible at a glance. Areas of low and high temperatures are easy to pick out. In addition, the amount of temperature change per unit of distance, called the *temperature gradient*, is easy to visualize. Closely spaced isotherms indicate a rapid rate of temperature change, whereas more widely spaced lines indicate a more gradual rate of change. You can see this in Figure 11.33. The isotherms are closer in Colorado and Utah (steeper temperature gradient), whereas the isotherms are spread farther in Texas (gentler temperature gradient). Without isotherms, a map would be covered with numbers representing temperatures at dozens or hundreds of places, which would make patterns difficult to see.

FIGURE 11.30 The left half of the graph (black line) shows global temperature changes for the twentieth century. The right half shows projected global warming in different emissions scenarios. The shaded zoned adjacent to each colored line shows the uncertainty range for each scenario. The basis for comparison (0.0 on the vertical axis) is the global average for the period 1980–1999. The orange line represents the scenario in which carbon dioxide concentrations were held constant at the values for the year 2000. (After IPCC, 2007)

WHY TEMPERATURES VARY: THE CONTROLS OF TEMPERATURE

Earth's Dynamic Atmosphere
▼ Temperature Data and the Controls of Temperature

A *temperature control* is any factor that causes temperature to vary from place to place and from time to time. Earlier in this chapter, we examined the single greatest cause for temperature variations—differences in the receipt of solar radiation. Because variations in Sun angle and length of daylight are a function of latitude, they are responsible for warm temperatures in the tropics and colder temperatures at more poleward locations. Of course, seasonal temperature changes at a given latitude occur as the Sun's vertical rays migrate toward and away from a place during the year.

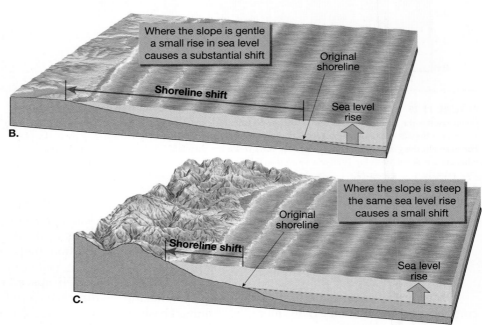

FIGURE 11.31 Research indicates that sea level has risen between 10 and 23 centimeters (4 and 8 inches) over the past century and that the trend will continue at an accelerated rate. **A.** Using data from satellites and floats, it was determined that sea level rose an average of 3 millimeters (0.1 inch) per year between 1993 and 2005. Researchers attributed about half the rise to melting glacial ice and the other half to thermal expansion. Rising sea level can adversely affect some of the most densely populated areas on Earth. (NASA/Jet Propulsion Laboratory) **B.** The slope of a shoreline is critical to determining the degree to which sea-level changes will affect it. When the slope is gentle, small changes in the sea level cause a substantial shift. **C.** The same sea-level rise along a steep coast results in only a small shoreline shift.

Table 11.2   Projected changes and effects of global warming in the twenty-first century

Projected Changes and Estimated Probability*	Examples of Projected Impacts
Higher maximum temperatures; more hot days and heat waves over nearly all land areas (*virtually certain*)	Increased incidence of death and serious illness in older age groups and urban poor. Increased heat stress in livestock and wildlife. Shift in tourist destinations. Increased risk of damage to a number of crops. Increased electric cooling demand and reduced energy supply reliability.
Higher minimum temperatures; fewer cold days, frost days, and cold waves over nearly all land areas (*virtually certain*)	Decreased cold-related human morbidity and mortality. Decreased risk of damage to a number of crops, and increased risk to others. Extended range and activity of some pest and disease vectors. Reduced heating energy demand.
Frequency of heavy precipitation events increases over most areas (*very likely*)	Increased flood, landslide, avalanche, and debris flow damage. Increased soil erosion. Increased flood runoff could increase recharge of some floodplain aquifers. Increased pressure on government and private flood insurance systems and disaster relief.
Area affected by drought increases (*likely*)	Decreased crop yields. Increased damage to building foundations caused by ground shrinkage. Decreased water-resource quantity and quality. Increased risk of forest fire.
Intense tropical cyclone activity (*likely*)	Increased risks to human life, risk of infectious-disease epidemics, and many other risks. Increased coastal erosion and damage to coastal buildings and infrastructure. Increased damage to coastal ecosystems, such as coral reefs and mangroves.

Virtually certain indicates a probability greater than 99 percent, *very likely* indicates a probability of 90–99 percent, and *likely* indicates a probability of 67–90 percent.

Source: IPCC, 2001, 2007

FIGURE 11.32 This modern shelter contains an electrical thermometer called a *thermistor*. A shelter protects instruments from direct sunlight and allows for the free flow of air. (Photo by Bobbé Christopherson)

But latitude is not the only control of temperature; if it were, we would expect that all places along the same parallel of latitude would have identical temperatures. This is clearly not the case. For example, Eureka, California, and New York City are both coastal cities at about the same latitude, and both have an average mean temperature of 11°C (52°F). However, New York City is 9°C (16°F) warmer than Eureka in July and 10°C cooler in January. In another example, two cities in Ecuador—Quito and Guayaquil—are relatively close to one another, but the mean annual temperatures at these two cities differ by 12°C (21°F). To explain these situations and countless others, we must understand that factors other than latitude exert a strong influence on temperature. Among the most important are the differential heating of land and water, altitude, geographic position, and ocean currents.*

Land and Water

The heating of Earth's surface directly influences the heating of the air above. Therefore, to understand variations in air temperature, we must understand the variations in heating properties of the different surfaces that Earth presents to the Sun—soil, water, trees, ice, and so on. Different land surfaces absorb varying amounts of incoming solar energy, which in turn cause variations in the temperature of the air above. The greatest contrast, however, is not between different land surfaces, but between land and water. *Land heats more rapidly and to higher temperatures than water and cools more rapidly and to lower temperatures than water.* Temperature variations, therefore, are considerably greater over land than over water.

*For a discussion of the effects of ocean currents on temperatures, see Chapter 10.

FIGURE 11.33 Temperature distribution using isotherms. Isotherms are lines that connect points of equal temperature. The temperatures on this map are in degrees Fahrenheit. Showing temperature distribution in this way makes patterns easier to see. On television, and in many newspapers, temperature maps are in color. Rather than labeling isotherms, the area *between* isotherms is labeled. For example, the zone between the 60° and 70° isotherms is labeled "60s."

Why do land and water heat and cool differently? Several factors are responsible:

1. The *specific heat* (amount of energy needed to raise 1 gram of a substance 1°C) is far greater for water than for land. Thus, water requires a great deal more heat to raise its temperature the same amount as an equal quantity of land.

2. Land surfaces are opaque, so heat is absorbed only at the surface. Water, being more transparent, allows heat to penetrate to a depth of many meters.

3. The water that is heated often mixes with water below, thus distributing the heat through an even larger mass.

4. Evaporation (a cooling process) from water bodies is greater than that from land surfaces.

All these factors collectively cause water to warm more slowly, store greater quantities of heat, and cool more slowly than land.

Monthly temperature data for two cities will demonstrate the moderating influence of a large water body and the extremes associated with land (**FIGURE 11.34**). Vancouver, British Columbia, is located along a windward coast, whereas Winnipeg, Manitoba, is in a continental position far from the

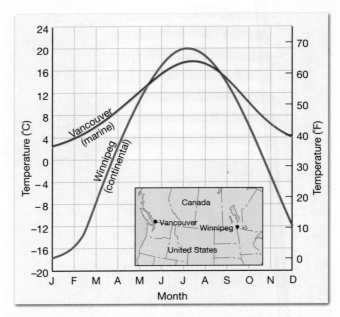

FIGURE 11.34 Mean monthly temperatures for Vancouver, British Columbia, and Winnipeg, Manitoba. Vancouver has a much smaller annual temperature range owing to the strong marine influence of the Pacific Ocean. The curve for Winnepeg illustrates the greater extremes associated with an interior location.

influence of water. Both cities are at about the same latitude and thus experience similar Sun angles and lengths of daylight. Winnipeg, however, has a mean January temperature that is 20°C (36°F) lower than Vancouver's. Winnipeg's July mean is 2°C (3.6°F) higher than Vancouver's. Although their latitudes are nearly the same, Winnipeg, which has no water influence, experiences much greater temperature extremes than Vancouver, which does. The key to Vancouver's moderate year-round climate is the Pacific Ocean.

On a different scale, the moderating influence of water may also be demonstrated when temperature variations in the Northern and Southern hemispheres are compared. In the Northern Hemisphere, 61 percent is covered by water, and land accounts for the remaining 39 percent. However, in the Southern Hemisphere, 81 percent is covered by water and 19 percent by land. The Southern Hemisphere is correctly called the *water hemisphere* (see Figure 9.1, p. 260). Table 11.3 portrays the considerably smaller annual temperature variations in the water-dominated Southern Hemisphere as compared with the Northern Hemisphere.

Altitude

The two cities in Ecuador mentioned earlier—Quito and Guayaquil—demonstrate the influence of altitude on mean temperatures (**FIGURE 11.35**). Although both cities are near the equator and not far apart, the annual mean at Guayaquil is 25°C (77°F), as compared to Quito's mean of 13°C (55°F). The difference is explained largely by the difference in the cities' elevations: Guayaquil is only 12 meters (40 feet) above sea level, whereas Quito is high in the Andes Mountains at 2800 meters (9200 feet).

Recall that temperatures drop an average of 6.5°C per kilometer (3.5°F per 1000 feet) in the troposphere; thus, cooler temperatures are to be expected at greater heights (see Figure 11.9 p. 316). Yet, the magnitude of the difference is not totally explained by the normal lapse rate. If this figure were used, we would expect Quito to be about 18°C (nearly 33°F) cooler than Guayaquil; the difference, however, is only 12°C. The fact that high-altitude places, such as Quito, are warmer than the value calculated using the normal lapse rate results from the absorption and reradiation of solar energy by the ground surface.

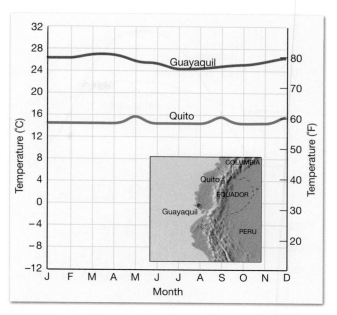

FIGURE 11.35 Because Quito is high in the Andes Mountains, it experiences much cooler temperatures than Guayaquil, which is near sea level. Because both cities are near the equator, they have a negligible annual temperature range.

Geographic Position

The geographic setting can greatly influence the temperatures experienced at a specific location. A coastal location where prevailing winds blow from the ocean onto the shore (a *windward* coast) experiences considerably different temperatures than does a coastal location where prevailing winds blow from the land toward the ocean (a *leeward* coast). The windward coast will experience the full moderating influence of the ocean—cool summers and mild winters—compared to an inland location at the same latitude.

A leeward coast, however, will have a more continental temperature regime because the winds do not carry the ocean's influence onshore. Eureka, California, and New York City, the two cities mentioned earlier, illustrate this aspect of geographic position. The annual temperature range at New York City is 19°C (34°F) greater than Eureka's (**FIGURE 11.36**).

Seattle and Spokane, both in Washington State, illustrate a second aspect of geographic position—mountains that act as barriers. Although Spokane is only about 360 kilometers (220 miles) east of Seattle, the towering Cascade Range separates the cities. Consequently, Seattle's temperatures show a marked marine influence, but Spokane's are more typically continental (**FIGURE 11.37**). Spokane is 7°C (13°F) cooler than Seattle in January and 4°C (7°F) warmer than Seattle in July. The annual range at Spokane is 11°C (20°F) greater than at Seattle. The Cascade Range effectively cuts Spokane off from the moderating influence of the Pacific Ocean.

Cloud Cover and Albedo

You may have noticed that clear days are often warmer than cloudy ones and that clear nights are usually cooler than cloudy ones. This demonstrates that cloud cover is another

Table 11.3 Variation in mean annual temperature range (°C) with latitude

Latitude	Northern Hemisphere	Southern Hemisphere
0	0	0
15	3	4
30	13	7
45	23	6
60	30	11
75	32	26
90	40	31

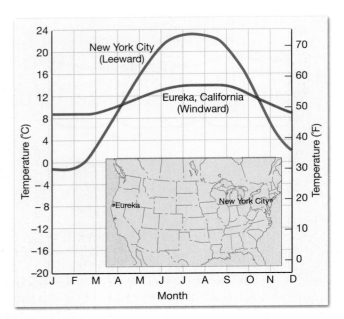

FIGURE 11.36 Monthly mean temperatures for Eureka, California, and New York City. Both cities are coastal and located at about the same latitude. Because Eureka is strongly influenced by prevailing winds from the ocean and New York City is not, the annual temperatures range at Eureka is much smaller.

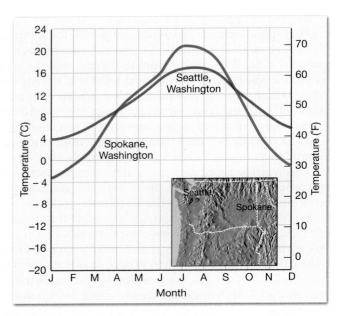

FIGURE 11.37 Monthly mean temperatures for Seattle and Spokane, Washington. Because the Cascade Mountains cut off Spokane from the moderating influence of the Pacific Ocean, its annual temperature range is greater than Seattle's.

factor that influences temperature in the lower atmosphere. Studies using satellite images show that at any particular time, about half of our planet is covered by clouds. Cloud cover is important because many clouds have a high albedo; therefore, clouds reflect a significant portion of the sunlight that strikes them back into space (see Figure 11.22, p. 324). By reducing the amount of incoming solar radiation, daytime

temperatures will be lower than if the clouds were not present and the sky were clear.

At night, clouds have the opposite effect as during daylight. They act as a blanket by absorbing radiation emitted by Earth's surface and reradiating a portion of it back to the surface. Consequently, some of the heat that otherwise would have been lost remains near the ground. Thus, nighttime air temperatures do not drop as low as they would on a clear night. The effect of cloud cover is to reduce the daily temperature range by lowering the daytime maximum and raising the nighttime minimum (**FIGURE 11.38**).

Clouds are not the only phenomenon that increases albedo and thereby reduces air temperatures. We also recognize that snow- and ice-covered surfaces have high albedos. This is one reason why mountain glaciers do not melt away in the summer and why snow may still be present on a mild spring day. In addition, during the winter, when snow covers the ground, daytime maximums on a sunny day are lower than they otherwise would be because energy that the land would have absorbed and used to heat the air is reflected and lost.

DID YOU KNOW?

The world's record-high temperature is nearly 59°C (138°F). It was recorded on September 13, 1922, at Azizia, Libya, in North Africa's Sahara Desert. The lowest recorded temperature on Earth is −89°C (−129°F). It should come as no surprise that this incredibly frigid temperature was recorded in Antarctica, at the Russian Vostok Station, on August 24, 1960.

FIGURE 11.38 The daily cycle of temperature at Peoria, Illinois, for two July days. Clouds reduce daily temperature range. During daylight hours, clouds reflect solar radiation back to space. Therefore, the maximum temperature is lower than if the sky were clear. At night, the minimum temperature will not fall as low because clouds retard the loss of heat.

WORLD DISTRIBUTION OF TEMPERATURE

Take a moment to study the two world maps (**FIGURES** 11.39 and 11.40). From hot colors near the equator to cool colors toward the poles, these maps portray sea-level temperatures in the seasonally extreme months of January and July.

Temperature distribution is shown by using isotherms. On these maps, you can study global temperature patterns and the effects of the controlling factors of temperature, especially latitude, the distribution of land and water, and ocean currents. Like most isothermal maps of large regions, all temperatures on these world maps have been reduced to sea level to eliminate the complications caused by differences in altitude.

FIGURE 11.39   World mean sea-level temperatures in January in degrees Celsius.

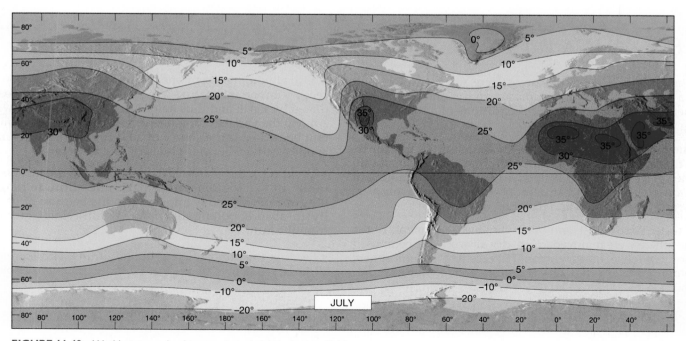

FIGURE 11.40   World mean sea-level temperatures in July in degrees Celsius.

On both maps, the isotherms generally trend east-west and show a decrease in temperatures poleward from the tropics. They illustrate one of the most fundamental aspects of world temperature distribution: that the effectiveness of incoming solar radiation in heating Earth's surface and the atmosphere above is largely a function of latitude.

Moreover, there is a latitudinal shifting of temperatures caused by the seasonal migration of the Sun's vertical rays. To see this, compare the color bands by latitude on the two maps. On the January map, the "hot spots" of 30°C are *south* of the equator, but in July they have shifted *north* of the equator.

If latitude were the only control of temperature distribution, our analysis could end here, but this is not the case. The added effect of the differential heating of land and water is also reflected on the January and July temperature maps. The warmest and coldest temperatures are found over land. Because temperatures do not fluctuate as much over water as over land, the seasonal north–south migration of isotherms is greater over the continents than over the oceans.

In addition, it is clear that the isotherms in the Southern Hemisphere, where there is little land and the oceans predominate, are much straighter and more stable than in the Northern Hemisphere, where they bend sharply northward in July and southward in January over the continents.

Isotherms also reveal the presence of ocean currents. Warm currents cause isotherms to be deflected poleward, whereas cold currents cause an equatorward bending. The horizontal transport of water poleward warms the overlying air and results in air temperatures that are higher than otherwise would be expected for the latitude. Conversely, currents moving toward the equator produce air temperatures cooler than expected.

Because Figures 11.39 and 11.40 show the seasonal extremes of temperature, they can be used to evaluate variations in the annual range of temperature from place to place. A comparison of the two maps shows that a station near the equator will record a very small annual temperature range. This is true because such a station experiences little variation in the length of daylight and always has a relatively high Sun angle. By contrast, a site in the middle latitudes experiences much wider variations in Sun angle and length of daylight and thus larger temperature variations. Therefore, we can state that the annual temperature range increases with an increase in latitude.

Land and water also affect seasonal temperature variations, especially outside the tropics. A continental location must endure hotter summers and colder winters than a coastal location. Consequently, the annual range will increase with an increase in continentality.

DID YOU KNOW?

A classic example of the effect of high latitude and continentality on annual temperature range is Yakutsk, a city in Siberia, approximately 60° north latitude and far from the influence of water. As a result, Yakutsk has an average annual temperature range of 62.2°C (112°F), one of the greatest in the world.

THE CHAPTER IN REVIEW

• *Weather* is the state of the atmosphere at a particular place for a short period of time. *Climate,* on the other hand, is a generalization of the weather conditions of a place over a long period of time.

• The most important *elements*—those quantities or properties that are measured regularly—of weather and climate are (1) air *temperature,* (2) *humidity,* (3) type and amount of *cloudiness,* (4) type and amount of *precipitation,* (5) air *pressure,* and (6) the speed and direction of the *wind.*

• If water vapor, dust, and other variable components of the atmosphere were removed, clean, dry air would be composed almost entirely of *nitrogen,* about 78 percent of the atmosphere by volume, and *oxygen* (O_2), about 21 percent. *Carbon dioxide* (CO_2), although present only in minute amounts (0.036 percent), is important because it has the ability to absorb heat radiated by Earth and thus helps keep the atmosphere warm. Among the variable components of air, *water vapor* is important because it is the source of all clouds and precipitation, and like carbon dioxide, it is also a heat absorber.

• *Ozone* (O_3), the triatomic form of oxygen, is concentrated in the 10-to 50-kilometer (6-to 31-mile) altitude range of the atmosphere and is important to life because of its ability to absorb potentially harmful ultraviolet radiation from the Sun.

• Because the atmosphere gradually thins with increasing altitude, it has no sharp upper boundary but simply blends into outer space. Based on temperature, the atmosphere is divided vertically into four layers. The *troposphere* is the lowermost layer. In the troposphere, temperature usually decreases with increasing altitude. This *environmental lapse rate* is variable but averages about 6.5°C per kilometer (3.5°F per 1000 feet). Essentially, all important weather phenomena occur in the troposphere. Beyond the troposphere is the *stratosphere,* which exhibits warming because of absorption of UV radiation by ozone. In the *mesosphere,* temperatures again decrease. Upward from the mesosphere is the *thermosphere,* a layer with only a tiny fraction of the atmosphere's mass and no well-defined upper limit.

• The two principal motions of Earth are (1) *rotation,* the spinning about its axis that produces the daily cycle of daylight and darkness; and (2) *revolution,* the movement in its orbit around the Sun.

• Several factors acting together cause the seasons. Earth's axis is inclined 23½ degrees from the perpendicular to the plane of its orbit around the Sun and remains pointed in the same direction (toward the North Star) as Earth journeys around the Sun. As a consequence, Earth's orientation to the Sun continually changes. Fluctuations in the Sun angle and length of daylight brought about by Earth's changing orientation to the Sun cause the seasons.

• The three mechanisms of heat transfer are (1) *conduction,* the transfer of heat through matter by molecular activity; (2) *convection,* the transfer of heat by the movement of a mass or substance from one place to another; and (3) *radiation,* the transfer of heat by electromagnetic waves.

• *Electromagnetic radiation* is energy emitted in the form of rays, or waves, called electromagnetic waves. All radiation is capable of transmitting energy through the vacuum of space. One of the most important differences between electromagnetic waves is their *wavelengths,* which range from

very long *radio waves* to very short *gamma rays. Visible light* is the only portion of the electromagnetic spectrum we can see. Some of the basic laws that govern radiation as it heats the atmosphere are (1) all objects emit radiant energy; (2) hotter objects radiate more total energy than do colder objects; (3) the hotter the radiating body, the shorter the wave lengths of maximum radiation; and (4) objects that are good absorbers of radiation are good emitters as well.

• The general drop in temperature with increasing altitude in the troposphere supports the fact that *the atmosphere is heated from the ground up.* Approximately 50 percent of the solar energy that strikes the top of the atmosphere reaches Earth's surface and is absorbed. Earth releases the absorbed radiation in the form of long-wave radiation. The atmospheric absorption of this long-wave *terrestrial radiation,* primarily by water vapor and carbon dioxide, is responsible for heating the atmosphere.

• Carbon dioxide, an important heat absorber in the atmosphere, is one of several gases that influence the heating of the atmosphere. By adding carbon dioxide to the atmosphere, primarily by burning fossil fuels and through deforestation, humans are likely contributing significantly to global warming. Some consequences of global warming include (l) shifts in temperature and rainfall patterns, (2) a gradual rise in sea level, (3) changing storm tracks and a higher frequency and greater intensity of hurricanes, and (4) an increase in the frequency and intensity of heat waves and droughts.

• The factors that cause temperature to vary from place to place, also called the *controls of temperature,* are (1) differences in the *receipt of solar radiation* due to latitude, (2) the unequal heating and cooling of *land and water,* (3) *altitude,* (4) *geographic position,* and (5) *ocean currents.*

• Temperature distribution is shown on a map by using *isotherms,* which are lines that connect equal temperatures.

KEY TERMS

aerosols (p. 313)

air (p. 311)

albedo (p. 324)

circle of illumination (p. 317)

climate (p. 310)

conduction (p. 322)

convection (p. 322)

diffused light (p. 325)

element (of weather and climate) (p. 311)

environmental lapse rate (p. 316)

equinox (spring or autumnal) (p. 319)

greenhouse effect (p. 325)

heat (p. 321)

inclination of the axis (p. 318)

infrared (p. 323)

isotherm (p. 329)

mesosphere (p. 316)

radiation or electromagnetic radiation (p. 322)

radiosonde (p. 316)

reflection (p. 324)

revolution (p. 317)

rotation (p. 317)

scattering (p. 324)

solstice (summer or winter) (p. 318)

stratosphere (p. 316)

temperature (p. 321)

thermosphere (p. 316)

Tropic of Cancer (p. 318)

Tropic of Capricorn (p. 318)

troposphere (p. 315)

ultraviolet (UV) (p. 323)

visible light (p. 323)

weather (p. 310)

QUESTIONS FOR REVIEW

1. Distinguish between weather and climate.

2. List the basic elements of weather and climate.

3. What are the two major components of clean, dry air (Figure 11.4, p. 312)? Are they important meteorologically?

4. Why are water vapor and aerosols important constituents of our atmosphere?

5. a. Why is ozone important to life on Earth?

   b. What are CFCs, and what is their connection to the ozone problem?

   c. What is the most serious threat to human health of a decrease in the stratosphere's ozone?

6. The atmosphere is divided vertically into four layers on the basis of temperature. List the names of these layers in order (from lowest to highest) and describe how temperatures change in each layer.

7. If the temperature at sea level were 23°C, what would the air temperature be at a height of 2 kilometers *under average conditions*?

8. Why do temperatures rise in the stratosphere?

9. Briefly explain the primary cause of the seasons.

10. After examining Table 11.1 (p. 321), write a general statement that relates the season, the latitude, and the length of daylight.

11. Describe the relationship between the temperature of a radiating body and the wavelengths it emits.

12. Distinguish among the three basic mechanisms of heat transfer.

13. Figure 11.20 (p. 324) illustrates what happens to incoming solar radiation. The percentages shown, however, are only global averages. In particular, the amount of solar radiation reflected (albedo) may vary considerably. What factors might cause variations in albedo?

14. Describe the basic process by which Earth's atmosphere is heated.

15. Why has the atmosphere's carbon dioxide level been rising for more than 150 years?

16. How are temperatures in the lower atmosphere likely to change as carbon dioxide levels continue to increase? Why?

17. List three possible consequences of global warming.

18. Quito, Ecuador, is located on the equator and is not a coastal city. It has an average annual temperature of only 13°C (55°F). What is the likely cause for this low average temperature?

19. In what ways can geographic position be considered a control of temperature?

COMPANION WEBSITE

The *Foundations of Earth Science* Website uses the resources and flexibility of the Internet to aid in your study of the topics in this chapter. Written and developed by the authors and other Earth science instructors, this site will help improve your understanding of Earth science. Visit **www.mygeoscienceplace.com** in order to:

- **Review** key chapter concepts.
- **Read** with links to the ebook and to chapter-specific web resources.

- **Visualize** and comprehend challenging topics using learning activities in *GEODe: Earth Science*.
- **Test** yourself with online quizzes.

GEODe: EARTH SCIENCE

GEODe: Earth Science is a valuable and easy to use learning aid that can be accessed from your book's Companion Website: **www.mygeoscienceplace.com.** It is a dynamic instructional tool that promotes understanding and reinforces important concepts by using tutorials, animations, and exercises that actively engage the student.

GEODe Earth Science
Earth's Dynamic Atmosphere

Heating Earth's Surface and Atmosphere
Solar Radiation

Experience tells us that the atmosphere is transparent to visible light because it readily reaches Earth's surface.

1575

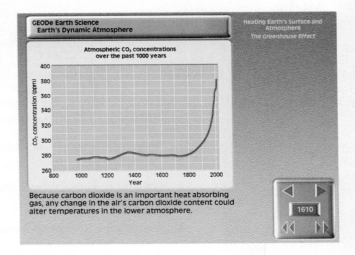

GEODe Earth Science
Earth's Dynamic Atmosphere

Heating Earth's Surface and Atmosphere
The Greenhouse Effect

Atmospheric CO₂ concentrations over the past 1000 years

Because carbon dioxide is an important heat absorbing gas, any change in the air's carbon dioxide content could alter temperatures in the lower atmosphere.

1610

MOISTURE, CLOUDS, AND PRECIPITATION

To assist you in learning the important concepts in this chapter, you will find it helpful to focus on the following questions:

1. Which processes cause water to change from one state of matter to another?

2. What is humidity? What is the most common method used to express humidity?

3. What is the basic cloud-forming process?

4. What controls the stability of the atmosphere?

5. What are three mechanisms that initiate the vertical movement of air?

6. What are the necessary conditions for condensation?

7. Which two criteria are used for cloud classification?

8. What is fog? How do fogs form?

9. How is precipitation produced in a cloud? What are the different forms of precipitation?

Lightning display associated with a thunderstorm (cumulonimbus clouds) near Colorado Springs, Colorado. (Photo by Sean Cayton/The Image Works)

Water vapor is an odorless, colorless gas that mixes freely with the other gases of the atmosphere. Unlike oxygen and nitrogen—the two most abundant components of the atmosphere—water can change from one state of matter to another (solid, liquid, or gas) at the temperatures and pressures experienced on Earth. By contrast, nitrogen will not condense to a liquid unless its temperature is lowered to −196°C (−321°F). Because of this unique property, water freely leaves the oceans as a gas and returns again as a liquid (**FIGURE 12.1**).

As you observe day-to-day weather changes, you might ask: Why is it generally more humid in the summer than in the winter? Why do clouds form on some occasions but not on others? Why do some clouds look thin and harmless whereas others form gray and ominous towers? Answers to these questions involve the role of water vapor in the atmosphere, the central theme of this chapter.

WATER'S CHANGES OF STATE

Earth's Dynamic Atmosphere
▼ Moisture and Cloud Formation

Water is the only substance that exists in the atmosphere as a solid (ice), liquid, and gas (water vapor). It is made of hydrogen and oxygen atoms that are bonded together to form water molecules (H_2O). In all three states of matter (even ice), these molecules are in constant motion—the higher the temperature, the more vigorous the movement. The chief difference among liquid water, ice, and water vapor is the arrangement of the water molecules.

Ice, Liquid Water, and Water Vapor

Ice is composed of water molecules that are held together by mutual molecular attractions. The molecules form a tight, orderly network, as shown in **FIGURE 12.2**. As a consequence,

FIGURE 12.1 Caught in a downpour. (Photo by ImageState/Alamy)

the water molecules in ice are not free to move relative to one another but rather vibrate about fixed sites. When ice is heated, the molecules oscillate more rapidly. When the rate of molecular movement increases sufficiently, the bonds between some of the water molecules are broken, resulting in melting.

In the liquid state, water molecules are still tightly packed but are moving fast enough that they are able to slide past one another. As a result, liquid water is fluid and will take the shape of its container.

As liquid water gains heat from its environment, some of the molecules will acquire enough energy to break the remaining molecular attractions and escape from the surface, becoming water vapor. Water-vapor molecules are widely spaced compared to liquid water and exhibit very energetic random motion. What distinguishes a gas from a liquid is its compressibility (and expandability). For example, you can easily put more and more air into a tire and increase its volume only slightly. However, do not try to put 10 gallons of gasoline into a five-gallon can.

To summarize, when water changes state, it does not turn into a different substance; only the distances and interactions among the water molecules change.

Latent Heat

Whenever water changes state, heat is exchanged between water and its surroundings. When water evaporates, heat is absorbed (Figure 12.2). Meteorologists often measure heat energy in calories. One **calorie** is the amount of heat required to raise the temperature of 1 gram of water 1°C (1.8°F). Thus, when 10 calories of heat are absorbed by 1 gram of water, the molecules vibrate faster and a 10°C (18°F) temperature rise occurs.

Under certain conditions, heat may be added to a substance without an accompanying rise in temperature. For example, when a glass of ice water is warmed, the temperature of the ice-water mixture remains a constant 0°C (32°F) until all the ice has melted. If adding heat does not raise the temperature, where does this energy go? In this case, the added energy went to break the molecular attractions between the water molecules in the ice cubes.

Because the heat used to melt ice does not produce a temperature change, it is referred to as **latent heat**. (*Latent* means "hidden," like the latent fingerprints hidden at a crime scene.) This energy can be thought of as being stored in liquid water, and it is not released to its surroundings as heat until the liquid returns to the solid state.

It requires 80 calories to melt one gram of ice, an amount referred to as *latent heat of melting*. Freezing, the reverse process, releases these 80 calories per gram to the environment as *latent heat of fusion*.

Evaporation and Condensation

We saw that heat is absorbed when ice is converted to liquid water. Heat is also absorbed during **evaporation**, the process of converting a liquid to a gas (vapor). The energy absorbed by water molecules during evaporation is used to give them

Sublimation
~680 cal

SOLID
(ice)

LIQUID
(water)

GAS
(water vapor)

Melting
80 cal

540–600 cal

Freezing
80 cal

Condensation
540–600 cal

Deposition
~680 cal

——— Releases latent heat to the environment
——— Absorbs latent heat from environment

FIGURE 12.2 Changes of state always involve an exchange of heat. The numbers shown here are the approximate amounts for the change of 1 gram of water from one state of matter to another.

the motion needed to escape the surface of the liquid and become a gas. This energy is referred to as the *latent heat of vaporization*. During the process of evaporation, it is the higher-temperature (faster-moving) molecules that escape the surface. As a result, the average molecular motion (temperature) of the remaining water is reduced—hence, the common expression "evaporation is a cooling process." You have undoubtedly experienced this cooling effect on stepping dripping wet from a swimming pool or bathtub. The energy used to evaporate water comes from the skin—and cools the body.

Condensation, the reverse process, occurs when water vapor changes to the liquid state. During condensation, water vapor molecules release energy (*latent heat of condensation*) in an amount equivalent to what was absorbed during evaporation. When condensation occurs in the atmosphere, it results in the

DID YOU KNOW?

"Freezer burn" is a common expression used to describe foods that have been left in a frost-free refrigerator for extended periods of time. Frost-free refrigerators circulate comparatively dry air through the freezer compartments. This causes ice on the freezer walls to sublimate (change from a solid to a gas) so it can be removed by the circulating air. Unfortunately, this process also removes moisture from those frozen foods that are not in airtight containers. Over a period of a few months these foods begin to dry out rather than actually being burned.

formation of such phenomena as fog and clouds.

As you will see, latent heat plays an important role in many atmospheric processes. In particular, when water vapor condenses to form cloud droplets, latent heat of condensation is released, warming the surrounding air and giving it buoyancy. When the moisture content of air is high, this process can spur the growth of towering storm clouds.

Sublimation and Deposition

You are probably least familiar with the last two processes illustrated in Figure 12.2—sublimation and deposition. **Sublimation** is the conversion of a solid directly to a gas without passing through the liquid state. Examples you may have observed include the gradual shrinking of unused ice cubes in the freezer and the rapid conversion of dry ice (frozen carbon dioxide) to wispy clouds that quickly disappear.

Deposition refers to the reverse process, the conversion of a vapor directly to a solid. This change occurs, for example, when water vapor is deposited as ice on solid objects such as grass or windows (**FIGURE 12.3**). These deposits are called *white frost* or *hoar frost* and are frequently referred to simply as *frost*. A household example of the process of deposition is the frost that accumulates in a freezer. As shown in Figure 12.2, deposition releases an amount of energy equal to the total amount released by condensation and freezing.

FIGURE 12.3 Frost on a window pane is an example of deposition. (Photo by Stockxpert/Jupiter Images Unlimited)

HUMIDITY: WATER VAPOR IN THE AIR

Earth's Dynamic Atmosphere
▼ Moisture and Cloud Formation

Water vapor constitutes only a small fraction of the atmosphere, varying from as little as one-tenth of 1 percent up to about 4 percent by volume. But the importance of water in the air is far greater than these small percentages would indicate. Indeed, scientists agree that *water vapor* is the most important gas in the atmosphere when it comes to understanding atmospheric processes.

Humidity is the general term for the amount of water vapor in air. Meteorologists employ several methods to express the water-vapor content of the air; we will examine three: mixing ratio, relative humidity, and dew-point temperature.

Saturation

Before we consider these humidity measures further, it is important to understand the concept of **saturation**. Imagine a closed jar half full of water and half full of dry air, both at the same temperature. As the water begins to evaporate from the water surface, a small increase in pressure can be detected in the air above. This increase is the result of the motion of the water-vapor molecules that were added to the air through evaporation. In the open atmosphere, this pressure is termed **vapor pressure** and is defined as that part of the total atmospheric pressure that can be attributed to the water-vapor content.

In the closed container, as more and more molecules escape from the water surface, the steadily increasing vapor pressure in the air above forces more and more of these molecules to return to the liquid. Eventually, the number of vapor molecules returning to the surface will balance the number leaving. At that point, the air is said to be *saturated*. If we add heat to the container, thereby increasing the temperature of the water and air, more water will evaporate before a balance is reached. Consequently, at higher temperatures, more moisture is required for saturation. The amount of water vapor required for saturation at various temperatures is shown in Table 12.1.

Mixing Ratio

Not all air is saturated, of course. Thus, we need ways to express how humid a parcel of air is. One method specifies the amount of water vapor contained in a unit of air. The **mixing ratio** is the mass of water vapor in a unit of air compared to the remaining mass of dry air.

$$\text{mixing ratio} = \frac{\text{mass of water vapor (grams)}}{\text{mass of dry air (kilograms)}}$$

Table 12.1 shows the mixing ratios of saturated air at various temperatures. For example, at 25°C (77°F), a

Table 12.1 Amount of water vapor (grams) required to saturate a kilogram of air at various temperatures

Temperature		Grams of Water Vapor per Kilogram of Air
(°C)	(°F)	
−40	−40	0.1
−30	−22	0.3
−20	−4	0.75
−10	14	2
0	32	3.5
5	41	5
10	50	7
15	59	10
20	68	14
25	77	20
30	86	26.5
35	95	35
40	104	47

saturated parcel of air (one kilogram) would contain 20 grams of water vapor.

Because the mixing ratio is expressed in units of mass (usually in grams per kilogram), it is not affected by changes in pressure or temperature. However, the mixing ratio is time consuming to measure by direct sampling. Other methods are employed to express the moisture content of the air. These include relative humidity and dew-point temperature.

Relative Humidity

The most familiar and, unfortunately, the most misunderstood term used to describe the moisture content of air is relative humidity. **Relative humidity** *is a ratio of the air's actual water-vapor content compared with the amount of water vapor required for saturation at that temperature (and pressure).* Thus, relative humidity indicates how near the air is to saturation, rather than the actual quantity of water vapor in the air.

To illustrate, we see from Table 12.1 that at 25°C (77°F), air is saturated when it contains 20 grams of water vapor per kilogram of air. Thus, if the air contains only 10 grams per kilogram on a 25°C day, the relative humidity is expressed as 10/20 or 50 percent. If air with a temperature of 25°C had a water-vapor content of 20 grams per kilogram, the relative humidity would be expressed at 20/20 or 100 percent. When the relative humidity reaches 100 percent, the air is saturated.

Because relative humidity is based on the air's water-vapor content, as well as the amount of moisture required for saturation, it can be changed in either of two ways. First, relative humidity can be changed by the addition or removal of water vapor. Second, because the amount of moisture required for saturation is a function of air temperature, relative humidity varies with temperature. (Recall that the amount of water vapor required for saturation is temperature dependent, such

A. Initial condition

B. Addition of 5 grams of water vapor

C. Addition of 10 grams of water vapor

FIGURE 12.4 Relative humidity. At a constant temperature, the relative humidity will increase as water vapor is added to the air. The saturation mixing ratio remains constant at 20 grams per kilogram and the relative humidity rises from 25 to 100 percent as the water-vapor content increases.

A. Initial condition

B. Cooled to 10°C

C. Cooled to 0°C

FIGURE 12.5 Relative humidity varies with temperature. When the water-vapor content (mixing ratio) remains constant, the relative humidity can be changed by increasing or decreasing the air temperature. In this example, when the temperature of the air in the flask was lowered from 20°C to 10°C, the relative humidity increased from 50 percent to 100 percent. Thus, 10°C is the dew point. Further cooling (from 10°C to 0°C) causes one-half of the water vapor to condense. In nature, cooling of air below its dew point generally causes condensation in the form of clouds, dew, or fog.

that at higher temperatures it takes more water vapor to saturate air than at lower temperatures.)

Adding or Subtracting Moisture

Notice in **FIGURE 12.4** that when water vapor is added to a parcel of air, its relative humidity increases until saturation occurs (100 percent relative humidity). What if even more moisture is added to this parcel of saturated air? Does the relative humidity exceed 100 percent? Normally, this situation does not occur. Instead, the excess water vapor condenses to form liquid water.

In nature, moisture is added to the air mainly via evaporation from the oceans. Plants, soil, and smaller bodies of water also make substantial contributions.

Changes with Temperature

The second condition that affects relative humidity is air temperature. Examine **FIGURE 12.5** carefully. Note in Part A that when air at 20°C contains 7 grams of water vapor per kilogram of air, it has a relative humidity of 50 percent. This can be verified by referring to Table 12.1. Here we can see that at 20°C, air is saturated when it contains 14 grams of water vapor per kilogram of air. Because the air in Figure 12.5A contains 7 grams of water vapor, its relative humidity is 7/14, or 50 percent.

When the flask is cooled from 20°C to 10°C as shown in Part B, it still contains 7 grams of water vapor, but the relative humidity increases from 50 percent to 100 percent. We can conclude from this that when the water-vapor content remains constant, *a decrease in temperature results in an increase in relative humidity.*

What happens when the air is cooled further, below the temperature at which saturation occurs? Part C of Figure 12.5 illustrates this situation. Notice from Table 12.1 that when the flask is cooled to 0°C, the air is saturated at 3.5 grams of water vapor per kilogram of air. Because this flask originally contained 7 grams of water vapor, 3.5 grams of water vapor have to go somewhere, because there is no room for them in the cooler air. They will condense to form liquid droplets that collect on the walls of the container. The relative humidity of the air inside remains at 100 percent.

FIGURE 12.6   Typical daily variations in temperature and relative humidity during a spring day at Washington, D.C. When temperature increases, relative humidity drops (see midafternoon) and vice versa.

FIGURE 12.7   Condensation, or "dew," occurs when a cold drinking glass chills the surrounding layer of air below the dew-point temperature. (Photo Elena Elisseeva/Shutterstock)

This raises an important concept. When air aloft is cooled below its saturation level, some of the water vapor condenses to form clouds. Therefore, the formation of liquid droplets (or ice crystals) within clouds reduces the *water-vapor* content of the air. (Clouds are composed of liquid water droplets, or ice crystals, too small to fall to Earth.)

We can summarize the effects of temperature on relative humidity as follows: When the water-vapor content of air remains at a constant level, a decrease in air temperature results in an increase in relative humidity, and an increase in temperature causes a decrease in relative humidity. **FIGURE 12.6** illustrates the relationship just described.

Dew-Point Temperature

Another important measure of humidity is the dew-point temperature. The **dew-point temperature** or simply the **dew point** is the temperature to which air needs to be cooled to reach saturation. For example, in Figure 12.5, the unsaturated air in the flask had to be cooled to 10°C before saturation occurred. Therefore, 10°C is the dew-point temperature for this air. In nature, cooling below the dew point causes water vapor to condense, typically as dew, fog, or clouds (**FIGURE 12.7**). The term *dew point* stems from the fact that during nighttime hours, objects near the ground often cool below the dew-point temperature and become coated with dew.

Unlike relative humidity, which is a measure of how near the air is to being saturated, dew-point temperature is a measure of the *actual moisture* content of a parcel of air. Because the dew-point temperature is directly related to the amount of water vapor in the air, and because it is easy to determine, it is one of the most useful measures of humidity.

Because dew point is the temperature at which saturation occurs, we can conclude that *high dew-point temperatures indicate moist air*, and *low dew-point temperatures indicate dry air*. In fact, for every 10°C (18°F) increase in dew-point temperature, the air's water-vapor content approximately doubles. This fact can be derived by examining Table 12.1 and noting that warm saturated air having a temperature of 20°C (68°F) contains twice the water vapor as cooler saturated air having a temperature of 10°C (50°F).

Because the dew-point temperature is a good measure of the amount of water vapor in the air, it is the measure of atmospheric moisture that appears on a variety of weather maps. Notice on the map in **FIGURE 12.8** that most of the places located near the warm Gulf of Mexico have dew-point temperatures that exceed 70°F (21°C). When the dew point exceeds 65°F (18°C), it is considered humid by most people, and air with a dew point 75°F (24°C) or higher is oppressive. Also notice in Figure 12.8 that although the Southeast is dominated by humid conditions (dew points above 65°F), most of the remainder of the country is experiencing comparatively drier air.

FIGURE 12.8 Surface map showing dew-point temperatures for September 15, 2005. Dew-point temperatures above 60°F dominate the southeastern United States, indicating that this region is blanketed with humid air.

difference that is observed between the thermometer readings, the lower the relative humidity; the smaller the difference, the higher the relative humidity. If the air is saturated, no evaporation will occur; and the two thermometers will have identical readings.

To determine the precise relative humidity from the thermometer readings, a standard table is used (Appendix C, pp. 484–485). With the same information, but using a different table, the dew-point temperature may also be calculated.

Measuring Humidity

Relative humidity is commonly measured using a **hygrometer**. One type of hygrometer, called a *sling psychrometer*, consists of two identical thermometers mounted side by side (**FIGURE 12.9**). One thermometer, the *dry-bulb*, gives the current air temperature. The other, called the *wet-bulb* thermometer, has a thin muslin wick tied around the end (see ends of thermometers in Figure 12.9).

To use the psychrometer, the cloth sleeve is saturated with water and a continuous current of air is passed over the wick. This is done either by spinning or swinging the instrument freely in the air or by fanning air past it. As a consequence, water evaporates from the wick, and the heat absorbed by the evaporating water makes the temperature of the wet bulb drop. The loss of heat that was required to evaporate water from the wet bulb lowers the thermometer reading.

The amount of cooling that takes place is directly proportional to the dryness of the air. The drier the air, the more moisture evaporates. The more heat the evaporating water absorbs, the greater the cooling. Therefore, the larger the

FIGURE 12.9 Sling psychrometer. **A.** Sling psychrometers are used to determine both relative humidity and dew point. **B.** The dry-bulb thermometer gives the current air temperature. The wet-bulb thermometer is covered with a cloth wick that is dipped in water. **C.** The thermometers are spun until the temperature of the wet-bulb thermometer stops declining. Then the thermometers are read and the data used in conjunction with the tables in Appendix C. (Photo by E. J. Tarbuck)

A different type of hygrometer is used in remote-sensing instrument packages such as radiosondes that transmit upper-air observations back to ground stations. The *electric hygrometer* contains an electrical conductor coated with a moisture-absorbing chemical. It works on the principle that the passage of current varies as the relative humidity varies.

THE BASIS OF CLOUD FORMATION: ADIABATIC COOLING

Earth's Dynamic Atmosphere
▼ Moisture and Cloud Formation

Up to this point, we have considered basic properties of water vapor and how its variability is measured. This section examines some of the important roles that water vapor plays in weather, especially in the formation of clouds.

Fog and Dew versus Cloud Formation

Recall that condensation occurs when water vapor changes to a liquid. Condensation may form dew, fog, or clouds. Although these three forms are different, all require that air reach saturation. As indicated earlier, saturation occurs either when sufficient water vapor is added to the air or, more commonly, when the air is cooled to its dew point.

Near Earth's surface, heat is readily exchanged between the ground and the air above. During evening hours, the surface radiates heat away, and the surface and adjacent air cool rapidly. This "radiation cooling" accounts for the formation of dew and some types of fog. Thus, surface cooling that occurs after sunset accounts for some condensation. However, cloud formation often takes place during the warmest part of the day. Some other mechanism must operate aloft that cools air sufficiently to generate clouds.

Adiabatic Temperature Changes

The process that is responsible for most cloud formation is easily demonstrated if you have ever pumped up a bicycle tire and noticed that the pump barrel became quite warm. The heat you felt was the consequence of the work you did on the air to compress it. When energy is used to compress air, the motion of the gas molecules increases and, therefore, the temperature of the air rises. Conversely, air that is allowed to escape from a bicycle tire *expands and cools* because the expanding air pushes (does work on) the surrounding air and must cool by an amount equivalent to the energy expended.

You have probably experienced the cooling effect of a propellant gas expanding as you applied hair spray or spray deodorant. As the compressed gas in the aerosol can is released, it quickly expands and cools. This drop in temperature occurs *even though heat is neither added nor subtracted.* Such variations are known as **adiabatic temperature changes** and result when air is compressed or allowed to expand. In summary, *when air is allowed to expand, it cools, and when it is compressed, it warms.*

Adiabatic Cooling and Condensation

To simplify the following discussion, it helps to imagine a volume of air enclosed in a thin elastic cover. Meteorologists call this imaginary volume of air a **parcel**. We typically consider a parcel to be a few hundred cubic meters in volume and assume that it acts independently of the surrounding air. It is also assumed that no heat is transferred into or out of the parcel. Although highly idealized, over short time spans, a parcel of air behaves in a manner much like an actual volume of air moving vertically in the atmosphere.

Dry Adiabatic Rate

As you travel from Earth's surface upward through the atmosphere, atmospheric pressure rapidly diminishes because there are fewer and fewer gas molecules. Thus, any time a parcel of air moves upward, it passes through regions of successively lower pressure, and the ascending air expands. As it expands, it cools adiabatically. Unsaturated air cools at the constant rate of 10°C for every 1000 meters of ascent (5.5°F per 1000 feet).

Conversely, descending air comes under increasingly higher pressures, compresses, and is heated 10°C for every 1000 meters of descent. This rate of cooling or heating applies only to unsaturated air and is known as the **dry adiabatic rate**.

Wet Adiabatic Rate

If a parcel of air rises high enough, it will eventually cool sufficiently to reach the dew point. Here the process of condensation begins. From this point on along its ascent, *latent heat of condensation* stored in the water vapor will be liberated. Although the air will continue to cool after condensation begins, the released latent heat works against the adiabatic process, thereby reducing the rate at which the air cools. This slower rate of cooling caused by the addition of latent heat is called the **wet adiabatic rate** of cooling. Because the amount of latent heat released depends on the quantity of moisture present in the air, the wet adiabatic rate varies from 5°C per 1000 meters for air with a high moisture content to 9°C per 1000 meters for dry air.

FIGURE 12.10 illustrates the role of adiabatic cooling in the formation of clouds. Note that from the surface up to the

FIGURE 12.10 Rising air cools at the dry adiabatic rate of 10°C per 1000 meters until the air reaches the dew point and condensation (cloud formation) begins. As air continues to rise, the latent heat released by condensation reduces the rate of cooling. The wet adiabatic rate is therefore always less than the dry adiabatic rate.

condensation level, the air cools at the dry adiabatic rate. The wet adiabatic rate begins at the condensation level.

PROCESSES THAT LIFT AIR

Earth's Dynamic Atmosphere
▼ Moisture and Cloud Formation

To review, when air rises, it expands and cools adiabatically. If air is lifted sufficiently, it will eventually cool to its dew-point temperature, saturation will occur, and clouds will develop. But why does air rise on some occasions and not on others?

It turns out that, in general, air tends to resist vertical movement. Therefore, air located near the surface tends to

stay near the surface, and air aloft tends to remain aloft. Exceptions to this rule, as we will see, include conditions in the atmosphere that give air sufficient buoyancy to rise without the aid of outside forces. In many situations, however, when you see clouds forming, there is some mechanical phenomenon at work that forces the air to rise (at least initially).

There are four mechanisms that cause air to rise:

1. *Orographic lifting*—air is forced to rise over a mountainous barrier.
2. *Frontal wedging*—warmer, less dense air is forced over cooler, denser air.
3. *Convergence*—a pileup of horizontal air flow results in upward movement.
4. *Localized convective lifting*—unequal surface heating causes localized pockets of air to rise because of their buoyancy.

In Chapter 13, we will examine other mechanisms that cause air to rise.

Orographic Lifting

Orographic lifting occurs when elevated terrains, such as mountains, act as barriers to the flow of air (**FIGURE 12.11**). As air ascends a mountain slope, adiabatic cooling often generates clouds and copious precipitation. In fact, many of the rainiest places in the world are located on windward mountain slopes.

By the time air reaches the leeward side of a mountain, much of its moisture has been lost. If the air descends, it warms adiabatically, making condensation and precipitation even less likely. As shown in Figure 12.11, the result can be a **rainshadow desert**. The Great Basin Desert of the western United States lies only a few hundred kilometers from the Pacific Ocean, but it is effectively cut off from the ocean's moisture by the imposing Sierra Nevada (Figure 12.11). The Gobi Desert of Mongolia, the Takla Makan of China, and the Patagonia Desert of Argentina are other examples of deserts

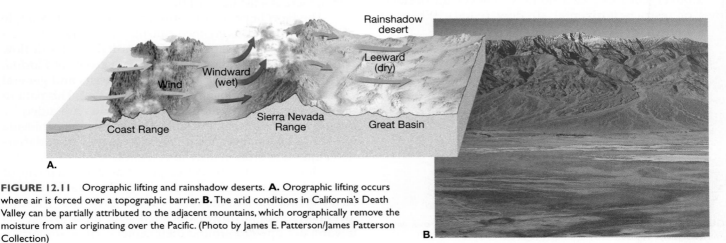

FIGURE 12.11 Orographic lifting and rainshadow deserts. **A.** Orographic lifting occurs where air is forced over a topographic barrier. **B.** The arid conditions in California's Death Valley can be partially attributed to the adjacent mountains, which orographically remove the moisture from air originating over the Pacific. (Photo by James E. Patterson/James Patterson Collection)

that exist because they are on the leeward sides of mountains.

Frontal Wedging

If orographic lifting were the only mechanism that forced air aloft, the relatively flat central portion of North America would be an expansive desert instead of the nation's breadbasket. Fortunately, this is not the case.

In central North America, masses of warm and cold air collide, producing a **front**. The cooler, denser air acts as a barrier over which the warmer, less dense air rises. This process, called **frontal wedging**, is illustrated in **FIGURE 12.12**.

Weather-producing fronts are associated with storm systems called *middle-latitude cyclones.* Because these storms are responsible for producing a high percentage of the precipitation in the middle latitudes, we will examine them closely in Chapter 14.

Convergence

We saw that the collision of contrasting air masses forces air to rise. In a more general sense, whenever air in the lower atmosphere flows together, lifting results. This phenomenon is called **convergence**. When air flows in from more than one direction, it must go somewhere. Because it cannot go down, it goes up (**FIGURE 12.13A**). This, of course, leads to adiabatic cooling and possibly cloud formation.

Convergence can also occur whenever an obstacle slows or restricts horizontal air flow (wind). When air

FIGURE 12.12 Frontal wedging. Colder, denser air acts as a barrier over which warmer, less dense air rises.

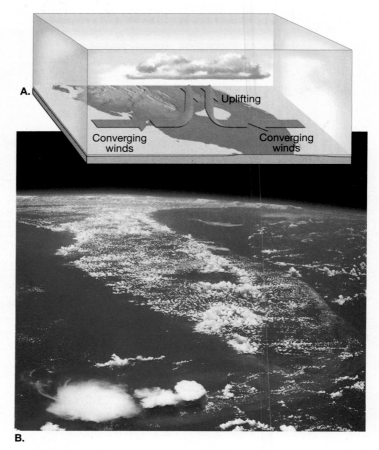

FIGURE 12.13 Convergence. **A.** When surface air converges, it increases in height to allow for the decreased area it occupies. **B.** Southern Florida viewed from the space shuttle. On warm days, airflow from the Atlantic Ocean and Gulf of Mexico onto the Florida peninsula generates many midafternoon thunderstorms. (Photo by NASA/Media Services)

moves from a relatively smooth surface, such as the ocean, onto an irregular landscape, its speed is reduced. The result is a pileup of air (convergence). This is similar to what happens when people leave a well-attended sporting event and pileup results at the exits. When air converges, the air molecules do not simply squeeze closer together (like people); rather, there is a net upward flow.

The Florida peninsula provides an excellent example of the role that convergence can play in initiating cloud development and precipitation. On warm days, the air flow is from the ocean to the land along both coasts of Florida. This leads to a pileup of air along the coasts and general convergence over the peninsula (**FIGURE 12.13B**). This pattern of air movement and the lifting that results are aided by intense solar heating of the land. This is why the peninsula of Florida experiences the greatest frequency of midafternoon thunderstorms in the United States.

More importantly, convergence as a mechanism of forceful lifting is a major contributor to the weather associated with middle-latitude cyclones and hurricanes. The low-level horizontal air flow associated with these systems is inward and upward around their centers. These important weather producers will be covered in more detail later, but

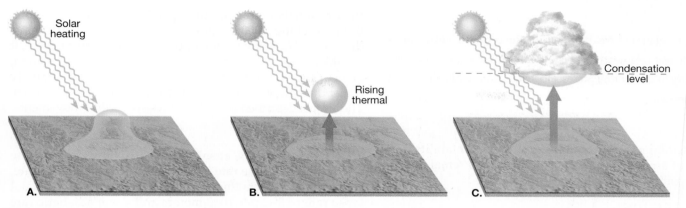

FIGURE 12.14 Localized convective lifting. **A.** Unequal heating of Earth's surface causes pockets of air to be warmed more than the surrounding air. **B.** These buoyant parcels of hot air rise, producing thermals. **C.** If they reach the condensation level, clouds form.

for now remember that convergence near the surface results in a general upward flow.

Localized Convective Lifting

On warm summer days, unequal heating of Earth's surface may cause pockets of air to be warmed more than the surrounding air. For instance, air above a paved parking lot will be warmed more than the air above an adjacent wooded park. Consequently, the parcel of air above the parking lot, which is warmer (less dense) than the surrounding air, will be buoyed upward (**FIGURE 12.14**). These rising parcels of warmer air are called *thermals*. Birds such as hawks and eagles use these thermals to carry them to great heights where they can gaze down on unsuspecting prey. People have learned to employ these rising parcels using hang gliders as a way to "fly."

The phenomenon that produces rising thermals is called **localized convective lifting**. When these warm parcels of air rise above the condensation level, clouds form, which can produce midafternoon rain showers. The accompanying rains, although occasionally heavy, are of short duration and widely scattered.

Although localized convective lifting by itself is not a major producer of precipitation, the added buoyancy that results from surface heating contributes significantly to the lifting initiated by the other mechanisms. It should also be remembered that even though the other mechanisms force air to rise, convective lifting occurs because the air is warmer (less dense) than the surrounding air and rises for the same reasons as does a hot-air balloon.

THE WEATHERMAKER: ATMOSPHERIC STABILITY

Earth's Dynamic Atmosphere
▼ Moisture and Cloud Formation

When air rises, it cools and eventually produces clouds. Why do clouds vary so much in size, and why does the resulting precipitation vary so much? The answers are closely related to the *stability* of the air.

Recall that a parcel of air can be thought of as having a thin flexible cover that allows it to expand but prevents it from mixing with the surrounding air. If this parcel were forced to rise, *its temperature would decrease because of expansion*. By comparing the parcel's temperature to that of the surrounding air, we can determine the stability of the bubble. If the parcel's temperature is lower than that of the surrounding environment, it will be denser, and if allowed to move freely, it would sink to its original position. Air of this type, called **stable air**, resists vertical displacement.

If, however, our imaginary rising parcel were *warmer* and hence less dense than the surrounding air, it would continue to rise until it reached an altitude where its temperature equaled that of its surroundings. This is exactly how a hot-air balloon works, rising as long as it is warmer and less dense than the surrounding air (**FIGURE 12.15**). This type of

FIGURE 12.15 As long as air is warmer than its surroundings, it will rise. Hot-air balloons rise up through the atmosphere for this reason. (Photo by Steve Vidler/SuperStock)

air is classified as **unstable air**. In summary, stability is a property of air that describes its tendency to remain in its original position (stable) or to rise (unstable).

Types of Stability

The stability of air is determined by examining the temperature of the atmosphere at various heights. Recall from Chapter 11 that this measure is termed the *environmental lapse rate*. The environmental lapse rate is the temperature of the atmosphere as determined from observations made by radiosondes and aircraft. It is important not to confuse this with *adiabatic temperature changes*, which are changes in temperature due to expansion or compression as a parcel of air rises or descends.

To illustrate, we will examine a situation in which the environmental lapse rate is 5°C per 1000 meters (**FIGURE 12.16**). When air at the surface has a temperature of 25°C, the air at 1000 meters will be 5 degrees cooler, or 20°C, the air at 2000 meters will have a temperature of 15°C, and so forth. At first glance, it appears that the air at the surface is less dense than the air at 1000 meters, because it is 5 degrees warmer. However, if the air near the surface is unsaturated and were to rise to 1000 meters, it would expand and cool at

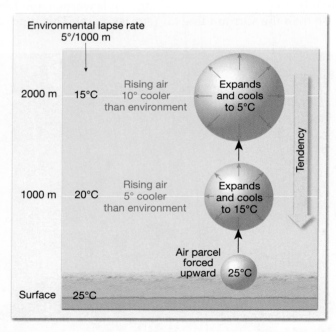

FIGURE 12.16 In a stable atmosphere, as an unsaturated parcel of air is lifted, it expands and cools at the dry adiabatic rate of 10°C per 1000 meters. Because the temperature of the rising parcel of air is lower than that of the surrounding environment, it will be heavier and, if allowed to do so, will sink to its original position.

the dry adiabatic rate of 10°C per 1000 meters. Therefore, upon reaching 1000 meters, its temperature would have dropped 10°C. Being 5 degrees cooler than its environment, it would be denser and tend to sink to its original position. Hence, we say that the air near the surface is potentially cooler than the air aloft and, therefore, will not rise on its own. The air just described is *stable* and resists vertical movement.

Absolute Stability

Stated quantitatively, **absolute stability** prevails when the environmental lapse rate is less than the wet adiabatic rate. **FIGURE 12.17** depicts this situation using an environmental lapse rate of 5°C per 1000 meters and a wet adiabatic rate of 6°C per 1000 meters. Note that at 1000 meters, the temperature of the surrounding air is 15°C, whereas the rising parcel of air has cooled to 10°C and is, therefore, the denser air. Even if this stable air were to be forced above the condensation level, it would remain cooler and denser than its environment, and it would tend to return to the surface.

Absolute Instability

At the other extreme, air is said to exhibit **absolute instability** when the environmental lapse rate is greater than the dry adiabatic rate. As shown in **FIGURE 12.18**, the ascending parcel of air is always warmer than its environment and will continue to rise because of its own buoyancy. However, absolute instability is generally found near Earth's surface. On hot, sunny days, the air above some surfaces, such as shopping center parking lots, is heated more than the air over adjacent surfaces. These invisible pockets of more intensely heated air, being less dense than the air aloft, will rise like a hot-air balloon. This phenomenon produces the small fluffy clouds we associate with fair weather. Occasionally, when the surface air is considerably warmer than the air aloft, clouds with considerable vertical development can form.

Conditional Instability

A more common type of atmospheric instability is called **conditional instability**. This occurs when moist air has an environmental lapse rate between the dry and wet adiabatic rates (between 5 and 10°C per 1000 meters). Simply, the atmosphere is said to be conditionally unstable when it is *stable* for an *unsaturated* parcel of air, but *unstable* for a *saturated* parcel of air. Notice in **FIGURE 12.19** that the rising parcel of air is cooler than the surrounding air for nearly 3000 meters. With the addition of latent heat above the lifting condensation level, the parcel becomes warmer than the surrounding air. From this point along its ascent, the

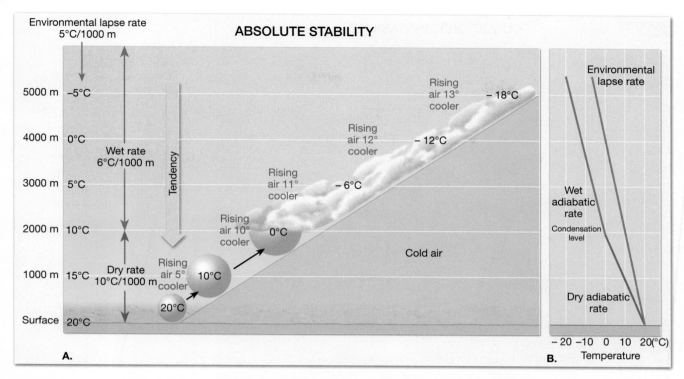

FIGURE 12.17   Absolute stability prevails when the environmental lapse rate is less than the wet adiabatic rate. **A.** The rising parcel of air is always cooler and denser than the surrounding air. When stable air is forced to rise, it produces flat, layered clouds. **B.** Graphic representation of the conditions shown in part **A**.

FIGURE 12.18   Illustration of *absolute instability*. **A.** Absolute instability develops when solar heating causes the lowermost layer of the atmosphere to be warmed to a higher temperature than the air aloft. The result is a steep environmental lapse rate that renders the atmosphere unstable. **B.** Graphic representation of the conditions shown in part **A**.

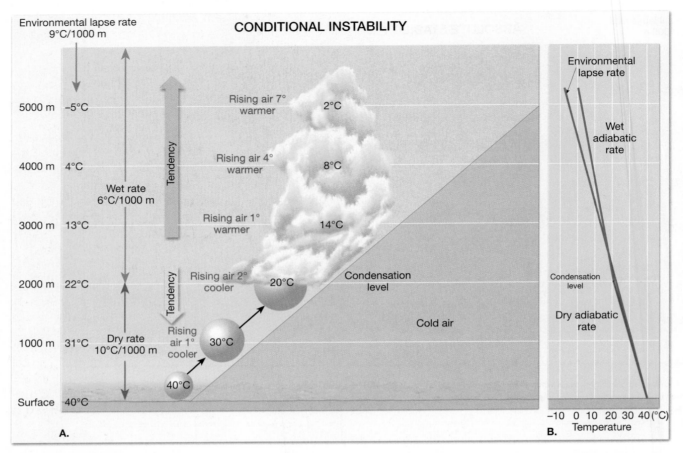

CONDITIONAL INSTABILITY

Environmental lapse rate
9°C/1000 m

5000 m −5°C

4000 m 4°C

Wet rate
6°C/1000 m

3000 m 13°C

2000 m 22°C

1000 m 31°C   Dry rate
10°C/1000 m

Surface −40°C

Rising air 7°
warmer   2°C

Rising air 4°
warmer   8°C

Rising air 1°
warmer   14°C

Rising air 2°
cooler   20°C   Condensation
                      level

Rising
air 1°   30°C   Cold air
cooler

40°C

Tendency

A.

Environmental
lapse rate

Wet
adiabatic
rate

Condensation
level

Dry adiabatic
rate

−10 0 10 20 30 40 (°C)
Temperature

B.

FIGURE 12.19   Illustration of *conditional instability* where warm air is forced to rise along a frontal boundary. **A.** Note that the environmental lapse rate of 9°C per 1000 meters lies between the dry and wet adiabatic rates. The parcel of air is cooler than the surrounding air up to nearly 3000 meters, where its tendency is to sink toward the surface (stable). Above this level, however, the parcel is warmer than its environment and will rise because of its own buoyancy (unstable). Thus, when conditionally unstable air is forced to rise, the result can be towering cumulus clouds. **B.** Graphic representation of the conditions shown in part **A**.

parcel will continue to rise because of its own buoyancy, without an outside force. Thus, conditional instability depends on whether or not the rising air is saturated. The word *conditional* is used because the air must be forced upward, such as over mountainous terrain, before it becomes unstable and rises because of its own buoyancy.

In summary, the stability of air is determined by examining the temperature of the atmosphere at various heights. In simple terms, a column of air is deemed unstable when the air near the bottom of this layer is significantly warmer (less dense) than the air aloft, indicating a steep environmental lapse rate. Under these conditions, the air actually turns over; the warm air below rises and displaces the colder air aloft. Conversely, the air is considered to be stable when the temperature drops gradually with increasing altitude.

Stability and Daily Weather

From the previous discussion, we can conclude that stable air resists vertical movement, whereas unstable air ascends freely because of its own buoyancy. But how do these facts manifest themselves in our daily weather?

Because stable air resists upward movement, we might conclude that clouds will not form when stable conditions prevail in the atmosphere. Although this seems reasonable, recall that processes exist that *force* air aloft. These include orographic lifting, frontal wedging, and convergence. When stable air is forced aloft, the clouds that form are widespread and have little vertical thickness when compared to their horizontal dimension, and precipitation, if any, is light to moderate.

By contrast, clouds associated with the lifting of unstable air are towering and often generate thunderstorms and occasionally even a tornado. For this reason, we can conclude that on a dreary, overcast day with light drizzle, stable air has been forced aloft. On the other hand, during a day when cauliflower-shaped clouds appear to be growing as if bubbles of hot air are surging upward, we can be fairly certain that the ascending air is unstable.

In summary, stability plays an important role in determining our daily weather. To a large degree, stability determines the type of clouds that develop and whether precipitation will come as a gentle shower or a heavy downpour.

CONDENSATION AND CLOUD FORMATION

GEODe
EARTH SCIENCE

Earth's Dynamic Atmosphere
▼ Forms of Condensation and Precipitation

To review briefly, condensation occurs when water vapor in the air changes to a liquid. The result of this process may be dew, fog, or clouds. For any of these forms of condensation to occur, the air must be saturated. Saturation occurs most commonly when air is cooled to its dew point, or less often when water vapor is added to the air.

Generally, there must be a surface on which the water vapor can condense. When dew occurs, objects at or near the ground, such as grass and car windows, serve this purpose. But when condensation occurs in the air above the ground, tiny bits of particulate matter, known as **condensation nuclei**, serve as surfaces for water-vapor condensation. These nuclei are important, for in their absence, a relative humidity well in excess of 100 percent is needed to produce clouds.

Condensation nuclei such as microscopic dust, smoke, and salt particles (from the ocean) are profuse in the lower atmosphere. Because of this abundance of particles, relative humidity rarely exceeds 101 percent. Some particles, such as ocean salt, are particularly good nuclei because they absorb water. These particles are termed **hygroscopic** ("water-seeking") **nuclei**.

When condensation takes place, the initial growth rate of cloud droplets is rapid. It diminishes quickly because the excess water vapor is quickly absorbed by the numerous competing particles. This results in the formation of a cloud consisting of millions upon millions of tiny water droplets, all so fine that they remain suspended in air. When cloud formation occurs at below-freezing temperatures, tiny ice crystals form. Thus, a cloud can consist of water droplets, ice crystals, or both.

The slow growth of cloud droplets by additional condensation and the immense size difference between cloud droplets and raindrops suggest that condensation alone is not responsible for the formation of drops large enough to fall as rain. We will first examine clouds and then return to the questions of how precipitation forms.

Types of Clouds

Clouds are among the most conspicuous and observable aspects of the atmosphere and its weather. **Clouds** are a form of condensation best described as *visible aggregates of minute droplets of water or tiny crystals of ice.* In addition to being prominent and sometimes spectacular features in the sky, clouds are of continual interest to meteorologists, because they provide a visible indication of what is going on in the atmosphere. Anyone who observes clouds with the hope of recognizing different types often finds that there are a bewildering variety of these familiar white and gray masses streaming across the sky. Still, once one comes to know the basic classification scheme for clouds, most of the confusion vanishes.

Clouds are classified on the basis of their *form* and *height* (**FIGURE 12.20**). Three basic forms are recognized: cirrus, cumulus, and stratus.

- **Cirrus** clouds are high, white, and thin. They can occur as patches composed of small cells or as delicate veil-like sheets or extended wispy fibers that often have a feathery appearance.
- **Cumulus** clouds consist of globular individual cloud masses. They normally exhibit a flat base and have the appearance of rising domes or towers. Such clouds are frequently described as having a cauliflower structure.
- **Stratus** clouds are best described as sheets or layers that cover much or all of the sky. While there may be minor breaks, there are no distinct individual cloud units.

All other clouds reflect one of these three basic forms or are combinations or modifications of them.

Three levels of cloud heights are recognized: high, middle, and low (Figure 12.20). **High clouds** normally have bases above 6000 meters (20,000 feet), **middle clouds** generally occupy heights from 2000 to 6000 meters (6500 to 20,000 feet), and **low clouds** form below 2000 meters (6500 feet). The altitudes listed for each height category are not hard and fast. There is some seasonal as well as latitudinal variation. For example, at high latitudes or during cold winter months in the midlatitudes, high clouds are often found at lower altitudes.

High Clouds

Three cloud types make up the family of high clouds (above 6000 meters [20,000 feet]): cirrus, cirrostratus, and cirrocumulus. *Cirrus* clouds are thin and delicate and sometimes appear as hooked filaments called "mares' tails" (**FIGURE 12.21A**). As the names suggest, *cirrocumulus* clouds consist of fluffy masses (**FIGURE 12.21B**), whereas *cirrostratus* clouds are flat layers (**FIGURE 12.21C**). Because of the low temperatures and small quantities of water vapor present at high altitudes, all high clouds are thin and white and are made up of ice crystals. Further, these clouds are not considered precipitation makers. However, when cirrus clouds are followed by cirrocumulus clouds and increased sky coverage, they may warn of impending stormy weather.

Middle Clouds

Clouds that appear in the middle range (2000 to 6000 meters [6500 to 20,000 feet]) have the prefix *alto* as part of their name. *Altocumulus* clouds are composed of globular masses that differ from cirrocumulus clouds in that they are larger and denser (**FIGURE 12.21D**). *Altostratus* clouds create a uniform white to grayish sheet covering the sky with the Sun or Moon visible as a bright spot (**FIGURE 12.21E**). Infrequent light snow or drizzle may accompany these clouds.

Low Clouds

There are three members in the family of low clouds: stratus, stratocumulus, and nimbostratus. *Stratus* are a uniform foglike layer of clouds that frequently covers much of the sky. These

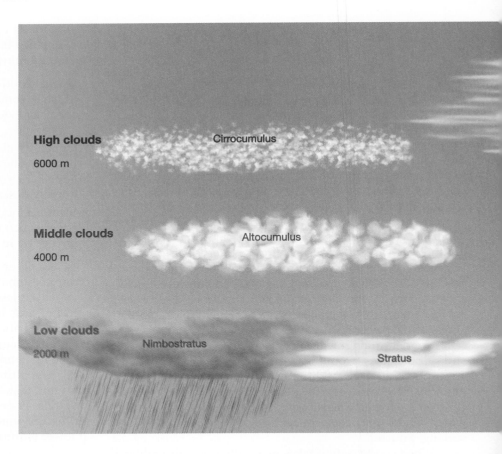

FIGURE 12.20   Classification of clouds according to height and form.

clouds may produce light precipitation. When stratus clouds develop a scalloped bottom that appears as long parallel rolls or broken globular patches, they are called *stratocumulus* clouds.

Nimbostratus clouds derive their name from the Latin *nimbus*, which means "rainy cloud," and *stratus*, which means "to cover with a layer" (**FIGURE 12.21F**). As the name suggests, nimbostratus clouds are one of the chief precipitation producers. Nimbostratus clouds form in association with stable conditions. We might not expect clouds to grow or persist in stable air, yet cloud growth of this type is

A. Cirrus

B. Cirrocumulus

FIGURE 12.21   These photos depict common forms of several different cloud types. (Photos **A**, **B**, **D**, **E**, **F**, and **G** by E. J. Tarbuck. Photo **C** by Jung-Pang Wu/Getty Images) Photo **H** by Doug Miller/Science Source/Photo Researchers, Inc.)

common when air is forced to rise, as occurs along a mountain range, a front, or near the center of a cyclone where converging winds cause air to ascend. Such forced ascent of stable air leads to the formation of a stratified cloud layer that is large horizontally compared to its depth.

C. Cirrostratus

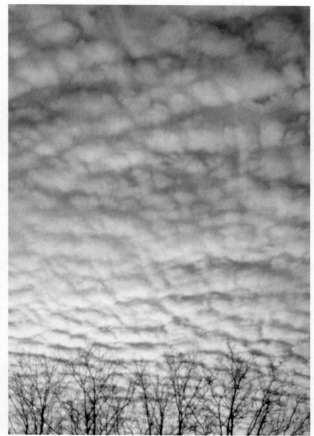

D. Altocumulus

FIGURE 12.21   (Continued).

E. Altostratus

F. Nimbostratus

G. Cumulus

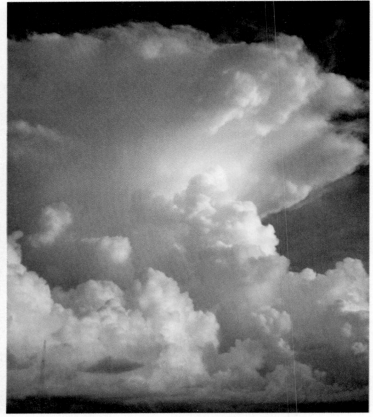

H. Cumulonimbus

FIGURE 12.21 (Continued).

Clouds of Vertical Development

Some clouds do not fit into any one of the three height categories mentioned. Such clouds have their bases in the low height range but often extend upward into the middle or high altitudes. Clouds in this category are called **clouds of vertical development**. They are all related to one another and are associated with unstable air. Although *cumulus* clouds are often connected with "fair" weather (**FIGURE 12.21G**), they may grow dramatically under the proper circumstances. Once upward movement is triggered, acceleration is powerful and clouds with great vertical extent form. The end result is often a towering cloud, called a *cumulonimbus*, that may produce rain showers or a thunderstorm (**FIGURE 12.21H**).

Definite weather patterns can often be associated with particular clouds or certain combinations of cloud types, so it is important to become familiar with cloud descriptions and characteristics.

FOG

Earth's Dynamic Atmosphere
▼ Forms of Condensation and Precipitation

Fog is generally considered to be an atmospheric hazard. When it is light, visibility is reduced to 2 or 3 kilometers (1 or 2 miles). However, when it is dense, visibility may be cut to a few dozen meters or less, making travel by any mode not only difficult but often dangerous. Officially, visibility must be reduced to 1 kilometer (0.6 mile) or less before fog is reported. Although this figure is arbitrary, it does provide an objective criterion for comparing fog frequencies at different locations.

Fog is defined as a *cloud with its base at or very near the ground*. There is no physical difference between a fog and a cloud; their appearance and structure are the same. The essential difference is the method and place of formation. Whereas clouds result when air rises and cools adiabatically, most fogs are the consequence of radiation cooling or the movement of air over a cold surface. (The exception is upslope fog.) In other circumstances, fogs form when enough water vapor is added to the air to bring about saturation (evaporation fogs).

Fogs Caused by Cooling

Three common fogs form when air at Earth's surface is chilled below its dew point. A fog is often a combination of these types.

Advection Fog

When warm, moist air moves over a cool surface, the result may be a blanket of fog called **advection fog** (**FIGURE 12.22**).

FIGURE 12.22 Advection fog rolling into San Francisco Bay. (Photo by Ed Pritchard/Getty Images Inc.—Stone Allstock)

Examples of such fogs are very common. The foggiest location in the United States, and perhaps in the world, is Cape Disappointment, Washington. The name is indeed appropriate, because this station averages 2552 hours of fog each year (there are 8760 hours in a year). The fog experienced at Cape Disappointment, and at other West Coast locations, is produced when warm, moist air from the Pacific Ocean moves over the cold California Current and is then carried onto shore by the prevailing winds. Advection fogs are also quite common in the winter season when warm air from the Gulf of Mexico blows across cold, often snow-covered surfaces of the Midwest and East.

Radiation Fog

Radiation fog forms on cool, clear, calm nights, when Earth's surface cools rapidly by radiation. As the night progresses, a thin layer of air in contact with the ground is cooled below its dew point. As the air cools and becomes denser, it drains into low areas, resulting in pockets of fog. The largest pockets are often river valleys, where thick accumulations may occur (**FIGURE 12.23**).

Radiation fog may also form when the skies clear after a rainfall. In these situations, the air near the surface is close to saturation and only a small amount of radiation cooling is needed to promote condensation. Radiation fog of this type often occurs around sunset and can make driving hazardous.

Upslope Fog

Upslope fog is created when relatively humid air moves up a gradually sloping plain or up the steep slopes of a mountain. Because of this upward movement, air expands and cools adiabatically. If the dew point is reached, an extensive layer of fog may form. In the United States, the Great Plains offers an excellent example. When humid easterly or southeasterly winds blow westward from the Mississippi River upslope toward the Rocky Mountains, the air gradually rises, resulting in an adiabatic temperature decrease of about 12°C (22°F). When the difference between the air temperature and dew point of westward-moving air is less than 12°C (22°F), an extensive fog can result in the western plains.

Evaporation Fogs

When the saturation of air occurs primarily because of the addition of water vapor, the resulting fogs may be called *evaporation fogs*. Two types of evaporation fogs are recognized: steam fog and frontal, or precipitation, fog.

Snow in Sierra Nevada

Fog

Pacific Ocean

A.

Fog

B.

FIGURE 12.23 Radiation fog. **A.** Satellite image of dense fog in California's San Joaquin Valley on November 20, 2002. This early morning radiation fog was responsible for several car accidents in the region, including a 14-car pileup. The white areas to the east of the fog are the snow-capped Sierra Nevadas. (NASA image) **B.** Radiation fog can make the morning commute hazardous. (Photo by Jeremy Walker/Getty Images Inc.—Stone Allstock)

FIGURE 12.24   Steam fog rising from Sparks Lake near Bend, Oregon. (Photo by Warren Morgan/CORBIS)

DID YOU KNOW?

On cold days when you "see your breath," you are actually creating steam fog. The moist air that you exhale saturates a small volume of cold air, causing tiny droplets to form. Like most steam fogs, the droplets quickly evaporate as the "fog" mixes with the unsaturated air around it.

Steam Fog

When cool air moves over warm water, enough moisture may evaporate from the water surface to produce saturation. As the rising water vapor meets the cold air, it immediately recondenses and rises with the air that is being warmed from below. Because the water has a steaming appearance, the phenomenon is called **steam fog**. Steam fog is fairly common over lakes and rivers in the fall and early winter, when the water may still be relatively warm and the air is rather crisp (**FIGURE 12.24**). Steam fog is often shallow because as the steam rises, it reevaporates in the unsaturated air above.

Frontal or Precipitation Fog

When frontal wedging occurs, warm air is lifted over colder air. If the resulting clouds yield rain, and the cold air below is near the dew point, enough rain will evaporate to produce fog. A fog formed in this manner is called **frontal fog**, or **precipitation fog**. The result is a more or less continuous zone of condensed water droplets reaching from the ground up through the clouds.

The frequency of dense fog varies considerably from place to place (**FIGURE 12.25**). As might be expected, fog

incidence is highest in coastal areas, especially where cold currents prevail, as along the Pacific and New England coasts. Relatively high frequencies are also found in the Great Lakes region and in the humid Appalachian Mountains of the East. In contrast, fogs are rare in the interior of the continent, especially in the arid and semiarid areas of the West.

PRECIPITATION

Earth's Dynamic Atmosphere
▼ Forms of Condensation and Precipitation

All clouds contain water. But why do some produce precipitation while others drift placidly overhead? This simple question perplexed meteorologists for many years. First, cloud droplets are very small, averaging less than 10 micrometers in diameter (for comparison, a human hair is about 75 micrometers in diameter). Because of their small size, cloud droplets fall incredibly slowly. In addition, clouds are made up of many billions of these droplets, all competing for the available water vapor; thus, their continued growth via condensation is extremely slow. So, what causes precipitation?

How Precipitation Forms

A raindrop large enough to reach the ground without completely evaporating contains roughly 1 million times more water than a single cloud droplet. Therefore, for precipitation to form, millions of cloud droplets must somehow coalesce (join together) into drops large enough to sustain themselves during their descent to the surface. Two mechanisms have been proposed to explain this phenomenon: the ice crystal process and the collision-coalescence process.

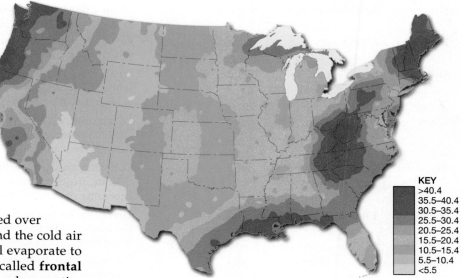

KEY
>40.4
35.5–40.4
30.5–35.4
25.5–30.4
20.5–25.4
15.5–20.4
10.5–15.4
5.5–10.4
<5.5

FIGURE 12.25   Map showing average number of days per year with heavy fog. Notice that the frequency of dense fog varies considerably from place to place. Coastal areas, particularly the Pacific Northwest and New England where cold currents prevail, have high occurrences of dense fog.

Ice Crystal Process

Meteorologists discovered that in the mid to high latitudes, precipitation often forms in clouds where the temperature is below 0°C (32°F). Although we would expect all cloud droplets to freeze in subzero temperatures, only those droplets that make contact with solid particles that have a particular structure (called *ice nuclei*) actually freeze. The remaining liquid droplets are said to be *supercooled* (below 0°C [32°F], but still liquid).

When ice crystals and supercooled water droplets co-exist in a cloud, the stage is set to generate precipitation. It turns out that ice crystals collect the available water vapor at a much faster rate than does liquid water. Thus, ice crystals grow larger at the expense of the water droplets. Eventually, this process generates ice crystals large enough to fall as snowflakes. During their descent, these ice crystals get bigger as they intercept supercooled cloud droplets that freeze on them. When the surface temperature is about 4°C (39°F) or higher, snowflakes usually melt before they reach the ground and continue their descent as rain.

Collision-Coalescence Process

Precipitation can form in warm clouds that contain large hygroscopic ("water-seeking") condensation nuclei, such as salt particles. Relatively large droplets form on these large nuclei. Because the bigger droplets fall faster, they collide and join with smaller water droplets. After many collisions, the droplets are large enough to fall to the ground as rain.

Forms of Precipitation

Because atmospheric conditions vary greatly from place to place as well as seasonally, several different forms of precipitation are possible (Table 12.2). Rain and snow are the most common and familiar, but other forms of precipitation are important as well. The occurrence of sleet, glaze, or hail is often associated with important weather events. Although limited in occurrence and sporadic in both time and space, these forms, especially glaze and hail, can cause considerable damage.

Rain and Drizzle

In meteorology, the term **rain** is restricted to drops of water that fall from a cloud and that have a diameter of at least 0.5 millimeter (0.02 inch). Most rain originates either in nimbostratus clouds or in towering cumulonimbus clouds that are capable of producing unusually heavy rainfalls known as *cloudbursts*. Raindrops rarely exceed about 5 millimeters (0.2 inch). Larger drops do not survive, because surface tension, which holds the drops together, is exceeded by the frictional drag of the air. Consequently, large raindrops regularly break apart into smaller ones.

Fine, uniform drops of water having a diameter less than 0.5 millimeter (0.02 inch) are called *drizzle*. Drizzle can be so fine that the tiny drops appear to float, and their impact is almost imperceptible. Drizzle and small raindrops generally are produced in stratus or nimbostratus clouds where precipitation may be continuous for several hours or, on rare occasions, for days.

Table 12.2 Forms of precipitation

Type	Approximate Size	State of Matter	Description
Mist	0.005 to 0.05 mm	Liquid	Droplets large enough to be felt on the face when air is moving 1 meter/second. Associated with stratus clouds.
Drizzle	Less than 0.5 mm	Liquid	Small uniform drops that fall from stratus clouds, generally for several hours.
Rain	0.5 to 5 mm	Liquid	Generally produced by nimbostratus or cumulonimbus clouds. When heavy, it can show high variability from one place to another.
Sleet	0.5 to 5 mm	Solid	Small, spherical to lumpy ice particles that form when raindrops freeze while falling through a layer of subfreezing air. Because the ice particles are small, damage, if any, is generally minor. Sleet can make travel hazardous.
Glaze	Layers 1 mm to 2 cm thick	Solid	Produced when supercooled raindrops freeze on contact with solid objects. Glaze can form a thick coating of ice having sufficient weight to seriously damage trees and power lines.
Rime	Variable accumulations	Solid	Deposits usually consisting of ice feathers that point into the wind. These delicate, frostlike accumulations form as supercooled cloud or fog droplets encounter objects and freeze on contact.
Snow	1 mm to 2 cm	Solid	The crystalline nature of snow allows it to assume many shapes including six-sided crystals, plates, and needles. Produced in supercooled clouds where water vapor is deposited as ice crystals that remain frozen during their descent.
Hail	5 mm to 10 cm or larger	Solid	Precipitation in the form of hard, rounded pellets or irregular lumps of ice. Produced in large convective, cumulonimbus clouds, where frozen ice particles and supercooled water coexist.
Graupel	2 to 5 mm	Solid	Sometimes called soft hail, graupel forms when rime collects on snow crystals to produce irregular masses of "soft" ice. Because these particles are softer than hailstones, they normally flatten out upon impact.

Snow

Snow is precipitation in the form of ice crystals (snowflakes) or, more often, aggregates of crystals. The size, shape, and concentration of snowflakes depend to a great extent on the temperature at which they form.

Recall that at very low temperatures, the moisture content of air is small. The result is the generation of very light and fluffy snow made up of individual six-sided ice crystals. This is the "powder" that downhill skiers talk so much about. By contrast, at temperatures warmer than about −5°C (23°F), the ice crystals join together into larger clumps consisting of tangled aggregates of crystals. Snowfalls consisting of these composite snowflakes are generally heavy and have a high moisture content, which makes them ideal for making snowballs.

Sleet and Glaze

Sleet is a wintertime phenomenon and refers to the fall of small particles of ice that are clear to translucent. For sleet to be produced, a layer of air with temperatures above freezing must overlie a subfreezing layer near the ground. When raindrops, which are often melted snow, leave the warmer air and encounter the colder air below, they freeze and reach the ground as small pellets of ice the size of the raindrops from which they formed.

On some occasions, when the vertical distribution of temperatures is similar to that associated with the formation of sleet, **freezing rain** or **glaze** results instead. In such situations, the subfreezing air near the ground is not thick enough to allow the raindrops to freeze. The raindrops, however, do become supercooled as they fall through the cold air and turn to ice upon colliding with solid objects. The result can be a thick coating of ice having sufficient weight to break tree limbs, down power lines, and make walking or driving extremely hazardous (**FIGURE 12.26**).

Hail

Hail is precipitation in the form of hard, rounded pellets or irregular lumps of ice. Moreover, large hailstones often consist of a series of nearly concentric shells of differing densities and degrees of opaqueness (**FIGURE 12.27**). Most hailstones have diameters between 1 centimeter (0.4 inch, pea size) and 5 centimeters (2 inches, golf ball size), although some can be as big as an orange or larger. Occasionally, hailstones weighing a pound or more have been reported. Many of these were probably composites of several stones frozen together.

The largest hailstone ever recorded in the United States fell during violent thunderstorms that pounded southeastern Nebraska on June 22, 2003. In the town of Aurora, a 17.8 centimeter (7 inch) wide chunk of ice, almost as large as a volleyball, was recovered. However, this hailstone was not the heaviest hailstone ever measured. Apparently, a chunk of this stone was broken off when it hit the gutter of a house.

FIGURE 12.26   Glaze forms when supercooled raindrops freeze on contact with objects. In January 1998, an ice storm of historic proportions caused enormous damage in New England and southeastern Canada. Nearly five days of freezing rain (glaze) left millions without electricity—some for as long as a month. (Photo by Syracuse Newspapers/The Image Works)

The heaviest hailstone in North America fell on Coffeyville, Kansas, in 1970. Having a 14 centimeter (5.5 inch) diameter, this hailstone weighed 766 grams (1.69 pounds). Even heavier hailstones have reportedly been recorded in Bangladesh, where a hailstorm in 1987 killed more than 90 people. It is estimated that large hailstones hit the ground at speeds exceeding 160 kilometers (100 miles) per hour.

The destructive effects of large hailstones are well known, especially to farmers whose crops have been devastated in a few minutes and to people whose windows and roofs have been damaged (**FIGURE 12.28**). In the United States, hail damage each year can run into the hundreds of millions of dollars.

Hail is produced only in large cumulonimbus clouds where updrafts can sometimes reach speeds approaching

A.

FIGURE 12.28 Hail damage in San Marcos, Texas, following a severe thunderstorm. (Photo by San Antonio Express-News/Newscom)

B.

FIGURE 12.27 Hailstones. **A.** Hailstones begin as small ice pellets that grow by adding supercooled water droplets as they move through a cloud. Strong updrafts may carry stones upward in several cycles, increasing the size of the hail by adding a new layer with each cycle. Eventually, the hailstones encounter a downdraft or grow too large to be supported by the updraft. **B.** A cross section of the Coffeyville hailstone. This huge hailstone fell over Kansas in 1970 and weighed 0.75 kilogram (1.65 pounds). (National Center for Atmospheric Research/University Corporation for Atmospheric Research/National Science Foundation)

temperature is below freezing. When rime forms on trees, it adorns them with its characteristic ice feathers, which can be spectacular to behold (**FIGURE 12.29**). Objects such as pine needles act as freezing nuclei, causing the supercooled droplets to freeze on contact. When the wind is blowing, only the windward surfaces of objects will accumulate the layer of rime.

Measuring Precipitation

The most common form of precipitation, rain, is the easiest to measure. Any open container having a consistent cross section throughout can be a rain gauge. In general practice, however, more sophisticated devices are used so that small amounts of rainfall can be measured accurately and losses from evaporation can be reduced. The *standard rain gauge*

160 kilometers (100 miles) per hour, and where there is an abundant supply of supercooled water (Figure 12.27A). Hailstones begin as small embryonic ice pellets that grow by collecting supercooled water droplets as they fall through the cloud. If they encounter a strong updraft, they may be carried upward again and begin the downward journey anew. Each trip through the supercooled portion of the cloud may be represented by an additional layer of ice. Hailstones can also form from a single descent through an updraft. Either way, the process continues until the hailstone encounters a downdraft or grows too heavy to remain suspended by the thunderstorm's updraft.

Rime

Rime is a deposit of ice crystals formed by the freezing of supercooled fog or cloud droplets on objects whose surface

FIGURE 12.29 Rime consists of delicate ice crystals that form when supercooled fog or cloud droplets freeze on contact with objects. (Photo by Siegfried Kramer/age fotostock)

FIGURE 12.30 Precipitation measurement. The standard rain gauge allows for accurate rainfall measurement to the nearest 0.025 centimeter (0.01 inch). Because the cross-sectional area of the measuring tube is only one-tenth as large as the collector, rainfall is magnified 10 times.

FIGURE 12.31 Weather radar display commonly seen on TV weathercasts. Colors indicate different intensities of precipitation. Note the band of heavy precipitation extending from southeastern Iowa to Milwaukee, Wisconsin.

(**FIGURE 12.30**) has a diameter of about 20 centimeters (8 inches) at the top. Once the water is caught, a funnel conducts the rain into a cylindrical measuring tube that has a cross-sectional area only one-tenth as large as the receiver. Consequently, rainfall depth is magnified 10 times, which allows for accurate measurements to the nearest 0.025 centimeter (0.01 inch). The narrow opening also minimizes evaporation. When the amount of rain is less than 0.025 centimeter, it is reported as a *trace* of precipitation.

Measurement Errors

In addition to the standard rain gauge, several types of recording gauges are routinely used. These instruments record not only the amount of rain but also its time of occurrence and intensity (amount per unit of time).

No matter which rain gauge is used, proper exposure is critical. Errors arise when the gauge is shielded from obliquely falling rain by buildings, trees, or other high objects. Hence, the instrument should be at least as far away from such obstructions as the objects are high. Another cause of error is the wind. It has been shown that with increasing wind and turbulence, it becomes more difficult to collect a representative quantity of rain.

Measuring Snowfall

When snow records are kept, two measurements are normally taken: depth and water equivalent. Usually the depth of snow is measured with a calibrated stick. The actual measurement is simple, but choosing a *representative* spot often poses a dilemma. Even when winds are light or moderate, snow drifts freely. As a rule, it is best to take several measurements in an open place away from trees and obstructions and then average them. To obtain the water

equivalent, samples may be melted and then weighed or measured as rain.

The quantity of water in a given volume of snow is not constant. A general ratio of 10 units of snow to 1 unit of water is often used when exact information is not available, but the actual water content of snow may deviate widely from this figure. It may take as much as 30 centimeters (12 inches) of light and fluffy dry snow or as little as 4 centimeters (1.6 inches) of wet snow to produce 1 centimeter (0.4 inch) of water.

Precipitation Measurement by Weather Radar

Today's TV weathercasts show helpful maps like the one in **FIGURE 12.31** to depict precipitation patterns. The instrument that produces these images is the *weather radar.*

The development of radar has given meteorologists an important tool to probe storm systems that may be up to a few hundred kilometers away. All radar units have a transmitter that sends out short pulses of radio waves. The specific wavelengths that are used depend on the objects the user wants to detect. When radar is used to monitor precipitation, wavelengths between 3 and 10 centimeters (1 and 4 inches) are employed.

These wavelengths can penetrate small cloud droplets but are reflected by larger raindrops, ice crystals, or

DID YOU KNOW?

Despite the impressive lake-effect snowstorms recorded in cities such as Buffalo and Rochester, New York, the greatest accumulations of snow generally occur in the mountainous regions of the western United States. The record for a single season goes to Mount Baker ski area north of Seattle, Washington, where 2896 cm (1140 in) of snow fell during the winter of 1998–1999.

hailstones. The reflected signal, called an *echo,* is received and displayed on a TV monitor. Because the echo is "brighter" when the precipitation is more intense, modern radar is able to depict not only the regional extent of the precipitation but also the rate of rainfall. Figure 12.31 is a typical radar display in which colors show precipitation intensity. Weather radar is also an important tool for determining the rate and direction of storm movement.

THE CHAPTER IN REVIEW

• *Water vapor,* an odorless, colorless gas, changes from one state of matter (solid, liquid, or gas) to another at the temperatures and pressures experienced near Earth's surface. The processes involved in *changing the state of matter* of water are *evaporation, condensation, melting, freezing, sublimation,* and *deposition.* During each change, *latent* (hidden) *heat* is either absorbed or released.

• *Humidity* is the general term used to describe the amount of water vapor in the air. The methods used to express humidity quantitatively include (a) *mixing ratio,* the mass of water vapor in a unit of air compared to the remaining mass of dry air; (b) *vapor pressure,* that part of the total atmospheric pressure attributable to its water-vapor content; (c) *relative humidity,* the ratio of the air's actual water-vapor content compared to the amount of water vapor required for saturation at that temperature; and (d) *dew point,* that temperature to which a parcel of air would need to be cooled to reach saturation. When air is saturated, the pressure exerted by the water vapor, called the *saturation vapor pressure,* produces a balance between the number of water molecules leaving the surface of the water and the number returning. Because the saturation vapor pressure is temperature dependent, at higher temperatures more water vapor is required for saturation to occur.

• *Relative humidity can be changed in two ways.* One is by *adding or subtracting water vapor.* The second is by *changing air temperature.* When air is cooled, its relative humidity increases.

• The basic cloud-forming process is the cooling of air as it rises. The cooling results from expansion because the pressure becomes progressively lower with height. Air temperature changes brought about by compressing or expanding the air are called *adiabatic temperature changes.* Unsaturated air warms by compression and cools by expansion at the rather constant rate of 10°C per 1000 meters of altitude change, a figure called the *dry adiabatic rate.* If air rises high enough, it will cool sufficiently to cause condensation and form a cloud. From this point on, air that continues to rise will cool at the *wet adiabatic rate,* which varies from 5°C to 9°C per 1000 meters of ascent. The difference in the two rates results because the condensing water vapor releases *latent heat,* thereby slowing the rate at which the rising air cools.

• Four mechanisms that can initiate the vertical movement of air are (a) *orographic lifting,* which occurs when flowing air encounters elevated terrains, such as mountains, and the air rises to go over the barrier; (b) *frontal wedging,* when cool air acts as a barrier over which warmer, less dense air rises; (c) *convergence,* which happens when volumes of air flow together and a general upward movement of air occurs; and (d) *localized convective lifting,* which occurs when unequal surface heating causes localized pockets of air to rise because of their buoyancy.

• The *stability of air* is determined by examining the temperature of the atmosphere at various altitudes. Air is said to be *unstable* when the *environmental lapse rate* (the rate of temperature decrease with increasing altitude in the troposphere) is greater than the *dry adiabatic rate.* Stated differently, a column of air is unstable when the air near the bottom is significantly warmer (less dense) than the air aloft. When stable air is forced aloft, precipitation, if any, is light, whereas unstable air generates towering clouds and stormy conditions.

• For condensation to occur, air must be saturated. Saturation takes place either when air is cooled to its dew point, which most commonly happens, or when water vapor is added to the air. There must also be a surface on which the water vapor can condense. In cloud and fog formation, tiny particles called *condensation nuclei* serve this purpose.

• *Clouds* are classified on the basis of their *appearance* and *height.* The three basic forms are *cirrus* (high, white, thin, wispy fibers), *cumulus* (globular, individual cloud masses), and *stratus* (sheets or layers that cover much or all of the sky). The four categories based on height are *high clouds* (bases normally above 6000 meters [20,000 feet]), *middle clouds* (from 2000 to 6000 meters [6500 to 20,000 feet]), *low clouds* (below 2000 meters [6500 feet]), and *clouds of vertical development.*

• *Fog* is a cloud with its base at or very near the ground. Fogs form when air is cooled below its dew point or when enough water vapor is added to the air to bring about saturation. Various types of fog include *advection fog, radiation fog, upslope fog, steam fog,* and *frontal fog* (or *precipitation fog*).

• For *precipitation* to form, millions of cloud droplets must somehow join together into large drops. Two mechanisms for the formation of precipitation have been proposed: First, in clouds where the temperatures are below freezing, ice crystals form and fall as snowflakes. At lower altitudes the snowflakes melt and become raindrops before they reach the ground. Second, large droplets form in warm clouds that contain large hygroscopic ("water-seeking") nuclei, such as salt particles. As these big droplets descend, they collide and join with smaller water droplets. After many collisions, the droplets are large enough to fall to the ground as rain.

• The forms of precipitation include *rain, snow, sleet, freezing rain (glaze), hail,* and *rime.*

• Rain, the most common form of precipitation, is probably easiest to measure. A common instrument is the *standard rain gauge,* which is read directly. Several types of *recording gauges,* which record the intensity and amount of rain, are also in use. The two most common measurements of snow are depth and water equivalent. Although the quantity of water in a given volume of snow is not constant, a general ratio of 10 units of snow to 1 unit of water is often used when exact information is not available.

KEY TERMS

absolute instability (p. 352)

absolute stability (p. 352)

adiabatic temperature change (p. 348)

advection fog (p. 359)

calorie (p. 342)

cirrus (p. 355)

cloud (p. 355)

clouds of vertical development (p. 359)

condensation (p. 343)

condensation nuclei (p. 355)

conditional instability (p. 352)

convergence (p. 350)

cumulus (p. 355)

deposition (p. 343)

dew-point temperature (p. 346)

dry adiabatic rate (p. 348)

evaporation (p. 342)

fog (p. 359)

freezing rain (p. 363)

front (p. 350)

frontal fog (p. 361)

frontal wedging (p. 350)

glaze (p. 363)

hail (p. 363)

high clouds (p. 355)

humidity (p. 344)

hygrometer (p. 347)

hygroscopic nuclei (p. 355)

latent heat (p. 342)

localized convective lifting (p. 351)

low clouds (p. 355)

middle clouds (p. 355)

mixing ratio (p. 344)

orographic lifting (p. 349)

parcel (p. 348)

precipitation fog (p. 361)

radiation fog (p. 360)

rain (p. 362)

rainshadow desert (p. 349)

relative humidity (p. 344)

rime (p. 364)

saturation (p. 344)

sleet (p. 363)

snow (p. 363)

stable air (p. 351)

steam fog (p. 361)

stratus (p. 355)

sublimation (p. 343)

unstable air (p. 352)

upslope fog (p. 360)

vapor pressure (p. 344)

wet adiabatic rate (p. 348)

QUESTIONS FOR REVIEW

1. Summarize the processes by which water changes from one state to another. Indicate whether heat energy is absorbed or liberated.

2. After studying Table 12.1 (p. 344), write a generalization relating temperature and the capacity of air to hold water vapor.

3. How do relative humidity and mixing ratio differ?

4. Referring to Figure 12.6 (p. 346), answer the following questions:

   a. During a typical day, when is the relative humidity highest? Lowest?

   b. At what time of day would dew most likely form?

5. If the air temperature remains unchanged and the mixing ratio decreases, how will relative humidity change?

6. On a cold winter day when the temperature is −10°C (14°F) and the relative humidity is 50 percent, what is the mixing ratio (refer to Table 12.1, p. 344)? What is the mixing ratio for a day when the temperature is 20°C (68°F) and the relative humidity is 50 percent?

7. Explain the principle of the sling psychrometer.

8. On a warm summer day when the relative humidity is high, it may seem even warmer than the thermometer indicates. Why do we feel so uncomfortable on a "muggy" day?

9. Why does air cool when it rises through the atmosphere?

10. Explain the difference between environmental lapse rate and adiabatic cooling.

11. If unsaturated air at 23°C were to rise, what would its temperature be at 500 meters? If the dew-point temperature at the condensation level were 13°C, at what altitude would clouds begin to form?

12. Why does the adiabatic rate of cooling change when condensation begins? Why is the wet adiabatic rate not a constant figure?

13. How do orographic lifting and frontal wedging act to force air to rise?

14. Explain why the Great Basin area of the western United States is so dry. What term is applied to such a situation?

15. How does stable air differ from unstable air? Describe the general nature of the clouds and precipitation expected with each.

16. What is the function of condensation nuclei in cloud formation? What is the function of the dew point?

17. As you drink an ice-cold beverage on a warm day, the outside of the glass or bottle becomes wet. Explain.

18. What is the basis for the classification of clouds?

19. Why are high clouds always thin?

20. List five types of fog and discuss the details of their formation.

21. What is the difference between precipitation and condensation?

22. List the forms of precipitation and the circumstances of their formation.

23. Sometimes, when rainfall is light, the amount is reported as a trace. When this occurs, how much (or little) rain has fallen?

COMPANION WEBSITE

The *Foundations of Earth Science* Website uses the resources and flexibility of the Internet to aid in your study of the topics in this chapter. Written and developed by the authors and other Earth science instructors, this site will help improve your understanding of Earth science. Visit **www.mygeoscienceplace.com** in order to

- **Review** key chapter concepts.
- **Read** with links to the ebook and to chapter-specific web resources.

- **Visualize** and comprehend challenging topics using learning activities in *GEODe: Earth Science*.
- **Test** yourself with online quizzes.

GEODe: EARTH SCIENCE

GEODe: Earth Science is a valuable and easy to use learning aid that can be accessed from your book's Companion Website: **www.mygeoscienceplace.com.** It is a dynamic instructional tool that promotes understanding and reinforces important concepts by using tutorials, animations, and exercises that actively engage the student.

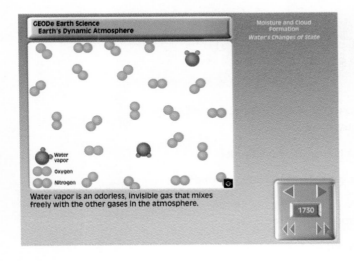

Water vapor is an odorless, invisible gas that mixes freely with the other gases in the atmosphere.

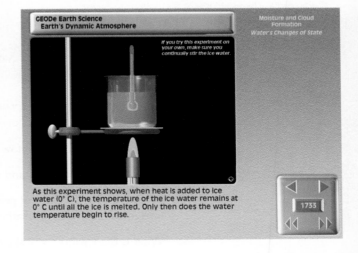

As this experiment shows, when heat is added to ice water (0° C), the temperature of the ice water remains at 0° C until all the ice is melted. Only then does the water temperature begin to rise.

THE ATMOSPHERE IN MOTION

To assist you in learning the important concepts in this chapter, you will find it helpful to focus on the following questions:

1. What is air pressure, and how does it change with altitude?

2. What force creates wind, and what other factors influence wind?

3. What are the two types of pressure centers? What is the air movement and general weather associated with each type?

4. What is the idealized global circulation?

5. What is the general atmospheric circulation in the midlatitudes?

6. What are the names and causes of some local winds?

Sailboats racing in the Rolex Cup Regatta.
(Photo by Neil Rabinowitz/CORBIS)

CHAPTER
13

Of the various elements of weather and climate, changes in air pressure are the least noticeable. When listening to a weather report, we are generally interested in moisture conditions (humidity and precipitation), temperature, and perhaps wind. It is the rare individual who wonders about air pressure. Although the hour-to-hour and day-to-day variations in air pressure are generally not noticed by people, they are very important in producing changes in our weather. Variations in air pressure from place to place cause the movement of air we call wind and are a significant factor in weather forecasting (**FIGURE 13.1**). As we will see, air pressure is closely tied to the other elements of weather in a cause-and-effect relationship.

UNDERSTANDING AIR PRESSURE

Earth's Dynamic Atmosphere
▼ Air Pressure and Wind

In Chapter 11 we noted that **air pressure** is simply the pressure exerted by the weight of air above. Average air pressure at sea level is about 1 kilogram per square centimeter, or 14.7 pounds per square inch. This is roughly the same pressure that is produced by a column of water 10 meters

(33 feet) in height. With some simple arithmetic, you can calculate that the air pressure exerted on the top of a small (50 centimeter by 100 centimeter [20 inch by 40 inch]) school desk exceeds 5000 kilograms (11,000 pounds), or about the weight of a 50-passenger school bus. Why doesn't the desk collapse under the weight of the ocean of air above? Simply, air pressure is exerted in all directions—down, up, and sideways. Thus, the air pressure pushing down on the desk exactly balances the air pressure pushing up on the desk.

To visualize this phenomenon better, imagine a tall aquarium that has the same dimensions as the desktop. When this aquarium is filled to a height of 10 meters (33 feet), the water pressure at the bottom equals 1 atmosphere (14.7 pounds per square inch). Now, imagine what will happen if this aquarium is placed on top of our student desk so that all the force is directed downward. Compare this to what results when the desk is placed inside the aquarium and allowed to sink to the bottom. In the latter example, the desk survives because the water pressure is exerted in all directions, not just downward as in our earlier example. The desk, like your body, is "built" to withstand the pressure of 1 atmosphere. It is important to note that although we do not generally notice the pressure exerted by the ocean of air around us, except when ascending or descending in an elevator or airplane, it is nonetheless substantial. The pressurized suits used by astronauts on space walks are designed to

FIGURE 13.1   Wind blowing snow off mountain cabin, Alto Adige, Italian Alps. (Photo by AGRfoto / Alex Rowbotham / Alamy)

duplicate the atmospheric pressure experienced at Earth's surface. Without these protective suits to keep body fluids from boiling away, astronauts would perish in minutes.

The concept of air pressure can also be understood if we examine the behavior of gas molecules. Gas molecules, unlike those of the liquid and solid phases, are not bound to one another but are freely moving about, filling all the space available to them. When two gas molecules collide, which happens frequently under normal conditions, they bounce off each other like elastic balls. If a gas is confined to a container, this motion is restricted by its sides, much like the walls of a handball court redirect the motion of the handball. The continuous bombardment of gas molecules against the sides of the container exerts an outward push that we call air pressure. Although the atmosphere is without walls, it is confined from below by Earth's surface and effectively from above because the force of gravity prevents its escape. Here, we can define *air pressure* as the force exerted against a surface by the continuous collision of gas molecules.

MEASURING AIR PRESSURE

Earth's Dynamic Atmosphere
▼ Air Pressure and Wind

When meteorologists measure atmospheric pressure, they employ a unit called the *millibar*. Standard sea-level pressure is 1013.2 millibars. Although the millibar has been the unit of measure on all U.S. weather maps since January 1940, the media use "inches of mercury" to describe atmospheric pressure. In the United States, the National Weather Service converts millibar values to inches of mercury for public and aviation use.

Inches of mercury is easy to understand. The use of mercury for measuring air pressure dates from 1643, when Torricelli, a student of the famous Italian scientist Galileo, invented the **mercury barometer**. Torricelli correctly described the atmosphere as a vast ocean of air that exerts pressure on us and all objects about us. To measure this force, he filled a glass tube, which was closed at one end, with mercury. The tube was then inverted into a dish of mercury (**FIGURE 13.2**). Torricelli found that the mercury flowed out of the tube until the weight of the column was balanced by the pressure that the atmosphere exerted on the surface of the mercury in the dish. In other words, the weight of mercury in the column equaled the weight of the same diameter column of air that extended from the ground to the top of the atmosphere.

When air pressure increases, the mercury in the tube rises. Conversely, when air pressure decreases, so does the height of the mercury column. With some refinements, the mercurial barometer invented by Torricelli is still the standard pressure-measuring instrument used today. Standard atmospheric pressure at sea level equals 29.92 inches of mercury.

The need for a smaller and more portable instrument for measuring air pressure led to the development of

FIGURE 13.2 Mercury barometer. The weight of the column of mercury is balanced by the pressure exerted on the container of mercury by the air above. If the pressure decreases, the column of mercury falls; if the pressure increases, the column rises.

the **aneroid barometer** (*aneroid* means "without liquid"). Instead of having a mercury column held up by air pressure, the aneroid barometer uses a partially evacuated metal chamber (**FIGURE 13.3**). The chamber is extremely sensitive to variations in air pressure and changes shape, compressing as the pressure increases and expanding as the pressure decreases. A series of levers transmits the movements of the chamber to a pointer on a dial that is calibrated to read in inches of mercury and/or millibars.

As shown in Figure 13.3, the face of an aneroid barometer intended for home use is inscribed with words such as *fair, change, rain,* and *stormy.* Notice that "fair" corresponds with high-pressure readings, whereas "rain" is associated with low pressures. Barometric readings, however, may not always indicate the weather. The dial may point to "fair" on a rainy day or to "rain" on a fair day. To "predict" the local weather, the change in air pressure over the past few hours is more important than the current pressure reading. Falling pressure is often associated with increasing cloudiness and the possibility of precipitation, whereas rising air pressure generally indicates clearing conditions. It is useful to remember, however, that particular barometer readings or trends do not always correspond to specific types of weather.

One advantage of the aneroid barometer is that it can easily be connected to a recording mechanism. The resulting instrument is a **barograph**, which provides a continuous record of pressure changes with the passage of time

FIGURE 13.3 Aneroid barometer. The aneroid barometer has a partially evacuated chamber that changes shape, compressing as atmospheric pressure increases and expanding as pressure decreases.

(**FIGURE 13.4**). Another important adaptation of the aneroid barometer is its use to indicate altitude for aircraft, mountain climbers, and mapmakers.

DID YOU KNOW?

A barometer could be constructed using any number of different liquids, including water. The problem with a water-filled barometer is size. Because water is 13.6 times less dense than mercury, the height of a water column at standard sea-level pressure would be 13.6 times taller than that of a mercurial barometer. Consequently, a water-filled barometer would need to be nearly 34 feet tall.

FIGURE 13.4 An aneroid barograph makes a continuous record of pressure changes. (Photo courtesy of Qualimetrics, Inc., Sacramento, California)

FACTORS AFFECTING WIND

Earth's Dynamic Atmosphere
▼ Air Pressure and Wind

In Chapter 12, we examined the upward movement of air and its role in cloud formation. As important as vertical motion is, far more air moves horizontally, the phenomenon we call **wind**. What causes wind?

Simply stated, wind is the result of horizontal differences in air pressure. *Air flows from areas of higher pressure to areas of lower pressure.* You may have experienced this when opening a vacuum-packed can of coffee. The noise you hear is caused by air rushing from the higher pressure outside the can to the lower pressure inside. Wind is nature's attempt to balance such inequalities in air pressure. Because unequal heating of Earth's surface generates these pressure differences, *solar radiation is the ultimate energy source for most wind.*

If Earth did not rotate, and if there were no friction between moving air and Earth's surface, air would flow in a straight line from areas of higher pressure to areas of lower pressure. But because Earth does rotate and friction does exist, wind is controlled by the following combination of forces: (1) pressure-gradient force, (2) Coriolis effect, and (3) friction. We will now examine each of these factors.

Pressure-Gradient Force

Pressure differences create wind, and the greater these differences, the greater the wind speed. Over Earth's surface, variations in air pressure are determined from barometric readings taken at hundreds of weather stations. These pressure data are shown on a weather map using **isobars**, lines that connect places of equal air pressure (**FIGURE 13.5**). The spacing of isobars indicates the amount of pressure change occurring over a given distance and is expressed as the **pressure gradient**.

To visualize a pressure gradient, think of it as the slope of a hill. A steep pressure gradient, like a steep hill, causes greater acceleration of an air parcel than does a weak pressure gradient. Thus, the relationship between wind speed and the pressure gradient is straightforward: *Closely spaced isobars indicate a steep pressure gradient and high winds, whereas widely spaced isobars indicate a weak pressure gradient and light winds.* Figure 13.5 illustrates the relationship between the spacing of isobars and wind speed. Notice that wind speeds are greater in Ohio, Kentucky, Michigan, and Illinois, where isobars are more closely spaced, than in the western states, where isobars are more widely spaced.

The pressure gradient is the driving force of wind, and it has both magnitude and direction. Its magnitude is determined from the spacing of isobars. The direction of force is always from areas of higher pressure to areas of lower pressure and at right angles to the isobars. Once the air starts to move, the Coriolis effect and friction come into play, but then only to modify the movement, not to produce it.

FIGURE 13.5 The black lines are isobars that connect places of equal barometric pressure. They show the distribution of pressure on weather maps. The lines usually curve and often close around cells of high and low pressure. Flags indicate the expected airflow surrounding cells of high and low pressure and are plotted like flags flying with the wind. Wind speed is indicated by flags and "feathers," as shown along the right-hand side of this map.

Coriolis Effect

Figure 13.5 shows the typical air movements associated with high- and low-pressure systems. As expected, the air moves out of the regions of higher pressure and into the regions of lower pressure. However, the wind does not cross the isobars at right angles as the pressure-gradient force directs it to do. The direction deviates as a result of Earth's rotation. This has been named the **Coriolis effect** after the French scientist who first thoroughly described it.

All free-moving objects or fluids, including the wind, are deflected to the *right* of their path of motion in the Northern Hemisphere and to the *left* in the Southern Hemisphere. The reason for this deflection can be illustrated by imagining the path of a rocket launched from the North Pole toward a target located on the equator (**FIGURE 13.6**). If the

rocket took an hour to reach its target, during its flight Earth would have rotated 15 degrees to the east. To someone standing on Earth, it would look as if the rocket veered off its path and hit Earth 15 degrees west of its target. The true path of the rocket is straight and would appear so to someone out in space looking at Earth. It was Earth turning under the rocket that gave it its *apparent* deflection.

Note that the rocket was deflected to the right of its path of motion because of the counterclockwise rotation of the Northern Hemisphere. In the Southern Hemisphere, the effect is reversed. Clockwise rotation produces a similar deflection, but to the *left* of the path of motion. The same deflection is experienced by wind regardless of the direction it is moving.

We attribute the apparent shift in wind direction to the Coriolis effect. This deflection (1) is always directed at right angles to the direction of airflow; (2) affects only wind direction, not wind speed; (3) is affected by wind speed (the stronger the wind, the greater the deflection); and (4) is strongest at the poles and weakens equatorward, becoming nonexistent at the equator.

It is of interest to point out that any free-moving object will experience a deflection caused by the Coriolis effect. This fact was dramatically discovered by the United States Navy in World War II. During target practice, long-range guns on battleships continually missed their targets by as much as several hundred yards until ballistic corrections were made for the changing position of a seemingly stationary target. Over a short distance, however, the Coriolis effect is relatively small.

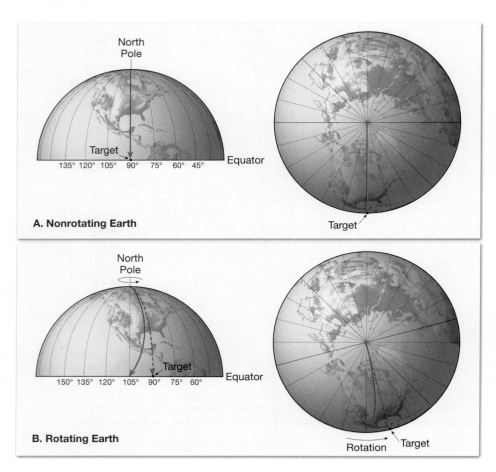

A. Nonrotating Earth

B. Rotating Earth

Friction with Earth's Surface

The effect of friction on wind is important only within a few kilometers of Earth's surface. Friction acts to slow air movement and, as a consequence, alters wind direction. To illustrate friction's effect on wind direction, let us look at a situation in which it has no role. Above the friction layer, the pressure-gradient force and Coriolis effect work together to direct the flow of air. Under these conditions, the pressure-gradient force causes air to start moving across the isobars. As soon as the air starts to move, the Coriolis effect acts at right angles to this motion. The faster the wind speed, the greater the deflection.

Eventually, the Coriolis effect will balance the pressure-gradient force and the wind will blow parallel to the isobars (**FIGURE 13.7**). Upper-air winds generally take this path and are called **geostrophic**

FIGURE 13.6 The Coriolis effect illustrated using a one-hour flight of a rocket traveling from the North Pole to a location on the equator. **A.** On a nonrotating Earth, the rocket would travel straight to its target. **B.** However, Earth rotates 15 degrees each hour. Thus, although the rocket travels in a straight line, when we plot the path of the rocket on Earth's surface, it follows a curved path that veers to the right of the target.

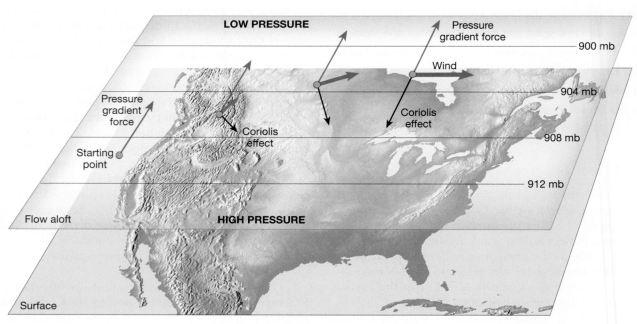

FIGURE 13.7 The geostrophic wind. The only force acting on a stationary parcel of air is the pressure-gradient force. Once the air begins to accelerate, the Coriolis effect deflects it to the right in the Northern Hemisphere. Greater wind speeds result in a stronger Coriolis effect (deflection) until the flow is parallel to the isobars. At this point, the pressure-gradient force and Coriolis effect are in balance and the flow is called a *geostrophic wind*. It is important to note that in the "real" atmosphere, airflow is continually adjusting for variations in the pressure field. As a result, the adjustment to geostrophic equilibrium is much more irregular than shown.

DID YOU KNOW?

The Coriolis effect could potentially affect the outcome of a baseball game. A ball hit a horizontal distance of 100 m (330 t) in four seconds down the right field line will be deflected 1.5 cm (more than one-half in) to the right. This could be just enough to turn a potential home run into a foul ball!

winds. The lack of friction with Earth's surface allows geostrophic winds to travel at higher speeds than do surface winds. This can be observed in **FIGURE 13.8** by noting the wind flags, many of which indicate winds of 50 to 100 miles per hour.

The most prominent features of upper-level flow are the **jet streams**. First encountered by high-flying bombers during World War II, these fast-moving "rivers" of air travel between 120 and 240 kilometers (75 and 150 miles) per hour

in a west-to-east direction. One such stream is situated over the polar front, which is the zone separating cool polar air from warm subtropical air.

Below 600 meters (2000 feet), friction complicates the airflow just described. Recall that the Coriolis effect is proportional to wind speed. Friction lowers the wind speed, so it reduces the Coriolis effect. Because the pressure-gradient force is not affected by wind speed, it wins the tug of war shown in **FIGURE 13.9**. The result is a movement of air at an angle across the isobars toward the area of lower pressure.

The roughness of the terrain determines the angle of airflow across the isobars. Over the smooth ocean surface, friction is low and the angle is small. Over rugged terrain, where friction is higher, the angle that air makes as it flows across the isobars can be as great as 45 degrees.

In summary, upper airflow is nearly parallel to the isobars, whereas the effect of friction causes the surface winds to move more slowly and cross the isobars at an angle.

ff	Miles per hour
◎	Calm
	1–2
	3–8
	9–14
	15–20
	21–25
	26–31
	32–37
	38–43
	44–49
	50–54
	55–60
	61–66
	67–71
	72–77
	78–83
	84–89
	119–123

A. Upper-level weather chart

B. Representation of upper-level chart

FIGURE 13.8   Upper-air weather chart. **A.** This simplified weather chart shows the direction and speed of the upper-air winds. Note from the flags that the airflow is almost parallel to the contours. Like most upper-air charts, this one shows variations in the height (in meters) at which a selected pressure (500 millibars) is found, instead of showing variations in pressure at a fixed height like surface maps. Do not let this confuse you, because there is a simple relationship between height contours and pressure. Places experiencing 500-millibar pressure at higher altitudes (toward the south) are experiencing higher pressures than places where the height contours indicate lower altitudes. Thus, *higher-elevation* contours indicate *higher* pressures, and *lower-elevation* contours indicate *lower* pressures. **B.** Representation of the 500-millibar surface shown in the upper-air weather chart above.

A. Upper-level wind (no friction)

B. Surface wind (effect of friction)

FIGURE 13.9 Comparison between upper-level winds and surface winds showing the effects of friction on airflow. Friction slows surface wind speed, which weakens the Coriolis effect, causing the winds to cross the isobars and move toward the lower pressure.

HIGHS AND LOWS

Earth's Dynamic Atmosphere
▼ Air Pressure and Wind

Among the most common features on any weather map are areas designated as pressure centers. **Cyclones**, or **lows**, are centers of low pressure, and **anticyclones**, or **highs**, are high-pressure centers. As **FIGURE 13.10** illustrates, the pressure decreases from the outer isobars toward the center in a cyclone. In an anticyclone, just the opposite is the case—the values of the isobars increase from the outside toward the

center. Knowing just a few basic facts about centers of high and low pressure greatly increases your understanding of current and forthcoming weather.

Cyclonic and Anticyclonic Winds

From the preceding section, you learned that the two most significant factors that affect wind are the pressure-gradient force and the Coriolis effect. Winds move from higher pressure to lower pressure and are deflected to the right or left by Earth's rotation. When these controls of airflow are applied to pressure centers in the Northern Hemisphere, the result is that winds blow inward and counterclockwise around a low (**FIGURE 13.11A**). Around a high, they blow outward and clockwise (Figure 13.10).

In the Southern Hemisphere, the Coriolis effect deflects the winds to the left; therefore, winds around a low blow clockwise, and winds around a high move counterclockwise (**FIGURE 13.11B**). In either hemisphere, friction causes a net inflow (**convergence**) around a cyclone and a net outflow (**divergence**) around an anticyclone.

Weather Generalizations About Highs and Lows

Rising air is associated with cloud formation and precipitation, whereas subsidence produces clear skies. This section will discuss how the movement of air can itself create

FIGURE 13.10 Cyclonic and anticyclonic winds in the Northern Hemisphere. Arrows show that winds blow into and counterclockwise around a low. By contrast, around a high, winds blow outward and clockwise.

A.

B.

FIGURE 13.11   Cyclonic circulation in the Northern and Southern hemispheres. The cloud patterns in these images allow us to "see" the circulation pattern in the lower atmosphere. **A.** This satellite image shows a large low-pressure center in the Gulf of Alaska on August 17, 2004. The cloud pattern clearly shows an inward and *counterclockwise* spiral. **B.** This image from March 26, 2004, shows a strong cyclonic storm in the South Atlantic near the coast of Brazil. The cloud pattern reveals an inward and *clockwise* circulation. (NASA)

pressure change and generate winds. After doing so, we will examine the relation between horizontal and vertical flow, and their effects on the weather.

Let us first consider a surface low-pressure system where the air is spiraling inward. The net inward transport of air causes a shrinking of the area occupied by the air mass, a process that is termed *horizontal convergence*. Whenever air converges horizontally, it must pile up—that is, increase in height to allow for the decreased area it now occupies. This generates a "taller" and therefore heavier air column. Yet, a surface low can exist only as long as the column of air exerts less pressure than that occurring in surrounding regions. We seem to have encountered a paradox—a low-pressure center causes a net accumulation of air, which increases its pressure. Consequently, a surface cyclone should quickly eradicate itself in a manner not unlike what happens when a vacuum-packed can is opened.

For a surface low to exist for very long, compensation must occur at some layer aloft. For example, surface convergence could be maintained if divergence (spreading out) aloft occurred at a rate equal to the inflow below. **FIGURE 13.12** shows the relationship between surface convergence and divergence aloft that is needed to maintain a low-pressure center.

Divergence aloft may even exceed surface convergence, thereby resulting in intensified surface inflow and accelerated vertical motion. Thus, divergence aloft can intensify storm centers as well as maintain them. On the other hand, inadequate divergence aloft permits surface flow to "fill" and weaken the accompanying cyclone.

Note that surface convergence about a cyclone causes a net upward movement. The rate of this vertical movement is slow, generally less than 1 kilometer (0.6 mile) per day. Nevertheless, because rising air often results in cloud formation and precipitation, a low-pressure center is generally related to unstable conditions and stormy weather (**FIGURE 13.13A**).

As often as not, it is divergence aloft that creates a surface low. Spreading out aloft initiates upflow in the atmosphere directly below, eventually working its way to the surface, where inflow is encouraged.

Like their cyclonic counterparts, anticyclones must be maintained from above. Outflow near the surface is accompanied by convergence aloft and general subsidence of the air column (Figure 13.12). Because descending air is compressed and warmed, cloud formation and precipitation are unlikely in an anticyclone. Thus, fair weather can usually be expected with the approach of a high-pressure center (**FIGURE 13.13B**).

For reasons that should now be obvious, it has been common practice to print on household barometers the words "stormy" at the low-pressure end and "fair" on the high-pressure end. By noting whether the pressure is rising, falling, or steady, we have a good indication of what the forthcoming weather will be. Such a determination, called the **pressure**, or **barometric**, **tendency**, is a useful aid in short-range weather prediction.

You should now be better able to understand why television weather reporters emphasize the positions and projected paths of cyclones and anticyclones. The "villain" on these weather programs is always the low-pressure center, which

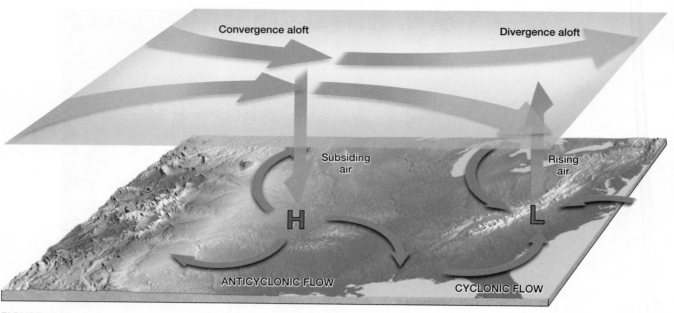

FIGURE 13.12 Airflow associated with surface cyclones and anticyclones. A low, or cyclone, has converging surface winds and rising air, causing cloudy conditions. A high, or anticyclone, has diverging surface winds and descending air, which leads to clear skies and fair weather.

produces "bad" weather in any season. Lows move in roughly a west-to-east direction across the United States and require a few days to more than a week for the journey. Because their paths can be somewhat erratic, accurate prediction of their migration is difficult, although essential, for short-range forecasting.

Meteorologists must also determine if the flow aloft will intensify an embryo storm or act to suppress its development.

Because of the close tie between conditions at the surface and those aloft, a great deal of emphasis has been placed on the importance and understanding of the total atmospheric circulation, particularly in the midlatitudes. We will now examine the workings of Earth's general atmospheric circulation and then again consider the structure of the cyclone in light of this knowledge.

A.

B.

FIGURE 13.13 These two photographs illustrate the basic weather generalizations associated with pressure centers. **A.** A rainy day in New York City. Centers of low pressure are frequently associated with cloudy conditions and precipitation. (Photo by David Grossman/Alamay) **B.** By contrast, clear skies and "fair" weather may be expected when an area is under the influence of high pressure. This scene is in New York City's Central Park. (Joseph A. Rosen/Ambient Images)

FIGURE 13.14   Global circulation on a nonrotating Earth. A simple convection system is produced by unequal heating of the atmosphere on a nonrotating Earth.

GENERAL CIRCULATION OF THE ATMOSPHERE

As noted, the underlying cause of wind is unequal heating of Earth's surface. In tropical regions, more solar radiation is received than is radiated back to space. In polar regions, the opposite is true—less solar energy is received than is lost. Attempting to balance these differences, the atmosphere acts as a giant heat-transfer system, moving warm air poleward and cool air equatorward. On a smaller scale, but for the same reason, ocean currents also contribute to this global heat transfer. The general circulation is complex, and a great deal has yet to be explained. We can, however, develop a general understanding by first considering the circulation that would occur on a nonrotating Earth having a uniform surface. We will then modify this system to fit observed patterns.

Circulation on a Nonrotating Earth

On a hypothetical nonrotating planet with a smooth surface of either all land or all water, two large thermally produced cells would form (**FIGURE 13.14**). The heated equatorial air would rise until it reached the tropopause, which acts like a lid and deflects the air poleward. Eventually, this upper-level airflow would reach the poles, sink, spread out in all directions at the surface, and move back toward the equator.

Once there, it would be reheated and start its journey over again. This hypothetical circulation system has upper-level air flowing poleward and surface air flowing equatorward.

If we add the effect of rotation, this simple convection system will break down into smaller cells. **FIGURE 13.15** illustrates the three pairs of cells proposed to carry on the task of heat redistribution on a rotating planet. The polar and tropical cells retain the characteristics of the thermally generated convection described earlier. The nature of the midlatitude circulation is more complex and will be discussed in more detail in a later section.

Idealized Global Circulation

Near the equator, the rising air is associated with the pressure zone known as the **equatorial low**—a region marked by abundant precipitation. As the upper-level flow from the equatorial low reaches 20 to 30 degrees latitude, north or south, it sinks back toward the surface. This subsidence and associated adiabatic heating produce hot, arid conditions. The center of this zone of subsiding dry air is the **subtropical high**, which encircles the globe near 30 degrees latitude, north and south (Figure 13.15). The great deserts of Australia, Arabia, and Africa exist because of the stable, dry condition caused by the subtropical highs.

At the surface, airflow is outward from the center of the subtropical high. Some of the air travels equatorward and is deflected by the Coriolis effect, producing the reliable

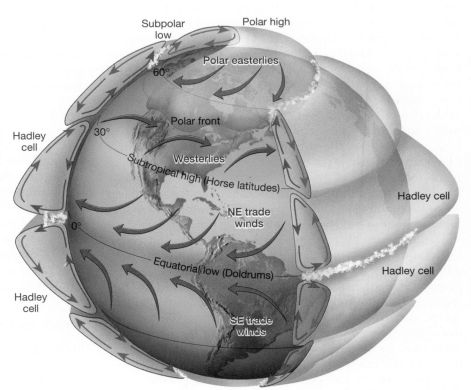

FIGURE 13.15   Idealized global circulation proposed for the three-cell circulation model of a rotating Earth.

trade winds. The remainder travels poleward and is also deflected, generating the prevailing **westerlies** of the midlatitudes. As the westerlies move poleward, they encounter the cool **polar easterlies** in the region of the **subpolar low**. The interaction of these warm and cool winds produces the stormy belt known as the **polar front**. The source region for the variable polar easterlies is the **polar high**. Here, cold polar air is subsiding and spreading equatorward.

In summary, this simplified global circulation is dominated by four pressure zones. The subtropical and polar highs are areas of dry subsiding air that flows outward at the surface, producing the prevailing winds. The low-pressure zones of the equatorial and subpolar regions are associated with inward and upward airflow accompanied by clouds and precipitation.

Influence of Continents

Up to this point, we have described the surface pressure and associated winds as continuous belts around Earth. However, the only truly continuous pressure belt is the subpolar low in the Southern Hemisphere, where the ocean is uninterrupted by landmasses. At other latitudes, particularly in the Northern Hemisphere, where landmasses break up the ocean surface, large seasonal temperature differences disrupt the pattern. **FIGURE 13.16** shows the resulting pressure and wind patterns for January and July. The circulation over the oceans is dominated by semipermanent cells of high pressure in the subtropics and cells of low pressure over the subpolar regions. The subtropical highs are responsible for the trade winds and westerlies, as mentioned earlier.

The large landmasses, on the other hand, particularly Asia, become cold in the winter and develop a seasonal high-pressure system from which surface flow is directed off the land (Figure 13.16). In the summer, the opposite occurs; the landmasses are heated and develop a low-pressure cell, which permits air to flow onto the land. These seasonal changes in wind direction are known as the **monsoons**. During warm months, areas such as India experience a flow of warm, water-laden air from the Indian Ocean, which produces the rainy summer monsoon. The winter monsoon is dominated by dry continental air. A similar situation exists, but to a lesser extent, over North America.

In summary, the general circulation is produced by semipermanent cells of high and low pressure over the oceans and is complicated by seasonal pressure changes over land.

THE WESTERLIES

The circulation in the midlatitudes, the zone of the westerlies, is complex and does not fit the convection system proposed for the tropics. Between 30 and 60 degrees latitude, the general west-to-east flow is interrupted by the migration of cyclones and anticyclones. In the Northern Hemisphere, these cells move from west to east around the globe, creating an anticyclonic (clockwise) flow or a cyclonic (counterclockwise) flow in their area of influence. A close correlation exists between the paths taken by these surface pressure systems and the position of the upper-level airflow, indicating that the upper air steers the movement of cyclonic and anticyclonic systems.

Among the most obvious features of the flow aloft are the seasonal changes. The steep temperature gradient across the middle latitudes in the winter months corresponds to a stronger flow aloft. In addition, the polar jet stream fluctuates seasonally such that its average position migrates southward with the approach of winter, and northward as summer nears. By midwinter, the jet core may penetrate as far south as central Florida.

Because the paths of low-pressure centers are guided by the flow aloft, we can expect the southern tier of states to experience more of their stormy weather in the winter season. During the hot summer months, the storm track is across the northern states, and some cyclones never leave Canada. The northerly storm track associated with summer also applies to Pacific storms, which move toward Alaska during the warm months, thus producing an extended dry season for much of the West Coast. The number of cyclones generated is seasonal as well, with the largest number occurring in the cooler months when the temperature gradients are greatest. This fact is in agreement with the role of cyclonic storms in the distribution of heat across the midlatitudes.

LOCAL WINDS

Now that we have examined Earth's large-scale circulation, let us turn briefly to winds that influence much smaller areas. Remember that all winds are produced for the same reason: pressure differences that arise because of temperature differences caused by unequal heating of Earth's surface. *Local winds* are simply small-scale winds produced by a locally generated pressure gradient. Those described here are caused either by topographic effects or by variations in surface composition in the immediate area.

Land and Sea Breezes

In coastal areas during the warm summer months, the land is heated more intensely during the daylight hours than the adjacent body of water. As a result, the air above the land surface heats, expands, and rises, creating an area of lower pressure. A **sea breeze** then develops, because cooler air over the water (higher pressure) moves toward the warmer land

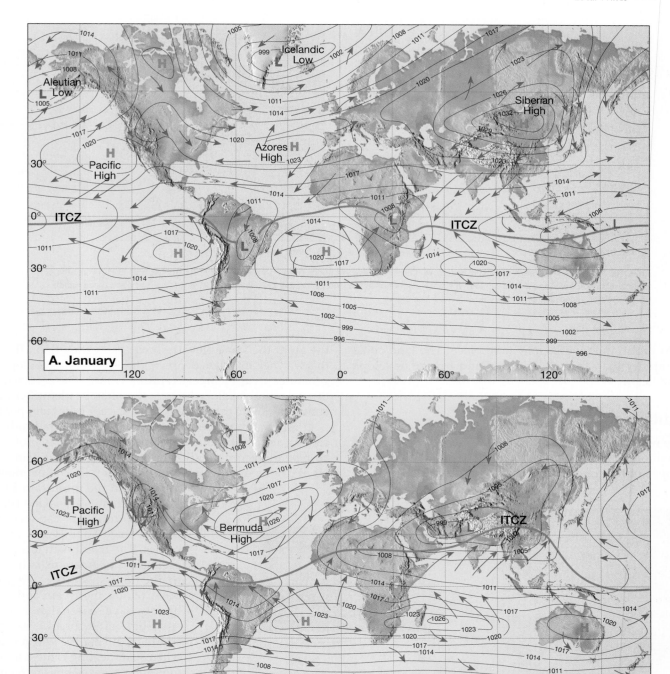

FIGURE 13.16 Average surface barometric pressure in millibars for **A.** January and **B.** July, with associated winds. The pressure zones clearly migrate north-south following the Sun's vertical rays. The line labeled "ITCZ" refers to the *intertropical convergence zone* and corresponds to the equatorial low. This region of ascending moist hot air is associated with abundant precipitation. It gets its name because it is the region where the trade winds converge.

(lower pressure) (**FIGURE 13.17A**). The sea breeze begins to develop shortly before noon and generally reaches its greatest intensity during the mid- to late afternoon. These relatively cool winds can be a significant moderating influence on afternoon temperatures in coastal areas. Small-scale sea breezes can also develop along the shores of large lakes. People who live in a city near the Great Lakes, such as Chicago, recognize this lake effect, especially in the summer. They are reminded daily by weather reports of the cool temperatures near the lake as compared to warmer outlying areas.

A. Sea breeze

B. Land breeze

FIGURE 13.17   A sea breeze and a land breeze. **A.** During the daylight hours, the air above the land heats and expands, creating an area of lower pressure. Cooler and denser air over the water moves onto the land, generating a *sea breeze*. **B.** At night, the land cools more rapidly than the water, generating an offshore flow called a *land breeze*.

At night, the reverse may take place. The land cools more rapidly than the sea, and the **land breeze** develops (**FIGURE 13.17B**).

Mountain and Valley Breezes

A daily wind similar to land and sea breezes occurs in many mountainous regions. During daylight hours, the air along the slopes of the mountains is heated more intensely than the air at the same elevation over the valley floor. Because this warmer air is less dense, it glides up along the slope and generates a **valley breeze** (**FIGURE 13.18A**). The occurrence of these daytime upslope breezes can often be identified by the cumulus clouds that develop on adjacent mountain peaks.

After sunset, the pattern may reverse. Rapid radiation cooling along the mountain slopes produces a layer of cooler air next to the ground. Because cool air is denser than warm air, it drains downslope into the valley. This movement of air is called the **mountain breeze** (**FIGURE 13.18B**). The same type of cool air drainage can occur in places that have very modest slopes. The result is that the coldest pockets of air are usually found in the lowest spots. Like many other winds, mountain and valley breezes have seasonal preferences. Although valley breezes are most common during the warm season when solar heating is most intense, mountain breezes tend to be more dominant in the cold season.

A. Valley breeze

FIGURE 13.18   Valley and mountain breezes. **A.** Heating during the daylight hours warms the air along the mountain slopes. This warm air rises, generating a valley breeze. **B.** After sunset, cooling of the air near the mountain can result in cool air drainage into the valley, producing the mountain breeze.

B. Mountain breeze

Chinook and Santa Ana Winds

Warm, dry winds sometimes move down the east slopes of the Rockies, where they are called **chinooks**. Such winds are often created when a strong pressure gradient develops in a mountainous region. As the air descends the leeward slopes of the mountains, it is heated adiabatically (by compression). Because condensation

"Snow eaters" is a local term for chinooks, the warm, dry winds that descend the eastern slopes of the Rockies. These winds have been known to melt more than a foot of snow in a single day. A chinook that moved through Granville, North Dakota, on February 21, 1918, caused temperatures to rise from $-33°F$ to $50°F$, an increase of $83°F!$

FIGURE 13.19   This satellite image shows strong Santa Ana winds fanning the flames of several large wildfires in Southern California on October 27, 2003. These fires scorched more than 740,000 acres and destroyed more than 3000 homes. (NASA)

may have occurred as the air ascended the windward side, releasing latent heat, the air descending the leeward slope will be warmer and drier than it was at a similar elevation on the windward side. Although the temperature of these winds is generally less than $10°C$ ($50°F$), which is not particularly warm, they occur mostly in the winter and spring when the affected areas may be experiencing below-freezing temperatures. Thus, by comparison, these dry, warm winds often bring a drastic change. When the ground has a snow cover, these winds are known to melt it in short order. The word *chinook* literally means "snow eater."

A chinooklike wind that occurs in southern California is the **Santa Ana.** These hot, desiccating winds greatly increase the threat of fire in this already dry area (**FIGURE 13.19**).

HOW WIND IS MEASURED

Two basic wind measurements, direction and speed, are particularly significant to weather observers. One simple device for determining both measurements is the *wind sock* that is a common sight at small airports and landing strips

(**FIGURE 13.20A**). The cone-shaped bag is open at both ends and is free to change position with shifts in wind direction. The degree to which the sock is inflated is an indication of wind speed.

Winds are always labeled by the direction from which they blow. A north wind blows *from* the north *toward* the south, an east wind *from* the east *toward* the west. The instrument most commonly used to determine wind direction is the **wind vane** (**FIGURE 13.20B**, upper right). This instrument, a common sight on many buildings, always points *into* the wind. The wind direction is often shown on a dial that is connected to the wind vane. The dial indicates wind direction, either by points of the compass (N, NE, E, SE, etc.) or by a scale of $0°$ to $360°$. On the latter scale, $0°$ or $360°$ are both north, $90°$ is east, $180°$ is south, and $270°$ is west.

Wind speed is commonly measured using a **cup anemometer** (Figure 13.20B, upper left). The wind speed is read from a dial much like the speedometer of an automobile. Places where winds are steady and speeds are relatively high are potential sites for tapping wind energy.

When the wind consistently blows more often from one direction than from any other, it is called a **prevailing wind**. You may be familiar with the prevailing westerlies that dominate the circulation in the midlatitudes. In the United States, for example, these winds consistently move the "weather" from west to east across the continent. Embedded within this general eastward flow are cells of high and low pressure with their characteristic clockwise and counterclockwise flow. As a result, the winds associated with the westerlies, as measured at the surface, often vary considerably from day to day and from place to place. By contrast, the direction of airflow associated with the belt of trade winds is much more consistent, as can be seen in **FIGURE 13.21**.

By knowing the locations of cyclones and anticyclones in relation to where you are, you can predict the changes in wind direction that will occur as a pressure center moves past. Because changes in wind direction often bring changes in temperature and moisture conditions, the ability to predict the winds can be very useful. In the Midwest, for example, a north wind may bring cool, dry air from Canada, whereas a south wind may bring warm, humid air from the Gulf of Mexico. Sir Francis Bacon summed it up nicely when he wrote, "Every wind has its weather."

The highest wind speed recorded at a surface station is 372 km (231 mi) per hour, measured April 12, 1934, at Mount Washington, New Hampshire. Located at an elevation of 1886 m (6288 ft), the observatory atop Mount Washington has an average wind speed of 56 km (35 mi) per hour. Faster wind speeds have undoubtedly occurred, but no instruments were in place to record them.

A.

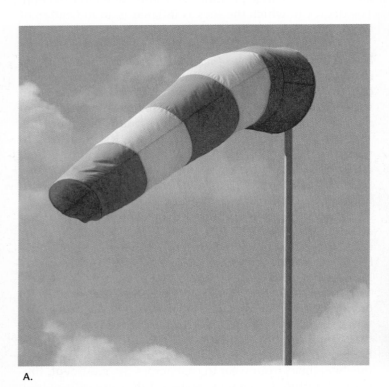

B.

FIGURE 13.20 **A.** A *wind sock* is a common device for determining wind direction and estimating wind speed. They are common sights at small airports and landing strips. **B.** Wind vane (right) and cup anemometer (left). The wind vane shows wind direction and the anemometer measures wind speed. (Photo by Belfort Instrument Company)

A. Westerlies (winter)

B. Southeast Trades (winter)

FIGURE 13.21 Wind roses showing the percentage of time airflow is from various directions. **A.** Wind frequency for the winter in the eastern United States. **B.** Wind frequency for the winter in northern Australia. Note the reliability of the southeast trades in Australia as compared to the westerlies in the eastern United States. (Data from G. T. Trewartha)

THE CHAPTER IN REVIEW

• Air has weight: At sea level, it exerts a pressure of 1 kilogram per square centimeter (14.7 pounds per square inch). *Air pressure* is the force exerted by the weight of air above. With increasing altitude, there is less air above to exert a force, and thus air pressure decreases with altitude, rapidly at first, then much more slowly. The unit used by meteorologists to measure atmospheric pressure is the *millibar. Standard sea-level pressure* is expressed as 1013.2 millibars. *Isobars* are lines on a weather map that connect places of equal air pressures.

• A *mercury barometer* measures air pressure using a column of mercury in a glass tube sealed at one end and inverted in a dish of mercury. It measures atmospheric pressure in *inches of mercury*, the height of the column of mercury in the barometer. Standard atmospheric pressure at sea level equals 29.92 inches of mercury. As air pressure increases, the mercury in the tube rises, and when air pressure decreases, so does the height of the column of mercury. *Aneroid* ("without liquid") *barometers* consist of partially evacuated metal chambers that compress as air pressure increases and expand as pressure decreases.

• *Wind* is the horizontal flow of air from areas of higher pressure toward areas of lower pressure. Winds are controlled by the following combination of forces: (1) the *pressure-gradient force* (amount of pressure change over a given distance), (2) *Coriolis effect* (deflective effect of Earth's rotation, to the right in the Northern Hemisphere and to the left in the Southern Hemisphere), and (3) *friction* with Earth's surface (slows the movement of air and alters wind direction).

• The two types of pressure centers are (1) *cyclones,* or *lows* (centers of low pressure), and (2) *anticyclones,* or *highs* (high-pressure centers). In the Northern Hemisphere, winds around a low (cyclone) are counterclockwise and inward. Around a high (anticyclone), they are clockwise and outward. In the Southern Hemisphere, the Coriolis effect causes winds to be clockwise around a low and counterclockwise around a high. Because air rises and cools adiabatically in a low-pressure center, cloudy conditions and precipitation are often associated with their passage. In a high-pressure center, descending air is compressed and warmed; therefore, cloud formation and precipitation are unlikely in an anticyclone, and "fair" weather is usually expected.

• Earth's *global pressure zones* include the *equatorial low, subtropical high, subpolar low,* and *polar high*. The *global surface winds* associated with these pressure zones are the *trade winds, westerlies,* and *polar easterlies.*

• Particularly in the Northern Hemisphere, large seasonal temperature differences over continents disrupt the idealized, or zonal, global patterns of pressure and wind. In winter, large, cold landmasses develop a seasonal high-pressure system from which surface airflow is directed off the land. In summer, landmasses are heated and a low-pressure system develops over them, which permits air to flow onto the land. These seasonal changes in wind direction are known as *monsoons.*

• In the middle latitudes, between 30 and 60 degrees latitude, the general west-to-east flow of the westerlies is interrupted by the migration of cyclones and anticyclones. The paths taken by these cyclonic and anticyclonic systems is closely correlated to upper-level airflow and the polar jet stream. The average position of the polar *jet stream,* and hence the paths followed by cyclones, migrates southward with the approach of winter and northward as summer nears.

• *Local winds* are small-scale winds produced by a locally generated pressure gradient. Local winds include *sea and land breezes* (formed along a coast because of daily pressure differences over land and water), *valley and mountain breezes* (in mountainous areas where the air along slopes heats differently than does the air at the same elevation over the valley floor), and *chinook and Santa Ana winds* (warm, dry winds created when air descends the leeward side of a mountain and warms by compression).

• The two basic wind measurements are *direction* and *speed*. Winds are always labeled by the direction *from* which they blow. Wind direction is measured with a *wind vane,* and wind speed is measured using a *cup anemometer.*

KEY TERMS

air pressure (p. 372)

aneroid barometer (p. 373)

anticyclone (high) (p. 378)

barograph (p. 373)

barometric tendency (p. 379)

chinook (p. 384)

convergence (p. 378)

Coriolis effect (p. 375)

cup anemometer (p. 385)

cyclone (low) (p. 378)

divergence (p. 378)

equatorial low (p. 381)

geostrophic wind (p. 376)

isobar (p. 374)

jet stream (p. 377)

land breeze (p. 384)

mercury barometer (p. 373)

monsoon (p. 382)

mountain breeze (p. 384)

polar easterlies (p. 382)

polar front (p. 382)

polar high (p. 382)

pressure gradient
  (p. 374)

pressure tendency
  (p. 379)

prevailing wind (p. 385)

Santa Ana (p. 385)

sea breeze (p. 382)

subpolar low (p. 382)

subtropical high (p. 381)

trade winds (p. 382)

valley breeze (p. 384)

westerlies (p. 382)

wind (p. 374)

wind vane (p. 385)

QUESTIONS FOR REVIEW

1. What is standard sea-level pressure in millibars? In inches of mercury? In pounds per square inch?

2. Mercury is 13 times heavier than water. If you built a barometer using water rather than mercury, how tall would it have to be to record standard sea-level pressure (in inches of water)?

3. Describe the principle of the aneroid barometer.

4. What force is responsible for generating wind?

5. Write a generalization relating the spacing of isobars to the speed of wind.

6. How does the Coriolis effect modify air movement?

7. Contrast surface winds and upper-air winds in terms of speed and direction.

8. Describe the weather that usually accompanies a drop in barometric pressure and a rise in barometric pressure.

9. Sketch a diagram (isobars and wind arrows) showing the winds associated with surface cyclones and anticyclones in both the Northern and Southern hemispheres.

10. If you live in the Northern Hemisphere and are directly west of a cyclone, what will the wind direction most probably be? What will the wind direction be if you are west of an anticyclone?

11. The following questions relate to the global pattern of air pressure and winds.

    a. From which pressure zone do the trade winds diverge?

    b. Which prevailing wind belts converge in the stormy region known as the polar front?

    c. Which pressure belt is associated with the equator?

12. What influence does upper-level airflow seem to have on surface pressure systems?

13. Describe the monsoon circulation of India.

14. What is a local wind? List three examples.

15. A northeast wind is blowing *from* the ___ (direction) *toward* the ___ (direction).

COMPANION WEBSITE

The *Foundations of Earth Science* Website uses the resources and flexibility of the Internet to aid in your study of the topics in this chapter. Written and developed by the authors and other Earth science instructors, this site will help improve your understanding of Earth science. Visit **www.mygeoscienceplace.com** in order to:

• **Review** key chapter concepts.

• **Read** with links to the ebook and to chapter-specific web resources.

• **Visualize** and comprehend challenging topics using learning activities in *GEODe: Earth Science*.

• **Test** yourself with online quizzes.

GEODe: EARTH SCIENCE

GEODe: Earth Science is a valuable and easy to use learning aid that can be accessed from your book's Companion Website: **www.mygeoscienceplace.com**. It is a dynamic instructional tool that promotes understanding and reinforces important concepts by using tutorials, animations, and exercises that actively engage the student.

GEODe Earth Science
Earth's Dynamic Atmosphere

Air Pressure and Wind

Measuring Air Pressure

Simple mercury barometer

Vacuum

29.92 inches (76 centimeters)

Mercury

Air pressure   Air pressure

Mercury

To measure the force exerted by air, Torricelli filled a glass tube, closed at one end, with mercury and inverted it into a dish of mercury.

1959

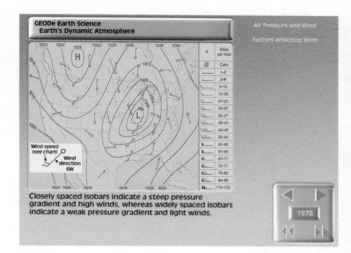

GEODe Earth Science
Earth's Dynamic Atmosphere

Air Pressure and Wind

Factors Affecting Wind

ft	Miles per hour
⊝	Calm
	1–2
	3–8
	9–14
	15–20
	21–25
	26–31
	32–37
	38–43
	44–49
	50–54
	55–60
	61–66
	67–71
	72–77
	78–83
	84–89
	119–123

Wind speed (see chart)   Wind direction SW

Closely spaced isobars indicate a steep pressure gradient and high winds, whereas widely spaced isobars indicate a weak pressure gradient and light winds.

1978

WEATHER PATTERNS AND SEVERE WEATHER

To assist you in learning the important concepts in this chapter, you will find it helpful to focus on the following questions:

1. What is an air mass?

2. How are air masses classified? What is the general weather associated with each air-mass type?

3. What are fronts? How do warm fronts and cold fronts differ?

4. What are the primary weather producers in the middle latitudes? What are the weather patterns associated with these systems?

5. What atmospheric conditions produce thunderstorms, tornadoes, and hurricanes?

Tornadoes are intense and destructive local storms of short duration that cause many deaths each year. (Photo by Alan R. Moller/Getty Images, Inc.— Stone Allstock)

Tornadoes and hurricanes rank among nature's most destructive forces. Each spring, newspapers report the death and destruction left in the wake of a "band" of tornadoes. During late summer and fall, we hear occasional news reports about hurricanes. Storms with names such as Katrina, Rita, Charley, and Ike make front-page headlines (**FIGURE 14.1**). Thunderstorms, although less intense and far more common than tornadoes and hurricanes, will also be part of our discussion of severe weather in this chapter. Before looking at violent weather, however, we will study those atmospheric phenomena that most often affect our day-to-day weather: air masses, fronts, and traveling middle-latitude cyclones. We will see the interplay of the elements of weather discussed in Chapters 11, 12, and 13.

FIGURE 14.1 Hurricane Rita became a Category 5 hurricane late on September 21, 2005, with sustained winds of 275 kilometers (170 miles) per hour and a central pressure of 897 millibars, making it the third most powerful Atlantic basin storm ever measured. When this image was taken about midday on September 22, the storm was slightly weaker. (NASA)

AIR MASSES

Earth's Dynamic Atmosphere
▼ Basic Weather Patterns

For many people who live in the middle latitudes, which include much of the United States, summer heat waves and winter cold spells are familiar experiences. In the first instance, several days of high temperatures and oppressive humidities may finally end when a series of thunderstorms pass through the area, followed by a few days of relatively cool relief. By contrast, the clear skies that often accompany a span of frigid subzero days may be replaced by thick gray clouds and a period of snow as temperatures rise to levels that seem mild when compared to those that existed just a day earlier. In both examples, what was experienced was a period of generally constant weather conditions followed by a relatively short period of change, and then the reestablishment of a new set of weather conditions that remained for perhaps several days before changing again.

What Is an Air Mass?

The weather patterns just described are the result of movements of large bodies of air, called air masses. An **air mass,** as the term implies, is an immense body of air, typically 1600 kilometers (1000 miles) or more across and perhaps several kilometers thick, that is characterized by a similarity of temperature and moisture at any given altitude. When this air moves out of its region of origin, it will carry these temperatures and moisture conditions elsewhere, eventually affecting a large portion of a continent.

An excellent example of the influence of an air mass is illustrated in **FIGURE 14.2**, which shows a cold, dry mass from northern Canada moving southward. With a beginning temperature of –46°C (–51°F), the air mass warms to –33°C (–27°F) by the time it reaches Winnipeg. It continues to warm as it moves southward through the Great Plains and into Mexico. Throughout its southward journey, the air mass becomes warmer. But it also brings some of the coldest weather of the winter to the places in its path. Thus, the air mass is modified, but it also modifies the weather in the areas over which it moves.

The horizontal uniformity of an air mass is not perfect, of course. Because air masses extend over large areas, small differences in temperature and humidity from place to place occur. Still, the differences observed within an air mass are small compared to the rapid changes experienced across air-mass boundaries.

Since it may take several days for an air mass to move across an area, the region under its influence will probably experience fairly constant weather, a situation called **air-mass weather.** Certainly, there may be some day-to-day variations, but the events will be very unlike those in an adjacent air mass.

The air-mass concept is an important one because it is closely related to the study of atmospheric disturbances. Most disturbances in the middle latitudes originate along the boundary zones that separate different air masses.

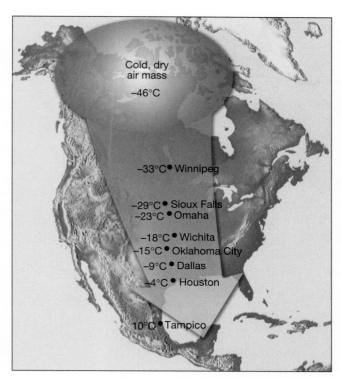

FIGURE 14.2 As this frigid Canadian air mass moved southward, it brought some of the coldest weather of the winter. (After Tom L. McKnight, *Physical Geography*, 5th ed. Upper Saddle River, NJ: Prentice Hall, 1996, p. 174)

A. Winter pattern

B. Summer pattern

FIGURE 14.3 Air-mass source regions for North America. Source regions are largely confined to subtropical and subpolar locations. The fact that the middle latitudes are the site where cold and warm air masses clash, often because the converging winds of a traveling cyclone draw them together, means that this zone lacks the conditions necessary to be a source region. The differences between polar and arctic are relatively small and serve to indicate the degree of coldness of the respective air masses. By comparing the winter (**A**) and summer (**B**) maps, it is clear that the extent and temperature characteristics fluctuate.

Source Regions

When a portion of the lower atmosphere moves slowly or stagnates over a relatively uniform surface, the air will assume the distinguishing features of that area, particularly with regard to temperature and moisture conditions.

The area where an air mass acquires its characteristic properties of temperature and moisture is called its **source region.** The source regions that produce air masses that influence North America are shown in **FIGURE 14.3.**

Air masses are classified according to their source region. **Polar (P)** and **arctic (A) air masses** originate in high latitudes toward Earth's poles, whereas those that form in low latitudes are called **tropical (T) air masses.** The designation *polar, arctic,* or *tropical* gives an indication of the temperature characteristics of an air mass. *Polar* and *arctic* indicate cold, and *tropical* indicates warm.

In addition, air masses are classified according to the nature of the surface in the source region. **Continental (c)**

DID YOU KNOW?

When a fast-moving frigid air mass advances from the Canadian arctic into the northern Great Plains, temperatures have been known to plunge 20° to 30°C (40° to 50°F) in a matter of just a few hours. One notable example is a drop of 55.5°C (100°F), from 6.7°C to −48.8°C (44° to −56°F), in 24 hours at Browning, Montana, on January 23–24, 1916.

air masses form over land, and **maritime (m) air masses** originate over water. The designation *continental* or *maritime* suggests the moisture characteristics of the air mass. Continental air is likely to be dry, and maritime air humid.

The basic types of air masses according to this scheme of classification are continental polar (cP), continental arctic (cA), continental tropical (cT), maritime polar (mP), and maritime tropical (mT).

Weather Associated with Air Masses

Continental polar and maritime tropical air masses influence the weather of North America most, especially east of the Rocky Mountains. Continental polar air masses originate in northern Canada, interior Alaska, and the Arctic—areas that are uniformly cold and dry in winter and cool and

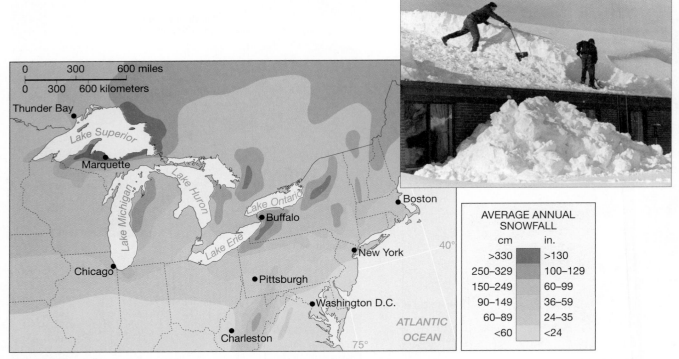

FIGURE 14.4 The snowbelts of the Great Lakes are easy to pick out on this snowfall map. (Data from NOAA) The photo was taken following a six-day lake-effect snowstorm in November 1996 that dropped 175 centimeters (nearly 69 inches) of snow on Chardon, Ohio, setting a new state record. (Photo by Tony Dejak/AP/Wide World Photos)

dry in summer. In winter, an invasion of continental polar air brings the clear skies and cold temperatures we associate with a cold wave as it moves southward from Canada into the United States. In summer, this air mass may bring a few days of cooling relief.

Although cP air masses are not normally associated with heavy precipitation, those that cross the Great Lakes in late autumn and winter sometimes bring snow to the leeward shores. These localized storms often form when the surface weather map indicates no apparent cause for a snowstorm to occur. These are known as **lake-effect snows,** and they make Buffalo and Rochester, New York, among the snowiest cities in the United States (**FIGURE 14.4**).

What causes lake-effect snow? During late autumn and early winter, the temperature contrast between the lakes and adjacent land areas can be large.* The temperature contrast can be especially great when a very cold cP air mass pushes southward across the lakes. When this occurs, the air acquires large quantities of heat and moisture from the relatively warm lake surface. By the time it reaches the opposite shore, the air mass is humid and unstable, and heavy snow showers are likely.

Maritime tropical air masses affecting North America most often originate over the warm waters of the Gulf of Mexico, the Caribbean Sea, or the adjacent Atlantic Ocean.

As you might expect, these air masses are warm, moisture-laden, and usually unstable. Maritime tropical air is the source of much, if not most, of the precipitation in the eastern two-thirds of the United States. In summer, when an mT air mass invades the central and eastern United States, and occasionally southern Canada, it brings the high temperatures and oppressive humidity typically associated with its source region.

Of the two remaining air masses, maritime polar and continental tropical, the latter has the least influence on the weather of North America. Hot, dry continental tropical air, originating in the Southwest and Mexico during the summer, only occasionally affects the weather outside its source region.

During winter, maritime polar air masses coming from the North Pacific often originate as continental polar air masses in Siberia. The cold, dry cP air is transformed into relatively mild, humid, unstable mP air during its long journey across the North Pacific. As this mP air arrives at the western shore of North America, it is often accompanied by low clouds and shower activity. When this air advances inland against the western mountains, orographic uplift produces heavy rain or snow on the windward slopes of the mountains. Maritime polar air also originates in the North Atlantic off the coast of eastern Canada and occasionally influences the weather of the northeastern United States. In winter, when New England is on the northern or northwestern side of a passing low, the counterclockwise cyclonic winds draw in maritime polar air. The result is a storm characterized by snow and cold temperatures, known locally as a *nor'easter.*

*Recall that land cools more rapidly and to lower temperatures than water. See the discussion of "Land and Water" in the section on "Why Temperatures Vary: The Controls of Temperature" in Chapter 11.

FRONTS

Earth's Dynamic Atmosphere
▽ Basic Weather Patterns

Fronts are boundaries that separate different air masses, one warmer than the other and often higher in moisture content. Fronts can form between any two contrasting air masses. Considering the vast size of the air masses involved, fronts are relatively narrow, being 15- to 200-kilometer-wide (9- to 120-mile) bands of discontinuity. On the scale of a weather map, they are generally narrow enough to be represented by a broad line (as in Figure 14.8, p. 398).

Above Earth's surface, the front slopes at a low angle so that warmer air overlies cooler air (**FIGURE 14.5**). In the ideal case, the air masses on both sides of the front move in the same direction and at the same speed. Under this condition, the front acts simply as a barrier, moving along between the two contrasting air masses. Generally, however, an air mass on one side of a front is moving faster relative to the frontal boundary than the air mass on the other side. Thus, one air mass actively advances into another and "clashes" with it. In

fact, these boundaries were tagged *fronts* during World War I by Norwegian meteorologists, who visualized them as analogous to battle lines between two armies. It is along these "battlegrounds" that cyclonic circulation (centers of low pressure) develop and generate much of the precipitation and severe weather in the middle latitudes.

As one air mass advances into another, limited mixing occurs along the frontal surface, but for the most part, the air masses retain their distinct identities as one is displaced upward over the other. No matter which air mass is advancing, *it is always the warmer (less dense) air that is forced aloft*, whereas *the cooler (denser) air acts as the wedge upon which lifting takes place*. The term **overrunning** is generally applied to warm air gliding up along a cold air mass. We will now take a look at different types of fronts.

Warm Fronts

When the surface position of a front moves so that warm air occupies territory formerly covered by cooler air, it is called a **warm front** (Figure 14.5). On a weather map, the surface position of a warm front is shown by a red line with red semicircles protruding into the cooler air.

East of the Rockies, warm tropical air often enters the United States from the Gulf of Mexico and overruns receding cool air. As the cold air retreats, friction with the ground slows the advance of the surface position of the front more so than its position aloft. Stated another way, less dense, warm air has a hard time displacing denser, cold air. For this reason, the boundary separating these air masses acquires a very gradual slope. The average slope of a warm front is about 1:200, which means that if you are 200 kilometers (120 miles) ahead of the surface location of a warm front, you will find the frontal surface at a height of 1 kilometer (0.6 mile).

As warm air ascends the retreating wedge of cold air, it expands and cools adiabatically to produce clouds and, frequently, precipitation. The sequence of clouds shown in

FIGURE 14.5   Warm front produced as warm air glides up over a cold air mass. Precipitation is moderate and occurs within a few hundred kilometers of the surface front.

Figure 14.5 typically precedes a warm front. The first sign of the approach of a warm front is the appearance of cirrus clouds overhead. These high clouds form 1000 kilometers (600 miles) or more ahead of the surface front, where the overrunning warm air has ascended high up the wedge of cold air.

As the front nears, cirrus clouds grade into cirrostratus, which blend into denser sheets of altostratus. About 300 kilometers (180 miles) ahead of the front, thicker stratus and nimbostratus clouds appear and rain or snow begins. Because of their slow rate of advance and very low slope, warm fronts usually produce light to moderate precipitation over a large area for an extended period. Warm fronts, however, are occasionally associated with cumulonimbus clouds and thunderstorms. This occurs when the overrunning air is unstable, and the temperatures on opposite sides of the front contrast sharply. At the other extreme, a warm front associated with a dry air mass could pass unnoticed at the surface.

A gradual increase in temperature occurs with the passage of a warm front. The increase is most noticeable when there is a large temperature difference between the adjacent air masses. The moisture content and stability of the encroaching warm air mass largely determine when clear skies will return. During the summer, cumulus, and occasionally cumulonimbus, clouds are embedded in the warm unstable air mass that follows the front. Precipitation from these clouds can be heavy but is usually scattered and of short duration.

Cold Fronts

When dense cold air is actively advancing into a region occupied by warmer air, the boundary is called a **cold front** (**FIGURE 14.6**). As with warm fronts, friction tends to slow the surface position of a cold front more so than its position aloft. However, because of the relative positions of the adjacent air masses, the cold front steepens as it moves. On the average, cold fronts are about twice as

steep as warm fronts, having a slope of perhaps 1:100. In addition, cold fronts advance at speeds around 35 to 50 kilometers (20 to 35 miles) per hour compared to 25 to 35 kilometers (15 to 20 miles) per hour for warm fronts. These two differences—rate of movement and steepness of slope—largely account for the more violent nature of cold-front weather compared to the weather generally accompanying a warm front.

As a cold front approaches, generally from the west or northwest, towering clouds often can be seen in the distance. Near the front, a dark band of ominous clouds foretells the ensuing weather. The forceful lifting of air along a cold front is often so rapid that the latent heat released when water vapor condenses will increase the air's buoyancy appreciably. The heavy downpours and vigorous wind gusts associated with mature cumulonimbus clouds frequently result. A cold front produces roughly the same amount of lifting as a warm front, but over a shorter distance. As a result, the intensity of precipitation is greater, but the duration is shorter. In addition, a marked temperature drop and a wind shift from the south to west or northwest accompany the passage of the front. The sometimes violent weather and sharp temperature contrast along the cold front are symbolized on a weather map by a blue line with blue triangle-shaped points that extend into the warmer air mass (Figure 14.6).

The weather behind a cold front is dominated by a subsiding and relatively cold air mass. Thus, clearing usually begins soon after the front passes. Although the compression of air due to subsidence causes some adiabatic heating, the effect on surface temperatures is minor. In winter, the long, cloudless nights that often follow the passage of a cold front allow for abundant radiation cooling that reduces surface temperatures. When a cold front moves over a relatively warm area, surface heating can produce shallow convection. This, in turn, may generate low cumulus or stratocumulus clouds behind the front.

FIGURE 14.6   Fast-moving cold front and cumulonimbus clouds. Thunderstorms may occur if the warm air is unstable.

Stationary Fronts and Occluded Fronts

Occasionally, the flow on both sides of a front is neither toward the cold air mass nor toward the warm air mass, but almost parallel to the line of the front. Thus, the surface position of the front does not move. This condition is called a **stationary front.** On a weather map, stationary fronts are shown with blue triangular points on one side of the front and red semicircles on the other. At times, some overrunning occurs along a stationary front, most likely causing gentle to moderate precipitation.

The fourth type of front is the **occluded front:** An active cold front overtakes a warm front, as shown in **FIGURE 14.7.** As the advancing cold air wedges the warm front upward, a new front emerges between the advancing cold air and the air over which the warm front is gliding. The weather of an occluded front is generally complex. Most precipitation is associated with the warm air being forced aloft. When

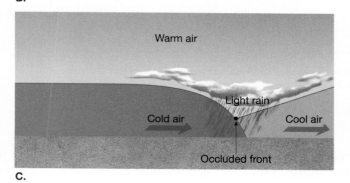

FIGURE 14.7 Stages in the formation of an occluded front. In this example, the air behind the cold front is colder (denser) than the cool air ahead of the warm front. As a result, the cold front wedges the warm front aloft.

conditions are suitable, however, the newly formed front is capable of initiating precipitation of its own.

A word of caution is in order concerning the weather associated with various fronts. Although the preceding discussion will help you recognize the weather patterns associated with fronts, remember that these descriptions are generalizations. The weather generated along any individual front may or may not conform fully to this idealized picture. Fronts, like all aspects of nature, never lend themselves to classification as easily as we would like.

THE MIDDLE-LATITUDE CYCLONE

Earth's Dynamic Atmosphere
▼ Basic Weather Patterns

So far, we have examined the basic elements of weather as well as the dynamics of atmospheric motions. We are now ready to apply our knowledge of these diverse phenomena to an understanding of day-to-day weather patterns in the middle latitudes. For our purposes, *middle latitudes* refers to the region between southern Florida and Alaska. The primary weather producers here are **middle-latitude,** or **midlatitude, cyclones.** On weather maps, such as those used on the Weather Channel, they are shown by an **L,** meaning *low-pressure system.*

Middle-latitude cyclones are large centers of low pressure that generally travel from west to east (**FIGURE 14.8**). Lasting from a few days to more than a week, these weather systems have a counterclockwise circulation with an airflow inward toward their centers. Most middle-latitude cyclones also have a cold front extending from the central area of low pressure, and frequently a warm front as well. Convergence and forceful lifting initiate cloud development and frequently cause abundant precipitation.

As early as the 1800s, it was known that middle-latitude cyclones were the bearers of precipitation and severe weather. But it was not until the early part of the 1900s that a model was developed to explain how cyclones form. A group of Norwegian scientists formulated and published this model in 1918. The model was created primarily from near-surface observations.

Years later, as data from the middle and upper troposphere and from satellite images became available, modifications were necessary. Yet, this model is still a useful working tool for interpreting the weather. If you keep this model in mind when you observe changes in the weather, the changes will no longer come as a surprise. You should begin to see some order in what had appeared to be disorder, and you might even occasionally "predict" the impending weather.

Idealized Weather of a Middle-Latitude Cyclone

The middle-latitude cyclone model provides a useful tool for examining the weather patterns of the middle latitudes. Figure 14.8 illustrates the distribution of clouds and thus the

FIGURE 14.8 Cloud patterns typically associated with a mature middle-latitude cyclone. The middle section is a map view. Note the cross-section lines (F–G, A–E). Above the map is a vertical cross section along line F–G. Below the map is a section along A–E. For cloud abbreviations, refer to Figures 14.5 and 14.6.

regions of possible precipitation associated with a mature system. Compare this drawing to the satellite image shown in **FIGURE 14.9**. It is easy to see why we often refer to the cloud pattern of a midlatitude cyclone as having a "comma" shape.

Guided by the westerlies aloft, cyclones generally move eastward across the United States, so we can expect the first signs of their arrival in the west. However, often in the region of the Mississippi valley, cyclones begin a more northeasterly path and occasionally move directly northward. A midlatitude cyclone typically requires two to four days to move completely across a given region. During that brief period, abrupt changes in atmospheric conditions may

FIGURE 14.9   Satellite view of a mature cyclone over the eastern United States. It is easy to see why we often refer to the cloud pattern of a cyclone as having a "comma" shape. (Photo courtesy of John Jensenius/National Weather Service)

be experienced. This is particularly true in the winter and spring, when the largest temperature contrasts occur across the middle latitudes.

Using Figure 14.8 as a guide, we will now consider these weather producers and what we should expect from them as they move over an area. To facilitate our discussion, Figure 14.8 includes two profiles along lines A–E and F–G.

- Imagine the change in weather as you move along profile A–E. At point A, the sighting of high cirrus clouds would be the first sign of the approaching cyclone. These high clouds can precede the surface front by 1000 kilometers (600 miles) or more, and they generally will be accompanied by falling pressure. As the warm front advances, a lowering and thickening of the cloud deck is noticed.

- Usually within 12 to 24 hours after the first sighting of cirrus clouds, light precipitation begins (point B). As the front nears, the rate of precipitation increases, a rise in temperature is noticed, and winds begin to change from east or southeast to south or southwest.

- With the passage of the warm front, an area is under the influence of a maritime tropical air mass (point C). Generally, the region affected by this sector of the cyclone experiences warm temperatures, south or southwest winds, and generally clear skies, although fair-weather cumulus or altocumulus are not uncommon.

- The relatively warm, humid weather of the warm sector passes quickly and is replaced by gusty winds and precipitation generated along the cold front. The approach of a rapidly advancing cold front is marked by a wall of dark clouds (point D). Severe weather accompanied by heavy

precipitation, hail, and an occasional tornado is a definite possibility at this time of year. The passage of the cold front is easily detected by a wind shift; the southwest winds are replaced by winds from the west to northwest and by a pronounced drop in temperature. Also, rising pressure hints of the subsiding cool, dry air behind the front.

- Once the front passes, skies clear as cooler air invades the region (point E). Often a day or two of almost cloudless deep blue skies occurs unless another cyclone is edging into the region.

A very different set of weather conditions will prevail in those regions north of the storm's center along profile F–G of Figure 14.8. Often the storm reaches its greatest intensity in this zone, and the area along profile F–G receives the brunt of the storm's fury. Temperatures remain cold during the passage of the system, and heavy snow, sleet, and/or freezing rain may develop during the winter months.

The Role of Airflow Aloft

When the earliest studies of midlatitude cyclones were made, little was known about the nature of the airflow in the middle and upper troposphere. Since then, a close relationship has been established between surface disturbances and the flow aloft. Airflow aloft plays an important role in maintaining cyclonic and anticyclonic circulation. In fact, more often than not, these rotating surface wind systems are actually generated by upper-level flow.

Recall that the airflow around a cyclone (low-pressure system) is inward, a fact that leads to mass convergence, or coming together (**FIGURE 14.10**). The resulting accumulation of air must be accompanied by a corresponding increase in surface pressure. Consequently, we might expect a low-pressure system to "fill" rapidly and be eliminated, just as the vacuum in a coffee can is quickly dissipated when we open it. However, this does not occur. On the contrary, cyclones often exist for a week or longer. For this to happen, surface convergence must be offset by a mass outflow at some level aloft (Figure 14.10). As long as divergence (spreading out) aloft is equal to or greater than the surface inflow, the low pressure and its accompanying convergence can be sustained.

Because cyclones are bearers of stormy weather, they have received far more attention than anticyclones. Nevertheless, a close relation exists, which makes it difficult to separate any discussion of these two types of pressure systems. The surface air that feeds a cyclone, for example, generally originates as air flowing out of an anticyclone. Consequently, cyclones and anticyclones typically are found adjacent to each other. Like the cyclone, an anticyclone depends on the flow far above to maintain its circulation. Divergence at the surface is balanced by convergence aloft and general subsidence of the air column (Figure 14.10).

FIGURE 14.10   Idealized diagram depicting the support that divergence and convergence aloft provide to cyclonic and anticyclonic circulation at the surface. Divergence aloft initiates upward air movement, reduced surface pressure, and cyclonic flow. On the other hand, convergence along the jet stream results in general subsidence of the air column, increased surface pressure, and anticyclonic surface winds.

WHAT'S IN A NAME?

Up to now we have examined the middle-latitude cyclones, which play such an important role in causing day-to-day weather changes. Yet the use of the term *cyclone* is often confusing. To many people, the term implies only an intense storm, such as a tornado or a hurricane. When a hurricane unleashes its fury on India or Bangladesh, for example, it is usually reported in the media as a cyclone (the term denoting a hurricane in that part of the world).

Similarly, tornadoes are referred to as cyclones in some places. This custom is particularly common in portions of the Great Plains of the United States. Recall that in *The Wizard of Oz*, Dorothy's house was carried from her Kansas farm to the land of Oz by a cyclone. Indeed, the nickname for the athletic teams at Iowa State University is the *Cyclones* (**FIGURE 14.11**). Although hurricanes and tornadoes are, in fact, cyclones, the vast majority of cyclones are *not* hurricanes or tornadoes. The term *cyclone* simply refers to the circulation around any low-pressure center, no matter how large or intense it is.

Tornadoes and hurricanes are both smaller and more violent than middle-latitude cyclones. Middle-latitude cyclones can have a diameter of 1600 kilometers (1000 miles) or more. By contrast, hurricanes average only 600 kilometers (375 miles) across, and tornadoes, with a diameter of just 0.25 kilometer (0.16 mile) are much too small to show up on a weather map.

The thunderstorm, a much more familiar weather event, hardly needs to be distinguished from tornadoes, hurricanes, and midlatitude cyclones. Unlike the flow of air about these latter storms, the circulation associated with thunderstorms is characterized by strong up-and-down movements. Winds in the vicinity of a thunderstorm do not follow the inward spiral of a cyclone, but they are typically variable and gusty.

Although thunderstorms form "on their own" away from cyclonic storms, they also form in conjunction with cyclones. For instance, thunderstorms are frequently spawned along the cold front of a midlatitude cyclone, where on rare occasions a tornado may descend from the thunderstorm's cumulonimbus tower. Hurricanes also generate widespread thunderstorm activity. Thus, thunderstorms are related in some manner to all three types of cyclones mentioned here.

DID YOU KNOW?

The term *extratropical cyclone* is another name that meteorologists use for a midlatitude cyclone. *Extratropical* means "outside the tropics." By contrast, hurricanes and tropical storms, which form in the lower latitudes are examples of *tropical cyclones*.

FIGURE 14.11   In parts of the Great Plains, cyclone is a synonym for tornado. The nickname for the athletic teams at Iowa State University is the *Cyclones*. (Iowa State University is the only Division I school to use Cyclones as its team name. The pictured logo was created to better communicate the school's image by combining the mascot, a cardinal bird named Cy and the Cyclone team name, a swirling twister in the bird's tail.) (Image courtesy of Iowa State University)

THUNDERSTORMS

Thunderstorms are the first of three severe weather types we will examine in this chapter. Sections on tornadoes and hurricanes follow.

Severe weather has a fascination that everyday weather phenomena cannot provide. The lightning display and booming thunder generated by a severe thunderstorm can be a spectacular event that elicits both awe and fear (**FIGURE 14.12**). Of course, hurricanes and tornadoes also attract a great deal of much deserved attention. A single tornado outbreak or hurricane can cause many deaths as well as billions of dollars in property damage. In a typical year, the United States experiences thousands of violent thunderstorms, hundreds of floods and tornadoes, and several hurricanes.

Thunderstorm Occurrence

Almost everyone has observed various small-scale phenomena that result from the vertical movements of relatively warm, unstable air. Perhaps you have seen a dust devil over an open field on a hot day whirling its dusty load to great heights. Or maybe you have noticed a bird glide effortlessly skyward on an invisible thermal of hot air. These examples illustrate the dynamic thermal instability that occurs during the development of a thunderstorm.

A **thunderstorm** is simply a storm that generates lightning and thunder. It frequently produces gusty winds, heavy rain, and hail. A thunderstorm may be produced by a single cumulonimbus cloud and influence only a small area, or it may be associated with clusters of cumulonimbus clouds covering a large area.

Thunderstorms form when warm, humid air rises in an unstable environment. Various mechanisms can trigger the upward air movement needed to create thunderstorm-producing cumulonimbus clouds. One mechanism, the unequal heating of Earth's surface, significantly contributes to the formation of *air-mass thunderstorms*. These storms are associated with the scattered puffy cumulonimbus clouds that commonly form

FIGURE 14.12   This lightning display occurred near Colorado Springs, Colorado. Lightning produces thunder. The electrical discharge of lightning superheats the air. In less than a second, the temperature rises by as much as 33,000°C. When air is heated this quickly, it expands explosively and produces the sound we hear as thunder. (Photo by Sean Cayton/The Image Works)

within maritime tropical air masses and produce scattered thunderstorms on summer days. Such storms are usually short-lived and seldom produce strong winds or hail.

Another type of thunderstorm not only benefits from uneven surface heating but is associated with the lifting of warm air, as occurs along a front or a mountain slope. Moreover, diverging winds aloft frequently contribute to the formation of these storms because they tend to draw air from lower levels upward beneath them. Some of the thunderstorms of this type may produce high winds, damaging hail, flash floods, and tornadoes. Such storms are described as *severe.*

At any given time, an estimated 2000 thunderstorms are in progress on Earth. As we would expect, the greatest number occur in the tropics, where warmth, plentiful moisture and instability are always present. About 45,000 thunderstorms take place each day, and more than 16 million occur annually around the world. The lightning from these storms strikes Earth 100 times each second (**FIGURE 14.13A**). Annually, the United States experiences about 100,000 thunderstorms and millions of lightning strikes. A glance at **FIGURE 14.13B** shows that thunderstorms are most frequent in Florida and the eastern Gulf Coast region, where such activity is recorded between 70 and 100 days each year. The region on the east side of the Rockies in Colorado and New Mexico is next, with

DID YOU KNOW?

Because lightning and thunder occur simultaneously, it is possible for you to estimate how far away a lightning stroke occurred. Lightning is seen instantaneously, but sound travels more slowly (about 1000 ft per sec) and reaches us later. If thunder is heard five seconds after lightning is seen, the lightning occurred about 5000 ft (1 mi) away.

thunderstorms occurring on 60 to 70 days each year. Most of the rest of the nation experiences thunderstorms on 30 to 50 days annually. Clearly, the western margin of the United States has little thunderstorm activity. The same is true for the northern tier of states and for Canada, where warm, moist, unstable mT air seldom penetrates.

Stages of Thunderstorm Development

All thunderstorms require warm, moist air, which, when lifted, will release sufficient latent heat to provide the buoyancy necessary to maintain its upward flight. This instability

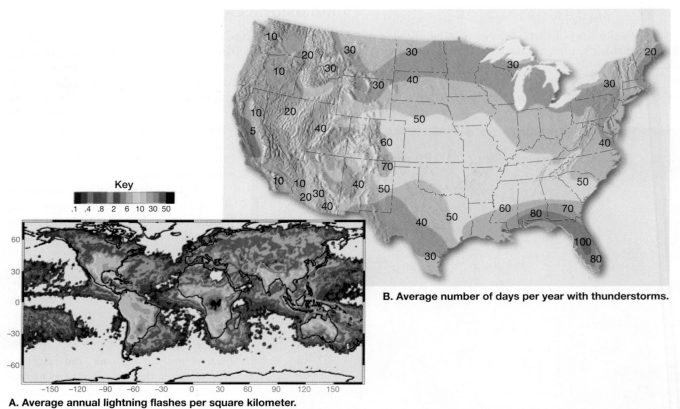

B. Average number of days per year with thunderstorms.

A. Average annual lightning flashes per square kilometer.

FIGURE 14.13   A. Data from space-based optical sensors show the worldwide distribution of lightning, with color variations indicating the average annual number of lightning flashes per square kilometer. The map includes data obtained from April 1995 to March 2000 from NASA's Optical Transient Detector, and from December 1997 to November 2000 from NASA's Lightning Imaging Sensor. Both are satellite-based sensors that use high-speed cameras capable of detecting brief lightning flashes even under daytime conditions. (NASA) **B.** Average number of days each year with thunderstorms. The humid subtropical climate that dominates the southeastern United States receives much of its precipitation in the form of thunderstorms. Most of the Southeast averages 50 or more days each year with thunderstorms. (Environmental Data Service, NOAA)

A.   B.

FIGURE 14.14   **A.** Buoyant thermals often produce fair-weather cumulus clouds that soon evaporate into the surrounding air, making it more humid. As this process of cumulus development and evaporation continues, the air eventually becomes sufficiently humid, so that newly forming clouds do not evaporate but continue to grow. (Photo by Henry Lansford/Photo Researchers, Inc.) **B.** This developing cumulonimbus cloud became a towering August thunderstorm over central Illinois. (Photo by E. J. Tarbuck)

and associated buoyancy are triggered by a number of different processes, yet most thunderstorms have a similar life history.

Because instability and buoyancy are enhanced by high surface temperatures, thunderstorms are most common in the afternoon and early evening (**FIGURE 14.14A**). However, surface heating alone is not sufficient for the growth of towering cumulonimbus clouds. A solitary cell of rising hot air produced by surface heating could, at best, produce a small cumulus cloud, which would evaporate within 10 to 15 minutes.

The development of 12,000-meter (40,000-foot) (or on rare occasions 18,000-meter [60,000-foot]) cumulonimbus towers requires a continual supply of moist air (**FIGURE 14.14B**). Each new surge of warm air rises higher than the last, adding to the height of the cloud (**FIGURE 14.15**). These updrafts must occasionally reach speeds over 100 kilometers (60 miles) per hour to accommodate the size of hailstones they are capable of carrying upward. Usually within an hour, the amount and size of precipitation that has accumulated is too much for the updrafts to support, and consequently downdrafts develop in one part of the cloud, releasing heavy precipitation. This represents the most active stage of the thunderstorm. Gusty winds, lightning, heavy precipitation, and sometimes hail are experienced.

Eventually the warm, moist air supplied by updrafts ceases as downdrafts dominate throughout the cloud. The cooling effect of falling precipitation, coupled with the influx of colder air aloft, marks the end of the thunderstorm activity. The life span of a typical cumulonimbus cell within a thunderstorm complex is only about an hour, but as the storm moves, fresh supplies of warm, water-laden air generate new cells to replace those that are dissipating.

TORNADOES

Tornadoes are local storms of short duration that must be ranked high among nature's most destructive forces (see the chapter-opening photo, p. 391). The sporadic occurrence and violent winds cause many deaths each year. Tornadoes are violent windstorms that take the form of a rotating column of air or *vortex* that extends downward from a cumulonimbus cloud.

Pressures within some tornadoes have been estimated to be as much as 10 percent lower than immediately outside the storm. Drawn by the much lower pressure in the center of the vortex, air near the ground rushes into the tornado

DID YOU KNOW?

During the 1988–2007 period, lightning officially claimed an average of 53 lives each year in the United States. However, the National Weather Service estimates that the actual number of lightning deaths each year is closer to 100 because many lightning-related fatalities go unreported. About 10 percent of lightning strike victims are killed. Among the 90 percent that survive, many suffer life-long injury and disability.

FIGURE 14.15 Stages in the development of a thunderstorm. During the cumulus stage, strong updrafts act to build the storm. The mature stage is marked by heavy precipitation and cool downdrafts in part of the storm. When the warm updrafts disappear completely, precipitation becomes light, and the cloud begins to evaporate.

from all directions. As the air streams inward, it is spiraled upward around the core until it eventually merges with the airflow of the parent thunderstorm deep in the cumulonimbus tower. Because of the tremendous pressure gradient associated with a strong tornado, maximum winds can sometimes approach 480 kilometers (300 miles) per hour.

Some tornadoes consist of a single vortex, but within many stronger tornadoes are smaller whirls called *suction vortices* that rotate within the main vortex (**FIGURE 14.16**). Suction vortices have diameters of only about 10 meters (33 feet) and rotate very rapidly. This structure accounts for occasional observations of virtually total destruction of one building while another one, just 10 meters (33 feet) away, suffers little damage.

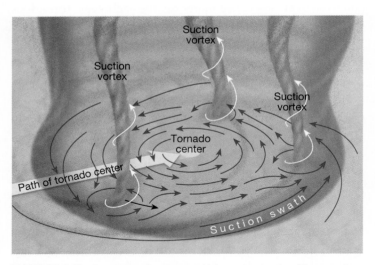

FIGURE L4.16 Some tornadoes have multiple suction vortices. These small and very intense vortices are roughly 10 meters (30 feet) across and move in a counterclockwise path around the tornado center. Because of this multiple vortex structure, one building might be heavily damaged and another one, just 10 meters (30 feet) away, might suffer little damage. (After Fujita)

Tornado Occurrence and Development

Tornadoes form in association with severe thunderstorms that produce high winds, heavy (sometimes torrential) rainfall, and often damaging hail. Fortunately, less than 1 percent of all thunderstorms produce tornadoes. Nevertheless, a much higher number must be monitored as potential tornado producers. Although meteorologists are still not sure what triggers tornado formation, it is apparent that they are the product of the interaction between strong updrafts in the thunderstorm and the winds in the troposphere.

Tornadoes can form in any situation that produces severe weather, including cold fronts and tropical cyclones (hurricanes). The most intense tornadoes are usually those that form in association with huge thunderstorms called *supercells*. An important precondition linked to tornado formation in severe thunderstorms is the development of a *mesocyclone*—a vertical cylinder of rotating air, typically about 3 to 10 kilometers (2 to 6 miles) across, that develops in the updraft of a severe thunderstorm (**FIGURE 14.17**). The formation of this large vortex often precedes tornado formation by 30 minutes or so.

The formation of a mesocyclone does not necessarily mean that tornado formation will follow. Only about half of all mesocyclones produce tornadoes. Forecasters cannot determine in advance which mesocyclones will spawn tornadoes.

General Atmospheric Conditions

Severe thunderstorms—and, hence, tornadoes—are most often spawned along the cold front of a middle-latitude cyclone or in association with a supercell thunderstorm such as pictured in Figure 14.17D. Throughout spring, air masses associated with middle-latitude cyclones are most likely to have greatly contrasting conditions. Continental polar air from Canada may still be very cold and dry, whereas maritime tropical air from the Gulf of Mexico is warm, humid, and unstable. The greater the contrast when these air masses meet, the more intense the storm. These two contrasting air masses are most likely to meet in the central United States, because there is no significant natural barrier separating the center of the country from the Arctic or the Gulf of Mexico. Consequently, this region generates more tornadoes than any other area of the country or, in fact, the world. The map in **FIGURE 14.18**, which depicts tornado incidence in the United States for a 27-year period, readily substantiates this fact.

Tornado Climatology

An average of between 1200 and 1300 tornadoes were reported annually in the United States between 2000 and 2009. Still, the actual number that occurs from one year to the next varies greatly. During this 10-year span, for example, yearly totals ranged from a low of 938 in 2002 to a high of 1820 in 2004.

FIGURE 14.17   The formation of a mesocyclone often precedes tornado formation. **A**. Winds are stronger aloft than at the surface (called speed wind shear), producing a rolling motion about a horizontal axis. **B**. Strong thunderstorm updrafts tilt the horizontally rotating air to a nearly vertical alignment. **C**. The mesocyclone, a vertical cylinder of rotating air, is established. **D**. If a tornado develops, it will descend from a slowly rotating wall cloud in the lower portion of the mesocyclone. A tornado is visible when it contains condensation or when it contains dust and debris. The appearance is often the result of both. When the column of air is aloft and does not produce damage, the visible portion is properly called a *funnel cloud*. (Photo © Howard B. Bluestein, professor of meteorology).

Tornadoes occur during every month of the year. April through June is the period of greatest tornado frequency in the United States; the number is lowest during December and January (Figure 14.18 graph inset). Of the 40,522 confirmed tornadoes reported over the contiguous 48 states during the 50-year period from 1950 through 1999, an average of almost 6 per day occurred during May. At the other extreme, a tornado was reported only about every other day in December and January.

Profile of a Tornado

An average tornado has a diameter of between 150 and 600 meters (500 and 2000 feet), travels across the landscape at approximately 45 kilometers (30 miles) per hour, and cuts a path about 10 kilometers (6 miles) long.* Because tornadoes

*The 10-kilometer (6-mile) figure applies to documented tornadoes. Because many small tornadoes go undocumented, the real average path of all tornadoes is unknown but is shorter than 10 kilometers.

usually occur slightly ahead of a cold front, in the zone of southwest winds, most move toward the northeast.

Of the hundreds of tornadoes reported in the United States annually, more than half are comparatively weak and short-lived. Most of these small tornadoes have lifetimes of three minutes or less and paths that seldom exceed 1 kilometer (0.6 mile) in length and 100 meters (330 feet) in width. Typical wind speeds are on the order of 150 kilometers (90 miles) per hour or less. On the other end of the tornado spectrum are the infrequent and often long-lived violent tornadoes. Although large tornadoes constitute only a small percentage of the total reported, their effects are often devastating. Such tornadoes may exist for periods in excess of

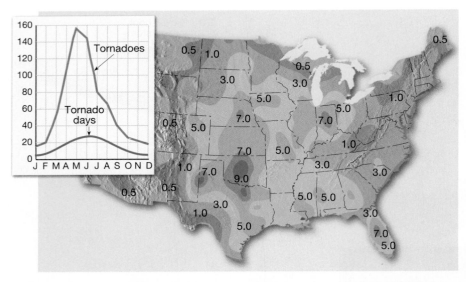

FIGURE 14.18 The map shows average annual tornado incidence per 26,000 square kilometers (10,000 square miles) for a 27-year period. The graph shows the average number of tornadoes and tornado days each month in the United States for the same period.

three hours and produce an essentially continuous damage path more than 150 kilometers (90 miles) long and perhaps a kilometer or more wide. Maximum winds range beyond 500 kilometers (310 miles) per hour.

Tornado Destruction

The potential for tornado destruction depends largely upon the strength of the winds generated by the storm. Because tornadoes generate the strongest winds in nature, they have accomplished many seemingly impossible tasks, such as driving a piece of straw through a thick wooden plank and

uprooting huge trees. Although it may seem impossible for winds to cause some of the extensive damage attributed to tornadoes, tests in engineering facilities have repeatedly demonstrated that winds in excess of 320 kilometers (200 miles) per hour are capable of incredible feats (**FIGURE 14.19**).

One commonly used guide to tornado intensity is the *Enhanced Fujita (EF) intensity scale* (Table 14.1). Because tornado winds cannot be measured directly, a rating on the EF-scale is determined by assessing the worst damage produced by a storm.

Although the greatest part of tornado damage is caused by violent winds, most tornado injuries and deaths result from flying debris. In the United States, the average annual death toll from tornadoes is about 60 to 70 people, but the actual number of deaths each year can depart significantly from the average. On April 3–4, 1974, for example, an outbreak of 148 tornadoes brought death and destruction to a 13-state region east of the Mississippi River. More than 300 people died and nearly 5500 people were injured in this worst disaster in half a century. Most tornadoes, however, do not result in a loss of life. In one statistical study that examined a 29-year period, 689 tornadoes resulted in deaths. This figure represents slightly less than 4 percent of the total 19,312 reported storms.

Although the percentage of tornadoes resulting in death is small, each tornado is potentially lethal. When tornado fatalities and storm intensities are compared, the results are quite interesting: The majority (63 percent) of tornadoes are weak (EF0 and EF1), and the number of storms decreases as tornado intensity increases. The

A.

B.

FIGURE 14.19 **A.** The force of the wind during a tornado near Wichita, Kansas, in April 1991 was enough to drive this piece of metal into a utility pole. (Photo by John Sokich/NOAA) **B.** The remains of a truck wrapped around a tree in Bridge Creek, Oklahoma, on May 4, 1999, following a major tornado outbreak. (AP Photo/L.M. Otero)

Table 14.1   Enhanced Fujita Intensity Scale*

Scale	Wind Speed Km/Hr	Mi/Hr	Damage
EF-0	105–137	65–85	*Light.* Some damage to siding and shingles.
EF-1	138–177	86–110	*Moderate.* Considerable roof damage. Winds can uproot trees and overturn single-wide mobile homes. Flagpoles bend.
EF-2	178–217	111–135	*Considerable.* Most single-wide homes destroyed. Permanent homes can shift off foundations. Flagpoles collapse. Softwood trees debarked.
EF-3	218–265	136–165	*Severe.* Hardwood trees debarked. All but small portions of houses destroyed.
EF-4	266–322	166–200	*Devastating.* Complete destruction of well-built residences, large sections of school buildings.
EF-5	>322	>200	*Incredible.* Significant structural deformation of mid- and high-rise buildings.

*The original Fujita scale was developed by T. Theodore Fujita in 1971 and put into use in 1973. The Enhanced Fujita Scale is a revision that was put into use in February 2007. Winds speeds are estimates (not measurements) based on damage, and represent 3-second gusts at the point of damage. More information about the criteria used to evaluate tornado intensity can be found at http://www.spc.noaa.gov/efscale/ and at http://www.spc.noaa.gov/faq/tornado/ef-scale.html.

distribution of tornado fatalities, however, is just the opposite. Although only 2 percent of tornadoes are classified as violent (EF4 and EF5), they account for nearly 70 percent of the deaths.

Tornado Forecasting

Because severe thunderstorms and tornadoes are small and relatively short-lived phenomena, they are among the most difficult weather features to forecast precisely. Nevertheless, the prediction, detection, and monitoring of such storms are among the most important services provided by professional meteorologists. Both the timely issuance and dissemination of watches and warnings are critical to the protection of life and property.

The Storm Prediction Center (SPC) located in Norman, Oklahoma, is part of the National Weather Service (NWS) and the National Centers for Environmental Prediction (NCEP). Its mission is to provide timely and accurate forecasts and watches for severe thunderstorms and tornadoes.

Severe thunderstorm outlooks are issued several times daily. *Day 1* outlooks identify those areas likely to be affected by severe thunderstorms during the next 6 to 30 hours, and *day 2* outlooks extend the forecast through the

DID YOU KNOW?

One tornado easily ranks above all others as the single most dangerous and destructive. Known as the Tri-State Tornado, it occurred on March 18, 1925. Starting in southeastern Missouri, the tornado remained on the ground for 352 km (219 mil), finally ending in Indiana. The losses included 695 dead and 2027 injured. Property losses were also great, with several small towns almost totally destroyed.

DID YOU KNOW?

The strongest tornadoes (EF5 on the Fujita scale) are rare. During the 30-year span, from 1970 through 1999, only 26 out of a total of 28,913 tornadoes were classified in the EF5 category. That is just 0.09 percent (nine one-hundredths of one percent)! No EF5 tornadoes are reported in many years. Nevertheless, during a single 16-hour span, April 3–4, 1974, there were seven EF5 storms.

following day. Both outlooks describe the type, coverage, and intensity of the severe weather expected. Many local NWS field offices also issue severe weather outlooks that provide a more local description of the severe weather potential for the next 12 to 24 hours.

Tornado Watches and Warnings

Tornado watches alert the public to the possibility of tornadoes over a specified area for a particular time interval. Watches serve to fine-tune forecast areas already identified in severe weather outlooks. A typical watch covers an area of about 65,000 square kilometers (25,000 square miles) for a four- to six-hour period. A tornado watch is an important part of the tornado alert system because it sets in motion the procedures necessary to deal adequately with detection, tracking, warning, and response. Watches are generally reserved for organized severe weather events where the tornado threat will affect at least 26,000 square kilometers (10,000 square miles) and/or persist for at least three hours. Watches typically are not issued when the threat is thought to be isolated and/or short-lived.

Whereas a tornado watch is designed to alert people to the possibility of tornadoes, a **tornado warning** is issued by local offices of the National Weather Service when a tornado has actually been sighted in an area or is indicated by weather radar. It warns of a high probability of imminent danger. Warnings are issued for much smaller areas than for watches, usually covering portions of a county or counties. In addition, they are in effect for much shorter periods, typically 30 to 60 minutes. Because a tornado warning may be based on an actual sighting, warnings are occasionally issued after a tornado has already developed. However, most warnings are issued prior to tornado formation, sometimes by several tens of minutes, based on Doppler radar data and/or spotter reports of funnel clouds.

If the direction and the approximate speed of the storm are known, an estimate of its most probable path can be made. Because tornadoes often move erratically, the warning area is fan-shaped downwind from the point where the tornado has been spotted. Improved forecasts and advances in technology have contributed to a significant decline in tornado deaths over the past 50 years.

Doppler Radar

Many of the difficulties that once limited the accuracy of tornado warnings have been reduced or eliminated by an advancement in radar technology called **Doppler radar.** Doppler radar not only performs the same tasks as conventional radar but also has the ability to detect motion directly (**FIGURE 14.20**). Doppler radar can detect the initial formation and subsequent development of a *mesocyclone,* the intense rotating wind system in the lower part of a thunderstorm that frequently precedes tornado development. Almost all mesocyclones produce damaging hail, severe winds, or tornadoes. Those that produce tornadoes (about 50 percent) can sometimes be distinguished by their stronger wind speeds and their sharper gradients of wind speeds.

It should also be pointed out that not all tornado-bearing storms have clear-cut radar signatures and that other storms can give false signatures. Detection, therefore, is sometimes a subjective process and a given display could be interpreted in several ways. Consequently, trained observers continue to form an important part of the warning system.

Although some operational problems exist, the benefits of Doppler radar are many. As a research tool, it is not only providing data on the formation of tornadoes but also helping meteorologists gain new insights into thunderstorm development, the structure and dynamics of hurricanes, and air-turbulence hazards that plague aircraft. As a practical tool for tornado detection, Doppler radar has significantly improved our ability to track thunderstorms and issue warnings.

HURRICANES

Most of us view the weather in the tropics with favor. Places such as the islands of the Caribbean are known for their lack of significant day-to-day variations. Warm breezes, steady temperatures, and rains that come as heavy but brief tropical showers are often the rule. It is ironic that these relatively tranquil regions sometimes produce the most violent storms on Earth.

The whirling tropical cyclones that on occasion have wind speeds attaining 300 kilometers (185 miles) per hour are known in the United States as **hurricanes**—the greatest storms on Earth. Out at sea, they can generate 15-meter (50-foot) waves capable of inflicting destruction hundreds of kilometers from their source. Should a hurricane smash onto land, strong winds coupled with extensive flooding can impose billions of dollars in damage and great loss of life (**FIGURE 14.21** and Figure 10.9, p. 288).

The vast majority of hurricane-related deaths and damage are caused by relatively infrequent, yet powerful, storms. Table 14.2 lists the deadliest hurricanes to strike the United States between 1900 and 2009. The storm that pounded an unsuspecting Galveston, Texas, in 1900 was not just the deadliest U.S. hurricane ever, but the deadliest natural disaster of *any kind* to affect the United States (Figure 14.21B). Of course, the deadliest and most costly storm in recent memory occurred in August 2005, when Hurricane Katrina devastated the Gulf Coast of Louisiana, Mississippi, and Alabama and took an estimated 1800 lives. Although hundreds of thousands fled before the storm made landfall, thousands of others were caught by the storm. In addition to the human suffering and tragic loss of life that were left in the wake of Hurricane Katrina, the financial losses caused by the storm are practically incalculable. Although imprecise, some suggest that the final accounting exceeded $100 billion.

| Reflectivity | Storm-relative velocity |

FIGURE 14.20 This is a dual Doppler radar image of a violent tornado near Moore, Oklahoma, on May 3, 1999. The left image (reflectivity) shows precipitation in the supercell thunderstorm. The right image shows motion of the precipitation along the radar beam, that is, how fast rain or hail is moving toward or away from the radar. In this example, the radar was unusually close to the tornado—close enough to make out the signature of the tornado itself (most of the time only the weaker and larger mesocyclone is detected). (After NOAA)

A.

B.

FIGURE 14.21 **A.** Storm surge damage along the Texas coast near Galveston from Hurricane Ike in September 2008. (USGS photo) **B.** Aftermath of the Galveston hurricane that struck an unsuspecting and unprepared city on September 8, 1900. It was the worst natural disaster in U.S. history. Entire blocks were swept clean, while mountains of debris accumulated around the few remaining buildings. (AP Photo)

Profile of a Hurricane

Most hurricanes form between the latitudes of 5 and 20 degrees over all the tropical oceans except the South Atlantic and the eastern South Pacific (**FIGURE 14.22**). The North Pacific has the greatest number of storms, averaging 20 each year. Fortunately for those living in the coastal regions of the southern and eastern United States, fewer than five hurricanes, on the average, develop annually in the warm sector of the North Atlantic.

These intense tropical storms are known in various parts of the world by different names. In the western Pacific, they are called *typhoons,* and in the Indian Ocean, including the Bay of Bengal and Arabian Sea, they are simply called *cyclones.* In the following discussion, these storms will be

referred to as hurricanes. The term *hurricane* is derived from Huracan, a Carib god of evil.

Although many tropical disturbances develop each year, only a few reach hurricane status. By international agreement, a hurricane has wind speeds in excess of 119 kilometers (74 miles) per hour and a rotary circulation. Mature hurricanes average 600 kilometers (375 miles) across, although they can range in diameter from 100 kilometers (60 miles) up to about 1500 kilometers (930 miles). From the outer edge to the center, the barometric pressure has on occasion dropped 60 millibars, from 1010 millibars to 950 millibars. The lowest pressures ever recorded in the Western Hemisphere are associated with these storms.

A steep pressure gradient generates the rapid, inward-spiraling winds of a hurricane (**FIGURE 14.23**). As the air

Table 14.2   The 10 deadliest hurricanes to strike the U.S. mainland 1900–2009

Rank	Hurricane	Year	Category	Deaths
1.	Texas (Galveston)	1900	4	8000*
2.	SE Florida (Lake Okeechobee)	1928	4	2500–3000
3.	Katrina	2005	4	1833
4.	Audrey	1957	4	At least 416
5.	Florida Keys	1935	5	408
6.	Florida (Miami)/Mississippi/Alabama/Florida (Pensacola)	1926	4	372
7.	Louisiana (Grande Isle)	1909	4	350
8.	Florida Keys/South Texas	1919	4	287
9. (tie)	Louisiana (New Orleans)	1915	4	275
9. (tie)	Texas (Galveston)	1915	4	275

Source: National Weather Service/National Hurricane Center NOAA Technical Memorandum NWS TPC-5.
*This number may actually have been as high as 10,000–12,000.

FIGURE 14.22 This world map shows the regions where most hurricanes form as well as their principal months of occurrence and the most common tracks they follow. Hurricanes do not develop within about 5° of the equator because the Coriolis effect is too weak. Because warm surface ocean temperatures are necessary for hurricane formation, they seldom form poleward of 20° latitude nor over the cool waters of the South Atlantic and the eastern South Pacific.

descends and heats by compression, making it the warmest part of the storm. Although many people believe that the eye is characterized by clear blue skies, this is usually not the case, because the subsidence in the eye is seldom strong enough to produce cloudless conditions. Although the sky appears much brighter in this region, scattered clouds at various levels are common.

Hurricane Formation and Decay

A hurricane is a heat engine that is fueled by the latent heat liberated when huge quantities of water vapor condense. The amount of energy produced by a typical hurricane in just a single day is truly immense. The release of latent heat warms the air and provides buoyancy for its upward flight. The result is to reduce the pressure near the surface, which encourages a more rapid inward flow of air. To get this engine started, a large quantity of warm, moisture-laden air is required, and a continual supply is needed to keep it going.

Hurricanes develop most often in the late summer when ocean waters have reached temperatures of 27°C (80°F) or higher and thus are able to provide the necessary heat and moisture to the air. This ocean-water temperature requirement accounts for the fact that hurricanes do not form over the relatively cool waters of the South Atlantic and the eastern South Pacific. For the same reason, few hurricanes form poleward of 20 degrees of latitude. Although water temperatures are sufficiently high, hurricanes do not form within 5 degrees of the equator, because the Coriolis effect is too weak to initiate the necessary rotary motion.

rushes toward the center of the storm, its velocity increases. This occurs for the same reason that skaters with their arms extended spin faster as they pull their arms in close to their bodies.

As the inward rush of warm, moist surface air approaches the core of the storm, it turns upward and ascends in a ring of cumulonimbus towers (Figure 14.23A). This doughnut-shaped wall of intense convective activity surrounding the center of the storm is called the **eye wall.** It is here that the greatest wind speeds and heaviest rainfall occur. Surrounding the eye wall are curved bands of clouds that trail away in a spiral fashion. Near the top of the hurricane, the airflow is outward, carrying the rising air away from the storm center, thereby providing room for more inward flow at the surface.

At the very center of the storm is the **eye** of the hurricane (Figure 14.23). This well-known feature is a zone about 20 kilometers (12.5 miles) in diameter where precipitation ceases and winds subside. It offers a brief but deceptive break from the extreme weather in the enormous curving wall clouds that surround it. The air within the eye gradually

DID YOU KNOW?

Hurricane season is different in different parts of the world. The Atlantic hurricane season officially extends from June through November. More than 97 percent of tropical activity in that region occurs during this six-month span. The "heart" of the season is August through October. During these three months, 87 percent of the minor hurricane (categories 1 and 2) days and 96 percent of the major hurricane (categories 3, 4, and 5) days occur. Peak activity is in early to mid-September.

Many tropical storms begin as disorganized arrays of clouds and thunderstorms that develop weak pressure gradients but exhibit little or no rotation. Such areas of low-level convergence and lifting are called *tropical disturbances.* Most of the time, these zones of convective activity die out. However, tropical disturbances occasionally grow larger and develop a strong cyclonic rotation.

What happens on those occasions when conditions favor hurricane development? As latent heat is released from the clusters of thunderstorms that make up the tropical disturbance, areas within the disturbance get warmer. As a consequence, air density lowers and surface pressure drops, creating a region of weak low pressure and cyclonic circulation. As pressure drops at the storm center, the pressure gradient steepens. If you were watching an animated weather map of the storm, you would see the isobars get closer together. In response, surface wind speeds

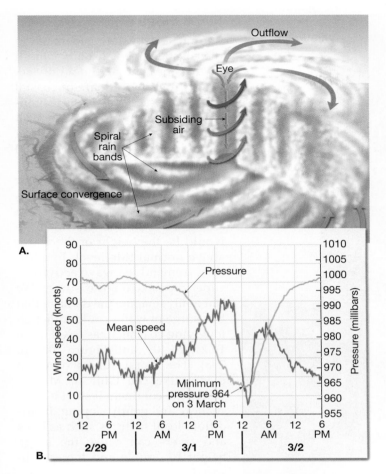

A.

B.

FIGURE 14.23 **A.** Cross section of a hurricane. Note that the vertical dimension is greatly exaggerated. The eye, the zone of relative calm at the center of the storm, is a distinctive hurricane feature. Sinking air in the eye warms by compression. Surrounding the eye is the eye wall, the zone where winds and rain are most intense. Tropical moisture spiraling inward creates rain bands that pinwheel around the storm center. Outflow of air at the top of the hurricane is important because it prevents the convergent flow at lower levels from filling in the storm. (After NOAA) **B.** Measurements of surface pressure and wind speed during the passage of Cyclone Monty at Mardi Station in Western Australia between February 29 and March 2, 2004. (Hurricanes are called "cyclones" in this part of the world.) The strongest winds are associated with the eye wall, and the weakest winds and lowest pressure are found in the eye. (Data from World Meteorological Organization)

increase and bring additional supplies of moisture to nurture storm growth. The water vapor condenses, releasing latent heat, and the heated air rises. Adiabatic cooling of rising air triggers more condensation and the release of more latent heat, which causes a further increase in buoyancy. And so it goes.

Meanwhile, at the top of the storm, air is diverging. Without this outward flow up top, the inflow at lower levels would soon raise surface pressures (that is, fill in the low) and thwart storm development.

Many tropical disturbances occur each year, but only a few develop into full-fledged hurricanes. By international agreement, lesser tropical cyclones are placed in different categories, based on wind strength. When a cyclone's strongest winds do not exceed 61 kilometers (38 miles) per hour, it is called a **tropical depression.** When winds are between 61 and 119 kilometers (38 and 74 miles) per hour, the cyclone is termed a **tropical storm.** It is during this phase that a name is given (Andrew, Floyd, Opal, etc.). Should the tropical storm become a hurricane, the name remains the same. Each year, between 80 and 100 tropical storms develop around the world. Of these, usually half or more eventually become hurricanes.

Hurricanes diminish in intensity whenever they (1) move over ocean waters that cannot supply warm, moist tropical air; (2) move onto land; or (3) reach a location where the large-scale flow aloft is unfavorable. Whenever a hurricane moves onto land, it loses its punch rapidly. The most important reason for this rapid demise is the fact that the storm's source of warm, moist air is cut off. When an adequate supply of water vapor does not exist, condensation and the release of latent heat must diminish. In addition, friction from the increased roughness of the land surface rapidly slows surface wind speeds. This factor causes the winds to move more directly into the center of the low, thus helping to eliminate the large pressure differences.

Hurricane Destruction

A location only a few hundred kilometers from a hurricane—just one day's striking distance away—may experience clear skies and virtually no wind. Prior to the age of weather satellites, such a situation made the task of warning people of impending storms very difficult (**FIGURE 14.24**).

The amount of damage caused by a hurricane depends on several factors, including the size and population density of the area affected and the shape of the ocean bottom near the shore. The most significant factor,

A.

B.

FIGURE 14.24 Satellite images of Hurricane Katrina in late August 2005 shortly before it devastated the Gulf Coast. **A**. Color-enhanced infrared image from the *GOES-East* satellite. The most intense activity is associated with red and orange. **B**. A more traditional satellite image from NASA's *Terra* satellite. (NASA)

Storm Surge

The most devastating damage in the coastal zone is usually caused by the storm surge. It not only accounts for a large share of coastal property losses but also is responsible for a high percentage of all hurricane-caused deaths. A **storm surge** is a dome of water 65 to 80 kilometers (40 to 50 miles) wide that sweeps across the coast near the point where the eye makes landfall. If all wave activity were smoothed out, the storm surge would be the height of the water above normal tide level. In addition, tremendous wave activity is superimposed on the surge. We can easily imagine the damage that this surge of water could inflict on low-lying coastal areas (see Figure 14.21, p. 409, and Figure 10.9, p. 288). The worst surges occur in places like the Gulf of Mexico where the continental shelf is very shallow and gently sloping. In addition, local features such as bays and rivers can cause the surge height to double and increase in speed.

As a hurricane advances toward the coast in the Northern Hemisphere, storm surge is always most intense on the right side of the eye where winds are blowing *toward* the shore. In addition, on this side of the storm, the forward movement of the hurricane also contributes to the storm surge. In **FIGURE 14.25** assume a hurricane with peak winds of 175 kilometers (109 miles) per hour is moving toward the shore at 50 kilometers (31 miles) per hour. In this case, the net wind speed on the right side of

of course, is the strength of the storm itself. By studying past storms, a scale has been established to rank the relative intensities of hurricanes. As Table 14.3 indicates, a *category 5* storm is the worst possible, whereas a *category 1* hurricane is least severe.

During the hurricane season it is common to hear scientists and reporters use the numbers from the *Saffir-Simpson Hurricane Scale*. When Hurricane Katrina made landfall, sustained winds were 225 kilometers (140 miles) per hour, making it a strong category 4 storm. Storms that fall into category 5 are rare. Damage caused by hurricanes can be divided into three categories: (1) storm surge, (2) wind damage, and (3) inland flooding.

Table 14.3 Saffir-Simpson Hurricane Scale

Scale Number (category)	Central Pressure (millibars)	Winds (km/hr)	Storm Surge (meters)	Damage
1	≥980	119–153	1.2–1.5	Minimal
2	965–979	154–177	1.6–2.4	Moderate
3	945–964	178–209	2.5–3.6	Extensive
4	920–944	210–250	3.7–5.4	Extreme
5	<920	>250	>5.4	Catastrophic

FIGURE 14.25 Winds associated with a Northern Hemisphere hurricane that is advancing toward the coast. This hypothetical storm, with peak winds of 175 kilometers (109 miles) per hour, is moving toward the coast at 50 kilometers (31 miles) per hour. On the right side of the advancing storm, the 175-kilometer-per-hour winds are in the same direction as the movement of the storm (50 kilometers per hour). Therefore, the *net* wind speed on the right side of the storm is 225 kilometers (140 miles) per hour. On the left side, the hurricane's winds are blowing opposite the direction of storm movement, so the *net* winds of 125 kilometers (78 miles) per hour are away from the coast. Storm surge will be greatest along that part of the coast hit by the right side of the advancing hurricane.

the advancing storm is 225 kilometers (140 miles) per hour. On the left side, the hurricane's winds are blowing opposite the direction of storm movement, so the net winds are *away* from the coast at 125 kilometers (78 miles) per hour. Along the shore facing the left side of the oncoming hurricane, the water level may actually decrease as the storm makes landfall.

Wind Damage

Destruction caused by wind is perhaps the most obvious of the classes of hurricane damage. Debris such as signs, roofing materials, and small items left outside become dangerous flying missiles in hurricanes. For some structures, the force of the wind is sufficient to cause total ruin. Mobile homes are particularly vulnerable. High-rise buildings are also susceptible to hurricane-force winds. Upper floors are most vulnerable because wind speeds usually increase with height. Recent research suggests that people should stay below the 10th floor but remain above any floors at risk for flooding. In regions with good building codes, wind damage is usually not as catastrophic as storm-surge damage. However, hurricane-force winds affect a much larger area than storm surge and can cause huge economic losses. For example, in 1992 it was largely the winds associated with Hurricane Andrew that produced more than $25 billion of damage in southern Florida and Louisiana.

Hurricanes sometimes produce tornadoes that contribute to the storm's destructive power. Studies have shown that more than half of the hurricanes that make landfall produce at least one tornado. In 2004 the number of tornadoes associated with tropical storms and hurricanes was extraordinary. Tropical Storm Bonnie and five landfalling hurricanes—Charley, Frances, Gaston, Ivan, and Jeanne—produced nearly 300 tornadoes that affected the southeast and mid-Atlantic states.

Heavy Rains and Inland Flooding

The torrential rains that accompany most hurricanes represent a third significant threat: flooding. Whereas the effects of storm surge and strong winds are concentrated in coastal areas, heavy rains may affect places hundreds of kilometers from the coast for up to several days after the storm has lost its hurricane-force winds.

In September 1999, Hurricane Floyd brought flooding rains, high winds, and rough seas to a large portion of the Atlantic seaboard. More than 2.5 million people evacuated their homes from Florida north to the Carolinas and beyond. It was the largest peacetime evacuation in U.S. history up to that time. Torrential rains falling on already saturated ground created devastating inland flooding. Altogether Floyd dumped more than 48 centimeters (19 inches) of rain on Wilmington, North Carolina, 33.98 cm (13.38 inches) in a single 24-hour span.

In summary, extensive damage and loss of life in the coastal zone can result from storm surge, strong winds, and torrential rains. When loss of life occurs, it is commonly caused by the storm surge, which can devastate entire barrier islands or zones within a few blocks of the coast. Although wind damage is usually not as catastrophic as the storm surge, it affects a much larger area. Where building codes are inadequate, economic losses can be especially severe. Because hurricanes weaken as they move inland, most wind damage occurs within 200 kilometers (125 miles) of the coast. Far from the coast, a weakening storm can produce extensive flooding long after the winds have diminished below hurricane levels. Sometimes the damage from inland flooding exceeds storm-surge destruction.

Tracking Hurricanes

Today we have the benefit of numerous observational tools for tracking tropical storms and hurricanes. Using input from satellites, aircraft reconnaissance, coastal radar, and remote data buoys in conjunction with sophisticated computer models, meteorologists monitor and forecast storm movements and intensity. The goal is to issue timely watches and warnings.

An important part of this process is the *track forecast*—the predicted path of the storm. The track forecast

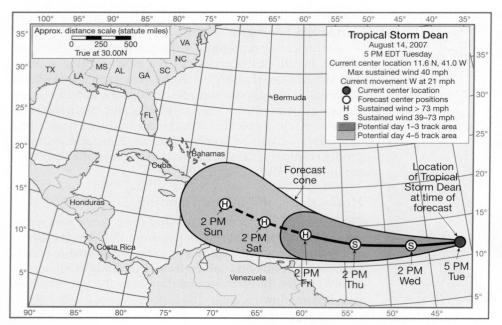

FIGURE 14.26 Five-day track forecast for Tropical Storm Dean issued at 5 PM EDT, Tuesday, August 14, 2007. When a hurricane track forecast is issued by the National Hurricane Center, it is termed a *forecast cone*. The cone represents the probable track of the center of the storm and is formed by enclosing the area swept out by a set of circles along the forecast track (at 12, 24, 36, hours, etc.). The size of each circle gets larger with time. Based on statistics from 2003 to 2007, the entire track of an Atlantic tropical cyclone can be expected to remain entirely within the cone roughly 60 to 70 percent of the time. (National Weather Service/National hurricane Center)

forecasts are important becase they can lead to timely evacuations from the surge zone where the greatest number of deaths usually occur. Fortunately, track forecasts have been steadily improving. During the span 2001–2005, forecast errors were roughly half of what they were in 1990. During the very active 2004 and 2005 Atlantic hurricane seasons, 12-to 72-hour track forecast accuracy was at or near record levels. Consequently, the length of official track forecasts issued by the National Hurricane Center was extended from three days to five days (**FIGURE 14.26**). Current five-day track forecasts are now as accurate as three-day forecasts were 15 years ago.

Despite improvements in accuracy, forecast uncertainty still requires that hurricane warnings be issued for relatively large coastal areas. During the span 2000–2005, the average length of coastline under a hurricane warning in the United States was 510 kilometers (316 miles). This represents a significant improvement over the preceding decade when the average was 730 kilometers (452 miles). Nevertheless, only about one-quarter of an average warning area experiences hurricane conditions.

is probably the most basic information because accurate prediction of other storm characteristics (winds and rainfall) is of little value if there is significant uncertainty as to where the storm is going. Accurate track

THE CHAPTER IN REVIEW

• An *air mass* is a large body of air, usually 1600 kilometers (1000 miles) or more across, that is characterized by a *sameness of temperature and moisture at any given altitude.* When this air moves out of its region of origin, called the *source region,* it will carry these temperatures and moisture conditions elsewhere, perhaps eventually affecting a large portion of a continent.

• Air masses are classified according to the nature of the surface in the source region and the latitude of the source region. *Continental (c)* designates an air mass of land origin, with the air likely to be dry; a *maritime (m)* air mass originates over water and, therefore, will be relatively humid. *Polar (P)* and *arctic (A)* air masses originate in high latitudes and are cold. *Tropical (T)* air masses form in low latitudes and are warm. According to this classification scheme, the *four basic types of air masses are continental polar (cP), continental tropical (cT), maritime polar (mP), and maritime tropical (mT).* Continental polar (cP) and maritime tropical (mT) air masses influence the weather of North

America most, especially east of the Rocky Mountains. Maritime tropical air is the source of much, if not most, of the precipitation received in the eastern two-thirds of the United States.

• *Fronts* are boundaries that separate air masses of different densities, one warmer and often higher in moisture content than the other. A *warm front* occurs when the surface position of the front moves so that warm air occupies territory formerly covered by cooler air. Along a warm front, a warm air mass overrides a retreating mass of cooler air. As the warm air ascends, it cools adiabatically to produce clouds and frequently light-to-moderate precipitation over a large area. A *cold front* forms where cold air is actively advancing into a region occupied by warmer air. Cold fronts are about twice as steep and move more rapidly than do warm fronts. Because of these two differences, precipitation along a cold front is generally more intense and of shorter duration than precipitation associated with a warm front.

• The primary weather producers in the middle latitudes are *large centers of low pressure* that generally travel from *west to east,* called *middle-latitude cyclones.* These *bearers of stormy weather,* which last from a few days to a week, have a *counterclockwise circulation* pattern in the Northern Hemisphere, with an *inward flow of air* toward their centers. Most middle-latitude cyclones have a *cold front and frequently a warm front* extending from the central area of low pressure. *Convergence* and *forceful lifting along the fronts* initiate cloud development and frequently cause precipitation. The particular weather experienced by an area depends on the path of the cyclone.

• *Thunderstorms* are caused by the upward movement of warm, moist, unstable air. They are associated with cumulonimbus clouds that generate heavy rainfall, lightning, thunder, and occasionally hail and tornadoes.

• *Tornadoes,* destructive local storms of short duration, are violent windstorms associated with severe thunderstorms that take the form of a rotating column of air that extends downward from a cumulonimbus cloud. Tornadoes are most often spawned along the cold front of a middle-latitude cyclone, most frequently during the spring months.

• *Hurricanes,* the greatest storms on Earth, are tropical cyclones with wind speeds in excess of 119 kilometers (74 miles) per hour. These complex tropical disturbances develop over tropical ocean waters and are fueled by the latent heat liberated when huge quantities of water vapor condense. Hurricanes form most often in late summer when ocean-surface temperatures reach 27°C (80°F) or higher and thus are able to provide the necessary heat and moisture to air. Hurricanes diminish in intensity whenever they move over cool ocean water that cannot supply adequate heat and moisture, move onto land, or reach a location where large-scale flow aloft is unfavorable. Hurricane damage is of three main types: storm surge, wind damage, and inland flooding.

KEY TERMS

air mass (p. 392)

air-mass weather (p. 392)

arctic (A) air mass (p. 393)

cold front (p. 396)

continental (c) air mass (p. 393)

Doppler radar (p. 408)

eye (p. 410)

eye wall (p. 410)

front (p. 395)

hurricane (p. 408)

lake-effect snow (p. 394)

maritime (m) air mass (p. 393)

middle-latitude or midlatitude cyclone (p. 397)

occluded front (p. 397)

overrunning (p. 395)

polar (P) air mass (p. 393)

source region (p. 393)

stationary front (p. 397)

storm surge (p. 412)

thunderstorm (p. 401)

tornado (p. 403)

tornado warning (p. 407)

tornado watch (p. 407)

tropical (T) air mass (p. 393)

tropical depression (p. 411)

tropical storm (p. 411)

warm front (p. 395)

QUESTIONS FOR REVIEW

1. Describe the weather associated with a continental polar air mass in the winter and in the summer. When would this air mass be most welcome in the United States?

2. What are the characteristics of a maritime tropical air mass? Where are the source regions for the maritime tropical air masses that affect North America? Where are the source regions for the maritime polar air masses?

3. Describe the weather along a cold front where very warm, moist air is being displaced.

4. For each weather element listed, describe the changes that an observer experiences when a middle-latitude cyclone passes with its center north of the observer: wind direction, pressure tendency, cloud type, cloud cover, precipitation, temperature.

5. Describe the weather conditions an observer would experience if the center of a middle-latitude cyclone passed to the south.

6. Briefly explain how the flow aloft aids the formation of cyclones at the surface.

7. What is the primary requirement for the formation of thunderstorms?

8. Based on your answer to Question 7, where would you expect thunderstorms to be most common on Earth? Where specifically in the United States?

9. Why do tornadoes have such high wind speeds?

10. What general atmospheric conditions are most conducive to the formation of tornadoes?

11. When is "tornado season"? That is, during what months is tornado activity most pronounced?

12. Distinguish between a *tornado watch* and a *tornado warning.*

13. Which has stronger winds, a tropical storm or a tropical depression?

14. Why does the intensity of a hurricane diminish rapidly when it moves onto land?

15. Name the three broad categories of hurricane damage. Which category is responsible for the highest percentage of hurricane-related deaths?

16. A hurricane has slower wind speeds than does a tornado, yet it inflicts more total damage. How might this be explained?

COMPANION WEBSITE

The Foundations of Earth Science Website uses the resources and flexibility of the Internet to aid in your study of the topics in this chapter. Written and developed by the authors and other Earth science instructors, this site will help improve your understanding of Earth science. Visit **www.mygeoscienceplace.com** in order to

- **Review** key chapter concepts.
- **Read** with links to the ebook and to chapter-specific web resources

- **Visualize** and comprehend challenging topics using learning activities in *GEODe: Earth Science*.
- **Test** yourself with online quizzes.

GEODe: EARTH SCIENCE

GEODe: Earth Science is a valuable and easy to use learning aid that can be accessed from your book's Companion Website: **www.mygeoscienceplace.com.** It is a dynamic instructional tool that promotes understanding and reinforces important concepts by using tutorials, animations, and exercises that actively engage the student.

THE NATURE OF THE SOLAR SYSTEM*

FOCUS ON LEARNING

To assist you in learning the important concepts in this chapter, you will find it helpful to focus on the following questions:

1. What was the geocentric theory of the universe held by many early Greeks?

2. What were the contributions to modern astronomy of Nicolaus Copernicus, Tycho Brahe, Johannes Kepler, Galileo Galilei, and Isaac Newton?

3. What are the two groups of planets in the solar system? What are the general characteristics of the planets in each group?

4. How is the solar system thought to have formed?

5. What are the major features of the lunar surface?

6. What are some distinguishing features of each planet in the solar system?

7. What are the minor members of the solar system?

*This chapter was revised with the assistance of Teresa Tarbuck and Mark Watry.

England's Stonehenge is one of the most famous prehistoric sites in the world. One of its functions was as an astronomical observatory.
(Photo by Ian Waldie/Reuters/ CORBIS)

The science of astronomy is a rational way of knowing and understanding the origins of the Earth, the solar system, and the universe. Earth was once thought to be unique, different in every way from anything else in the universe. However, through the science of astronomy, we have discovered that Earth and the Sun are similar to other objects in the universe and that the physical laws that apply on Earth seem to apply everywhere in the universe.

Today we know that Earth is one of eight planets and numerous smaller bodies that orbit the Sun, that the Sun is just one of perhaps 100 billion stars that make up the Milky Way Galaxy, and that the Milky Way is only one of billions of galaxies in an incomprehensibly large universe. This view of Earth's position in space is radically different from the one held only a few hundred years ago, when Earth was believed to occupy a privileged position at the center of the universe.

How did our understanding of the universe change so drastically and so quickly? In this chapter we examine the transformation from the ancient view of the universe, which focused on the positions and movements of celestial objects, to the modern perspective, which focuses on *understanding how* these objects came to be and *why* they move the way they do.

ANCIENT ASTRONOMY

Astronomy probably began long before recorded history (more than 5000 years ago) when humans began to track the motion of celestial objects so they knew when to plant their crops or prepare to hunt migrating herds. The ancient Chinese, Egyptians, and Babylonians are well known for their record keeping. These cultures recorded the locations of the Sun, Moon, and the five visible planets as these objects moved slowly against the background of "fixed" stars. Eventually, it was not enough to track the motions of celestial objects; predicting their future positions (to avoid getting married at an unfavorable time, for example) became important.

A study of Chinese archives shows that the Chinese recorded every appearance of the famous Halley's Comet for at least 10 centuries. However, because this comet appears only once every 76 years, they were unable to link these appearances to establish that what they saw was the same object multiple times. Like most ancients, the Chinese considered comets to be mystical. Generally, comets were seen as bad omens and were blamed for a variety of disasters, from wars to plagues (**FIGURE 15.1**). In addition, the Chinese kept quite accurate records of "guest stars." Today we know that a "guest star" is a normal star, usually too faint to be visible, which increases its brightness as it explosively ejects gases from its surface, a phenomenon we call a *nova* (*novus* = new) or *supernova* (**FIGURE 15.2**).

The Golden Age of Astronomy

The "Golden Age" of early astronomy (600 B.C.–A.D. 150) was centered in Greece. Although the early Greeks have been criticized, and rightly so, for using purely philosophical arguments to explain natural phenomena, they employed observational data as well. The basics of geometry and trigonometry, which they developed, were used to measure the sizes of and distances to the largest-appearing bodies in the heavens—the Sun and the Moon.

The early Greeks held the incorrect **geocentric** (*geo* = Earth, *centric* = centered) view of the universe—which professed that Earth was a sphere that remained motionless at the center of the universe. Orbiting Earth were the Moon, Sun, and known planets—Mercury, Venus, Mars, Jupiter, and Saturn. The Sun and Moon were thought to be perfect crystal spheres. Beyond the planets was a transparent, hollow **celestial sphere** on which the stars were attached and traveled daily around Earth. (Although it appears that the stars and planets move across the sky, this effect is actually caused by Earth's rotation on its axis.) Some early Greeks realized that the motion of the stars could be explained just as easily by a rotating Earth, but they rejected that idea because Earth exhibits no sense of motion and seemed too large to be movable. In fact, proof of Earth's rotation was not demonstrated until 1851.

To the Greeks, all of the heavenly bodies, except seven, appeared to remain in the same relative position to one

FIGURE 15.1 The Bayeux Tapestry that hangs in Bayeux, France, shows the apprehension caused by Halley's Comet in A.D. 1066. This event preceded the defeat of King Harold by William the Conqueror. ("Sighting of a comet." Detail from Bayeux Tapestry. Musee de la Tapisserie, Bayeux. "With special authorization of the City of Bayeux." Bridgeman-Giraudon/Art Resource, NY)

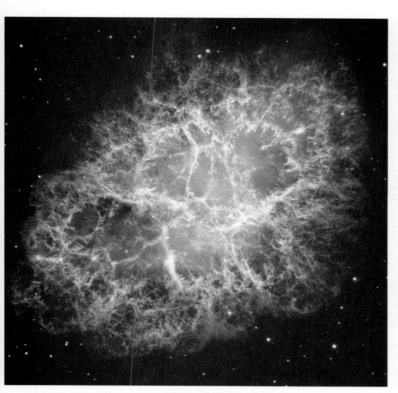

FIGURE 15.2   The Chinese recorded the sudden appearance of a "guest star" in A.D. 1054 The scattered remains of that supernova is the Crab Nebula in the constellation Taurus. This image comes from the Hubble Space Telescope. (NASA)

another. These seven wanderers (*planetai* in Greek) included the Sun, the Moon, Mercury, Venus, Mars, Jupiter, and Saturn. Each was thought to have a circular orbit around Earth.

Although this system was incorrect, the Greeks refined it to the point that it explained the apparent movements of all celestial bodies.

Ptolemy's Model

Much of our knowledge of Greek astronomy comes from a 13-volume treatise, *Almagest* (the great work), which was compiled by Ptolemy in A.D. 141. In addition to presenting a summary of Greek astronomical knowledge, Ptolemy is credited with developing a model of the universe that accounted for the observable motions of the celestial bodies (**FIGURE 15.3**).

In the Greek tradition, the Ptolemaic model had the planets moving in perfect circular orbits around a motionless Earth. (The Greeks considered the circle to be the pure and perfect shape.) However, the motion of the planets, as seen against the background of stars, is not so simple. Each planet, if watched night after night, moves slightly eastward among the stars. Periodically, each planet appears to stop, reverse direction for a period of time, and then resume an eastward motion. The apparent westward drift is called **retrograde** (*retro* = to go back, *gradus* = walking) **motion**. This rather odd apparent motion results from the combination of the motion of Earth and the planet's own motion around the Sun.

The retrograde motion of Mars is shown in **FIGURE 15.4**. Because Earth has a faster orbital speed than Mars, it overtakes its neighbor. While doing so, Mars *appears* to be moving backward, in retrograde motion. This is analogous to what a driver sees out the side window when passing a slower car. The slower planet, like the slower car, appears to

A.

B.

FIGURE 15.3   The universe according to Ptolemy, second century A.D. **A.** Ptolemy believed that the star-studded celestial sphere made a daily trip around a motionless Earth. In addition, he proposed that the Sun, Moon, and planets made trips of various lengths along individual orbits. **B.** A three-dimensional model of an Earth-centered system. Ptolemy likely utilized something similar to this to calculate the motions of the heavens. (Photo by PAL Photo)

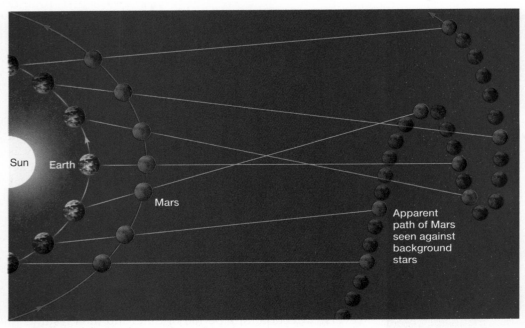

FIGURE 15.4 Retrograde (backward) motion of Mars as seen against the background of distant stars. When viewed from Earth, Mars moves eastward among the stars each day, then periodically appears to stop and reverse direction. This apparent westward drift is a result of the fact that Earth has a faster orbital speed than Mars and overtakes it. As this occurs, Mars appears to be moving backward, that is, it exhibits retrograde motion.

combination of two circular motions, a fact that can be verified by anyone who has used the Spirograp design-drawing toy.)

It is a tribute to Ptolemy's genius that he was able to account for the planets' motions as well as he did, considering that he used an incorrect model. The precision with which his model was able to predict planetary motion is attested to by the fact that it went virtually unchallenged, in principle if not in detail, until the seventeenth century. When Ptolemy's predicted positions for the planets became out of step with the observed positions (which took 100 years or more) his model was simply recalibrated using the new observed positions as a starting point.

With the decline of the Roman Empire around the fourth century, much of the accumulated knowledge disappeared as libraries were destroyed. After the decline of Greek and Roman civilizations, the center of astronomical study moved east to Baghdad where, fortunately, Ptolemy's work was translated into Arabic. Later, Arabic astronomers expanded Hipparchus's star catalog and divided the sky into 48 constellations—the foundation of our present-day constellation system. It wasn't until some time after the tenth century that the ancient Greeks' contributions to astronomy were reintroduced to Europe through the Arabic community. The **Ptolemaic model** soon dominated European thought as the correct representation of the heavens, which created problems for anyone who found errors in it.

be going backward, although its actual motion is in the same direction as the faster-moving body.

It is difficult to accurately represent retrograde motion using the incorrect Earth-centered model, but that is what Ptolemy was able to accomplish (**FIGURE 15.5**). Rather than using a single circle for each planet's orbit, he proposed that the planets orbited on small circles (*epicycles*), revolving along large circles (*deferents*). By trial and error, he found the right combination of circles to produce the amount of retrograde motion observed for each planet. (An interesting note is that almost any closed curve can be produced by the

FIGURE 15.5 Ptolemy's explanation of retrograde motion—the backward motion of planets against the background of fixed stars. In Ptolemy's model, the planets move on small circles (epicycles) while they orbit Earth on larger circles (deferents). Through trial and error, Ptolemy discovered the right combination of circles to produce the retrograde motion observed for each planet.

THE BIRTH OF MODERN ASTRONOMY

Ptolemy's Earth-centered universe was not discarded overnight. Modern astronomy's development was more than a scientific endeavor, it required a break from deeply entrenched philosophical and religious views that had been a basic part of Western society for thousands of years. Its development was brought about by the discovery of a new and much larger universe governed by discernible laws. We examine the work of five noted scientists involved in this transition from an astronomy that merely describes what is observed, to an astronomy that tries to explain what is observed and more importantly why the universe behaves the way it does. They include Nicolaus Copernicus,

Tycho Brahe, Johannes Kepler, Galileo Galilei, and Sir Isaac Newton.

Nicolaus Copernicus

For almost 13 centuries after the time of Ptolemy, very few astronomical advances were made in Europe—some were even lost, including the notion of a spherical Earth. The first great astronomer to emerge after the Middle Ages was Nicolaus Copernicus (1473–1543) from Poland (**FIGURE 15.6**). After discovering Aristarchus's writings, Copernicus became convinced that Earth is a planet, just like the other five then-known planets. The daily motions of the heavens, he reasoned, could be more simply explained by a rotating Earth.

Having concluded that Earth is a planet, Copernicus constructed a *heliocentric* model for the solar system with the Sun at the center and the planets Mercury, Venus, Earth, Mars, Jupiter, and Saturn orbiting it. This was a major break from the ancient and prevailing idea that a motionless Earth lies at the center of all movement in the universe. However, Copernicus retained a link to the past and used circles to represent the orbits of the planets. Because of this Copernicus was unable to accurately predict the future locations of the planets. Copernicus found it necessary to add smaller circles (epicycles) like those used by Ptolemy. The discovery that the planets actually have *elliptical* orbits occurred a century later and is credited to Johannes Kepler.

Like his predecessors, Copernicus also used philosophical justifications to support his point of view: " . . . In the midst of all stands the Sun. For who could in this most beautiful temple place this lamp in another or better place than that from which it can at the same time illuminate the whole?"

FIGURE 15.6 Polish astronomer Nicolaus Copernicus (1473–1543) believed that Earth was just another planet. (Detlev van Ravenswaay/Photo Researchers, Inc.)

Copernicus's monumental work, *De Revolutionibus, Orbium Coelestium* (*On the Revolution of the Heavenly Spheres*), which set forth his controversial Sun-centered solar system, was published as he lay on his deathbed. Hence, he never suffered the criticisms that fell on many of his followers. Although Copernicus's model was a vast improvement over Ptolemy's, it did not attempt to explain how planetary motions occurred or why.

The greatest contribution of the Copernican system to modern science is its challenge of the primacy of Earth in the universe. At the time this was considered heretical by many Europeans. Professing the Sun-centered model cost at least one person his life. Giordano Bruno was seized by the Inquisition, a Church tribunal, in 1600, and refusing to denounce the Copernican theory, was burned at the stake.

Tycho Brahe

Tycho Brahe (1546–1601) was born of Danish nobility three years after the death of Copernicus. Reportedly, Tycho became interested in astronomy while viewing a solar eclipse that had been predicted by astronomers. He persuaded King Frederick II to establish an observatory near Copenhagen, which Tycho headed. There he designed and built pointers (the telescope would not be invented for a few more decades), which he used for 20 years to systematically measure the locations of the heavenly bodies in an effort to disprove the Copernican theory (**FIGURE 15.7**). His observations, particularly of Mars, were far more precise than any made previously and are his legacy to astronomy.

Tycho did not believe in the Copernican model, because he was unable to observe an apparent shift in the position of stars that should result if Earth traveled around the Sun. His argument went like this: If Earth orbits the Sun, the position of a nearby star, when observed from two locations in Earth's orbit six months apart, should shift with respect to the more distant stars. Tycho was correct, but his measurements did not have great enough precision to show any displacement. The apparent shift of the stars is called *stellar parallax* (see Figure 16.2, p. 459), and today it is used to measure distances to the nearest stars.

The principle of parallax is easy to visualize: Close one eye, and with your index finger vertical, use your eye to line up your finger with some distant object. Now, without moving your finger, view the object with your other eye and notice that the object's position appears to change. The farther away you hold your finger, the less the object's position seems to shift. Herein lay the flaw in Tycho's argument. He was right about parallax, but the distance to even the nearest stars is enormous compared to the width of Earth's orbit. Consequently, the shift that Tycho was looking for is too small to be detected without the aid of a telescope—which had not yet been invented.

With the death of his patron, the King of Denmark, Tycho was forced to leave his observatory. It was probably his arrogant and extravagant nature that caused a conflict with the new ruler. Tycho moved to Prague in the present-day Czech Republic, where, in the last year of his life, he

FIGURE 15.7   Tycho Brahe (1546–1601) in his observatory, in Uraniborg, on the Danish island of Hveen. Tycho (central figure) and the background are painted on the wall of the observatory within the arc of the sighting instrument called a quadrant. In the far right, Tycho can be seen "sighting" a celestial object through the "hole" in the wall. Tycho's accurate measurements of Mars enabled Johannes Kepler to formulate his three laws of planetary motion. (Courtesy of The Bridgeman Library International)

acquired an able assistant, Johannes Kepler. Kepler retained most of the observations made by Tycho and put them to exceptional use. Ironically, the data Tycho collected to refute the Copernican view of the solar system would later be used by Kepler to support it.

Johannes Kepler

If Copernicus ushered out the old astronomy, Johannes Kepler (1571–1630) ushered in the new (**FIGURE 15.8**). Armed with Tycho's data, a good mathematical mind, and, of greater importance, a strong belief in the accuracy of Tycho's work, Kepler derived three basic laws of planetary motion. The first two laws resulted from his inability to fit Tycho's observations of Mars to a circular orbit. Unwilling to concede that the discrepancies were a result of observational

FIGURE 15.8   German astronomer Johannes Kepler (1571–1630) helped establish the era of modern astronomy by deriving three laws of planetary motion. (Photo by Imagno/Getty Images)

error, he searched for another solution. This endeavor led him to discover that the orbit of Mars is not a perfect circle but is slightly elliptical (**FIGURE 15.9**). About the same time, he realized that the orbital speed of Mars varies in a predictable way. As it approaches the Sun, it speeds up, and as it moves away, it slows down.

In 1609, after almost a decade of work, Kepler proposed his first two laws of planetary motion:

1. The path of each planet around the Sun, while almost circular, is actually an ellipse, with the Sun at one focus (Figure 15.9).

2. Each planet revolves so that an imaginary line connecting it to the Sun sweeps over equal areas in equal intervals of time (**FIGURE 15.10**). This *law of equal areas* geometrically expresses the variations in orbital speeds of the planets.

Figure 15.10 illustrates the second law. Note that in order for a planet to sweep equal areas in the same amount of time, it must travel more rapidly when it is nearer the Sun and more slowly when it is farther from the Sun.

Kepler was devout and believed that the Creator made an orderly universe and that this order would be reflected in the positions and motions of the planets. The uniformity he tried to find eluded him for nearly a decade.

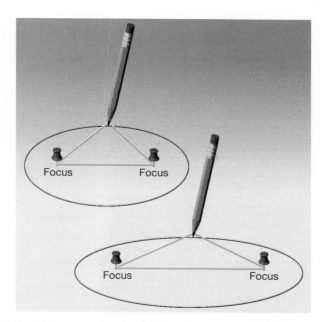

FIGURE 15.9 Drawing ellipses with various eccentricities. Using two straight pins for foci and a loop of string, trace out a curve while keeping the string taut, and you will have drawn an ellipse. The farther the pins (the foci) are moved apart, the more flattened (more eccentric) is the resulting ellipse.

Table 15.1	Period of revolution and solar distances of planets		
Planet	Solar Distance (AU)*	Period (years)	Ellipticity 0 = circle
Mercury	0.39	0.24	0.205
Venus	0.72	0.62	0.007
Earth	1.00	1.00	0.017
Mars	1.52	1.88	0.094
Jupiter	5.20	11.86	0.049
Saturn	9.54	29.46	0.057
Uranus	19.18	84.01	0.046
Neptune	30.06	164.80	0.011

*AU = astronomical unit

Then in 1619, Kepler published his third law in *The Harmony of the Worlds*:

3. The orbital periods of the planets and their distances to the Sun are proportional. In its simplest form, the orbital period is measured in Earth years, and the planet's distance to the Sun is expressed in terms of Earth's mean distance to the Sun. The latter "yardstick" is called the **astronomical unit (AU)** and is equal to about 150 million kilometers (93 million miles). Using these units, Kepler's third law states that the planet's orbital period squared is equal to its mean solar distance cubed. Consequently, the solar distances of

the planets can be calculated when their periods of revolution are known. For example, Mars has an orbital period of 1.88 years, which squared equals 3.54. The cube root of 3.54 is 1.52, and that is the average distance from Mars to the Sun, in astronomical units (Table 15.1).

Kepler's laws assert that the planets revolve around the Sun, and therefore support the Copernican theory. Kepler, however, did not determine the *forces* that act to produce the planetary motion he had so ably described. That task would remain for Galileo Galilei and Sir Isaac Newton.

Galileo Galilei

Galileo Galilei (1564–1642) was the greatest Italian scientist of the Renaissance (**FIGURE 15.11**). He was a contemporary of Kepler and, like Kepler, strongly supported the Copernican theory of a Sun-centered solar system. Galileo's greatest contributions to science were his descriptions of the behavior of moving objects, which he derived from experimentation. The method of using experiments to determine natural laws had essentially been lost since the time of the early Greeks.

All astronomical discoveries before Galileo's time were made without the aid of a telescope. In 1609, Galileo heard that a Dutch lens maker had devised a system of lenses that magnified objects. Apparently without ever seeing a telescope, Galileo constructed his own, which magnified distant objects three times the size seen by the unaided eye. He immediately made others, the best having a magnification of about 30 (**FIGURE 15.12**).

With the telescope, Galileo was able to view the universe in a new way. He made many important discoveries that supported the Copernican view of the universe, including the following:

1. The discovery of Jupiter's four largest satellites, or moons (**FIGURE 15.13**). This finding dispelled the old idea that Earth was the sole center of motion in the universe; for here, plainly visible, was another center of motion—Jupiter. It also countered the frequently

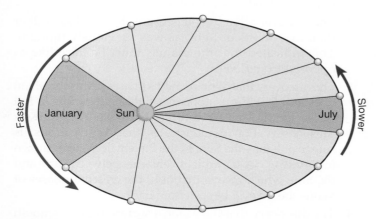

FIGURE 15.10 Kepler's law of equal areas. A line connecting a planet (Earth) to the Sun sweeps out an area in such a manner that equal areas are swept out in equal times. Thus, Earth revolves slower when it is farther from the Sun (aphelion) and faster when it is closest (perihelion). The eccentricity of Earth's orbit is greatly exaggerated in this diagram.

FIGURE 15.11 Italian scientist Galileo Galilei (1564–1642) used a new invention, the telescope, to observe the Sun, Moon, and planets in more detail than ever before. (Nimatallah/Art Resource N.Y.)

FIGURE 15.12 One of Galileo's telescopes. Although Galileo did not invent the telescope, he built several—the largest of which had a magnification of 30. (Photo by Gianni Tortoli/Photo Researchers, Inc.)

FIGURE 15.13 Sketch by Galileo of how he saw Jupiter and its four largest satellites through his telescope. The positions of Jupiter's four largest Moons (drawn as stars) change nightly. You can observe these same changes with binoculars. (Yerkes Observatory Photograph/University of Chicago)

used argument that the Moon would be left behind if Earth revolved around the Sun.

2. The discovery that the planets are circular disks rather than just points of light, as was previously thought. This indicated that the planets must be Earthlike as opposed to starlike.

3. The discovery that Venus exhibits phases just as the Moon does and that Venus appears smallest when it is in full phase and thus is farthest from Earth (**FIGURE 15.14B,C**). This observation demonstrates that Venus orbits its source of light—the Sun. In the Ptolemaic system, shown in **FIGURE 15.14A**, the orbit of Venus lies between Earth and the Sun, which means that only the crescent phases of Venus should ever be seen from Earth.

4. The discovery that the Moon's surface is not a smooth glass sphere, as the ancients had proclaimed. Rather, Galileo saw mountains, craters, and plains indicating that the Moon was Earthlike. He thought the plains might be bodies of water, and this idea was strongly promoted by others, as we can tell from the names

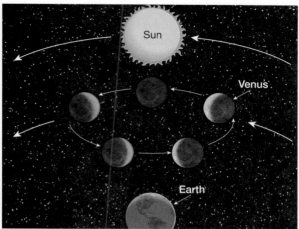

A. Phases of Venus as seen from Earth in the Earth-centered model.

FIGURE 15.14 Using a telescope, Galileo discovered that Venus has phases just like the Moon. **A.** In the Ptolemaic (Earth-centered) system, the orbit of Venus lies between the Sun and Earth. Thus, in an Earth-centered solar system, only the crescent phase of Venus would be visible from Earth. **B.** In the Copernican (Sun-centered) system, Venus orbits the Sun and hence all of the phases of Venus should be visible from Earth. **C.** As Galileo observed, Venus goes through a series of Moonlike phases. Venus appears smallest during the full phase when it is farthest from Earth and largest in the crescent phase when it is closest to Earth. This verified Galileo's belief that the Sun was the center of the solar system. (Photo courtesy of Lowell Observatory)

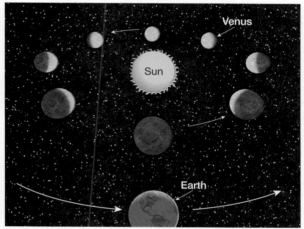

B. Phases of Venus as seen from Earth in the sun-centered model.

C.

given to these features (Sea of Tranquility, Sea of Storms, etc.).

5. The discovery that the Sun (the viewing of which may have caused the eye damage that later blinded him) had sunspots—dark regions caused by slightly lower temperatures. He tracked the movement of these spots and estimated the rotational period of the Sun as just under a month. Hence, another heavenly body was found to have both "blemishes" and rotational motion.

Each of these observations eroded a bedrock principle held by the prevailing view on the nature of the universe.

In 1616, the Church condemned the Copernican theory as contrary to Scripture because it did not put humans at their rightful place at the center of Creation, and Galileo was told to abandon this theory. Undeterred, Galileo began writing his most famous work, *Dialogue of the Great World Systems*. Despite poor health, he completed the project and in 1630 went to Rome, seeking permission from Pope Urban VIII to publish. Since the book was a dialogue that expounded both the Ptolemaic and Copernican systems, publication was allowed. However, Galileo's detractors were quick to realize that he was promoting the Copernican view at the expense of the Ptolemaic system. Sale of the book was quickly halted, and Galileo was called before the Inquisition. Tried and convicted of proclaiming doctrines contrary to religious teachings, he was sentenced to permanent house arrest, under which he remained for the last 10 years of his life.

Despite this restriction, and his grief following the death of his eldest daughter, Galileo continued to work. In 1637 he became totally blind, yet during the next few years he completed his finest scientific work, a book on the study of motion in which he stated that the natural tendency of an object in motion is to remain in motion. Later, as more scientific evidence in support of the Copernican system was discovered, the Church allowed Galileo's works to be published.

Sir Isaac Newton

Sir Isaac Newton (1642–1727) was born in the year of Galileo's death (**FIGURE 15.15**). His many accomplishments in mathematics and physics led a successor to say that "Newton was the greatest genius that ever existed."

DID YOU KNOW?

Through experimentation, Galileo discovered that the acceleration of falling objects does not depend on their weight. According to some accounts, Galileo made this discovery by dropping balls of iron and wood from the Leaning Tower of Pisa to show that they would fall together and hit the ground at the same time. Despite the popularity of this legend, Galileo probably did not attempt this experiment. In fact, it would have been inconclusive because of the effect of air resistance. However, nearly four centuries later, this experiment was performed most dramatically on the airless Moon when David Scott, an *Apollo 15* astronaut, demonstrated that a feather and a hammer do, indeed, fall at the same rate.

Although Kepler and those who followed attempted to explain the forces involved in planetary motion, their explanations were less than satisfactory. Kepler believed that some force pushed the planets along in their orbits. Galileo, however, correctly reasoned that no force is required to keep an object in motion. Instead, Galileo proposed that the natural tendency for a moving object that is unaffected by an outside force is to continue moving at a uniform speed and in a straight line. This concept, *inertia*, was later formalized by Newton as his first law of motion.

The problem, then, was not to explain the force that keeps the planets moving but rather to determine the force that *keeps them from going in a straight line out into space*. It was to this end that Newton conceptualized the force of gravity. At the early age of 23, he envisioned a force that extends from Earth into space and holds the Moon in orbit around Earth. Although others had theorized the existence of such a force, he was the first to formulate and test the *law of universal gravitation*. It states:

> Every body in the universe attracts every other body with a force that is directly proportional to their masses and inversely proportional to the square of the distance between them.

Thus, gravitational force decreases with distance, so that two objects 3 kilometers apart have 3^2, or 9, times less gravitational attraction than if the same objects were 1 kilometer apart.

The law of gravitation also states that the greater the mass of an object, the greater its gravitational force. For example, the large mass of the Moon has a gravitational force strong enough to cause ocean tides on Earth, whereas the tiny mass of a communications satellite has very little effect on Earth.

With his laws of motion, Newton proved that the force of gravity—combined with the tendency of a planet to remain in straight-line motion—would result in a planet having an elliptical orbit as established by Kepler. Earth, for example, moves forward in its orbit about 30 kilometers (18.5 miles) each second, and during the same second, the force of gravity pulls it toward the Sun about 0.5 centimeter (1/8 inch). Therefore, as Newton concluded, it is the combination of Earth's forward motion and its "falling" motion that defines its orbit (**FIGURE 15.16**). If gravity were somehow eliminated, Earth would move in a straight line out into space. Conversely, if Earth's forward motion suddenly stopped, gravity would pull it crashing into the Sun.

Newton used the law of universal gravitation to express Kepler's third law, which defines the relationship between the orbital periods of the planets and their solar distances. In its new form, Kepler's third law takes into account the masses of the bodies involved and thereby provides a method for determining the mass of a body when the orbit of one of its satellites is known. For example, the mass of the Sun is known from Earth's orbit, and Earth's mass has been determined from the orbit of the Moon. In fact, the mass of any body with a satellite can be determined.

OUR SOLAR SYSTEM: AN OVERVIEW

GEODe
EARTH SCIENCE

Earth's Place in the Universe
▼ The Planets: An Overview

The Sun is at the center of a revolving system, trillions of miles wide, consisting of eight planets, their satellites, and numerous smaller asteroids, comets, and meteoroids

FIGURE 15.15 English scientist Sir Isaac Newton (1642–1727) explained gravity as the force that holds planets in orbit around the Sun. (Getty Images)

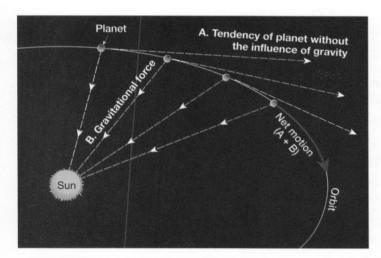

FIGURE 15.16   Orbital motion of Earth and other planets.

(FIGURE 15.17). An estimated 99.85 percent of the mass of our solar system is contained within the Sun. Collectively, the planets account for most of the remaining 0.15 percent. Starting from the Sun, the planets are Mercury, Venus, Earth, Mars, Jupiter, Saturn, Uranus, and Neptune. Pluto was recently reclassified as a member of a new class of solar system bodies called *dwarf planets*.

Tethered to the Sun by gravity, all of the planets travel in the same direction on slightly elliptical orbits (Table 15.2).

Gravity causes objects nearest the Sun to travel fastest. Therefore, Mercury has the highest orbital velocity, 48 kilometers per second, and the shortest period of revolution around the Sun, 88 Earth-days. By contrast, the distant dwarf planet Pluto has an orbital speed of just 5 kilometers per second and requires 248 Earth-years to complete one revolution. Most large bodies orbit the Sun approximately in the same plane. The planets' inclination with respect to the Earth–Sun orbital plane, known as the *ecliptic*, is shown in Table 15.2.

Nebular Theory: Formation of the Solar System

The **nebular theory**, which explains the formation of the solar system, states that the Sun and planets formed from a rotating cloud of interstellar gases (mainly hydrogen and helium) and dust called the **solar nebula**. As the solar nebula contracted due to gravity, most of the material collected in the center to form the hot *protosun*. The remaining materials formed a thick, flattened, rotating disk, within which matter gradually cooled and condensed into grains and clumps of icy, rocky material. Repeated collisions resulted in most of the material eventually collecting into asteroid-sized objects called **planetesimals.**

The composition of planetesimals was largely determined by their proximity to the protosun. As you might expect, temperatures were highest in the inner solar system

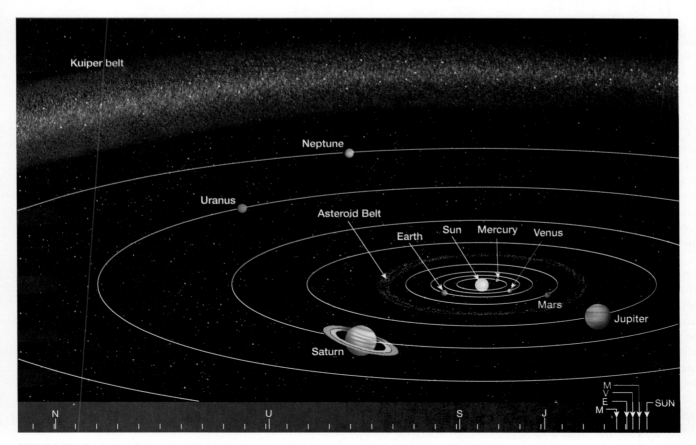

FIGURE 15.17   Orbits of the planets. Positions of the planets are shown to scale along bottom of diagram.

Table 15.2   Planetary data

Planet	Symbol	Mean Distance from Sun			Period of Revolution	Inclination of Orbit	Orbital Velocity	
		AU*	Millions of Miles	Millions of Kilometers			mi/s	km/s
Mercury	☿	0.39	36	58	88^d	7°00'	29.5	47.5
Venus	♀	0.72	67	108	225^d	3°24'	21.8	35.0
Earth	⊕	1.00	93	150	365.25^d	0°00'	18.5	29.8
Mars	♂	1.52	142	228	687^d	1°51'	14.9	24.1
Jupiter	♃	5.20	483	778	12^{yr}	1°18'	8.1	13.1
Saturn	♄	9.54	886	1427	30^{yr}	2°29'	6.0	9.6
Uranus	♅	19.18	1783	2870	84^{yr}	0°46'	4.2	6.8
Neptune	♆	30.06	2794	4497	165^{yr}	1°46'	3.3	5.3

Planet	Period of Rotation	Diameter		Relative Mass (Earth = 1)	Average Density (g/cm^3)	Polar Flattening (%)	Eccentricity†	Number of Known Satellites††
		Miles	Kilometers					
Mercury	59^d	3015	4878	0.06	5.4	0.0	0.206	0
Venus	243^d	7526	12,104	0.82	5.2	0.0	0.007	0
Earth	23^{h}53^{m}04^s	7920	12,756	1.00	5.5	0.3	0.017	1
Mars	24^{h}37^{m}23^s	4216	6794	0.11	3.9	0.5	0.093	2
Jupiter	9^{h}56^m	88,700	143,884	317.87	1.3	6.7	0.048	63
Saturn	10^{h}30^m	75,000	120,536	95.14	0.7	10.4	0.056	61
Uranus	17^{h}14^m	29,000	51,118	14.56	1.2	2.3	0.047	27
Neptune	16^{h}07^m	28.900	50,530	17.21	1.7	1.8	0.009	13

*AU—astronomical unit. Earth's mean distance from Sun.

†Eccentricity is a measure of the amount an orbit deviates from a circular shape. The larger the number, the less circular the orbit.

††Includes all satellites discovered as of August 2009.

and decreased toward the outer edge of the disk. Therefore, between the present orbits of Mercury and Mars, the planetesimals were composed of materials with high melting temperatures—metals and rocky substances. Then, through repeated collisions and accretion (sticking together) these asteroid-sized rocky bodies combined to form the four **protoplanets** that eventually became Mercury, Venus, Earth, and Mars.

The planetesimals that formed beyond the orbit of Mars, where temperatures are low, contained high percentages of ices—water, carbon dioxide, ammonia, and methane—as well as small amounts of rocky and metallic debris. It was mainly from these planetesimals that the four outer planets eventually formed. The accumulation of ices accounts, in part, for the large sizes and low densities of the outer planets. The two most massive planets, Jupiter and Saturn, had surface gravities sufficient to attract and retain large quantities of hydrogen and helium, the lightest elements.

It took roughly a billion years after the protoplanets formed for the planets to gravitationally accumulate most of the interplanetary debris. This was a period of intense bombardment as the planets cleared their orbits of much of the leftover material. The "scars" of this period are still evident on the Moon's surface. Small bodies were flung into planet-crossing orbits, or into interstellar space. A small fraction of the interplanetary matter that escaped this violent period became asteroids, comets, and meteoroids. By comparison, the present-day solar system is a much quieter place, although these processes continue today at a greatly reduced pace.

The Planets: Internal Structures and Atmospheres

The planets fall into two groups based on location, size, and density: the **terrestrial** (Earthlike) **planets** (Mercury, Venus, Earth, and Mars), and the **Jovian** (Jupiter-like) **planets** (Jupiter, Saturn, Uranus, and Neptune). Because of their relative locations, the four terrestrial planets are also known as *inner planets* and the four Jovian planets are known as *outer planets*. A correlation exists between planetary locations and sizes—the inner planets are substantially smaller than the outer planets, also known as *gas giants*. For example, the

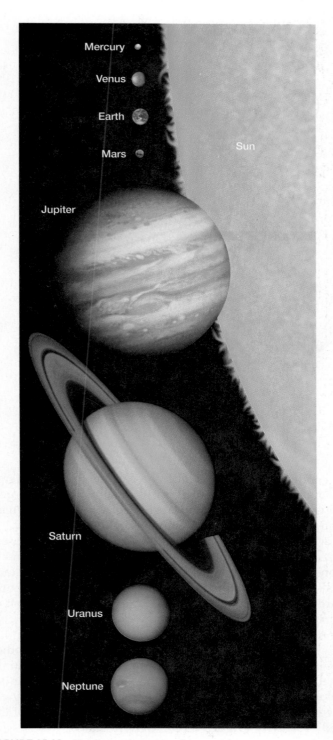

FIGURE 15.18 The planets drawn to scale.

of water, whereas the average density of the Jovian planets is only 1.5 times that of water. Saturn has a density only 0.7 times that of water, which means that it would float if placed in a large enough tank of water. The outer planets are also characterized by long orbital periods and numerous satellites.

Internal Structures

Shortly after Earth formed, the segregation of material resulted in the formation of three major layers defined by their chemical composition—the crust, mantle, and core. This type of chemical separation occurred in the other planets as well. However, because the terrestrial planets are compositionally different than the Jovian planets, the nature of these layers differs between these two groups (**FIGURE 15.19**).

The terrestrial planets are dense, having relatively large cores of iron and iron compounds. From their centers outward, the amount of metallic iron decreases while the amount of rocky silicate minerals increase. The outer cores of Earth and Mercury are liquid, whereas the cores of Venus and Mars are thought to be partially molten. This difference is attributable to Venus and Mars having lower internal temperatures than those of Earth and Mercury. Silicate minerals and other lighter compounds make up the mantles of the terrestrial planets. Finally, the silicate crusts of terrestrial planets are relatively thin compared to their mantles.

The two largest Jovian planets, Jupiter and Saturn, have small metallic inner cores consisting of iron compounds at extremely high temperatures and pressures. The outer cores of these two giants are thought to be liquid metallic hydrogen, whereas the mantles are comprised of liquid hydrogen and helium. The outermost layers are gases and ices of hydrogen, helium, water, ammonia, and methane—which account for the low densities of these planets. Uranus and Neptune also have small metallic cores but their mantles are likely hot dense water and ammonia. Above their mantles, the amount of hydrogen and helium increases, but exists in much lower concentrations than those of Jupiter and Saturn.

The Atmospheres of the Planets

The Jovian planets have very thick atmospheres composed mainly of hydrogen and helium, with lesser amounts of water, methane, ammonia, and other hydrocarbons. The Jovian atmospheres are so thick that they do not show a clear boundary between "atmosphere" and "planet." By contrast, the terrestrial planets, including Earth, have relatively meager atmospheres composed of carbon dioxide, nitrogen, and oxygen.

Two factors explain these significant differences—solar heating (temperature) and gravity (**FIGURE 15.20**). These variables determine what planetary gases, if any, were captured by planets during the formation of the solar system and which were ultimately retained.

During planetary formation, the inner regions of the developing solar system were too hot for ices and gases to condense. In contrast, the Jovian planets formed where temperatures were low and solar heating of planetesimals was minimal. This allowed water vapor, ammonia, and methane

diameter of Neptune (the smallest Jovian planet) is three times larger than the diameter of Earth or Venus. Further, Neptune's mass is 17 times greater than that of Earth or Venus (**FIGURE 15.18**).

Other properties that differ include densities, chemical compositions, orbital periods, and numbers of satellites. Variations in the chemical composition of planets are largely responsible for their density differences. Specifically, the average density of the terrestrial planets is about five times the density

TERRESTRIAL PLANETS

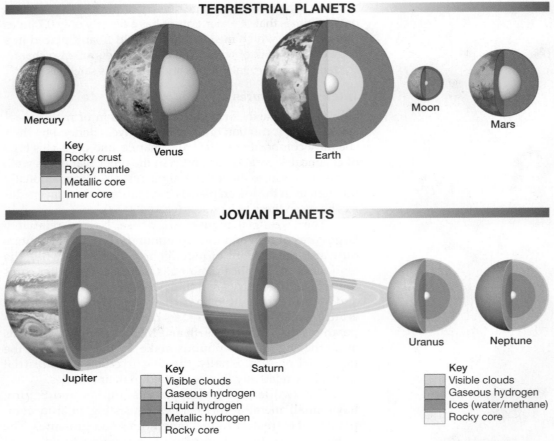

Mercury

Venus

Earth

Moon

Mars

Key
Rocky crust
Rocky mantle
Metallic core
Inner core

FIGURE 15.19   Comparison of the internal structures of the planets.

JOVIAN PLANETS

Jupiter

Saturn

Uranus

Neptune

Key
Visible clouds
Gaseous hydrogen
Liquid hydrogen
Metallic hydrogen
Rocky core

Key
Visible clouds
Gaseous hydrogen
Ices (water/methane)
Rocky core

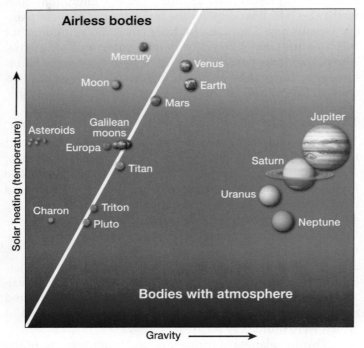

Airless bodies

Mercury

Venus

Moon

Earth

Mars

Jupiter

Asteroids

Galilean moons

Europa

Saturn

Titan

Uranus

Charon

Triton

Neptune

Pluto

Solar heating (temperature) →

Gravity →

Bodies with atmosphere

FIGURE 15.20   The factors that explain why some bodies have thick atmospheres, whereas others are airless include solar heating (temperature) and gravity. Airless worlds are comparatively warm and have weak gravity, whereas bodies with significant atmospheres have weak heating and strong gravity.

to condense into ices. Hence, the gas giants contain large amounts of these volatiles. As the planets grew, the largest Jovian planets, Jupiter and Saturn, also attracted large quantities of the lightest gases, hydrogen and helium.

How did Earth acquire water and other volatile gases? It seems that early in the history of the solar system, gravitational tugs by the developing protoplanets sent planetesimals into very eccentric orbits. As a result, Earth was bombarded with icy objects that originated beyond the orbit of Mars. This was a fortuitous event for organisms that currently inhabit our planet.

Mercury, our Moon, and numerous other small bodies lack significant atmospheres even though they certainly would have been bombarded by icy bodies early in their development. Airless bodies develop where solar heating exceeds a certain level, which depends on the strength of the body's gravity (Figure 15.20). Simply stated, *less massive planets* have a better chance of losing their atmosphere because gas molecules need less speed to escape their weak gravities. Comparatively warm bodies with small surface gravity, such as our Moon, are unable to hold even heavy gases such as carbon dioxide and nitrogen. Mercury holds trace amounts of gas.

The slightly larger terrestrial planets Earth, Venus, and Mars retain some heavy gases including water vapor, nitrogen, and carbon dioxide. However, their atmospheres are miniscule compared to their total mass. Early in their development, the terrestrial planets probably had much thicker atmospheres. Over time, however, these primitive atmospheres gradually changed as certain gases trickled away into space. For example, Earth's atmosphere continues to leak hydrogen and helium (the two lightest gases) into space. This phenomenon occurs near the top of Earth's atmosphere where air is so tenuous that nothing stops the fastest moving ions from flying off into space. The speed required to escape a planet's gravity is called **escape velocity**. Because hydrogen is the lightest gas, it most easily reaches the speed needed to overcome Earth's gravity.

Planetary Impacts

Planetary impacts have occurred throughout the history of the solar system. On bodies that have little or no atmosphere, such as the Moon and Mercury, even the smallest pieces of interplanetary debris (meteorites) can produce microscopic cavities on individual mineral grains. By contrast, large **impact craters** are the result of collisions with massive bodies, such as asteroids and comets.

Planetary impacts were considerably more common in the early history of the solar system than they are today, with the heaviest bombardment occurring 3.8 to 4.1 billion years ago. Following that period, the rate of cratering diminished dramatically and now remains essentially constant. Because weathering and erosion are almost nonexistent on the Moon and Mercury, their cratered past is clearly evident.

On larger bodies, thick atmospheres may cause the impacting objects to break up and/or decelerate. For example, Earth's atmosphere causes meteoroids with masses of less than 10 kilograms (22 pounds) to lose up to 90 percent of their speed as they penetrate the atmosphere. Therefore, impacts of low-mass bodies produce only small craters on Earth. Earth's atmosphere is much less effective in slowing large bodies—fortunately, they make very rare appearances.

The formation of a large impact crater is illustrated in **FIGURE 15.21**. The meteoroid's high-speed impact compresses the material it strikes, causing an almost instantaneous rebound that ejects material from the surface. Craters excavated by objects that are several kilometers across often exhibit a central peak, such as the one in the large crater in **FIGURE 15.22**. Much of the material expelled, called *ejecta*, lands in or near the crater, where it accumulates to form a rim. Large meteoroids may generate sufficient heat to melt

FIGURE 15.21 Formation of an impact crater. The energy of the rapidly moving meteoroid is transformed into heat energy and compressional waves. The rebound of the compressed rock causes debris to be ejected from the crater. Heat melts some material, producing glass beads. Small secondary craters are formed by the material "splashed" from the impact crater. (After E. M. Shoemaker)

DID YOU KNOW?

Although it was long suspected, it was not until recently that the presence of extrasolar planets has been verified. Astronomers have found these bodies by measuring the telltale wobbles of nearby stars. The first apparent planet outside the solar system was discovered in 1995, orbiting the star 51 Pegasi, 42 light-years from Earth. Since that time, numerous Jupiter-size bodies have been identified, most of them surprisingly close to the stars they orbit.

some of the impacted rock. Samples of glass beads produced in this manner, as well as rocks consisting of broken fragments welded together by the heat of impacts, have been collected from the Moon, allowing planetary geologists to learn about such events.

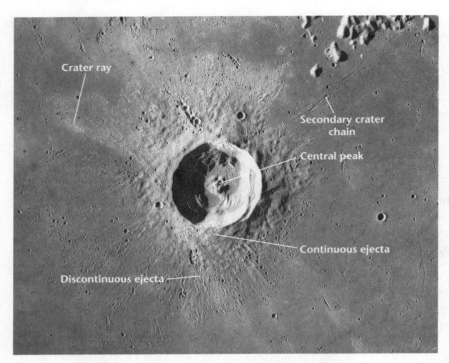

FIGURE 15.22   The 20-kilometer-wide lunar crater Euler in the southwestern part of Mare Imbrium. Clearly visible are the bright rays, central peak, secondary craters, and large accumulation of ejecta near the crater rim. (Courtesy of NASA)

EARTH'S MOON: A CHIP OFF THE OLD BLOCK

Earth's Place in the Universe
▼ Earth's Moon

The Earth–Moon system is unique because the Moon is the largest satellite relative to its planet. Mars is the only other terrestrial planet with moons, but its tiny satellites are likely captured asteroids. Most of the 150 or so satellites of the Jovian planets are composed of low-density rock-ice mixtures, none of which resemble the Moon. As we will see later, our unique planet–satellite system is closely related to the mechanism that created it.

The diameter of the Moon is 3475 kilometers (2160 miles), about one-fourth of Earth's 12,756 kilometers (7926 miles). The Moon's surface temperature averages about 107°C (225°F) for daylight hours and −153°C (−243°F) for night. Because its period of rotation on its axis equals its period of revolution around Earth, the same lunar hemisphere always faces Earth. All of the landings of manned *Apollo* missions were confined to the side of the Moon facing Earth.

The Moon's density is 3.3 times that of water, comparable to that of *mantle* rocks on Earth, but considerably less than Earth's average density (5.5 times that of water). The Moon's relatively small iron core is thought to account for much of this difference.

The Moon's low mass relative to Earth results in a lunar gravitational attraction that is one-sixth that of Earth. A person weighing 150 pounds on Earth weighs only 25 pounds on the Moon, although their mass remains the same. This difference allows an astronaut to carry a heavy life-support system with relative ease. If not burdened with such a load, an astronaut could jump six times higher on the Moon than on Earth. The Moon's small mass (and low gravity) is the primary reason it was not able to retain an atmosphere.

How Did the Moon Form?

Until recently, the origin of the Moon—our nearest planetary neighbor—was a topic of considerable debate among scientists. Current models show that Earth is too small to have formed with a moon, particularly one so large. Furthermore, a captured moon would likely have an eccentric orbit similar to the captured moons that orbit the Jovian planets.

The current consensus is that the Moon formed as the result of a collision between a Mars-sized body and a youthful, semimolten Earth about 4.5 billion years ago. (Collisions of this type were probably frequent at that time.) During this explosive event, some of the ejected debris was thrown into Earth's orbit and gradually coalesced to form the Moon. Computer simulations show that most of the ejected material would have come from the rocky mantle of the impactor, whereas its core became part of the growing Earth. This *impact model* is consistent with the Moon's low density and internal structure, which consists of a large mantle and a small iron-rich core.

The Lunar Surface

When Galileo first pointed his telescope toward the Moon, he observed two different types of terrain—dark lowlands and brighter, highly cratered highlands (**FIGURE 15.23**). Because the dark regions appeared smooth, resembling seas on Earth, they were called **maria** (*mar* = sea, singular **mare**). The *Apollo 11* mission showed conclusively that the maria are exceedingly smooth plains composed of basaltic lavas. These vast plains are strongly concentrated on the side of the Moon facing Earth and cover about 16 percent of the lunar surface. The lack of large volcanic cones on these surfaces is evidence of very fluid basaltic lavas similar to the Columbia Plateau flood basalts on Earth.

By contrast, the Moon's light-colored areas resemble Earth's continents, so the first observers dubbed them **terrae** (Latin for "land"). These areas are now generally referred to as the **lunar highlands**, because they are elevated several kilometers above the maria. Rocks retrieved from the highlands are mainly breccias, pulverized by massive bombardment early in the Moon's history. The arrangement of terrae and maria result in the legendary "face" of the "man in the moon."

Some of the most obvious lunar features are impact craters. The larger craters shown in Figure 15.23 are about 250 kilometers (150 miles) in diameter, roughly the width of Indiana. A meteoroid 3 meters (10 feet) in diameter can blast out a crater 50 times larger, or about 150 meters (500 feet) in diameter. Larger craters, such as Kepler and Copernicus (32 and 93 kilometers diameter, respectively) were created

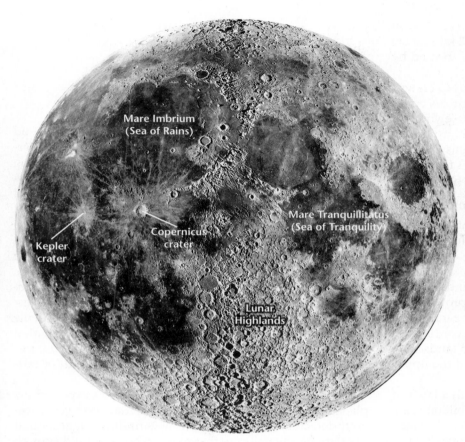

FIGURE 15.23 Telescopic view of the lunar surface from Earth. The major features are the dark "seas" (maria) and the light, highly cratered highlands. (UCO/Lick Observatory Image)

ocean began to cool and underwent magmatic differentiation (see Chapter 2). Most of the dense minerals, olivine and pyroxene, sank while less dense silicate minerals floated to form the Moon's primitive crust. The highlands are made of these igneous rocks that rose buoyantly like "scum" from the crystallizing magma. The most common highland rock-type is *anorthosite*, which is composed mainly of calcium-rich feldspar.

Once formed, the lunar crust was continually impacted as the Moon swept up debris from the solar nebula. During this time, several large impact basins were created. Then about 3.8 billion years ago, the Moon, as well as the rest of the solar system, experienced a sudden drop in the rate of meteoritic bombardment.

The Moon's next major event was the filling of the large impact basins created at least 300 million years earlier (**FIGURE 15.24**). Radiometric dating of the maria basalts puts their age between 3.0 billion and 3.5 billion years, considerably younger than the initial lunar crust.

The mare basalts are thought to have originated at depths between 200 and 400 kilometers. They were likely generated by a slow rise in temperature attributed to the decay of radioactive elements. Partial melting probably occurred in several isolated pockets as indicated by the diverse chemical makeup of the rocks retrieved during the *Apollo* missions. Recent evidence suggests that some mare-forming eruptions may have occurred as recently as one billion years ago.

from bombardment by bodies 1 kilometer or more in diameter (Figure 15.23). These two craters are thought to be relatively young because of the bright *rays* (lightly colored ejected material) that radiate from them for hundreds of kilometers.

History of the Lunar Surface

The evidence used to unravel the history of the lunar surface comes primarily from radiometric dating of rocks returned from *Apollo* missions and studies of crater densities—counting the number of craters per unit area. The greater the crater density, the older the feature. Such evidence suggests that after the Moon coalesced, it passed through the following four phases: (1) formation of the original crust and lunar highlands, (2) excavation of the large impact basins, (3) filling of mare basins, and (4) formation of rayed craters.

During the late stages of its accretion, the Moon's outer shell was most likely completely melted—literally a magma ocean. Then about 4.4 billion years ago, the magma

FIGURE 15.24 Formation of lunar maria. **A.** Impact of an asteroid-size mass produced a huge crater hundreds of kilometers in diameter and disturbed the lunar crust far beyond the crater. **B.** Filling of the impact area with fluid basalts, perhaps derived from partial melting deep within the lunar mantle. **C.** Today such basins make up the lunar maria and a few similar large structures on Mercury.

Other lunar surface features related to this period of volcanism include small shield volcanoes (8–12 kilometers in diameter), pyroclastic eruptions, and rilles formed by localized lava channels.

The last prominent features to form were rayed craters, as exemplified by the 90-kilometer-wide Copernicus crater shown in Figure 15.23. Material ejected from these younger depressions blankets the maria surfaces and many older, rayless craters. The relatively young Copernicus crater is thought to be about one billion years old. Had it formed on Earth, erosional forces would have long since obliterated it.

Today's Lunar Surface: Weathering and Erosion

The Moon's small mass and low gravity account for its lack of an atmosphere or flowing water. Therefore, the processes of weathering and erosion that continually modify Earth's surface are absent on the Moon. In addition, tectonic forces are no longer active on the Moon, so quakes and volcanic eruptions have ceased. Because the Moon is unprotected by an atmosphere, erosion is dominated by the impact of tiny particles from space (*micrometeorites*) that continually bombard its surface and gradually smooth the landscape. This activity has crushed and repeatedly mixed the upper portions of the lunar crust.

Both the maria and terrae are mantled with a layer of gray, unconsolidated debris derived from a few billion years of meteoric bombardment (**FIGURE 15.25**). This soil-like layer, called **lunar regolith** (*rhegos* = blanket, *lithos* = stone) is composed of igneous rocks, breccia, glass beads, and fine *lunar dust*. The lunar regolith is anywhere from 2 to 20 meters thick depending on the age of the surface.

PLANETS AND MOONS

Earth's Place in the Universe
▼ A Brief Tour of the Planets

Mercury: The Innermost Planet

Mercury, the innermost and smallest planet, revolves around the Sun quickly (88 days) but rotates slowly on its axis. Mercury's day-night cycle, which lasts 176 Earth-days, is very long compared to Earth's 24-hour cycle. One "night" on Mercury is roughly equivalent to three months on Earth, and is followed the same duration of daylight. Mercury has the greatest temperature extremes of any planet. Nighttime temperatures drop as low as −173°C (−280°F) and noontime temperatures exceed 427°C (800°F), hot enough to melt tin and lead. These extreme temperatures make life "as we know it" impossible on Mercury.

Mercury absorbs most of the sunlight that strikes it, reflecting only 6 percent into space, a characteristic of terrestrial bodies that have little or no atmosphere. The minuscule amount of gas present on Mercury may have originated from several sources: ionized gas emitted from the Sun; ices that vaporized during a recent comet impact; and/or outgassing of the planet's interior.

Although Mercury is small and scientists expected the planet's interior to have already cooled, the *Messenger* spacecraft detected a magnetic field. This finding suggests that Mercury has a large core that remains hot and fluid enough to generate a magnetic field.

Mercury resembles Earth's Moon in that it has very low reflectivity, no sustained atmosphere, numerous volcanic

FIGURE 15.25 Astronaut Harrison Schmitt sampling the lunar surface. Notice the footprints (inset) in the lunar "soil." (Courtesy of NASA)

FIGURE 15.26   Mercury. This view of Mercury looks remarkably similar to Earth's Moon. (Courtesy of NASA)

extreme *greenhouse effect*. As a consequence, Venus's surface temperature averages about 450°C (900°F). Temperature variations at the surface are generally minimal because of the intense mixing within the planet's dense atmosphere. Investigations of the extreme and uniform surface temperatures led scientists to more fully understand how the greenhouse effect operates on Earth.

The composition of the Venusian interior is probably similar to Earth's. However, Venus's weak magnetic field means its internal dynamics must be very different. Mantle convection is thought to operate on Venus, but the processes of plate tectonics, which recycle rigid lithosphere, do not appear to have contributed to the present Venusian topography.

The surface of Venus is completely hidden from view by a thick cloud layer composed mainly of tiny sulfuric acid droplets. In the 1970s, despite extreme temperatures and pressures, four Russian spacecraft landed successfully and obtained surface images. (As expected, however, all of the probes were crushed by the planet's immense atmospheric pressure within an hour of landing.) Using radar imaging, the unmanned spacecraft *Magellan* mapped Venus's surface in amazing detail (**FIGURE 15.27**).

Approximately 1000 impact craters have been identified on Venus, far fewer than Mercury and Mars, but more than Earth. Researchers, who expected that Venus would

features, and a heavily cratered terrain (**FIGURE 15.26**). The youngest and largest (1300 kilometers in diameter) known impact crater on Mercury is Caloris Basin. Images and other data gathered by *Mariner 10* show evidence of volcanism in and around Caloris Basin and a few other smaller basins. Also like our Moon, Mercury has smooth plains that cover nearly 40 percent of the area imaged by *Mariner 10*. Most of these smooth areas are associated with large impact basins, including Caloris Basin, where lava partially filled the basins and the surrounding lowlands. Consequently, these smooth plains appear to be similar in origin to lunar maria. Hopefully, data gathered by *Messenger* during its orbit around Mercury in 2011 will shed additional light on the relationship between cratering and volcanism.

Venus: The Veiled Planet

Venus, second only to the Moon in brilliance in the night sky, is named after the Roman goddess of love and beauty. It orbits the Sun in a nearly perfect circle once every 225 Earth-days. However, Venus rotates in the opposite direction of the other planets (*retrograde motion*) at an agonizingly slow pace—one Venus-day is equivalent to about 244 Earth-days. Venus has the densest atmosphere of the terrestrial planets, consisting mostly of carbon dioxide (97 percent)—the prototype for an

Planetary Radius (km)
6048 6050 6052 6054 6056 6058 6060 6062

FIGURE 15.27   This global view of the surface of Venus is computer-generated from years of investigations culminating with the *Magellan* mission. The twisting bright features that cross the planet are highly fractured mountains and canyons of the eastern Aphrodite highland. (Courtesy of NASA/JPL) show evidence of extensive cratering from the heavy bombardment period, found instead that a period of extensive volcanism was responsible for resurfacing Venus. Its thick atmosphere also limits the number of impacts by breaking up large incoming meteoroids and incinerating most of the small debris.

About 80 percent of the Venusian surface consists of low-lying plains covered by lava flows, some of which traveled along lava channels that extend for hundreds of kilometers. Venus's Baltis Vallis, the longest known lava channel in the solar system, meanders 6800 kilometers (4225 miles) across the planet. More than 100 large volcanoes have been identified on Venus. However, high surface temperatures and pressures inhibit explosive volcanism. In addition, Venus's extreme conditions result in volcanoes that tend to be shorter and wider than those on Earth or Mars (**FIGURE 15.28**). Maat Mons, the largest volcano on Venus, is about 8.5 kilometers high and 400 kilometers wide. By comparison, Mauna Loa, the largest volcano in Earth is about 9 kilometers high and only 120 kilometers wide.

Venus also has major highlands that consist of plateaus, ridges, and topographic rises that stand above the plains. The rises are thought to have formed where hot mantle plumes encountered the base of the planet's crust, causing uplift. Much like mantle plumes on Earth, abundant volcanism is associated with mantle upwelling on Venus. Recent data collected by the European Space Agency's *Venus Express* suggest that Venus's highlands contain silica-rich granitic rock. As such, these elevated landmasses resemble Earth's continents, albeit on a much smaller scale.

FIGURE 15.28 Venus's Sapas Mons (center) is a broad volcano 400 kilometers (250 miles) wide. The bright areas in the foreground are lava flows. Another large volcano, Maat Mons, is in the background. This computer-generated view was constructed from data acquired by the *Magellan* spacecraft. (Courtesy of NASA/JPL)

Mars: The Red Planet

Mars, approximately one-half the diameter of Earth, revolves around the Sun in 687 Earth-days. Mean surface temperatures range from lows of −140°C (−220°F) in the winter to highs of 20°C (68°F) in the summer. Daily temperature variations are greater due to the planet's very thin atmosphere (only 1 percent as dense as Earth's). The tenuous Martian atmosphere consists primarily of carbon dioxide (95 percent), with small amounts of nitrogen, oxygen, and water vapor.

Mars' Topography

Mars, like the Moon, is pitted with impact craters. The smaller craters are usually filled with wind-blown dust—confirming that Mars is a dry, desert world. The reddish color of the Martian landscape is iron oxide (rust). Large impact craters provide information about the nature of the Martian surface. Ejecta like that surrounding lunar craters is what would be expected from a surface composed of dry dust and rocky debris. By contrast, the ejecta surrounding some Martian craters has the appearance of a muddy slurry that splashed from the crater. Planetary geologists believe that a layer of *permafrost* (frozen, icy soil) lies below the surface. The impact heated and melted the ice, producing the fluidlike appearance of the ejecta.

About two-thirds of the surface of Mars consists of heavily cratered highlands, concentrated mostly in its southern hemisphere (**FIGURE 15.29**). The period of extreme cratering occurred early in the planet's history and ended about 3.8 billion years ago as it did in the rest of the solar system. Thus, Martian highlands are similar in age to the lunar highlands.

Based on relatively low crater counts, the northern plains, which account for the remaining one-third of the planet, are younger than the highlands (Figure 15.29). The plains' relatively flat topography is consistent with vast outpouring of fluid basaltic lava flows. Visible on these plains are volcanic cones, some with summit pits and lava flows with wrinkled edges.

Located along the Martian equator is an enormous elevated region, about the size of North America, called the *Tharsis bulge* (Figure 15.29). This feature, about 10 kilometers high, appears to have been uplifted and capped with a massive accumulation of volcanic rock that includes the planet's five largest volcanoes.

The tectonic forces that created the Tharsis region also produced fractures that radiate from its center, like spokes on a bicycle wheel. Along the eastern flanks of the bulge, a series of vast canyons called *Valles Marineris* (Mariner Valleys) developed. Valles Marineris is so vast that it can be seen in the image of Mars in Figure 15.29. This canyon network was largely created by downfaulting, not by stream erosion as is the case for Arizona's Grand Canyon. Thus, it consists of grabenlike valleys similar to the East

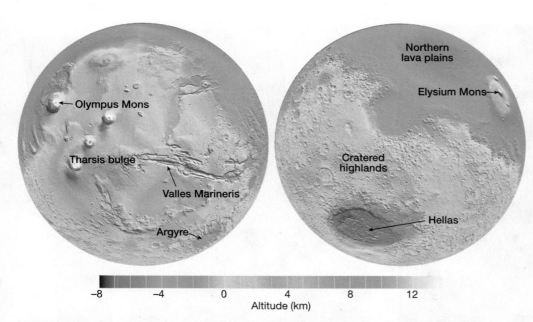

FIGURE 15.29 Two computer-generated globes of Mars with some major surface features labeled. Color represents height above (or below) the mean planetary radius—white is about 12 kilometers above average and dark blue 8 kilometers below average. (Courtesy of NASA/JPL)

Dust devils have also been photographed. Most of the Martian landscape resembles Earth's rocky deserts, with abundant dunes and low areas partially filled with dust.

Yes, Water Ice on Mars!

Liquid water does not appear to exist anywhere on the Martian surface. However, poleward of about 30 degrees latitude ice can be found within a meter of the surface. In the polar regions water ice forms small permanent ice caps along with carbon dioxide ice. In addition, considerable evidence indicates that in the first billion years of the planet's history, liquid water flowed on the surface creating stream valleys and related features.

One location where running water was involved in carving valleys can be seen in the *Mars Reconnaissance Orbiter* image in **FIGURE 15.31**. Researchers have proposed that melting of subsurface ice caused springlike seeps to emerge along the valley wall, slowly creating the gullies—a process that may still be active today.

Other channels have streamlike banks and contain numerous teardrop-shaped islands (**FIGURE 15.32**). These valleys appear to have been cut by catastrophic floods with discharge rates that were more than 1000 times greater than those of the Mississippi River. Most of these large flood channels emerge from areas of chaotic topography that appear to

African Rift Valleys. Once formed, Valles Marineris grew by water erosion and collapse of the rift walls. The main canyon is more than 5000 kilometers long, 7 kilometers deep, and 100 kilometers wide (Figure 15.29).

Other prominent features on the Martian landscape are large impact basins. Hellas, the largest identifiable impact structure on the planet, is about 2300 kilometers (1400 miles) in diameter and is the planet's lowest elevation (Figure 15.29). Debris ejected from this basin contributed to the elevation of the adjacent highlands. Other buried crater basins that are even larger than Hellas probably exist.

Volcanism was prevalent on Mars during most of its history. The scarcity of impact craters on some volcanic surfaces suggests that the planet is still active. Mars has several of the largest known volcanoes in the solar system, including the largest, Olympus Mons, which is about the size of Arizona and stands nearly three times higher than Mount Everest. This gigantic volcano was last active about 100 million years ago and resembles Earth's Hawaiian shield volcanoes (**FIGURE 15.30**).

How did the volcanoes on Mars grow so much larger than similar structures on Earth? The largest volcanoes on the terrestrial planets tend to form where plumes of hot rock rise from deep within their interiors. On Earth, moving plates keep the crust in constant motion. Consequently, mantle plumes tend to produce a chain of volcanic structures, such as the Hawaiian Islands. By contrast, on Mars plate tectonics is absent so successive eruptions build up in the same location. As a result, enormous volcanoes such as Olympus Mons come into being rather than a chain of smaller volcanoes.

Currently, the dominant force shaping the Martian surface is wind erosion. Extensive dust storms, with winds up to 270 kilometers (170 miles) per hour, can persist for weeks.

FIGURE 15.30 Image of Olympus Mons, an inactive shield volcano on Mars that covers an area about the size of the state of Arizona. (Courtesy of the U.S. Geological Survey)

FIGURE 15.31 Image obtained by Mars *Reconnaissance Orbiter* shows gullies emanating from rocky cliffs near a crater's rim (upper left) that have meandering and braided patterns typical of water-carved channels. (Courtesy of NASA/JPL)

FIGURE 15.32 Streamlike channels are strong evidence that Mars once had flowing water. Inset shows close-up of streamlined island where running water encountered resistant material along its channel. (Courtesy of NASA/JPL)

have formed when the surface collapsed. The most likely source of water for these flood-created valleys was the melting of subsurface ice. If the melt water was trapped beneath a thick layer of permafrost, pressure could mount until a catastrophic release occurred. As the water escaped, the overlying surface would collapse, creating the chaotic terrain.

Not all Martian valleys appear to be the result of water released in this manner. Some exhibit branching treelike patterns that resemble dendritic drainage networks on Earth. In addition, the *Opportunity* rover investigated structures similar to features created by water on Earth. These included layered sedimentary rocks, playas (salt flats), and lake beds. Minerals that form only in the presence of water such as hydrated sulfates were also detected. Small spheres of hematite, dubbed "blueberries," were found that probably precipitated from water to form lake sediments. Nevertheless, with the exception of the polar regions, water does not appear to have significantly altered the topography of Mars for more than a billion years.

Jupiter: Lord of the Heavens

The giant among planets, Jupiter has a mass two and a half times greater than the combined mass of all other planets, satellites, and asteroids in the solar system. In fact, had

Jupiter been about 10 times larger, it would have become a small star. However, it pales in comparison to the Sun with only 1/800 of the Sun's mass.

Jupiter orbits the Sun once every 12 Earth-years, and rotates more rapidly than any other planet, completing one rotation in slightly less than 10 hours. When viewed telescopically, the effect of this fast spin is noticeable. The bulge of the equatorial region and the contraction of the polar dimension are evident (see the Polar Flattening column in Table 15.2).

Jupiter's appearance is mainly attributable to the colors of light reflected from its three main cloud layers (**FIGURE 15.33**). The warmest, and lowest, layer is composed mainly of water ice and appears blue-grey—generally not seen in visible-light images. A little higher, where temperatures are

Belts
(dark clouds)

Strong winds

Zones
(bright clouds)

Strong winds

Belts
(dark clouds)

North polar region

North temperate zone
North temperate belt
North tropical zone

North equitorial belt

Equitorial zone

South equitorial belt

South tropical zone

South temperate belt

South temperate zone

South polar region

FIGURE 15.33   The structure of Jupiter's atmosphere. The areas of light clouds (*zones*) are regions where gases are ascending and cooling. Sinking dominates the flow in the darker cloud layers (*belts*). This convective circulation, along with the rapid rotation of the planet, generates the high-speed winds observed between the belts and zones.

cooler, is a layer of brown to orange-brown clouds of ammonium hydrosulfide droplets. These colors are thought to be by-products of chemical reactions occurring in Jupiter's atmosphere. Near the top of its atmosphere lie white wispy clouds of ammonia ice.

Because of its immense gravity, Jupiter is shrinking a few centimeters each year. This contraction generates most of the heat that drives Jupiter's atmospheric circulation. Thus, unlike winds on Earth, which are driven by solar energy, the heat emanating from Jupiter's interior produces the huge convection currents observed in its atmosphere.

Jupiter's convective flow produces alternating dark-colored *belts* and light-colored *zones* as shown in Figure 15.33. The light clouds (*zones*) are regions where warm material is ascending and cooling, whereas the dark belts represent cool material that is sinking and warming. This convective circulation, along with Jupiter's rapid rotation,

generates the high-speed, east–west flow observed between the belts and zones.

The largest storm on the planet is the Great Red Spot. This enormous, anticyclonic storm that is twice the size of Earth, has been known for 300 years. In addition to the Great Red Spot, there are various white and brown oval-shaped storms (Figure 15.33). The white ovals are the cold cloud tops of huge storms many times larger than hurricanes on Earth. The brown storm clouds reside at lower levels in the atmosphere. Lightning in various white oval storms has been photographed by the *Cassini* spacecraft, but the strikes appear to be less frequent than on Earth.

Jupiter's Moons

Jupiter's satellite system, consisting of 63 moons discovered thus far, resembles a miniature solar system. Galileo discovered the four largest satellites, referred to as Galilean satellites,

A. **Io**   B. **Europa**   C. **Ganymede**   D. **Callisto**

FIGURE 15.34   Jupiter's four largest moons (from left to right) are called the Galilean moons because they were discovered by Galileo. **A.** The innermost moon, Io, is one of only three volcanically active bodies in the solar system. **B.** Europa, smallest of the Galilean moons, has an icy surface that is crisscrossed by many linear features. **C.** Ganymede, the largest Jovian satellite, contains cratered areas, smooth regions, and areas covered by numerous parallel grooves. **D.** Callisto, the outermost of the Galilean satellites, is densely cratered, much like Earth's moon. (Courtesy of NASA/NGS Image Collection)

in 1610 (**FIGURE 15.34**). The two largest, Ganymede and Callisto, are roughly the size of Mercury, whereas the two smaller ones, Europa and Io, are about the size of Earth's Moon. The eight largest moons appear to have formed around Jupiter as the solar system condensed.

Jupiter also has many very small satellites (about 20 kilometers in diameter) that revolve in the opposite direction (*retrograde motion*) of the largest moons and have eccentric orbits steeply inclined to the Jovian equator. These satellites appear to be asteroids or comets that passed near enough to be gravitationally captured by Jupiter or are remnants of the collisions of larger bodies.

The Galilean moons can be observed with binoculars or a small telescope and are interesting in their own right. Images from *Voyagers 1* and 2 revealed, to the surprise of most geoscientists, that each of the four Galilean satellites is a unique world (Figure 15.34). The *Galileo* mission also unexpectedly revealed that the composition of each satellite is strikingly different, implying a different evolution for each. For example, Ganymede has a dynamic core that generates a strong magnetic field not observed in other satellites.

The innermost of the Galilean moons, Io, is perhaps the most volcanically active body in our solar system. In all, more than 80 active sulfurous volcanic centers have been discovered. Umbrella-shaped plumes have been observed rising from Io's surface to heights approaching 200 kilometers (**FIGURE 15.35A**). The heat source for volcanic activity is tidal energy generated by a relentless "tug of war" between Jupiter and the other Galilean satellites—with Io as the rope. The gravitational field of Jupiter and the other nearby satellites pull and push on Io's tidal bulge as its slightly eccentric orbit takes it alternately closer to, then farther from Jupiter. This gravitational flexing of Io is transformed into heat (similar to the back-and-forth bending of a piece of

sheet metal) and results in Io's spectacular sulfurous volcanic eruptions. Moreover, lava thought to be mainly composed of silicate minerals regularly erupts on its surface (**FIGURE 15.35B**).

Jupiter's Rings

One of the surprising aspects of the *Voyager 1* mission was the discovery of Jupiter's ring system. More recently, the ring system was thoroughly investigated by the Galileo Mission. By analyzing how these rings scatter light, researchers determined that the rings are composed of fine, dark particles, similar in size to smoke particles. Furthermore, the faint nature of the rings indicates that these minute particles are widely dispersed. The main ring is composed of particles believed to be fragments blasted from the surfaces of Metis and Adrastea, two small moons of Jupiter. Impacts on Jupiter's moons Amalthea and Thebe are believed to be the source of the debris from which the outer Gossamer ring formed.

Saturn: The Elegant Planet

Requiring more than 29 Earth-years to make one revolution, Saturn is almost twice as far from the Sun as Jupiter, yet their atmospheres, compositions, and internal structures are remarkably similar. The most striking feature of Saturn is its system of rings first observed by Galileo in 1610 (**FIGURE 15.36**). With his primitive telescope, the rings appeared as two small bodies adjacent to the planet. Their ring nature was determined 50 years later by the Dutch astronomer Christian Huygens.

Saturn's atmosphere, like Jupiter's, is dynamic (Figure 15.36). Although the bands of clouds are fainter and wider near the equator, rotating "storms" similar to Jupiter's Great Red Spot occur in Saturn's atmosphere as does intense

A.

B.

FIGURE 15.35 A volcanic eruption on Jupiter's Moon Io. **A.** This plume of volcanic gases and debris is rising over 100 kilometers (60 miles) above Io's surface. **B.** The bright red area on the left side of the image is newly erupted hot lava. (Courtesy of NASA)

lightning. Although the atmosphere is nearly 75 percent hydrogen and 25 percent helium, the clouds are composed of ammonia, ammonia hydrosulfide, and water, each segregated by temperature. Like Jupiter, the atmosphere's dynamics are driven by the heat released by gravitational compression.

Saturn's Moons

The Saturnian satellite system consists of 61 known moons of which 53 have been named. The moons vary significantly in size, shape, surface age, and origin. Twenty-three of the moons are "original" satellites that formed in tandem with their parent planet. At least two (Dione and Tethys) show evidence of tectonic activity, where internal forces have ripped apart their icy surfaces. Others, like Hyperion, are so porous that impacts punch into their surfaces, and Rhea

may have its own rings. Many of Saturn's smallest moons have irregular shapes and are only a few tens of kilometers in diameter.

Saturn's largest moon, Titan, is larger than Mercury and is the second-largest satellite in the solar system. Titan, and Neptune's Triton, are the only satellites in the solar system known to have substantial atmospheres. Titan was visited and photographed by the *Huygens* probe in 2005. The atmospheric pressure at Titan's surface is about 1.5 times that at Earth's surface, and the atmospheric composition is about 98 percent nitrogen and 2 percent methane with trace organic compounds. Titan has Earthlike geological landforms and geological processes, such as dune formation and streamlike erosion caused by methane "rain." In addition, the northern latitudes appear to have lakes of liquid methane.

Enceladus is another unique satellite of Saturn—one of the few where active eruptions have been observed (**FIGURE 15.37**). The outgassing, comprised mostly of water, is thought to be the main source replenishing the material in Saturn's E ring. The geyserlike activity occurs in an area called "tiger stripes" that consists of four large fractures with ridges on either side.

Saturn's Ring System

In the early 1980s, the nuclear-powered *Voyagers* 1 and 2 explored Saturn within 100,000 miles of its surface. More information was collected about Saturn in that short time than had been acquired since Galileo first viewed this "elegant planet" in the early 1600s. More recently, observations from ground-based telescopes, the Hubble Space Telescope, and the *Cassini-Huygens* spacecraft have added to our knowledge of Saturn's ring system. In 1995 and 1996, when the positions of Earth and Saturn allowed the rings to be viewed edge-on, Saturn's faintest rings and satellites became visible. (The rings were visible edge-on again in 2009.)

Saturn's ring system is more like a large rotating disk of varying density and brightness than a series of independent ringlets. Each ring is composed of individual particles—mainly water ice with lesser amounts of rocky debris—that circle the planet while regularly impacting one another. There are only a few gaps—most of the areas that look like empty space contain either fine dust particles or coated ice particles that are inefficient reflectors of light.

Most of Saturn's rings fall into one of two categories based on density. Saturn's main (bright) rings, designated A and B, are tightly packed and contain particles that range in size from a few centimeters (pebble-size) to tens of meters (house-size), with most of the particles being roughly the size of a large snowball. In the dense rings, particles collide frequently as they orbit the planet. Although Saturn's main rings (A and B) are 40,000 kilometers wide, they are very thin, only 10 to 30 meters from top to bottom.

At the other extreme are the faint rings (C, D, F, G, and E). Saturn's outermost rings (F, G, and E), not visible in Figure 15.36, are composed of widely dispersed, smoke-size particles. The faint rings are thought to be thicker (100 to 1000 meters) than Saturn's bright rings, but conclusive evidence is not yet available.

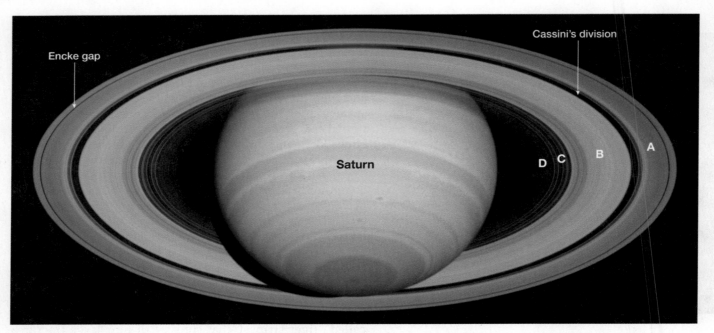

FIGURE 15.36 Image taken by the Earth orbiting Hubble Space Telescope shows Saturn's dynamic ring system. The two bright rings, called A ring (outer) and B ring (inner) are separated by the Cassini division. A second small gap (Encke gap) is also visible as a thin line in the outer portion of the A ring. (Courtesy of NASA)

Studies have shown that the gravitational tugs of nearby moons tend to shepherd the ring particles by gravitationally altering their orbits (**FIGURE 15.38**). For example, the F ring, which is very narrow, appears to be the work of satellites located on either side that confine the ring by pulling back particles that try to escape. Whereas the Cassini Division, a clearly visible gap in Figure 15.36, arises from the gravitational pull of Jupiter's moon Mimas.

Some of the ring particles are believed to be debris ejected from the moons imbedded in them. It is also possible that material is continually recycled between the rings and the ring moons. The ring moons gradually sweep up particles, which are subsequently ejected by collisions with large chunks of ring material, or perhaps by energetic collisions with other moons. It seems then, that planetary rings are not the timeless features that we once thought—rather, they are continually recycled.

Uranus and Neptune: Twins

Although Earth and Venus have many similar traits, Uranus and Neptune are perhaps more deserving of being called twins. They are nearly equal in diameter (both about four times the size of Earth) and are both bluish in appearance—a result of methane in their atmospheres. Their days are nearly the same length and their cores are made of rocky silicates and iron—similar to the other gas giants. Their mantles, comprised mainly of water, ammonia, and methane, are thought to be very different from Jupiter and Saturn (see Figure 15.19). One of the most pronounced differences between Uranus and Neptune is the time they take to complete one revolution around the Sun—84 and 165 Earth-years, respectively.

Uranus: The Sideways Planet

Unique to Uranus is its axis of rotation, which lies nearly parallel to the ecliptic ("lying on its side"). Its rotational motion, therefore, resembles a rolling ball instead of a spinning toy top (**FIGURE 15.39**). This unusual characteristic of Uranus is likely due to a huge impact that essentially knocked the planet sideways from its original orbit early in its evolution.

Uranus, once thought to be weatherless, shows evidence of huge storm systems the size of the United States. Recent photographs from the Hubble Space Telescope also reveal banded clouds composed mainly of ammonia and methane ice—similar to the cloud systems of the other gas giants.

Uranus's Rings

A surprise discovery in 1977 showed that Uranus has a ring system (Figure 15.39). The find occurred as Uranus passed in front of a distant star and blocked its view, a process called *occultation* (*occult* = hidden). Observers saw the star "wink" briefly five times (meaning five rings) before the primary occultation and again five times afterward. More recent ground- and space-based observations indicate that Uranus has at least ten sharp-edged distinct rings orbiting its equatorial region. Interspersed among these distinct structures are broad sheets of dust.

Neptune: The Windy Planet

Because of its great distance from Earth, astronomers knew very little about Neptune until 1989. Twelve years and nearly 3 billion miles of *Voyager 2* travel provided investigators an amazing opportunity to view the outermost planet in the solar system.

FIGURE 15.39 Uranus surrounded by its major rings and 10 of its 17 known moons. Also visible are cloud patterns and several oval storm systems. This false-color image was generated from data obtained by Hubble's Near Infrared Camera. (Image by Hubble Space Telescope courtesy of NASA)

FIGURE 15.37 NASA's *Cassini Orbiter* captured this mosaic of Saturn's tectonically active, icy satellite Enceladus. The northern hemisphere contains a one-kilometer deep chasm (Labtya + Suki), and the tiger stripe features are visible in the lower right. Inset image show jest spurting ice particles, water vapor, and organic compounds from the area of the tiger stripes. (Courtesy of NASA/JPL)

Neptune has a dynamic atmosphere, much like that of the other Jovian planets (**FIGURE 15.40**). Record wind speeds that exceed 2400 kilometers (1500 miles) per hour encircle the planet, making Neptune one of the windiest places in the solar system. Recall that Neptune exhibits large dark spots thought to be rotating storms similar to Jupiter's Great Red Spot. However, Neptune's storms appear to have comparatively short life spans—usually only a few years. Another feature that Neptune has in common with the other Jovian planets are layers of white, cirruslike clouds (probably frozen methane) about 50 kilometers above the main cloud deck.

Neptune's Moons

Neptune has 13 known satellites, the largest of which is the moon Triton, the remaining 12 are small, irregularly shaped bodies. Triton is the only large moon in the solar system that exhibits retrograde motion, indicating that it most likely formed independently, and was later gravitationally captured by Neptune.

Triton and a few other icy moons erupt "fluid" ices—an amazing manifestation of

FIGURE 15.38 Two of Saturn's ring moons. **A.** Saturn's moon Pan is a small moon about 30 kilometers in diameter that orbits in the Encke gap, located in the A ring. It is responsible for keeping the Encke gap open. **B.** Prometheus, a potato-shaped moon, acts as a ring shepherd. Its gravity helps confine the moonlets in Saturn's thin F ring. (Courtesy of NASA/JPL)

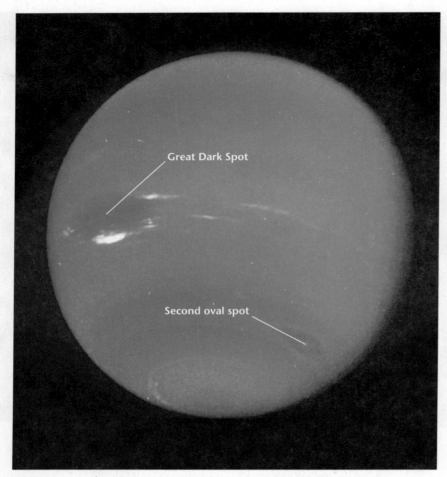

FIGURE 15.40   This image of Neptune shows the Great Dark Spot (left center). Also visible are bright cirruslike clouds that travel at high speed around the planet. A second oval spot is at south latitude on the east side of the planet. (Courtesy of the Jet Propulsion Laboratory)

molten rock does on Earth. In fact, upon reaching the surface these magmas can generate quiet outpourings of ice lavas, or occasionally, produce explosive eruptions. An explosive eruptive column can generate the ice equivalent of volcanic ash. In 1989, *Voyager* 2 detected active plumes on Triton that rose 8 kilometers above the surface and were blown downwind for more than 100 kilometers. In other environments, ice lavas develop that can flow great distances from their source—similar to the fluid basaltic flows on Hawaii.

Neptune's Rings

Neptune has five named rings, two of which are broad, and three that are narrow, perhaps no more than 100 kilometers wide. The outermost ring appears to be partially confined by the satellite Galatea. Neptune's rings are most similar to Jupiter's in that they appear faint, which suggests they are composed mostly of micrometer dust-size particles. Neptune's rings also display red colors that indicate the dust is composed of organic compounds.

MINOR MEMBERS OF THE SOLAR SYSTEM

There are countless chunks of debris in the vast spaces separating the eight planets and in the outer reaches of the solar system. In 2006, the International Astronomical Union organized solar system objects not classified as planets or moons into two broad categories: (1) **dwarf planets** and (2) **small solar system bodies** that include *asteroids, comets,* and *meteoroids.* The newest grouping, dwarf planets, includes Ceres, the largest known object in the asteroid belt, and Pluto, a former planet.

Asteroids and meteoroids are composed of rocky and/or metallic material with compositions somewhat like the terrestrial planets. They are distinguished according to size: asteroids are larger than 100 meters in diameter, whereas meteoroids have diameters less than 100 meters. Comets, on the other hand, are loose collections of ices, dust, and small rocky particles that originate in the outer reaches of the solar system.

volcanism. **Cryovolcanism** (from the Greek *Kryos,* meaning "frost") describes the eruption of magmas derived from the partial melting of ice instead of silicate rocks. Triton's icy magma is a mixture of water ice, methane, and probably ammonia. When partially melted, this mixture behaves as

DID YOU KNOW?

In the last few decades, it has become increasingly clear that comets and asteroids have collided with Earth far more frequently than was previously known. The dangers of living with these small but deadly objects from space came to public attention in 1989 when an asteroid nearly 1 km (0.6 mi) across shot past Earth. It was a near miss as it crossed our orbit just six hours ahead of Earth. Traveling at 71,000 km per hour (44,000 mi per hour), it could have produced a crater 8 km (5 mi) in diameter and perhaps 2 km (1 mi) deep. As an observer noted, "Sooner or later it will be back." Statistics show that collisions of this tremendous magnitude should take place every few hundred million years and could have drastic consequences for life on Earth.

Asteroids: Leftover Planetesimals

Asteroids are small bodies (planetesimals) remaining from the formation of the solar system, making them about 4.6 billion years old. Most asteroids orbit the Sun between Mars and Jupiter in the region known as the **asteroid belt** (**FIGURE 15.41**). There are only five that are more than 400 kilometers in diameter, but the solar system hosts an estimated 1 to 2 million asteroids larger than 1 kilometer, and many millions that are smaller. Some travel along eccentric orbits that take them very near the Sun, and others regularly pass close to Earth and the Moon (Earth-crossing asteroids).

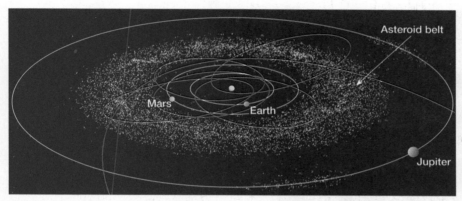

FIGURE 15.41   The orbits of most asteroids lie between Mars and Jupiter. Also shown are the orbits of a few known near-Earth asteroids. Perhaps a thousand or more asteroids have near-Earth orbits. Luckily, only a few dozen are thought to be larger than 1 kilometer in diameter.

Many of the recent large-impact craters on the Moon and Earth were probably the result of collisions with asteroids. About 2000 Earth-crossing asteroids are known, one-third of which are more than one kilometer in diameter. Inevitably, Earth–asteroid collisions will occur again.

Because most asteroids have irregular shapes, planetary geologists initially speculated that they might be fragments of a broken planet that once orbited between Mars and Jupiter (**FIGURE 15.42**). However, the combined mass of all asteroids is now estimated to be only 1/1000 of the modest-sized Earth. Today, most researchers agree that asteroids are leftover debris from the solar nebula. Asteroids have lower densities than scientists originally thought, suggesting they are porous bodies, like piles of rubble, loosely bound together.

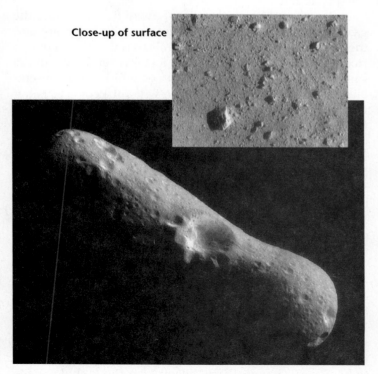

Close-up of surface

FIGURE 15.42   Image of asteroid Eros obtained by the *NEAR Shoemaker* probe. Inset shows a close-up of Eros's barren rocky surface. (Courtesy of NASA)

In February 2001 an American spacecraft became the first visitor to an asteroid. Although it was not designed for landing, *NEAR Shoemaker* landed successfully on Eros and collected information that has planetary geologists both intrigued and perplexed. Images obtained as the spacecraft drifted toward the surface of Eros revealed a barren, rocky surface composed of particles ranging in size from fine dust to boulders up to 10 meters (30 feet) across (Figure 15.42). Researchers unexpectedly discovered that fine debris tends to concentrate in the low areas where it forms flat deposits resembling ponds. Surrounding the low areas, the landscape is marked by an abundance of large boulders.

One of several hypotheses to explain the boulder-strewn topography is seismic shaking, which would cause the boulders to move upward as the finer materials sink. This is analogous to what happens when a jar of sand and various sized pebbles is shaken—the larger pebbles rise to the top and the smaller sand grains settle to the bottom.

Indirect evidence from meteorites suggests some asteroids might have been heated by a large impact event. A few large asteroids may have completely melted, causing them to differentiate into a dense iron core and a rocky mantle. In November 2005, the Japanese probe *Hayabusa* landed on a small near-Earth asteroid named 25143 Itokawa and is scheduled to return samples to Earth by June 2010.

Comets: Dirty Snowballs

Comets, like asteroids, are leftover material from the formation of the solar system. They are loose collections of rocky material, dust, water ice, and frozen gases (ammonia, methane, and carbon dioxide), thus the nickname "dirty snowballs." Recent space missions to comets have shown their surfaces to be dry and dusty, which indicates that their ices are hidden beneath a layer of rock debris.

Most comets reside in the outer reaches of the solar system and take hundreds of thousands of years to complete a single orbit around the Sun. However, a smaller number of *short-period comets* (those having orbital periods of less than 200 years), such as the famous Halley's Comet, make regular encounters with the inner solar system (**FIGURE 15.43**). The shortest period comet (Encke's Comet) orbits around the Sun once every three years.

All of the phenomena associated with comets come from a small central body called the **nucleus**. These structures are typically 1 to 10 kilometers in diameter, but nuclei 40 kilometers across have been observed. When comets reach the inner solar system, solar energy begins to vaporize their ices. The escaping gases carry dust from the comet's surface, producing a highly reflective halo called the **coma** (**FIGURE 15.44**). Within the coma, the small glowing nucleus with a diameter of only a few kilometers can sometimes be detected.

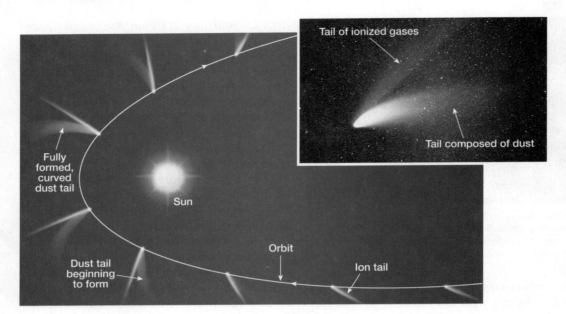

Tail of ionized gases

Tail composed of dust

Fully formed, curved dust tail

Sun

Orbit

Dust tail beginning to form

Ion tail

FIGURE 15.43   Orientation of a comet's tail as it orbits the Sun. (Photo by Eric Clifton and Craig Neaveill)

As comets approach the Sun, most develop tails that can extend for millions of kilometers. The tail of a comet points away from the Sun in a slightly curved manner (Figure 15.43), which led early astronomers to believe that the Sun has a repulsive force that pushes away particles of the coma to form the tail. Scientists have identified two solar forces known to contribute to tail formation. One is *radiation pressure* caused by radiant energy (light) emitted by the Sun, and the second is the *solar wind*, a stream of charged particles ejected from the Sun. Sometimes a single tail composed of both dust and ionized gases is produced, but two tails are often observed (Figure 15.43). The heavier dust particles produce a slightly curved tail that follows the comet's orbit, whereas the extremely light ionized gases are "pushed" directly away from the Sun, forming the second tail.

As a comet's orbit carries it away from the Sun, the gases forming the coma recondense, the tail disappears, and the comet returns to cold storage. Material that was blown from the coma to form the tail is lost forever. When all the gases are expelled, the inactive comet, which closely resembles an asteroid, continues its orbit without a coma or tail. It is believed that few comets remain active for more than a few hundred close orbits of the Sun.

The very first samples from a comet's coma (Comet Wild 2) were returned to Earth in January of 2006 by NASA's *Stardust* spacecraft (**FIGURE 15.45**). Images from *Stardust* show that the comet's surface was riddled with flat-bottomed depressions and appeared dry, although at least 10 gas jets were active. Laboratory studies revealed that the coma contained a wide range of organic compounds and substantial amounts of silicate crystals.

Most comets originate in one of two regions—the *Kuiper belt* or the *Oort cloud*. Named in honor of astronomer Gerald Kuiper, who predicted its existence, the **Kuiper belt** hosts comets that orbit in the outer solar system, beyond Neptune (see Figure 15.17). This disc-shaped structure is thought to contain about a billion objects over one kilometer in size. However, most comets are too small and too distant to be observed from Earth, even using the Hubble Space Telescope. Like the asteroids in the inner solar system, most Kuiper belt comets move in slightly elliptical orbits that lie

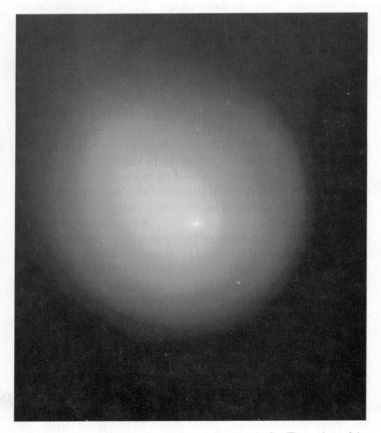

FIGURE 15.44   Coma of comet Holmes as it orbits the Sun. The nucleus of the comet is within the bright spot in the center. Comet Holmes, which orbits the Sun every six years, was uncharacteristically active during its most recent entry into the inner solar system. (Image by Spitzer Space Telescope, courtesy of NASA)

FIGURE 15.45   Comet Wild 2, as seen by NASA's *Stardust* spacecraft, during its flyby of the comet. Inset, artist's concept depicting jets of gas and dust erupting from comet Wild 2. (Courtesy of NASA)

roughly in the same plane as the planets. A chance collision between two Kuiper belt comets, or the gravitational influence of one of the Jovian planets, occasionally alters their orbits sufficiently to send them into our view.

Halley's Comet most likely originated in the Kuiper belt. Its orbital period averages 76 years, and every one of its 29 appearances since 240 B.C. has been recorded by Chinese astronomers—testimony to their dedication as astronomical observers and the endurance of Chinese culture. When seen in 1910, Halley's Comet had developed a tail nearly 1.6 million kilometers (1 million miles) long and was visible during the daytime.

Named for Dutch astronomer Jan Oort, the **Oort cloud** consists of comets that are distributed in all directions from the Sun, forming a spherical shell around the solar system. Most Oort cloud comets orbit the Sun at distances greater than 10,000 times the Earth–Sun distance. The gravitational effect of a distant passing star may send an occasional Oort cloud comet into a highly eccentric orbit that carries it toward the Sun. However, only a tiny fraction of Oort cloud comets have orbits that bring them into the inner solar system.

Meteoroids: Visitors to Earth

Nearly everyone has seen a **meteor**, commonly (but inaccurately) called "shooting stars." These streaks of light can be observed in as little as the blink of an eye or can last as long as few seconds. They occur when a small solid particle, a

meteoroid, enters Earth's atmosphere from interplanetary space. Heat, created by friction between the meteoroid and the air, produces the light we see trailing across the sky. Most meteoroids originate from one of the following three sources: (1) interplanetary debris missed by the gravitational sweep of the planets during formation of the solar system, (2) material that is continually being ejected from the asteroid belt, or (3) the rocky and/or metallic remains of comets that once passed through Earth's orbit. A few meteoroids are probably fragments of the Moon, Mars, or possibly Mercury, ejected by a violent asteroid impact. Before *Apollo* astronauts brought Moon rocks back to Earth, meteorites were the only extraterrestrial materials that could be studied in the laboratory.

Meteoroids less than about a meter in diameter generally vaporize before reaching Earth's surface. Some, called *micrometeorites,* are so tiny and their rate of fall so slow that they drift to Earth continually as space dust. Researchers estimate that thousands of meteoroids enter Earth's atmosphere every day. After sunset on a clear, dark night, many are bright enough to be seen with the naked eye anywhere on Earth.

Occasionally, meteor sightings increase dramatically to 60 or more per hour. These displays, called **meteor showers**, result when Earth encounters a swarm of meteoroids traveling in the same direction at nearly the same speed as Earth. The close association of these swarms to the orbits of some short-term comets strongly suggests that they represent material lost by these comets (Table 15.3). Some swarms, not associated with the orbits of known comets, are probably the scattered remains of the nucleus of a long-defunct comet. The notable *Perseid meteor shower* that occurs each year around August 12 is likely material ejected from of the Comet *Swift-Tuttle* on previous approaches to the Sun.

Most meteoroids large enough to survive probably originate among the asteroids, where chance collisions or gravitational interactions with Jupiter modify their orbits and project them toward Earth. Earth's gravity does the rest.

Table 15.3   Major meteor showers

Shower	Approximate Dates	Associated Comet
Quadrantids	January 4–6	—
Lyrids	April 20–23	Comet 1861 I
Eta Aquarids	May 3–5	Halley's comet
Delta Aquarids	July 30	—
Parseids	August 12	Comet 1862 III
Draconids	October 7–10	Comet Giacobini-Zinner
Orionids	October 20	Halley's comet
Taurids	November 3–13	Comet Encke
Andromedids	November 14	Comet Biela
Leonids	November 18	Comet 1866 I
Geminids	December 4–16	—

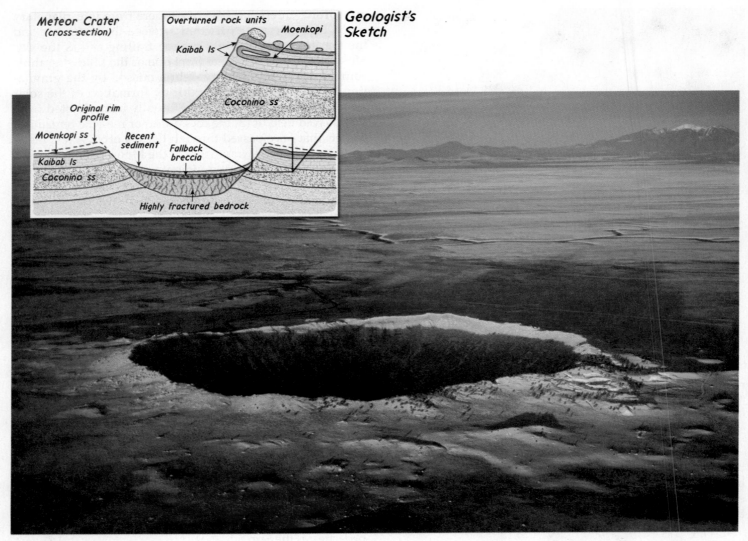

Geologist's Sketch

Meteor Crater (cross-section)

Overturned rock units — Moenkopi

Kaibab ls

Original rim profile

Moenkopi ss

Recent sediment

Fallback breccia

Kaibab ls

Coconino ss

Coconino ss

Highly fractured bedrock

FIGURE 15.46 Meteor Crater, near Winslow, Arizona. This cavity is about 1.2 kilometers (0.75 mile) across and 170 meters (560 feet) deep. The solar system is cluttered with meteoroids and other objects that can strike Earth with explosive force. (Photo by Michael Collier)

A few very large meteoroids have blasted craters on Earth's surface that strongly resemble those on our Moon. At least 40 terrestrial craters exhibit features that could only be produced by an explosive impact of a large asteroid, or perhaps a comet nucleus. More than 250 others may be of impact origin. Most notable is Arizona's Meteor Crater, a huge cavity more than 1 kilometer wide, 170 meters (560 feet) deep, with an upturned rim that rises above the surrounding countryside (**FIGURE 15.46**). More than 30 tons of iron fragments have been found in the immediate area, but attempts to locate the main body have been unsuccessful. Based on the amount of erosion observed on the crater rim, the impact likely occurred within the last 50,000 years.

The remains of meteoroids, when found on Earth, are referred to as **meteorites** (**FIGURE 15.47**). Classified by their composition, meteorites are: (1) *irons*, mostly iron with 5 to 20 percent nickel; (2) *stony* (also called *chondrites*), silicate minerals with inclusions of other minerals, or (3) *stony–irons*, mixtures of the two. Although stony meteorites are the most common, irons are found in large numbers because metallic meteorites withstand impacts better, weather more slowly, and are easily distinguished from terrestrial rocks. Iron meteorites are probably fragments of once molten cores of large asteroids or small planets.

One type of stony meteorite, called a *carbonaceous chondrite*, contains organic compounds and occasionally simple amino acids, which are the basic building blocks of life. This discovery confirms similar findings in observational astronomy, which indicate that numerous organic compounds exist in interstellar space.

Data from meteorites have been used to ascertain the internal structure of Earth and the age of the solar system. If meteorites represent the composition of the terrestrial planets, as some planetary geologists suggest, our planet must contain a much larger percentage of iron than

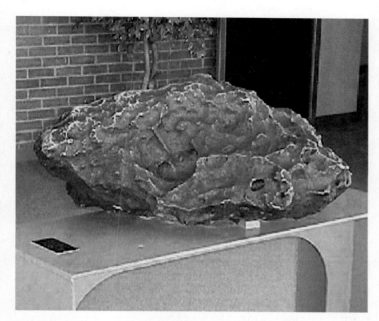

FIGURE 15.47 Iron meteorite found near Meteor Crater, Arizona. (Courtesy of Meteor Crater Enterprises, Inc.)

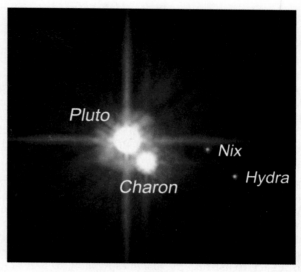

FIGURE 15.48 Pluto, with three of its known moons. Image by the Hubble Space Telescope. (Courtesy of NASA)

is indicated by surface rocks. This is one reason that geologists think Earth's core is mostly iron and nickel. In addition, radiometric dating of meteorites indicates the age of our solar system is about 4.6 billion years. This "old age" has been confirmed by data obtained from lunar samples.

Dwarf Planets

Since its discovery in 1930, Pluto has been a mystery to astronomers who were searching for another planet in order to explain irregularities in Neptune's orbit. At the time of its discovery, Pluto was thought to be the size of Earth—too small to significantly alter Neptune's orbit. Later, estimates of Pluto's diameter, adjusted because of improved satellite images, indicated that it was less than half Earth's diameter. Then, in 1978, astronomers realized that Pluto appeared much larger than it really is because of the brightness of its newly discovered satellite, Charon (**FIGURE 15.48**). Most recently, calculations based on images obtained by the Hubble Space Telescope show that Pluto's diameter is 2300 kilometers (1430 miles), about one-fifth the diameter of Earth and less than half that of Mercury (long considered the solar system's "runt"). In fact, seven moons in the solar system, including Earth's, are larger than Pluto.

Even more attention was given to Pluto's status as a planet when astronomers discovered another large icy body in orbit beyond Neptune. Soon over a thousand of these *Kuiper belt objects* were discovered forming a band of objects—a second asteroid belt, but located at the outskirts of the solar system. The Kuiper belt objects are rich in ices

and have physical properties similar to those of comets. Many other planetary objects, some perhaps larger than Pluto, are thought to exist in this belt of icy worlds beyond Neptune's orbit.

The International Astronomical Union, the group responsible for naming and classifying celestial objects, voted in 2006 to create a new class of solar system objects called *dwarf planets*. These are celestial bodies that orbit the Sun, are essentially round due to their own gravity, but are not large enough to sweep their orbits clear of other debris. By this definition, Pluto is recognized as a dwarf planet and the prototype of this new category of planetary objects. Other dwarf planets include Eros, a Kuiper belt object, and Ceres, the largest known asteroid.

Pluto's reclassification was not the first such "demotion." In the mid-1800s, astronomy textbooks listed as many as 11 planets in our solar system, including the asteroids Vesta, Juno, Ceres, and Pallas. Astronomers continued to discover dozens of other "planets," a clear signal that these small bodies represent a class of objects separate from the planets.

Researchers now recognize that Pluto was unique among the classical planets—completely different from the four rocky innermost planets, as well as the four gaseous giants. The new classification will give a home to the hundreds of additional dwarf planets astronomers assume exist in the solar system. *New Horizons,* the first spacecraft designed to explore the outer solar system, was launched in January 2006. Scheduled to fly by Pluto in July 2015, and later explore the Kuiper belt, *New Horizons* carries tremendous potential for aiding researchers in further understanding the solar system.

THE CHAPTER IN REVIEW

• Early Greeks held the *geocentric* ("Earth-centered") view of the universe, believing that Earth was a sphere that stayed motionless at the center of the universe. Orbiting Earth were the Moon, the Sun, and the known planets—Mercury, Venus, Mars, Jupiter, and Saturn. To the early Greeks, the stars traveled daily around Earth on a transparent, hollow *celestial sphere.* In A.D. 141, *Claudius Ptolemy* documented this geocentric view called the Ptolemaic system.

• Modern astronomy evolved during the 1500s and 1600s. *Nicolaus Copernicus* (1473–1543) reconstructed the solar system with the Sun at the center and the planets orbiting around it, but he erroneously continued to use circles to represent the orbits of planets. *Tycho Brahe*'s (1546–1601) observations were far more precise than any made previously and are his legacy to astronomy. *Johannes Kepler* (1571–1630) ushered in the new astronomy with his three laws of planetary motion. After constructing his own telescope, *Galileo Galilei* (1564–1642) made many important discoveries that supported the Copernican view of a Sun-centered solar system. *Sir Isaac Newton* (1642–1727) developed laws of motion and showed that the force of gravity, combined with the tendency of an object to move in a straight line, causes the elliptical orbits of the planets.

• The planets can be arranged into two groups: the *terrestrial* (Earthlike) *planets* (Mercury, Venus, Earth, and Mars) and the *Jovian* (Jupiter-like) *planets* (Jupiter, Saturn, Uranus, and Neptune). When compared to the Jovian planets, the terrestrial planets are smaller, more dense, contain proportionally more rocky material, have slower rates of rotation, and meager atmospheres.

• The *nebular theory* describes the formation of the solar system. The planets and the Sun began forming about 5 billion years ago from a large cloud of dust and gases called a *nebula.* As the nebular cloud contracted, it began to rotate and flatten into a disk. Material that was gravitationally pulled toward the center became the *protosun.* Within the rotating disk, small centers formed, called *protoplanets,* sweeping up more and more of the nebular debris. Because of their high temperatures and weak gravitational fields, the inner planets (Mercury, Venus, Earth, and Mars) were unable to accumulate much of the lighter components (hydrogen, ammonia, methane, and water) of the nebula. However, because of the very cold temperatures existing far from the Sun, the fragments from which the Jovian planets formed contained a high percentage of ices of water, carbon dioxide, ammonia, and methane.

• The lunar surface exhibits several types of features. Most *craters* were produced by the impact of rapidly moving in-terplanetary debris (meteoroids and asteroids). Bright, densely cratered highlands make up most of the lunar surface. Dark, fairly smooth lowlands are called *maria.* Maria basins are enormous impact craters that have been flooded with layer upon layer of fluid basaltic lava. All lunar terrains are mantled with a soil-like layer of gray, unconsolidated debris, called *lunar regolith,* which has been derived from a few billion years of meteoric bombardment.

• Closest to the Sun, *Mercury* is a small, dense planet that has virtually no atmosphere and exhibits the greatest temperature extremes of any planet. *Venus,* the brightest planet in the sky, has a thick, heavy atmosphere composed of 97 percent carbon dioxide; a surface of relatively subdued plains and inactive volcanoes; a surface atmospheric pressure 90 times that of Earth's; and surface temperatures of 475°C (890°F). *Mars,* the red planet, has a carbon dioxide atmosphere only 1 percent as dense as Earth's, extensive dust storms, numerous inactive volcanoes, many large canyons, and several valleys resembling drainage patterns similar to stream valleys on Earth. *Jupiter,* the largest planet, rotates rapidly, has a banded appearance, a Great Red Spot that varies in size, a ring system, and at least 63 moons (one of which, Io, is volcanically active). *Saturn,* best known for its rings, also has a dynamic atmosphere, with winds up to 1500 kilometers per hour (930 miles per hour) and "storms" similar to Jupiter's Great Red Spot. *Uranus* and *Neptune* are often called the twins because of their similar structures and compositions. Uranus is unique in rotating "on its side." Neptune has white, cirruslike clouds above its main cloud deck and large dark spots, assumed to be large rotating storms similar to Jupiter's Great Red Spot.

• The minor members of the solar system include *asteroids, comets, meteoroids,* and *dwarf planets.* Most asteroids lie between the orbits of Mars and Jupiter. Asteroids are leftover rocky and metallic debris from the solar nebula that never accreted into a planet. Comets are made of ices (water, ammonia, methane, carbon dioxide, and carbon monoxide) with small pieces of rocky and metallic material. Most comets are thought to reside in the outer solar system in one of two locations, the *Kuiper belt,* or the *Oort cloud.* Meteoroids, small solid particles that are mainly remnants of comets or pieces ejected from larger bodies during planetary impacts. Meteoroids become *meteors* when they enter Earth's atmosphere and vaporize with a flash of light. *Meteor showers* occur when Earth encounters a swarm of meteoroids, probably material lost by a comet. *Meteorites* are the remains of meteoroids found on Earth. Recently, Pluto was placed into a new class of solar system objects called *dwarf planets.*

KEY TERMS

asteroid (p. 446)

asteroid belt (p. 446)

astronomical unit (AU) (p. 425)

celestial sphere (p. 420)

coma (p. 447)

comet (p. 447)

cryovolcanism (p. 446)

dwarf planet (p. 446)

escape velocity (p. 433)

geocentric (p. 420)

impact crater (p. 433)

Jovian planet (p. 430)

Kuiper belt (p. 448)

lunar highlands (p. 434)

lunar regolith (p. 436)

maria (mare) (p. 434)

meteor (p. 449)

meteorite (p. 450)

meteoroid (p. 449)

meteor shower (p. 449)

nucleus (p. 447)

nebular theory (p. 429)

Oort cloud (p. 449)

planetesimals (p. 429)

protoplanets (p. 430)

Ptolemaic model (p. 422)

retrograde motion (p. 421)

small solar system bodies (p. 446)

solar nebula (p. 429)

terrae (p. 434)

terrestrial planet (p. 430)

QUESTIONS FOR REVIEW

1. Why did the ancients think that celestial objects had some control over their lives?

2. Describe what produces the retrograde motion of Mars. What geometric arrangement did Ptolemy use to explain this motion?

3. What major change did Copernicus make in the Ptolemaic system?

4. What was Tycho Brahe's contribution to science?

5. Did Galileo invent the telescope?

6. Explain how Galileo's discovery of Jupiter's four largest moons supported the Copernican view of a Sun-centered universe.

7. Newton learned that the orbits of the planets are the result of two actions. Describe these actions.

8. Compare the rotational periods of the terrestrial and Jovian planets.

9. How fast (in kilometers per hour) does a location on the equator of Jupiter rotate? Note that Jupiter's circumference equals approximately 452,000 kilometers.

10. By what criteria are planets considered either Jovian or terrestrial?

11. What accounts for the large density differences between the terrestrial and Jovian planets?

12. Explain why the terrestrial planets have meager atmospheres, as compared to the Jovian planets.

13. How is crater density used in the relative dating of surface features on the Moon?

14. Briefly outline the history of the Moon.

15. In what way are maria on the Moon similar to the Columbia Plateau?

16. Venus was once referred to as "Earth's twin." How are these two planets similar? How do they differ?

17. What surface features do Mars and Earth have in common?

18. Why are the largest volcanoes on Earth so much smaller than the largest ones on Mars?

19. Why might astrobiologists be intrigued by evidence that groundwater has seeped onto the surface of Mars?

20. What is the nature of Jupiter's Great Red Spot?

21. Why are the Galilean satellites of Jupiter so named?

22. What is distinctive about Jupiter's satellite, Io?

23. Why are many of Jupiter's small satellites thought to have been captured?

24. How are Jupiter and Saturn similar?

25. What two roles do ring moons play in the nature of planetary ring systems?

26. How are Saturn's satellite Titan and Neptune's satellite Triton similar?

27. Name three bodies in the solar system that exhibit active volcanism.

28. Where are most asteroids found?

29. What do you think would happen if Earth passed through the tail of a comet?

30. Where are most comets thought to reside? What eventually becomes of comets that orbit close to the Sun?

31. Compare meteoroid, meteor, and meteorite.

32. What are the three main sources of meteoroids?

33. Why are impact craters more common on the Moon than on Earth, even though the Moon is a much smaller target and has a weaker gravitational field?

34. It has been estimated that Halley's Comet has a mass of 100 billion tons. Further, this comet is estimated to lose 100 million tons of material during the few months that its orbit brings it close to the Sun. With an orbital period of 76 years, what is the maximum remaining life span of Halley's Comet?

COMPANION WEBSITE

The *Foundations of Earth Science* Website uses the resources and flexibility of the Internet to aid in your study of the topics in this chapter. Written and developed by the authors and other Earth science instructors, this site will help improve your understanding of Earth science. Visit **www.mygeoscienceplace.com** in order to:

• **Review** key chapter concepts.

• **Read** with links to the ebook and to chapter-specific web resources.

• **Visualize** and comprehend challenging topics using learning activities in *GEODe: Earth Science*.

• **Test** yourself with online quizzes.

GEODe: EARTH SCIENCE

GEODe: Earth Science is a valuable and easy to use learning aid that can be accessed from your book's Companion Website: **www.mygeoscienceplace.com.** It is a dynamic instructional tool that promotes understanding and reinforces important concepts by using tutorials, animations, and exercises that actively engage the student.

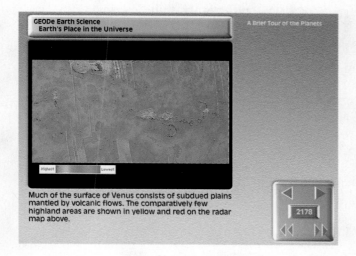

Much of the surface of Venus consists of subdued plains mantled by volcanic flows. The comparatively few highland areas are shown in yellow and red on the radar map above.

Tectonic deformation is also evident on Venus. Shown is a large fault valley, called a **graben**, which extends from the lower left to the upper right of the photo. Countless smaller faults that trend perpendicular to the **graben** can also be seen.

BEYOND OUR SOLAR SYSTEM*

FOCUS ON LEARNING

To assist you in learning the important concepts in this chapter, you will find it helpful to focus on the following questions:

1. How is the principle of parallax used to measure the distance to a star?

2. What are the major intrinsic properties of stars?

3. What are the size categories of stars?

4. What are the different types of nebulae?

5. What is the most plausible model for stellar evolution? What are the stages in the life cycle of a star?

6. What are the possible final states that a star may assume after it consumes its nuclear fuel and collapses?

7. What is our own Milky Way Galaxy like?

8. What are the different types of galaxies?

9. What is the Doppler shift?

10. What is the big bang theory for the origin of the universe?

*This chapter was revised with the assistance of Teresa Tarbuck and Mark Watry.

Spectacular view of a spiral galaxy called M81. (NASA)

Aside from the Sun, Moon, several planets, and the occasional comet or meteor, every celestial object we see with our naked eye lies beyond our solar system. The closest star to Earth, other than the Sun, is Proxima Centauri, which is about 4.3 light-years away—roughly 100 million times farther than the Moon. To appreciate how far this is, imagine that the Earth and Moon are dots on a sheet of paper one millimeter apart. On this scale, the Sun is 390 millimeters (about 15 inches) away, and Proxima Centauri is about 100,000 kilometers (62,000 miles) away! That is one long sheet of paper! It would wrap around Earth two and one-half times. Also on this scale, the *nearest galaxy* lies 60 billion kilometers away. These facts suggest that the universe is incomprehensibly large. It is also incomprehensibly empty, containing on average about one hydrogen atom per cubic centimeter.

Astronomers and cosmologists* study the nature of this vast cosmos, trying to answer questions such as: Is our Sun a typical star? Do other stars have solar systems with planets like Earth? How large is the universe? Did it have a beginning? Will it have an end? This chapter explores the answers to these questions.

*Cosmologists study the origin and evolution of the universe.

STARS LIKE THE SUN

The Sun is the only star close enough to Earth for us to observe its surface features. Nevertheless, a great deal is known about other stars in the universe. This knowledge relies on the fact that stars and hot clouds of gas radiate tremendous amounts of energy in all directions into space (**FIGURE 16.1**). The key to understanding the universe is to collect this radiation and unravel the clues it holds. Astronomers have devised many ingenious methods to do just that.

Measuring Distances to the Closest Stars

Measuring the distance to a star is difficult. Obviously, we cannot journey to the star, and even if we had an extremely powerful laser range finder, it would take over eight years to receive the return signal from the nearest star. Even then, we would have to be in the right place to catch the return signal. Nevertheless, astronomers have developed some indirect methods to measure stellar distances. The most basic of these measurements is called *stellar parallax*, a measurement that is limited to determining the distances to only the closest stars.

Recall from Chapter 15 that **stellar parallax** is the very slight back-and-forth shift of the apparent position of a nearby star due to the orbital motion of Earth around the Sun. The principle of parallax is easy to visualize. Close one eye, and with your index finger in a vertical position, use your open eye to line up your finger with some distant object. Without moving your finger or your head, view the object with your other eye and notice that its position appears to have changed. Now repeat the exercise holding your finger farther away, and notice that the farther away you hold your finger, the less its position seems to shift.

FIGURE 16.1 Lagoon Nebula. It is in glowing clouds like these that gases and dust particles become concentrated into stars. (Courtesy of National Optical Astronomy Observatories)

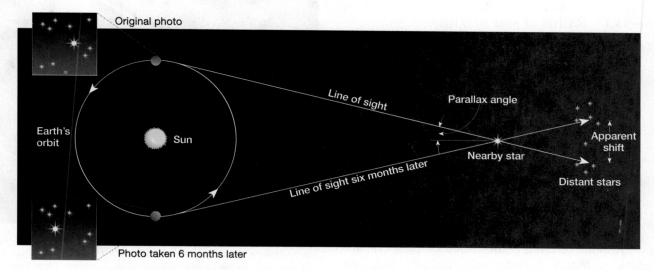

FIGURE 16.2 Geometry of stellar parallax. The parallax angle shown here is enormously exaggerated to illustrate the principle. Because distances to even the nearest stars are thousands of times greater than the Earth–Sun distance, the triangles that astronomers work with are extremely long and narrow, making the angles that are measured very small.

In principle, this method of measuring stellar distances is elementary and was known to the ancient Greeks. Today, parallax is determined by photographing a nearby star against the background of distant stars. Then, six months later, when Earth has moved halfway around its orbit, a second photograph is taken. When these photographs are compared, the position of the nearby star appears to have shifted with respect to the background stars. **FIGURE 16.2** illustrates this shift and the parallax angle determined from it. The nearest stars have the largest parallax angles, whereas those of distant stars are much too small to measure. Recall that the sixteenth-century astronomer Tycho Brahe was unable to detect stellar parallax for any stars, leading him to reject the idea that Earth orbits the Sun.

In practice, parallax measurements are greatly complicated because of the tiny angles involved and because the Sun and the star being measured are moving in different directions. The first accurate stellar parallax was not determined until 1838. Even today, parallax angles for only a few thousand of the nearest stars are known with certainty. Almost all the other stars have such small parallax shifts that accurate measurements are not possible. Fortunately, other methods have been developed to estimate distances to more distant stars. In addition, the Hubble Space Telescope, which is not hindered by Earth's light-distorting atmosphere, has obtained accurate parallax distances for many more stars.

Minute parallax angles prove that the distances to stars are enormous, so large that conventional units of length, such as kilometers or astronomical units, are too cumbersome to use. A better unit to express stellar distances is the **light-year**, which is the distance light travels in one Earth-year—about 9.5 trillion kilometers (5.8 trillion miles).

Stellar Brightness

The oldest means of classifying stars is based on their *brightness*, also called *luminosity* or *magnitude*. It is natural to assume that very bright stars are somehow different from very dim stars. Three factors control the brightness of a star as seen from Earth: *how big* it is, *how hot* it is, and *how far away* it is. The stars in the night sky come in a grand assortment of sizes, temperatures, and distances, so their apparent brightnesses vary widely.

Apparent Magnitude

Stars have been classified according to their apparent brightness since at least the second century B.C., when Hipparchus placed about 850 of them into six categories based on his ability to see differences in brightness. Because he could only reliably see six different brightness levels, he created six categories. These categories were later called **magnitudes**, with *first magnitude (low numerical value) being the brightest and sixth magnitude (high numerical value) the dimmest*. Since some stars may appear dimmer than others only because they are farther away, a star's brightness, *as it appears when viewed from Earth*, is called its **apparent magnitude**. With the invention of the telescope, many stars fainter than the sixth magnitude were discovered.

In the mid-1800s, a method was developed to standardize the magnitude scale. An absolute comparison was made between the light coming from stars of the first magnitude and stars of the sixth magnitude. It was determined that a first-magnitude star was about 100 times brighter than a sixth-magnitude star. On the scale that was devised, any two stars that differ by 5 magnitudes have a ratio in brightness of 100 to 1. Hence, a third-magnitude star is 100 times brighter than an eighth-magnitude star. It follows, then, that the brightness ratio of two stars differing by only one magnitude is about 2.5.* A star of the first magnitude is about 2.5 times brighter than a star of the second magnitude. Table 16.1 shows how differences in magnitude correspond to brightness ratios.

*Calculations: or $2.512 \times 2.512 \times 2.512 \times 2.512 \times 2.512$, or 2.512 raised to the fifth power, equals 100.

Table 16.1   Ratios of star brightness

Difference in Magnitude	Brightness Ratio
0.5	1.6:1
1	2.5:1
2	6.3:1
3	16:1
4	40:1
5	100:1
10	10,000:1
20	100,000,000:1

FIGURE 16.3   Time-lapse photograph of stars in the constellation Orion. These star trails show some of the various star colors. It is important to note that the eye sees color somewhat differently than does photographic film. (Courtesy of National Optical Astronomy Observatories)

Because some celestial bodies, such as the Moon and Sun, are brighter than first-magnitude stars, zero and negative magnitudes were introduced. On this scale, the Sun has an apparent magnitude of −26.7. At its brightest, Venus has a magnitude of −4.3. At the other end of the scale, the 5-meter (200-inch) Hale Telescope can view stars with an apparent magnitude of 23, approximately 100 million times dimmer than stars that are visible to the unaided eye, and the Hubble Space Telescope can "see" stars with an apparent magnitude of 30!

Absolute Magnitude

Apparent magnitudes were good approximations of the true brightness of stars when astronomers thought that the universe was very small—containing no more than a few thousand stars that were all at very similar distances from Earth. However, we now know that the universe is unimaginably large and contains innumerable stars at wildly varying distances. Since astronomers are interested in the "true" brightness of stars, they devised a measure called **absolute magnitude**.

Stars of the same apparent magnitude usually do not have the same brightness because their distances from us are not equal. Imagine that you see a plane flying overhead at night. Although the lights on the plane may look brighter than the stars behind them, we know they are not as luminous.

Table 16.2   Distance, apparent magnitude, and absolute magnitude of some stars

Name	Distance (light-years)	Apparent Magnitude*	Absolute Magnitude*
Sun	NA	−26.7	5.0
Alpha Centauri	4.27	0.0	4.4
Sirius	8.70	−1.4	1.5
Arcturus	36	−0.1	−0.3
Betelgeuse	520	0.8	−5.5
Deneb	1600	1.3	−6.9

*The more negative (smaller) the number, the brighter; the more positive (larger) the number, the dimmer.

Astronomers correct for distance by determining what brightness (magnitude) the stars would have if they were at a standard distance—about 32.6 light-years away from Earth. For example, the Sun, which has an apparent magnitude of −26.7, would, if located at a distance of 32.6 light-years, have an absolute magnitude of about +5. Thus, stars with absolute magnitudes greater than +5 (smaller numerical value) are intrinsically brighter than the Sun. It is only because of their distance that they appear much dimmer. Table 16.2 lists the absolute and apparent magnitudes of some stars as well as their distances from Earth. Most stars have an absolute magnitude between −5 (very bright) and +15 (very dim). The Sun is near the middle of this range.

Stellar Color and Temperature

The next time you are outdoors on a clear night, take a good look at the stars and note their color (**FIGURE 16.3**). Because our eyes do not respond to color very well in low-intensity light, look at the brightest stars. Some that are quite colorful can be found in the constellation Orion. Of the two brightest stars in Orion, Rigel (β Orionis) appears blue, whereas Betelgeuse (α Orionis) is definitely red.

Very hot stars with surface temperatures above 30,000 K (kelvin) emit most of their energy in the form of short-wavelength light and therefore appear blue. On the other hand, cooler red stars, with surface temperatures generally less than 3000 K, emit most of their energy as longer-wavelength red light. Stars, such as the Sun, with surface temperatures between 5000 and 6000 K, appear yellow. Because color is primarily a manifestation of a star's surface temperature, this characteristic provides astronomers with useful information about a star. As you will see, combining temperature data with stellar magnitude tells us a great deal about the size and mass of a star.

Variable Stars   **461**

Binary Stars and Stellar Mass

One of the night sky's best-known constellations, the Big Dipper, appears to consist of seven stars. But those with good eyesight can recognize that the second star in the handle is actually two stars. During the eighteenth century, astronomers used their new tool, the telescope, to discover numerous such star pairs. One of the stars in the pair was usually fainter than the other, and for this reason it was considered to be farther away. In other words, the stars were not considered true pairs but were thought only to lie along the same line of sight.

In the early nineteenth century, careful examination of numerous star pairs by William Herschel showed that many stars found in pairs actually orbit one another. The two stars are in fact united by their mutual gravitation. These pairs of stars, in which the members are far enough apart to be resolved telescopically, are called **visual binaries** (*binaries* = double). The idea of one star orbiting another may seem unusual, but more than half of the stars in the universe exist in pairs or multiples.

Binary stars can be used to determine the star property most difficult to calculate—its *mass*. The mass of a body can be established if it is gravitationally attached to a partner. Binary stars orbit each other around a common point called the *center of mass* (**FIGURE 16.4**). For stars of equal mass, the center of mass lies exactly halfway between them. When one star is more massive than its partner, their common center will be located closer to the more massive one. Thus, if the sizes of their orbits can be observed, a determination of their individual masses can be made. You can experience this relationship on a seesaw by trying to balance a person who has a much greater (or smaller) mass.

For illustration, when one star has an orbit half the size (radius) of its companion, it is twice as massive as its companion. If their combined masses are equal to three solar masses, then the larger will be twice as massive as the Sun, and the smaller will have a mass equal to that of the Sun. Most stars have a mass that falls in a range between 1/10 and 50 times the mass of the Sun.

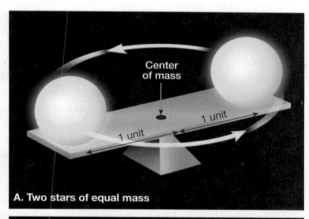

A. Two stars of equal mass

B. One star twice as massive as its companion

FIGURE 16.4   Binary stars orbit each other around their common center of mass. **A.** For stars of equal mass, the center of mass lies exactly halfway between them. **B.** If one star is twice as massive as its companion, it is twice as close to their common center of mass. Therefore, more massive stars have proportionately smaller orbits than do their less massive companions.

VARIABLE STARS

Not all stars release a relatively steady stream of energy like our Sun. Stars that fluctuate in brightness are known as variable stars. Some, called **pulsating variables**, fluctuate regularly in brightness by expanding and contracting in size. Astronomers study variable stars for many reasons, including trying to determine whether average stars such as the Sun spend some of their lives as variable stars, and if so, what kind.

The most spectacular variable stars belong to a group known as **eruptive variables**. When one of these explosive events occurs, it appears as a sudden brightening of a star, called a **nova** (**FIGURE 16.5**). The term *nova*, meaning "new," was used by the ancients because these stars were unknown to them before their abrupt increase in luminosity.

During a nova event, the outer shell of the star is ejected outward at high speed. A nova generally reaches maximum brightness in a couple of days, remains bright for only a few weeks, then slowly returns in a year or so to its original brightness. Because the star returns to its prenova brightness, we can assume that only a small amount of its mass is lost during the flare-up. Some stars have experienced more than one such event. In fact, the process probably occurs repeatedly.

The modern explanation for novae proposes that they occur in binary systems consisting of an expanding *red giant* and a hot *white dwarf*. Hydrogen-rich gas from the oversized giant encroaches near enough to the white dwarf to be gravitationally transferred. Eventually, enough hydrogen-rich gas is transferred to the hot dwarf to cause it to explosively ignite. Such a thermonuclear reaction rapidly heats and expands the outer gaseous envelope of the white dwarf to produce a nova event. In a relatively short time, the white dwarf returns to its prenova state, where it remains inactive until the next buildup occurs.

Like a nova, a **supernova** is a star that dramatically increases in brightness. However, the two phenomena are different. A supernova is a catastrophic event radiating as much energy in a few months as the Sun will radiate in its entire lifetime. In addition, during a supernova event the star's outer shell is explosively ejected, a topic we will consider later (**FIGURE 16.6**).

March 10, 1935

May 6, 1935

FIGURE 16.5 Photographs of Nova Herculis (a nova in the constellation Hercules), taken about two months apart, showing the decrease in brightness. (Courtesy of Lick Observatory)

FIGURE 16.6 This false-color image from three of NASA's Great Observatories provides one example of a star that died in a fiery supernova blast. Called Cassiopeia A, this supernova remnant is located 10,000 light-years away in the constellation Cassiopeia. At the center, visible only as a tiny turquoise dot, is the leftover corpse of the now-dead star, called a neutron star. (NASA)

HERTZSPRUNG-RUSSELL DIAGRAM

Early in the twentieth century, Einar Hertzsprung and Henry Russell independently studied the relationship between the true brightness (absolute magnitude) of stars and their temperatures. From this research each developed a graph, now called a **Hertzsprung-Russell diagram (H-R diagram)**, that displays these intrinsic stellar properties. By studying H-R diagrams, we can learn a great deal about the relationships among the sizes, colors, and temperatures of stars.

To produce an H-R diagram, astronomers survey a portion of the sky and plot each star according to its luminosity (brightness) and temperature (**FIGURE 16.7**). Notice that the stars in Figure 16.7 are not uniformly distributed. Rather, about 90 percent of all stars fall along a band that runs from the upper-left corner to the lower-right corner of the H-R diagram. These "ordinary" stars are called **main-sequence stars**. As shown in Figure 16.7, the hottest main-sequence stars are intrinsically the brightest, and the coolest are intrinsically the dimmest.

The luminosity of the main-sequence stars is also related to their mass. The hottest (blue) stars are about 50 times more massive than the Sun, whereas the coolest (red) stars are only 1/10 as massive. Therefore, on the H-R diagram, the main-sequence stars appear in decreasing order, from hotter, more massive blue stars to cooler, less massive red stars.

Note the location of the Sun in Figure 16.7. The Sun is a yellow main-sequence star with an absolute magnitude of about 5. Because the magnitude of a vast majority of main-sequence stars lie between −5 and 15, and because the Sun falls midway in this range, the Sun is often considered an average star.

Just as all humans do not fall into the normal size range, some stars are clearly different than main-sequence stars. Above and to the right of the main sequence in the H-R diagram (Figure 16.7) lies a group of very luminous stars called *giants*, or, on the basis of their color, **red giants**. The size of these giants can be estimated by comparing them with stars of known size that have the same surface temperature. We know that objects having equal surface temperatures radiate the same amount of energy per unit area. Therefore, any difference in the brightness of two stars having the same surface temperature is attributable to their relative sizes.

For example, a red main-sequence star and another red star that is 100 times more luminous radiate the same amount of energy per unit area. Therefore, in order for the

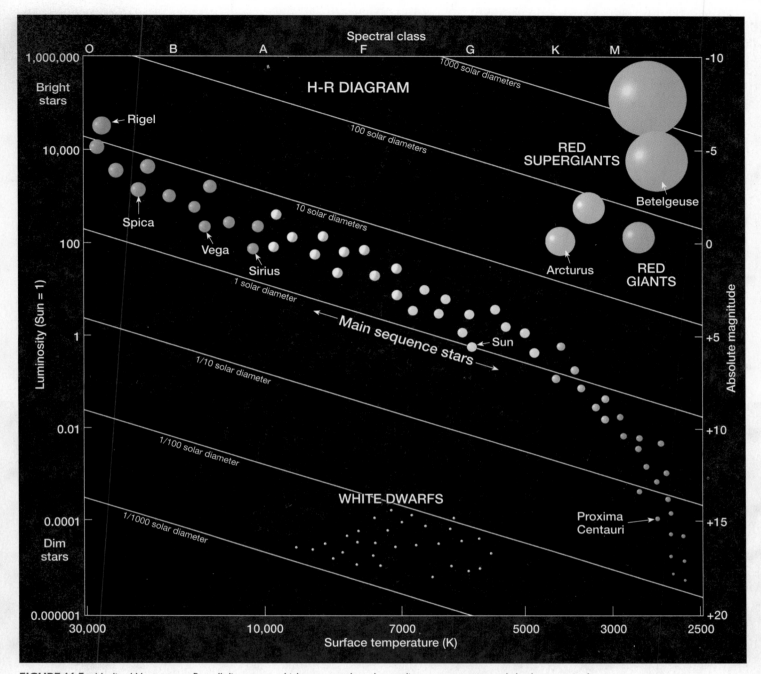

FIGURE 16.7 Idealized Hertzsprung-Russell diagram on which stars are plotted according to temperature and absolute magnitude.

more luminous star to be 100 times brighter than the less luminous star, it must have 100 times more surface area. Stars with large radiating surfaces appear in the upper-right position of an H-R diagram and are appropriately called *giants*.

Some stars are so large that they are called **supergiants**. Betelgeuse, a bright red supergiant in the constellation Orion, has a radius about 800 times that of the Sun. If this star were at the center of our solar system, it would extend beyond the orbit of Mars, and Earth would find itself inside the star! Other red giants that are easy to locate are Arcturus in the constellation Bootes and Antares in Scorpius.

In the lower-left portion of the H-R diagram, the opposite situation arises. These stars are much fainter than main-sequence stars of the same temperature, and by using the same reasoning, they must be much smaller. Some probably approximate Earth in size. This group has come to be called **white dwarfs**.

Soon after the first H-R diagrams were developed, astronomers realized their importance in interpreting stellar evolution. Just as with living things, a star is born, ages, and dies. Owing to the fact that almost 90 percent of the stars lie on the main sequence, we can be relatively certain that stars spend most of their active years as main-sequence stars.

Only a few percent are giants, and perhaps 10 percent are white dwarfs. After a brief discussion of interstellar matter, we will come back to stellar evolution and the life cycle of stars.

INTERSTELLAR MATTER

Lying between the stars is "the vacuum of space." However, it is far from a perfect vacuum, for it is populated with accumulations of dust and gases. The name applied to these concentrations of interstellar matter is **nebula** (*nebula* = cloud). If this interstellar matter is close to very hot (blue) stars, it will glow and is called a **bright nebula** (**FIGURE 16.8**). The two main types of bright nebulae are known as *emission nebulae* and *reflection nebulae*.

Emission nebulae are gaseous masses that consist largely of hydrogen. They absorb *ultraviolet radiation* emitted by embedded or nearby hot stars. Because these gases are under very low pressure, they reradiate, or emit, this energy as *visible light*. This conversion of ultraviolet light to visible light is known as *fluorescence*, an effect you observe daily in fluorescent lights.

Reflection nebulae, as the name implies, merely reflect the light of nearby stars (**FIGURE 16.9**). Reflection nebulae are likely composed of relatively dense clouds of large particles called **interstellar dust**. This view is supported by the fact that atomic gases with low densities could not reflect light sufficiently to produce the glow observed.

FIGURE 16.8 The Trifid Nebula, in the constellation Sagittarius. This colorful nebula is a cloud consisting mostly of hydrogen and helium gases. These gases are excited by the radiation of the hot, young stars within and produce a reddish glow. (Courtesy of National Optical Astronomy Observatories)

FIGURE 16.9 A faint blue reflection nebula, in the Pleiades star cluster, is caused by the reflection of starlight from dust in the nebula. The Pleiades star cluster, just visible to the naked eye in the constellation Taurus, is spectacular when viewed through binoculars or a small telescope. (Palomar Observatories/California Institute of Technology [Caltech])

When a cloud of interstellar material is not close enough to a bright star to be illuminated, it is referred to as a **dark nebula**. Exemplified by the Horsehead Nebula in Orion, dark nebulae appear as opaque objects silhouetted against a bright background (**FIGURE 16.10**). Dark nebulae can also easily be seen as starless regions—"holes in the heavens" when viewing the Milky Way.

Although nebulae appear very dense, they actually consist of very thinly scattered matter. Because of their enormous size, however, the total mass of rarefied particles and molecules are many times that of the Sun. Interstellar matter is of great interest to astronomers because it is from this material that stars and planets are formed.

STELLAR EVOLUTION

The idea of describing how a star is born, ages, and then dies may seem a bit presumptuous, for many of these objects have life spans that exceed billions of years. However, by studying stars of different ages, at different points in their life cycles, astronomers have been able to piece together a plausible model for stellar evolution.

The method that was used to create this model is analogous to what an alien being, upon reaching Earth, might use to determine the developmental stages of human life. By examining a large number of humans, this stranger would be able to observe the birth of human life, the activities of children and adults, and the death of the elderly. From this information, the alien could put the stages of human development into their proper sequence. Based on the relative abundance of humans in each stage of development, it would even be possible to conclude that humans spend more of their lives as adults than as toddlers. In a similar fashion, astronomers have pieced together the life story of stars.

In the simplest sense, every stage of a star's life is ruled by gravity. The mutual gravitational attraction of particles in a thin, gaseous cloud causes the cloud to collapse. As the cloud is squeezed to unimaginable pressures, its temperature rises, igniting its nuclear furnace, and a star is born. A star is a ball of very hot gases, caught between the opposing forces of gravity trying to contract it and thermal nuclear energy trying to expand it. Eventually, all of a star's nuclear fuel will be exhausted and gravity takes control, collapsing the stellar remnant into a comparatively small, dense body.

Stellar Birth

The birthplaces of stars are dark, cool interstellar clouds, which are rich in dust and gases (**FIGURE 16.11**). In the Milky Way, these gaseous clouds consist of 92 percent hydrogen, 7 percent helium, and less than 1 percent of the remaining heavier elements. One mechanism thought to trigger stellar formation is a shock wave generated by a catastrophic explosion (supernova) of a nearby star. Regardless of the force that initiates the process, once it is started, mutual gravitational attraction of the particles causes the cloud to contract, pulling every particle toward the center. As the cloud shrinks, gravitational energy (potential energy) is converted into energy of motion, or heat energy, and the contracting gases slowly heat up.

The initial contraction spans a million years. With the passage of time, the temperature of this gaseous body slowly and continuously rises, eventually reaching a temperature sufficiently high to cause it to radiate energy from its surface in the form of long-wavelength red light. Because this large red object is not hot enough to engage in nuclear fusion, it is not yet a star. The name **protostar** is applied to these bodies.

Protostar Stage

During the protostar stage, gravitational contraction continues, slowly at first, then much more rapidly (Figure 16.11). This collapse causes the core of the developing star to heat much more intensely than the outer envelope. When the core reaches a temperature of 10 million K, the pressure within is so great that groups of four hydrogen nuclei fuse together into single helium nuclei. Astronomers refer to this nuclear reaction as **hydrogen burning** because an enormous amount of energy is released. However, keep in mind that thermonuclear "burning" is not burning in the usual chemical sense of a wood or coal fire.

Immense heat released by hydrogen fusion causes the gases inside the star to move with increased vigor, resulting

FIGURE 16.10 The Horsehead Nebula, a dark nebula in a region of glowing nebulosity in Orion. (© Anglo-Australian Observatory/Royal Observatory, photography by David Malin)

in an increase in the internal gas pressure. At some point, the increased atomic motion produces an outward force (pressure) that exactly balances the inward-directed force of gravity. When this balance is reached, the star becomes a *stable main-sequence star* (Figure 16.11). In other words, a main-sequence star is one in which the force of gravity, which is trying to squeeze the star into the smallest possible ball, is balanced by gas pressure created by hydrogen burning in the star's interior.

Main-Sequence Stage

During the main-sequence stage, the star experiences very little change in size or energy output. Hydrogen is continually being converted into helium, and the energy that is released keeps the gas pressure sufficiently high to prevent gravitational collapse. How long can the star maintain this balance? Hot, massive blue stars radiate energy at such an enormous rate that they substantially deplete their hydrogen fuel in only a few million years, approaching the end of their main-sequence stage rapidly. By contrast, the very smallest (red) main-sequence stars may take hundreds of billions of years to burn their hydrogen, living practically forever. A yellow star, such as the Sun, remains a main-sequence star for about 10 billion years before consuming most of its usable hydrogen fuel. Since the solar system is about 5 billion years old, the Sun will remain a stable main-sequence star for another 5 billion years.

The average star spends 90 percent of its life as a hydrogen-burning main-sequence star. Once the hydrogen fuel in the star's core is depleted, it will evolve rapidly and die. However, with the exception of the least-massive stars, death is delayed when another type of nuclear reaction is triggered and the star becomes a red giant.

Red Giant Stage

The evolution to the red giant stage begins when the usable hydrogen in the star's interior is consumed, leaving a helium-rich core. Although hydrogen fusion is still progressing in the star's outer shell, no fusion is taking place in the core. Without a source of energy, the core no longer has the gas pressure necessary to support itself against the inward force of gravity. As a result, the core begins to contract.

The collapse of the star's interior causes its temperature to rapidly increase as gravitational energy is converted into heat. Some of this energy is radiated outward, initiating a more vigorous level of hydrogen fusion in the star's outer shell. The additional energy from the accelerated rate of hydrogen burning heats and enormously expands the star's outer gaseous shell. The result is a bloated red giant hundreds, and occasionally even thousands, of times its main-sequence size (Figure 16.11).

As the star expands, its surface cools, which explains the star's red color—comparatively cool objects radiate more of their energy as long-wavelength radiation. Eventually the star's gravitational force stops this outward expansion and the two opposing forces, gravity and gas pressure, are once again in balance. The star enters a stable state, only much larger in size. Some red giants overshoot the equilibrium point and then rebound like an overextended spring. Such stars continue to expand and contract, never reaching equilibrium. Instead, they become variable stars.

While the envelope of a red giant expands, the core continues to collapse and the internal temperature eventually reaches 100 million K. At this incredible temperature, it is hot enough to start a nuclear reaction in which helium is converted to carbon. At this point, a red giant consumes both hydrogen and helium to produce energy. In stars more massive than the Sun, other thermonuclear reactions are also triggered. The result is the generation of all the elements on the periodic table up to number 26, iron. Nuclear reactions that generate elements heavier than iron require an additional source of energy.

Eventually, all the usable nuclear fuel in a star will be consumed. The Sun, for example, will spend less than a billion years as a giant while more massive stars will pass through this stage even more rapidly. Once all the fuel is gone, the force of gravity will squeeze the star into the smallest, most dense piece of matter possible.

Burnout and Death

What happens to a star after the red giant phase? We know that a star, regardless of its size, must eventually exhaust all of its usable nuclear fuel and collapse in response to its immense gravitational field. Since the gravitational field of a star is dependent on its mass, low-mass stars have different fates than high-mass stars. With this in mind, we will consider the final stage for stars in three different mass categories.

Death of Low-Mass Stars

Stars less than one-half the mass of the Sun (0.5 solar mass) consume their fuel at a comparatively slow rate (**FIGURE 16.12A**). Consequently, these small, *cool red stars* may remain a main-sequence star for up to 100 billion years. Because the interior of a low-mass star never attains sufficiently high temperatures and pressures to fuse helium, its only energy source is hydrogen fusion. Thus, a low-mass star never evolves to become a bloated red giant. Rather, it remains a stable main-sequence star until it has consumed its usable hydrogen fuel and collapses into a hot, dense *white dwarf*. As you shall see, white dwarfs are small, compact objects unable to support hydrogen burning.

Death of Medium-Mass (Sun-like) Stars

All main-sequence stars with masses ranging between one-half to eight times that of the Sun evolve in essentially the same way (**FIGURE 16.12B**). During their giant phase, Sun-like stars fuse hydrogen and helium fuel at an accelerated rate. Once this fuel is exhausted, these stars (like low-mass stars) collapse into an Earth-size body of great density—a white dwarf. The gravitational energy supplied to a collapsing white dwarf is reflected in its high surface temperature, hence its white color. However, without a source of nuclear energy, a white dwarf becomes cooler and dimmer as it continually radiates its remaining thermal energy into space.

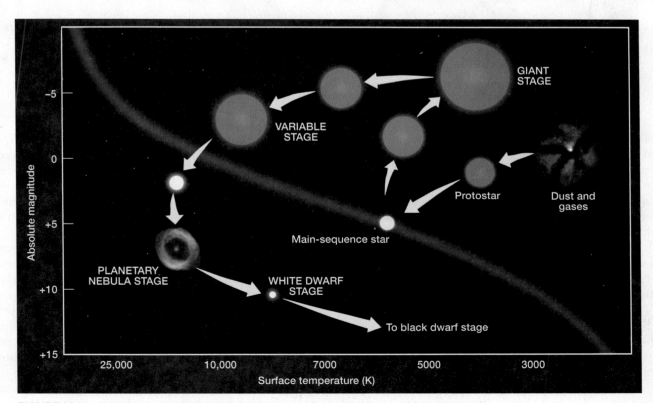

FIGURE 16.11   H-R diagram showing stellar evolution for a star about as massive as the Sun.

468   **CHAPTER 16**   Beyond Our Solar System

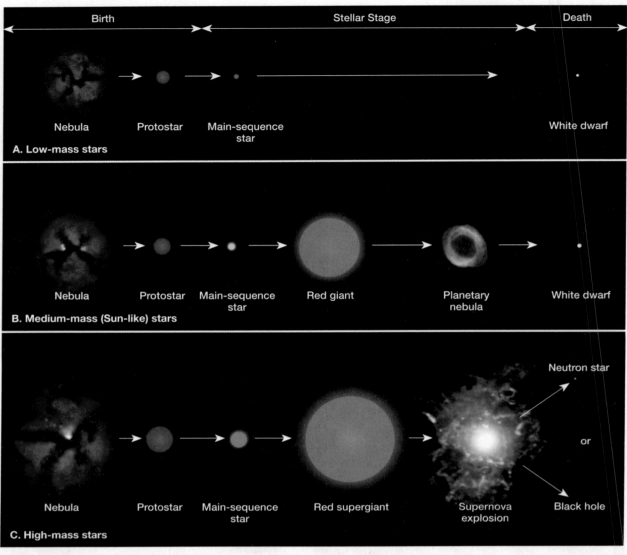

FIGURE 16.12   The evolutionary stages of stars having various masses.

During their collapse from red giants to white dwarfs, medium-mass stars are believed to cast off their bloated outer atmosphere, creating an expanding spherical cloud of gas. The remaining hot, central white dwarf heats the gas cloud, causing it to glow. These spectacular, gleaming spherical clouds are called **planetary nebulae**. A good example of a planetary nebula is the Helix Nebula in the constellation Aquarius (**FIGURE 16.13**). This nebula appears as a ring because our line of sight through the center traverses less gaseous material than at the nebula's edge. It is, nevertheless, spherical in shape.

Death of Massive Stars

In contrast to Sun-like stars, which expire nonviolently, stars exceeding eight solar masses have relatively short life spans and terminate in a brilliant explosion called a *supernova* (**FIGURE 16.12C**). During a supernova event, a star becomes millions of times brighter than its prenova stage. If one of the nearest stars to Earth produced such an outburst, its brilliance would surpass that of the Sun. Fortunately for us, supernovae are relatively rare events; none have been observed in our galaxy since the advent of the telescope, although Tycho Brahe and Kepler each recorded one about 30 years apart. An even brighter supernova was recorded in A.D. 1054 by the Chinese. Today, the remnant of this great outburst is the Crab nebula, shown in **FIGURE 16.14**.

A supernova event is likely triggered when a massive star has consumed most of its nuclear fuel. Without a heat engine to generate the gas pressure required to balance its immense gravitational field, it collapses. This implosion is cataclysmic, resulting in a shock wave that moves out from the star's interior. This energetic shock wave blasts the star's outer shell into space, generating the supernova event.

Theoretical work predicts that during a supernova, the star's interior condenses into a very hot object, possibly no larger than 20 kilometers in diameter. These incomprehensibly dense bodies have been named *neutron stars*. Some supernovae events are thought to produce even smaller and more

FIGURE 16.13 The Helix Nebula, the nearest planetary nebula to our solar system. A planetary nebula is the ejected outer envelope of a Sun-like star that formed during the star's collapse from a red giant to a white dwarf. (© Anglo-Australian Observatory, photography by David Malin)

Figure 16.11 shows the evolution of a star about the size of the Sun on an H-R diagram. Keep in mind that the star does not physically follow this path, but rather that its position on the H-R diagram represents the color (temperature) and absolute magnitude (brightness) of the star at various stages in its evolution.

Using the H-R diagram, the protostar that became the Sun would be located to the right and above the main sequence (Figure 16.11). It appears to the right because of its relatively cool surface temperature (red color), and above because it would be more luminous than a main-sequence star of the same color, because it is still a large collection of gas with a large surface area. As it shrinks and its nuclear furnace turns on, its surface gets hotter, turning yellow, and its total luminosity decreases because its total surface area is much smaller. You should be able to follow Figure 16.11 to visualize the remaining evolutionary changes experienced by a star the size of the Sun. In addition, Table 16.3 provides a summary of the evolutionary history of stars having various masses.

intriguing objects called *black holes*. We will consider the nature of neutron stars and black holes in the following section on stellar remnants.

H-R Diagrams and Stellar Evolution

Hertzsprung-Russell diagrams have been very helpful in formulating and testing models of stellar evolution. They are also useful for illustrating the changes that take place in an individual star during its life span.

DID YOU KNOW?

The first naked-eye supernova in 383 years was discovered in the southern sky in February 1987. This stellar explosion was officially named SN 1987A (SN stands for supernova, and 1987A indicates that it was the first supernova observed in 1987). Naked-eye supernovae are rare. Only a few have been recorded in historic times. Arab observers saw one in 1006, and the Chinese recorded one in 1054 at the present location of the Crab Nebula. In addition, the astronomer Tycho Brahe observed a supernova in 1572, and Kepler saw one shortly thereafter in 1604.

STELLAR REMNANTS

Eventually, all stars consume their nuclear fuel and collapse into one of three final forms—a *white dwarf*, *neutron star*, or *black hole*. How a star's life ends, and what final form it takes, depends largely on the star's mass. Generally, low- and medium-mass stars die nonviolently, whereas high-mass stars die catastrophically. The dividing line between these two dramatically different possibilities is approximately eight solar masses.

White Dwarfs

Once low- and medium-mass stars consume their remaining thermal fuel, gravity causes them to collapse into *white dwarfs*. These Earth-sized objects have a mass roughly equal to the Sun. Thus, their densities may be a million times greater than water. A spoonful of such matter would weigh several tons. Densities this great are possible only when electrons are displaced inward from their regular orbits around an atom's nucleus. Material in this state is called **degenerate matter**.

The atoms in degenerate matter have been squeezed together so tightly that the electrons are pushed very close to the nucleus. Electrical repulsion, between the negatively

FIGURE 16.14   Crab Nebula in the constellation Taurus: the remains of the supernova of A.D. 1054. (NASA)

for this is that more massive stars, because of their greater gravitational fields, are squeezed into a smaller, more densely packed object than are less massive stars. Thus, the smallest white dwarfs were produced from the collapse of larger, more massive main-sequence stars than were the larger white dwarfs.

This conclusion led to the prediction that stars even smaller and more massive than white dwarfs must exist. Named **neutron stars**, these objects are the remnants of explosive supernova events. In a white dwarf, the electrons are pushed close to the nucleus, whereas in a neutron star the electrons are forced to combine with protons in the nucleus to produce neutrons (hence the name neutron star). If Earth were to collapse to the density of a neutron star, it would have a diameter equivalent to the length of a football field. A pea-size sample of this matter would weigh 100 million tons. This is approximately the density of an atomic nucleus; thus, a neutron star can be thought of as a large atomic nucleus, composed of only neutrons.

During a supernova implosion, the outer envelope of the star is ejected (**FIGURE 16.15**), and the core collapses into a very hot star about 20 kilometers (12.4 miles) in diameter. Although neutron stars have high surface temperatures, their small size greatly limits their luminosity, making them almost impossible to locate visually.

However, theoretical models predict that a neutron star would have a very strong magnetic field and a high rate of rotation. As a star collapses, it rotates faster, for the same reason ice skaters rotate faster as they pull in their arms. If the Sun were to collapse to the size of a neutron star, it would increase its rate of rotation from once every 25 days to nearly 1000 times per second. Radio waves generated by the rotating magnetic fields of a neutron star are concentrated into two narrow zones that align with the star's magnetic poles. Consequently, these stars resemble a rapidly rotating beacon emitting strong radio waves. If Earth happened to be in the path of these beacons, the star would appear to blink on and off, or pulsate, as the waves swept past.

In the early 1970s, a source that radiates short pulses of radio energy, named a **pulsar** (pulsating radio source), was discovered in the Crab Nebula. Visual inspection of this radio source indicated that it was a small star centered in the

charged electrons and the positively charged nucleus, rather than molecular motion supports the star against even further gravitational collapse. Although atomic particles in degenerate matter are much closer together than in "normal" matter, they still are not packed as tightly as possible. Stars made of matter of an even greater density are known to exist.

As a main-sequence star contracts into a white dwarf, its surface becomes very hot, sometimes exceeding 25,000 K. Even so, without a source of energy, it slowly becomes cooler and dimmer. Eventually a white dwarf becomes a small, cold, burned-out ember in space called a *black dwarf*.

Neutron Stars

A study of white dwarfs produced what might appear to be a surprising conclusion. The *smallest white dwarfs* are the *most massive*, and the *largest* are the *least massive*. The explanation

Table 16.3   Summary of evolution for stars of various masses

Initial Mass of Main-Sequence Star (Sun =1)*	Main-Sequence Stage	Giant Phase	Evolution After Giant Phase	Terminal State (Final Mass)
0.001	None (Planet)	No	Not applicable	Planet (0.001)
0.1	Red	No	Not applicable	White dwarf (0.1)
1–3	Yellow	Yes	Planetary Nebula	White dwarf (<1.4)
8	White	Yes	Supernova	Neutron star (1.4–3)
25	Blue	Yes (Supergiant)	Supernova	Black hole (>3.0)

*These mass numbers are estimates.

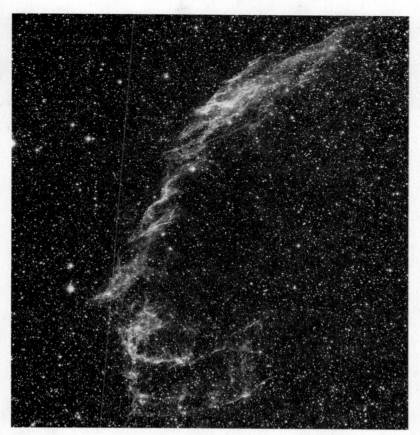

FIGURE 16.15 Veil Nebula in the constellation Cygnus is the remnant of an ancient supernova implosion. (Palomar Observatories/California Institute of Technology [Caltech])

nebula. The pulsar found in the Crab Nebula is very likely the remains of the supernova of A.D. 1054 (see Figure 16.14). Since then several other neutron stars have been discovered.

Black Holes

Although neutron stars are extremely dense, they are not the densest objects in the universe. Stellar evolutionary theory predicts that the mass of a neuron star cannot be greater than three times that of the Sun. Above this mass, not even tightly packed neutrons can withstand the star's gravitational pull. When the core of a star left behind after a supernova explosion exceeds the three-solar-mass limit, gravity wins the battle with pressure, and the stellar remnant collapses. (Although the precise figure is uncertain, the pre-supernova mass of such a star likely exceeded 25 solar masses.) The incredible object created by such a collapse is called a **black hole**.

Even though black holes are extremely hot, their surface gravity is so immense that even light cannot escape. Consequently, they literally disappear from sight. Anything that moves too close to a black hole will be swept in by its irresistible gravitational field and be devoured.

How did astronomers find objects whose gravitational field prevents the escape of all matter and energy? Theory predicts that as matter is pulled into a black hole, it should become very hot and emit a flood of x-rays before being engulfed. Because isolated black holes do not have a source of matter to engulf, astronomers decided to look at binary-star systems for evidence of matter being rapidly swept into a region of apparent nothingness.

A likely candidate for a black hole is Cygnus X-1, a strong x-ray source in the constellation Cygnus. This x-ray source can be detected orbiting a red supergiant companion once every 5.6 days. It appears that gases are pulled from the giant companion and spiral into a disc-shaped structure around a "void," thought to be a black hole (**FIGURE 16.16**). The result is the emission of a steady stream of x-rays. Because x-rays cannot penetrate our atmosphere efficiently, the existence of black holes was not confirmed until the advent of orbiting observatories. The first x-ray sources were discovered in 1971 by detectors on satellites, and soon after, Cygnus X-1 was determined to be a black hole.

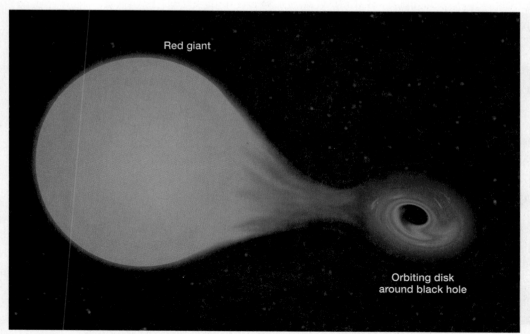

Red giant

Orbiting disk
around black hole

FIGURE 16.16 This illustration shows how astronomers suggest a binary pair consisting of a red giant and black hole might function.

FIGURE 16.17 Panorama of our galaxy, the Milky Way. Notice the dark band caused by the presence of interstellar dark nebulae. (Courtesy of Axel Mellinger)

THE MILKY WAY GALAXY

On a clear and moonless night away from city lights, you can see a truly marvelous sight—a band of light stretching from horizon to horizon. With his telescope, Galileo discovered that this band of light was composed of countless individual stars. Today, we realize that the Sun is actually a part of this vast system of stars, the Milky Way Galaxy (**FIGURE 16.17**).

The Milky Way is a spiral galaxy containing about 100 billion stars (**FIGURE 16.18A**). Its milky appearance is a result of the solar system's location within the flat galactic disk. When we look *along the plane* of the galaxy, we see a band of stars. You can see this in the edge-on view in **FIGURE 16.18B**. However, when we look *out of the plane* of the galaxy, we do not see as many stars.

When astronomers began to telescopically survey the stars located along the plane of the Milky Way, it appeared that equal numbers lay in every direction, and people wondered if Earth was actually at the center of the galaxy. It turns out the Earth is not in the center of the galaxy, and a simple illustration shows the fallacy of this argument. Imagine that the trees in an enormous forest represent the stars in the galaxy. After hiking into this forest a short distance, you look around. What you see is an equal number of trees in every direction. Are you really in the center of the forest? Not necessarily; from anywhere in the forest, except at the very edge, it will look as though you are in the middle.

Attempts to visually inspect the Milky Way are hindered by the large quantities of interstellar matter that lie in our line of sight. Nevertheless, with the aid of radio telescopes, the gross structure of our galaxy has been determined. The Milky Way is a relatively large spiral galaxy whose disk is about 100,000 light-years wide and about 10,000 light-years thick at the nucleus (Figure 16.18). As viewed from Earth, the center of the galaxy lies beyond the constellation Sagittarius.

Radio telescopes also show that the Milky Way has at least three distinct spiral arms. (**FIGURE 16.19**). The Sun is positioned in one of these arms about two-thirds of the way from the center, at a distance of about 30,000 light-years. The stars in the arms of the Milky Way rotate around the galactic nucleus, with the most outward ones moving the slowest, such that the ends of the arms appear to trail. The Sun takes about 200 million years to orbit around the galactic center.

FIGURE 16.18 Structure of the visible portion of the Milky Way Galaxy.

FIGURE 16.19 If the Milky Way were photographed from a distance, it might appear like the spiral galaxy NGC 2997. (© Anglo-Australian Observatory, photography by David Malin)

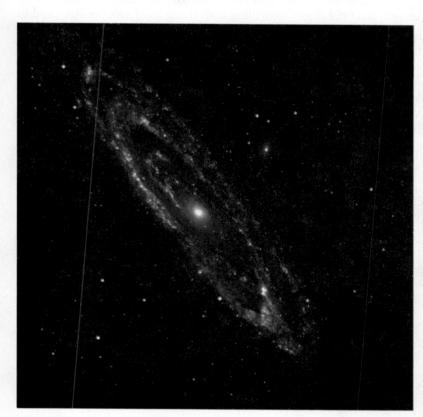

FIGURE 16.20 Andromeda Galaxy, a large spiral galaxy. A dwarf elliptical galaxy is located to the right of Andromeda. (NASA)

Surrounding the galactic disk is a nearly spherical halo made of very tenuous gas and numerous globular clusters. These star clusters do not participate in the rotating motion of the arms but rather have their own orbits that carry them through the disk. Although some clusters are very dense, they pass among the stars of the galactic arms with plenty of room to spare.

NORMAL GALAXIES

In the mid-1700s, German philosopher Immanuel Kant proposed that the telescopically visible fuzzy patches of light scattered among the stars were actually distant galaxies like the Milky Way. Kant described them as island universes. Each galaxy, he believed, contained billions of stars and, as such, was a universe in itself. The weight of opinion, however, favored the hypothesis that they were dust and gas clouds (nebulae) within our galaxy because Earth was still considered a special and privileged place in the universe. Admitting that other galaxies existed would reduce Earth's (and humankind's) stature.

This matter was not resolved until the 1920s, when American astronomer Edwin Hubble was able to locate, within one of these fuzzy patches (the nebula in Andromeda), some unique stars that are known to be intrinsically very bright. Because these bright stars appeared to be faint when viewed telescopically, Hubble concluded that they must lie outside the Milky Way. The fuzzy patch Hubble observed lies more than two million light-years away and has been named the *Andromeda Galaxy* (**FIGURE 16.20**).

Hubble had extended the universe far beyond the limits of our imagination, to include hundreds of billions of galaxies, each containing hundreds of billions of stars. It has been said that a million galaxies are found in that portion of the sky bounded by the cup of the Big Dipper. There truly are more stars in the heavens than grains of sand in all the beaches on Earth.

Types of Galaxies

Among the hundreds of billions of galaxies, three basic types of *normal galaxies* have been identified: *spiral*, *elliptical*, and *irregular*. In addition, scattered throughout the universe, a few galaxies differ considerably from the norm. These very luminous objects are known collectively as *active galaxies*.

A.

B.

FIGURE 16.21   Two views illustrating the idealized structure of spiral galaxies. **A.** Spiral galaxy known as Messier 81, or M81. **B.** Edge-on view of a spiral galaxy captured by Hubble Space Telescope. (NASA)

Spiral Galaxies

The Milky Way and the Andromeda Galaxy are examples of large **spiral galaxies** (**FIGURE 16.21**). (Andromeda can be seen with the unaided eye as a fuzzy fifth-magnitude object.) Spiral galaxies are generally large, ranging from 20,000 to about 125,000 light-years in diameter. Typically, they are disk-shaped, with a greater concentration of stars near their centers, but there are numerous variations. Viewed broadside, arms are often seen extending from the central nucleus and sweeping gracefully away. The outermost stars of these arms rotate most slowly, giving the galaxy the appearance of a fireworks pinwheel.

One type of spiral galaxy, however, has the stars arranged in the shape of a bar, which rotates as a rigid system. This requires that the outer stars move faster than the inner ones, a fact not easily reconciled with the laws of motion. Attached to each end of these bars are curved spiral arms. These have become known as **barred spiral galaxies** (**FIGURE 16.22**). About 10 percent of all galaxies are thought to be barred spirals with another 20 percent regular spiral galaxies like the Milky Way.

Elliptical Galaxies

The most numerous group, making up 60 percent of the total, are the **elliptical galaxies**. These are generally smaller than spiral galaxies. Some are so much smaller, in fact, that the term *dwarf galaxy* has been applied to them. Because these dwarf galaxies are not visible at great distances, a visual survey of the sky shows more of the conspicuous large spiral galaxies. However, if one looks at the galaxies in any given volume of the universe, elliptical galaxies are the most numerous.

Although most elliptical galaxies are small, the very largest known galaxies (200,000 light-years in diameter) are also elliptical. As their name implies, elliptical galaxies have an ellipsoidal shape that ranges to nearly spherical, and they lack spiral arms. The dwarf companion of Andromeda shown in Figure 16.20 is an elliptical galaxy.

Irregular Galaxies

Only 10 percent of the known galaxies show no symmetry and are classified as **irregular galaxies**. The best-known irregular galaxies, the

FIGURE 16.22   Barred spiral galaxy. (NASA)

Large and Small Magellanic Clouds in the Southern Hemisphere, are easily visible with the unaided eye. Named after the explorer Ferdinand Magellan, who observed them when he circumnavigated Earth in 1520, they are our nearest galactic neighbors—only 150,000 light-years away.

One of the major differences among the galactic types is the age of the stars that make them up. The irregular galaxies are composed mostly of young stars, whereas the elliptical galaxies contain old stars. The Milky Way and other spiral galaxies consist of both young and old stars, with the youngest located in the arms.

Galactic Clusters

Once astronomers discovered that stars were associated in groups (galaxies), they set out to determine whether galaxies were also grouped or just randomly distributed throughout the universe. They found that galaxies are grouped into clusters (**FIGURE 16.23**). Some large **galactic clusters** contain thousands of galaxies. Our own, called the **Local Group**, contains at least 28 galaxies. Of these, 3 are spirals, 11 are irregulars, and 14 are ellipticals. Galactic clusters also reside in huge swarms called *superclusters*. From visual observations, it appears that superclusters may be the largest entities in the universe.

FIGURE 16.23   A cluster of galaxies located about 1 billion light-years from Earth. (Courtesy of NASA)

THE BIG BANG AND THE FATE OF THE UNIVERSE

The universe is more than simply a collection of dust clouds, stars, stellar remnants, and galaxies. It is an entity with its own properties. **Cosmology** is the branch of science that studies these properties, and cosmologists have developed a comprehensive theory about the nature of the universe. Some of the questions cosmologists try to answer with this theory include: Did the universe have a beginning? If so, how did it start? How did the universe evolve to its present state? How long has it been around and how long will it last?

These are basic questions that many cultures have asked, in one form or another. Modern cosmology addresses these important issues and helps us understand the universe we inhabit. Today, there is only one theory describing the birth and current state of the universe that is seriously considered by most scientists—*the big bang*. We will look at some of the evidence that led to the development of the big bang theory, one tested prediction that supports it, and one implication of this theory that is currently being tested.

The Expanding Universe

Before we can discuss the evidence suggesting that the universe is expanding, we have to examine how astronomers measure relative motion in the universe. Here on Earth, you can tell if something is approaching because it appears to grow larger as it approaches or smaller as it recedes. Most objects in the universe are so distant that their apparent size never changes. Instead, astronomers look at the changes in the wavelengths of light emitted by these bodies to determine relative motion.

You have probably noticed the change in pitch of an ambulance siren as it passes by. When it is approaching, the sound seems to have a higher pitch than if you were standing next to it, and when it is moving away, it seems to have a lower pitch. This effect, which occurs for all wave motion, including sound and light waves, was first explained by Christian Doppler in 1842 and is called the *Doppler effect*. The reason for the difference in pitch is that it takes time for the wave to be emitted. If the source of the wave is moving away, the beginning of the wave is emitted nearer to you than the end of the wave, "stretching" the wave and giving it a longer wavelength (**FIGURE 16.24**). For an approaching wave source, the wave is compressed.

In the case of light, when a source is moving away, the light we see is of lower energy than the originally emitted light (the light is shifted to the red end of the spectrum) because the emitted waves are lengthened. Approaching objects have their light waves shifted toward the blue end of the spectrum (shorter wavelength). Therefore, the Doppler effect reveals whether Earth and another celestial body are approaching one another or moving apart. In addition, the amount of shift allows us to determine the relative velocity between Earth and the object. Large Doppler shifts indicate high velocities; small Doppler shifts indicate low velocities.

One of the most important discoveries of modern astronomy was made in 1929 by Edwin Hubble. Using observational data collected several years earlier, Hubble showed that almost all galaxies have Doppler shifts toward the red end of the spectrum. The red shift occurs because the

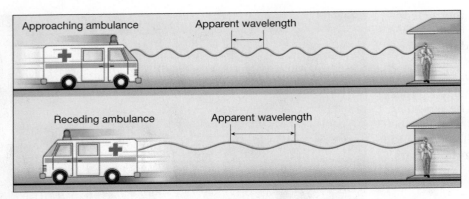

FIGURE 16.24   The Doppler effect, illustrating the apparent lengthening and shortening of wavelengths caused by the relative motion between a source and an observer.

light waves are "stretched," indicating that Earth and the source are moving away from each other (galaxies in the Local Group are an exception). Hubble set out to determine what the predominance of red shifts tells us about the universe.

Hubble realized that dimmer galaxies were probably farther away than brighter galaxies, so he tried to determine whether there was a relation between the distance to a galaxy and its red shift. Using estimated distances based on relative brightness, Hubble discovered that the red shifts of galaxies increase with distance and that the most distant galaxies are receding the fastest and at enormous speeds. This idea, termed **Hubble's law**, states that galaxies are receding from us at speeds that are proportional to their distances.

Hubble was surprised at this discovery because it implied that the most distant galaxies are moving away from us many times faster than those nearby. At the time, conventional wisdom was that the universe was unchanging. It had always existed much like it is now, and would continue to exist, relatively unchanged, indefinitely. What cosmological theory could explain Hubble's findings? It did not take long to realize that an expanding universe adequately accounts for the observed red shifts. The theory of the expanding universe states that new space is being created between objects

that are very far apart (Earth and objects outside the Local Group of galaxies, for example).

To help visualize the nature of this expanding universe, we will employ a popular analogy. Imagine a loaf of raisin bread dough that has been set out to rise for a few hours (**FIGURE 16.25**). Also imagine that the raisins are galaxies and the dough is space. As the dough doubles in size, so does the distance between all of the raisins. In addition, the raisins that were originally farthest apart traveled a greater distance in the same time span than those located closer together. We therefore conclude that in an expanding universe, as in our analogy, those objects located farther apart move away from each other more rapidly.

Another feature of the expanding universe can be demonstrated using the raisin bread analogy. No matter which raisin you select, it moves away from all the other raisins. Likewise, no matter where you are located in the universe, all the other galaxies (except those in the same cluster) will be receding from you. Edwin Hubble changed our understanding of the universe, and *The Hubble Space Telescope* is named in his honor.

The Origin of the Universe

First and foremost, any viable theory regarding the origin of the universe must account for the fact that all galaxies are moving away from us. Does this observation put our planet in the center of the universe? Probably not. Since all clusters of galaxies are moving away from all the other galactic groups, every point in the universe looks like the center of the universe just like every point in the forest looks like the center of the forest. In addition, if we are not in the center of our solar system or our galaxy, it is unlikely that we would be at the center of the universe. A more probable explanation exists: the expanding universe described above. If the universe is expanding, every galaxy would be moving away from every other galaxy.

The concept of an expanding universe has led to the widely accepted **big bang theory**. According to this theory, the entire universe was once confined to a dense, hot, supermassive point. Then, about 14 billion years ago, a cataclysmic explosion occurred, expanding the universe in all directions. The big bang marks the inception of the universe; everything in the universe was created at that instant. Some of the energy became matter that cooled and condensed, forming the stars that compose the galactic systems we now observe fleeing from their birthplace.

A good scientific theory makes predictions that can be tested. One prediction of the big bang theory is that if there was a cataclysmic explosion at the beginning of time, we should be able to detect the afterglow.

A. Raisin bread dough before it rises.

B. Raisin bread dough a few hours later.

FIGURE 16.25   Illustration of the raisin bread analogy of an expanding universe. As the dough rises, raisins originally farther apart travel a greater distance in the same time span as those located closer together. Thus, raisins (like galaxies in a uniform expanding universe) that are located farther apart move away from each other more rapidly than those located nearer to each other.

The name Big Bang was originally coined by cosmologist Fred Hoyle as a sarcastic comment on the believability of the theory. The Big Bang Theory proposes that our universe began as a violent explosion, from which the universe continues to expand, evolve, and cool. Through decades of experimentation and observation, scientists have gathered substantial evidence that supports this theory. Despite this fact, the Big Bang Theory, like all other scientific theories, can never be proved. It is always possible that a future observation will disprove a previously accepted theory. Nevertheless, the Big Bang has replaced all alternative theories and remains the only widely accepted scientific model for the origin of the universe.

would follow, causing the galaxies to eventually collide and coalesce into the high-energy, high-density mass from which the universe began. This fiery death of the universe, the big bang operating in reverse, has been called the "*big crunch.*"

Whether or not the universe will expand forever, or eventually collapse upon itself, depends on its average density. If the average density of the universe is more than an amount known as its *critical density* (about one atom for every cubic meter), gravitational attraction is sufficient to stop the outward expansion and cause the universe to collapse. On the other hand, if the density of the universe is less than the critical value, it will expand forever. Current estimates of the density of the universe place it below the critical density, which predicts an ever expanding, or *open universe*. Additional support for an open universe comes from studies that indicate the universe is expanding faster now than in the past. Hence, the view currently favored by most cosmologists is an expanding universe with no ending point.

However, the methods used to determine the density of the universe have substantial uncertainties. It is possible that previously undetected matter (dark matter) exists in great quantities in the universe. *Dark matter* may sound very mysterious, even sinister, but all that the term means is that there may be matter out there that does not interact with electromagnetic radiation. Recall that almost all the information about the universe comes to us as light. If there is a form of matter that does not interact with light, we cannot "see" it, and it would be dark. However, all is not lost. It is possible that dark matter will show itself by gravitational interactions with the type of matter that we are familiar with. Many astronomers are presently looking for these interactions. If there is enough dark matter in the universe, the universe could, in fact, collapse in the "big crunch." Consider the following phrase as astronomers search for dark matter— "*Absence of evidence is not evidence of absence.*"

Although the light released in the big bang had very high energy and very short wavelengths, the expansion of the universe should have stretched out the waves so that today they would be "seen" as long-wavelength radio waves. In 1965 this radiation was detected and found to fill the entire visible universe just as predicted. Most cosmologists consider this strong evidence for the big bang theory.

The End of the Universe

If the universe began with a big bang, how will it end? One possibility is that the universe will expand forever. In this scenario, the stars will slowly burn out, being replaced by invisible degenerate matter and black holes that travel outward through an endless, dark, cold universe. The other possibility is that the outward flight of the galaxies will slow and eventually stop due to gravity. Gravitational contraction

THE CHAPTER IN REVIEW

• One method for determining the distance to a star is to use a measurement called *stellar parallax*, the extremely slight back-and-forth shifting in a nearby star's position due to the orbital motion of Earth. *The farther away a star is, the less its parallax.* A unit used to express stellar distance is the *light-year*, the distance light travels in a year, which is about 9.5 trillion kilometers (5.8 trillion miles).

• The intrinsic properties of stars include *brightness, color, temperature, mass,* and *size.* Three factors control the brightness of a star as seen from Earth: how big it is, how hot it is, and how far away it is. *Magnitude* is the measure of a star's brightness. *Apparent magnitude* is how bright a star appears when viewed from Earth. *Absolute magnitude* is the "true" brightness of a star if it were at a standard distance of about 32.6 light-years. The difference between the two magnitudes is directly related to a star's distance. Color is a manifestation of a star's temperature. Very hot stars (surface temperatures above 30,000 K) appear blue; red stars

are much cooler (surface temperatures generally less than 3000 K). Stars with surface temperatures between 5000 and 6000 K appear yellow, like our Sun. The center of mass of orbiting *binary stars* (two stars revolving around a common center of mass under their mutual gravitational attraction) is used to determine the mass of the individual stars in a binary system.

• *Variable stars* fluctuate in brightness. Some, called *pulsating variables*, fluctuate regularly in brightness by expanding and contracting in size. When a star explosively brightens, it is called a *nova*. During the outburst, the outer layer of the star is ejected at high speed. After reaching maximum brightness in a few days, the nova slowly returns in a year or so to its original brightness.

• A *Hertzsprung-Russell diagram* is constructed by plotting the absolute magnitudes and temperatures of stars on a graph. A great deal about the sizes of stars can be learned from H-R diagrams. Stars located in the upper-right position of an H-R diagram are called *giants*, luminous stars of large radius. *Supergiants* are very large. Very small *white dwarf* stars are located in the lower-central portion of an H-R diagram. Ninety percent of all stars, called *main-sequence stars*, are in a band that runs from the upper-left corner to the lower-right corner of an H-R diagram.

• New stars are born out of enormous accumulations of dust and gases, called *nebula*, that are scattered between existing stars. A *bright nebula* glows because the matter is close to a very hot (blue) star. The two main types of bright nebulae are *emission nebulae* (which derive their visible light from the fluorescence of the ultraviolet light from a star in or near the nebula) and *reflection nebulae* (relatively dense dust clouds in interstellar space that are illuminated by reflecting the light of nearby stars). When a nebula is not close enough to a bright star to be illuminated, it is referred to as a *dark nebula*.

• Stars are born when their nuclear furnaces are ignited by the unimaginable pressures and temperatures in collapsing nebulae. New stars not yet hot enough for nuclear fusion are called *protostars*. When collapse causes the core of a protostar to reach a temperature of at least 10 million K, the fusion of hydrogen nuclei into helium nuclei begins a process called *hydrogen burning*. The opposing forces acting on a star are *gravity* trying to contract it and *gas pressure* (*thermal nuclear energy*) trying to expand it. When the two forces are balanced, the star becomes a stable *main-sequence star*. When the hydrogen in a star's core is consumed, its outer envelope expands enormously and a *red giant* star, hundreds to thousands of times larger than its main-sequence size, forms. When all the usable nuclear fuel in these giants is exhausted and gravity takes over, the stellar remnant collapses into a small, dense body.

• The *final fate of a star is determined by its mass*. Stars with less than one-half the mass of the Sun collapse into hot, dense *white dwarf* stars. Medium-mass stars, like the Sun, become red giants, collapse, and end up as white dwarf stars, often surrounded by expanding spherical clouds of glowing gas called *planetary nebulae*. Massive stars terminate in a brilliant explosion called a *supernova*. Supernovae events can produce small, extremely dense *neutron stars*, composed entirely of subatomic particles called neutrons, or even smaller and more dense *black holes*, objects that have such immense gravity that light cannot escape their surface.

• The *Milky Way Galaxy* is a large, disk-shaped *spiral galaxy* about 100,000 light-years wide and about 10,000 light-years thick at the center. There are three distinct *spiral arms* of stars, with some showing splintering. The Sun is positioned in one of these arms about two-thirds of the way from the galactic center, at a distance of about 30,000 light-years. Surrounding the galactic disk is a nearly spherical halo made of very tenuous gas and numerous *globular clusters* (nearly spherically shaped groups of densely packed stars).

• The various types of galaxies include (1) *irregular galaxies*, which lack symmetry and account for only 10 percent of the known galaxies; (2) *spiral galaxies*, which are typically disk-shaped with a somewhat greater concentration of stars near their centers, often containing arms of stars extending from their central nucleus; and (3) *elliptical galaxies*, the most abundant type, which have an ellipsoidal shape that ranges to nearly spherical and that lack spiral arms.

• Galaxies are not randomly distributed throughout the universe. They are grouped in *galactic clusters*, some containing thousands of galaxies. Our own, called the *Local Group*, contains at least 28 galaxies.

• By applying the *Doppler effect* (the apparent change in wavelength of radiation caused by the motions of the source and the observer) to the light of galaxies, galactic motion can be determined. Most galaxies have Doppler shifts toward the red end of the spectrum, indicating increasing distance. The amount of Doppler shift is dependent on the velocity at which the object is moving. Because the most distant galaxies have the greatest red shifts, Edwin Hubble concluded in the early 1900s that they were retreating from us with greater recessional velocities than were more nearby galaxies. It was soon realized that an *expanding universe* can adequately account for the observed red shifts.

• The realizations that the universe is expanding led to the widely accepted *big bang theory*. According to this theory, the entire universe was at one time confined in a dense, hot, supermassive concentration. Almost 14 billion years ago, a cataclysmic explosion hurled this material in all directions, creating all matter and space. Eventually the ejected masses of gas cooled and condensed, forming the stellar systems we now observe fleeing from their place of origin.

KEY TERMS

absolute magnitude (p. 460)

apparent magnitude (p. 459)

barred spiral galaxy (p. 474)

big bang theory (p. 476)

black hole (p. 471)

bright nebula (p. 464)

cosmology (p. 475)

dark nebula (p. 465)

degenerate matter (p. 469)

elliptical galaxy (p. 474)

emission nebula (p. 464)

eruptive variables (p. 461)

galactic cluster (p. 475)

Hertzsprung-Russell (H-R) diagram (p. 462)

Hubble's law (p. 476)

hydrogen burning (p. 465)

interstellar dust (p. 464)

irregular galaxy (p. 474)

light-year (p. 459)

Local Group (p. 475)

magnitude (p. 459)

main-sequence stars (p. 462)

nebula (p. 464)

neutron star (p. 470)

nova (p. 461)

planetary nebula (p. 468)

protostar (p. 465)

pulsar (p. 470)

pulsating variables (p. 461)

red giant (p. 462)

reflection nebula (p. 464)

spiral galaxy (p. 474)

stellar parallax (p. 458)

supergiant (p. 463)

supernova (p. 461)

visual binary (p. 461)

white dwarf (p. 463)

QUESTIONS FOR REVIEW

1. How far away in light-years is our nearest stellar neighbor, Proxima Centauri? Convert your answer to kilometers.

2. What is the most basic method of determining stellar distances?

3. Explain the difference between a star's apparent and absolute magnitudes. Which one is an intrinsic property of a star?

4. Which star is the most luminous, one having an absolute magnitude of five, or one with an absolute magnitude of ten?

5. What information about a star can be determined from its color?

6. What color are the hottest stars? Medium-temperature stars like the Sun? Coolest stars?

7. Which property of a star can be determined from binary-star systems?

8. Make a generalization relating the mass and luminosity of main-sequence stars.

9. The disk of a star cannot be resolved telescopically. Explain the method that astronomers use to estimate the size of stars.

10. Where on an H-R diagram does a star spend most of its lifetime?

11. How does the Sun compare in size and brightness to other main-sequence stars?

12. What role does interstellar matter play in stellar evolution?

13. Compare a bright nebula and a dark nebula.

14. What element is the fuel for main-sequence stars?

15. What causes a star to become a giant?

16. Why are less massive stars thought to age more slowly than more massive stars, even though they have much less "fuel"?

17. Enumerate the steps thought to be involved in the evolution of Sun-like stars.

18. What is the final state of a low-mass (red) main-sequence star?

19. What is the final state of a medium-mass (Sun-like) star?

20. How do the "lives" of the most massive stars end? What are the two possible products of this event?

21. Describe the general structure of the Milky Way Galaxy.

22. Compare the three general types of galaxies.

23. Explain why astronomers consider elliptical galaxies more abundant than spiral galaxies, even though more spiral galaxies have been sighted.

24. How did Edwin Hubble determine that the Andromeda Galaxy is located beyond the Milky Way?

25. What evidence supports the big bang theory?

COMPANION WEBSITE

The *Foundations of Earth Science* Website uses the resources and flexibility of the Internet to aid in your study of the topics in this chapter. Written and developed by the authors and other Earth science instructors, this site will help improve your understanding of Earth science. Visit **www.mygeoscienceplace.com** in order to:

- **Review** key chapter concepts.
- **Read** with links to the ebook and to chapter-specific web resources.

- **Visualize** and comprehend challenging topics using learning activities in *GEODe: Earth Science*.
- **Test** yourself with online quizzes.

A METRIC AND ENGLISH UNITS COMPARED

UNITS

1 kilometer (km)	= 1000 meters (m)
1 meter (m)	= 100 centimeters (cm)
1 centimeter (cm)	= 0.39 inch (in.)
1 mile (mi)	= 5280 feet (ft)
1 foot (ft)	= 12 inches (in.)
1 inch (in.)	= 2.54 centimeters (cm)
1 square mile (mi^2)	= 640 acres (a)
1 kilogram (kg)	= 1000 grams (g)
1 pound (lb)	= 16 ounces (oz)
1 fathom	= 6 feet (ft)

CONVERSIONS

When you want to convert:	multiply by:	to find:
Length		
inches	2.54	centimeters
centimeters	0.39	inches
feet	0.30	meters
meters	3.28	feet
yards	0.91	meters
meters	1.09	yards
miles	1.61	kilometers
kilometers	0.62	miles
Area		
square inches	6.45	square centimeters
square centimeters	0.15	square inches
square feet	0.09	square meters
square meters	10.76	square feet
square miles	2.59	square kilometers
square kilometers	0.39	square miles
Volume		
cubic inches	16.38	cubic centimeters
cubic centimeters	0.06	cubic inches
cubic feet	0.028	cubic meters
cubic meters	35.3	cubic feet
cubic miles	4.17	cubic kilometers
cubic kilometers	0.24	cubic miles
liters	1.06	quarts
liters	0.26	gallons
gallons	3.78	liters
Masses and Weights		
ounces	20.33	grams
grams	0.035	ounces
pounds	0.45	kilograms
kilograms	2.205	pounds

Temperature

When you want to convert degrees Fahrenheit (°F) to degrees Celsius (°C), subtract 32 degrees and divide by 1.8.

When you want to convert degrees Celsius (°C) to degrees Fahrenheit (°F), multiply by 1.8 and add 32 degrees.

When you want to convert degrees Celsius (°C) to kelvins (K), delete the degree symbol and add 273. When you want to convert kelvins (K) to degrees Celsius (°C), add the degree symbol and subtract 273.

FIGURE A.1   Temperature scales.

B MINERAL IDENTIFICATION KEY

Group I Metallic Luster

Hardness	Streak	Other Diagnostic Properties	Name (Chemical Composition)
Harder than glass	Black streak	Black; magnetic; hardness = 6; specific gravity = 5.2; often granular	Magnetite (Fe_3O_4)
	Greenish-black streak	Brass yellow; hardness = 6; specific gravity = 5.2; generally an aggregate of cubic	Pyrite (FeS_2) fool's gold
	Red-brown streak	Gray or reddish brown; hardness = 5–6; specific gravity = 5; platy appearance	Hematite (Fe_2O_3)
Softer than glass	Greenish-black streak	Golden yellow; hardness = 4; specific gravity = 4.2; massive	Chalcopyrite ($CuFeS_2$)
	Gray-black streak	Silvery gray; hardness = 2.5; specific gravity = 7.6 (very heavy); good cubic cleavage	Galena (PbS)
	Yellow-brown streak	Yellow brown to dark brown; hardness variable (1–6); specific gravity = 3.5–4; often found in rounded masses; earthy appearance	Limonite ($Fe_2O_3 \cdot H_2O$)
	Gray-black streak	Black to bronze; tarnishes to purples and greens; hardness = 3; specific gravity = 5; massive	Bornite (Cu_5FeS_4)
Softer than your fingernail	Dark gray streak	Silvery gray; hardness = 1 (very soft); specific gravity = 2.2; massive to platy; writes on paper (pencil lead); feels greasy	Graphite (C)

Group II Nonmetallic Luster (Dark-Colored)

Hardness	Cleavage	Other Diagnostic Properties	Name (Chemical Composition)
Harder than glass	Cleavage present	Black to greenish black; hardness = 5–6; specific gravity = 3.4; fair cleavage, two directions at nearly 90 degrees	Augite (Ca, Mg, Fe, Al silicate)
		Black to greenish black; hardness = 5–6; specific gravity = 3.2; fair cleavage, two directions at nearly 60 degrees and 120 degrees	Hornblende (Ca, Na, Mg, Fe, OH, Al silicate)
		Red to reddish brown; hardness = 6.5–7.5; conchoidal fracture; glassy luster	Garnet (Fe, Mg, Ca, Al silicate)
	Cleavage not prominent	Gray to brown; hardness = 9; specific gravity = 4; hexagonal crystals common	Corundum (Al_2O_3)
		Dark brown to black; hardness = 7; conchoidal fracture; glassy luster	Smoky quartz (SiO_2)
		Olive green; hardness = 6.5–7; small glassy grains	Olivine $(Mg,Fe)_2 SiO_4$
	Cleavage present	Yellow brown to black; hardness = 4; good cleavage in six directions; light yellow streak that has the smell of sulfur	Sphalerite (ZnS)
Softer than glass		Dark brown to black; hardness = 2.5–3; excellent cleavage in one direction; elastic in thin sheets; black mica	Biotite (K, Mg, Fe, OH, Al silicate)

(continued)

Group II Nonmetallic Luster (Dark-Colored) (Continued)

Hardness	Cleavage	Other Diagnostic Properties	Name (Chemical Composition)
	Cleavage absent	Generally tarnished to brown or green; hardness = 2.5; specific gravity = 9; massive	Native copper (Cu)
	Cleavage not prominent	Reddish brown; hardness = 1–5; specific gravity = 4–5; red streak; earthy appearance	Hematite (Fe_2O_3)
Softer than your fingernail		Yellow brown; hardness = 1–3; specific gravity = 3.5; earthy appearance; powders easily	Limonite ($Fe_2O_3 \cdot H_2O$)

Group III Nonmetallic Luster (Light Colored)

Hardness	Cleavage	Other Diagnostic Properties	Name (Chemical Composition)
	Cleavage present	Salmon colored or white to gray; hardness = 6; specific gravity = 2.6; two directions of cleavage at nearly right angles	Potassium feldspar ($KAlSi_3O_8$)
Harder than glass			Plagioclase feldspar ($NaAlSi_3O_8$ to $CaAl_2Si_2O_8$)
	Cleavage absent	Any color; hardness = 7; specific gravity = 2.65; conchoidal fracture; glassy appearance; varieties; milky, rose, smoky, amethyst (violet)	Quartz (SiO_2)
		White, yellowish to colorless; hardness = 3; three directions of cleavage at 75 degrees (rhombohedral); effervesces in HCl; often transparent	Calcite ($CaCO_3$)
Softer than glass	Cleavage present	White to colorless; hardness = 2.5; three directions of cleavage at 90 degrees (cubic); salty taste	Halite (NaCl)
		Yellow, purple, green, colorless; hardness = 4; white streak; translucent to transparent; four directions of cleavage	Fluorite (CaF_2)
	Cleavage present	Colorless; hardness = 2–2.5; transparent and elastic in thin sheets; excellent cleavage in one direction; light mica	Muscovite (K, OH, Al silicate)
		White to transparent; hardness = 2; when in sheets, is flexible but not elastic; varieties: selenite (transparent, three directions of cleavage); satin spar (fibrous, silky luster); alabaster (aggregate of small crystals)	Gypsum ($CaSO_4 \cdot 2H_2O$)
Softer than your fingernail	Cleavage not prominent	White, pink, green; hardness = 1; forms in thin plates; soapy feel; pearly luster	Talc (Mg silicate)
		Yellow; hardness = 1–2.5	Sulfur (S)
		White; hardness = 2; smooth feel; earthy odor when moistened, has typical clay texture	Kaolinite (Hydrous Al silicate)
		Green; hardness = 2.5; fibrous; variety of serpentine	Asbestos (Mg, Al silicate)
		Pale to dark reddish brown; hardness = 1–3; dull luster; earthy; often contains spheroidal-shaped particles; not a true mineral	Bauxite (Hydrous Al oxide)

RELATIVE HUMIDITY AND DEW-POINT TABLES

Table C.1   Relative humidity (percent)

Dry bulb (°C)	Depression of Wet-Bulb Temperature (Dry-Bulb Temperature Minus Wet-Bulb Temperature = Depression of the Wet Bulb)																					
	1	2	3	4	5	6	7	8	9	10	11	12	13	14	15	16	17	18	19	20	21	22
−20	28																					
−18	40																					
−16	48	0																				
−14	55	11																				
−12	61	23																				
−10	66	33	0																			
−8	71	41	13																			
−6	73	48	20	0																		
−4	77	54	32	11																		
−2	79	58	37	20	1																	
0	81	63	45	28	11																	
2	83	67	51	36	20	6																
4	85	70	56	42	27	14																
6	86	72	59	46	35	22	10	0														
8	87	74	62	51	39	28	17	6														
10	88	76	65	54	43	33	24	13	4													
12	88	78	67	57	48	38	28	19	10	2												
14	89	79	69	60	50	41	33	25	16	8	1											
16	90	80	77	62	54	45	37	29	21	74	7	1										
18	91	81	72	64	56	48	40	33	26	19	12	6	0									
20	91	82	74	66	58	51	44	36	30	23	17	11	5									
22	92	83	75	68	60	53	46	40	33	27	21	15	10	4	0							
24	92	84	76	69	62	55	49	42	36	30	25	20	14	9	4	0						
26	92	85	77	70	64	57	51	45	39	34	28	23	18	13	9	5						
28	93	86	78	71	65	59	53	45	42	36	31	26	21	17	12	8	4					
30	93	86	79	72	66	61	55	49	44	39	34	29	25	20	16	12	8	4				
32	93	86	80	73	68	62	56	51	46	41	36	32	27	22	19	14	11	8	4			
34	93	86	81	74	69	63	58	52	48	43	38	34	30	26	22	18	14	11	8	5		
36	94	87	81	75	69	64	59	54	50	44	40	36	32	28	24	21	17	13	10	7	4	
38	94	87	82	76	70	66	60	55	51	46	42	38	34	30	26	23	20	16	13	10	7	5
40	94	89	82	76	71	67	61	57	52	48	44	40	36	33	29	25	22	19	16	13	10	7

Relative Humidity Values

*To determine the relative humidity, or dew point, find the air (dry-bulb) temperature on the vertical axis (far left) and the depression of the wet bulb on the horizontal axis (top). Where the two meet, the relative humidity (Table C.1) or dew point (Table C.2) is found. For example, when the dry-bulb temperature is 20°C and a wet-bulb temperature is 14°C, then the depression of the wet bulb is 6°C (20° − 14°C). From Table C.1, the relative humidity is 51 percent and from Table C.2, the dew point is 10°C.

Table C.2   Dew-point temperature (°C)*

Dry bulb (°C)   (Dry-Bulb Temperature Minus Wet-Bulb Temperature = Depression of the Wet Bulb)

Dry-Bulb (Air) Temperature

Dew-Point Values

Dry bulb (°C)	1	2	3	4	5	6	7	8	9	10	11	12	13	14	15	16	17	18	19	20	21	22
−20	−33																					
−18	−28																					
−16	−24																					
−14	−21	−36																				
−12	−18	−28																				
−10	−14	−22																				
−8	−12	−18	−29																			
−6	−10	−14	−22																			
−4	−7	−12	−17	−29																		
−2	−5	−8	−13	−20																		
0	−3	−6	−9	−15	−24																	
2	−1	−3	−6	−11	−17																	
4	1	−1	−4	−7	−11	−19																
6	4	1	−1	−4	−7	−13	−21															
8	6	3	1	−2	−5	−9	−14															
10	8	6	4	1	−2	−5	−9	−14	−18													
12	10	8	6	4	1	−2	−5	−9	−16													
14	12	11	9	6	4	1	−2	−5	−10	−17												
16	14	13	11	9	7	4	1	−1	−6	−10	−17											
18	16	15	13	11	9	7	4	2	−2	−5	−10	−19										
20	19	17	15	14	12	10	7	4	2	−2	−5	−10	−19									
22	21	19	17	16	74	12	10	8	5	3	−1	−5	−10	−19								
24	23	21	20	18	16	14	12	10	8	6	2	−1	−5	−10	−18							
26	25	23	22	20	18	17	15	13	11	9	6	3	0	−4	−9	−18						
28	27	25	24	22	27	19	17	16	14	11	9	7	4	1	−3	−9	−16					
30	29	27	26	24	23	21	19	18	16	14	12	70	8	5	1	−2	−8	−15				
32	31	29	28	27	25	24	22	21	19	17	15	13	11	8	5	2	−2	−7	−14			
34	33	31	30	29	27	26	24	23	21	20	18	16	14	12	9	6	3	−1	−5	−12	−29	
36	35	33	32	31	29	28	27	25	24	22	20	19	17	15	13	10	7	4	0	−4	−10	
38	37	35	34	33	32	30	29	28	26	25	23	21	19	17	15	13	11	8	5	1	−3	−9
40	39	37	36	35	34	32	31	30	28	37	25	24	22	20	18	16	14	12	9	6	2	−2

D EARTH'S GRID SYSTEM

A glance at any globe reveals a series of north–south and east–west lines that together make up Earth's grid system, a universally used scheme for locating points on Earth's surface. The north–south lines of the grid are called **meridians** and extend from pole to pole (**FIGURE D.1**). All are halves of great circles. A **great circle** is the largest possible circle that can be drawn on a globe; if a globe were sliced along one of these circles, it would be divided into two equal parts called **hemispheres**. By viewing a globe or Figure D.1, it can be seen that meridians are spaced farthest apart at the equator and converge toward the poles. The east–west lines (circles) of the grid are known as **parallels**. As their names imply, these circles are parallel to one another (Figure D.1). Although all meridians are parts of great circles, all parallels are not. In fact, only one parallel, the equator, is a great circle.

LATITUDE AND LONGITUDE

Latitude may be defined as distance, measured in degrees, *north* and *south* of the equator. Parallels are used to show latitude. Because all points that lie along the same parallel are an identical distance from the equator, they all have the same latitude designation. The latitude of the equator is

0 degrees, and the north and south poles lie 90 degrees N and 90 degrees S, respectively.

Longitude is defined as distance, measured in degrees, *east* and *west* of the zero or prime meridian. Because all meridians are identical, the choice of a zero line is obviously arbitrary. However, the meridian that passes through the Royal Observatory at Greenwich, England, is universally accepted as the reference meridian. Thus, the longitude for any place on the globe is measured east or west from this line. Longitude can vary from 0 degrees along the prime meridian to 180 degrees, halfway around the globe.

It is important to remember that when a location is specified, directions must be given—that is, north or south latitude and east or west longitude (**FIGURE D.2**). If this is not done, more than one point on the globe is being designated. The only exceptions, of course, are places that lie along the equator, the prime meridian, or the 180-degree meridian. Although it is not incorrect to use fractions, a degree of latitude or longitude is usually divided into minutes and seconds. A minute (') is 1/60 of a degree, and a second (") is 1/60 of a minute. When locating a place on a map, the degree of exactness will depend on the scale of the map. When using a small-scale world map or globe, it may be difficult to estimate latitude and longitude to the nearest whole degree or two. On the other hand, when a large-scale map of an area is used, it is often possible to estimate latitude and longitude to the nearest minute or second.

DISTANCE MEASUREMENT

The length of a degree of longitude depends on where the measurement is taken. At the equator, which is a great circle, a degree of east–west distance is equal to approximately 111 kilometers (69 miles). This figure is found by dividing Earth's circumference—40,075 kilometers (24,900 miles)—by 360. However, with an increase in latitude, the parallels become smaller, and the length of a degree of longitude diminishes (see Table D.1). Thus, at about latitude 60 degrees N and S, a degree of longitude has a value equal to about half of what it was at the equator.

As all meridians are halves of great circles, a degree of latitude is equal to about 111 kilometers (69 miles), just as is a degree of longitude along the equator. However, Earth is not a perfect sphere but is slightly flattened at the poles and bulges slightly at the equator. Because of this, there are small differences in the length of a degree of latitude.

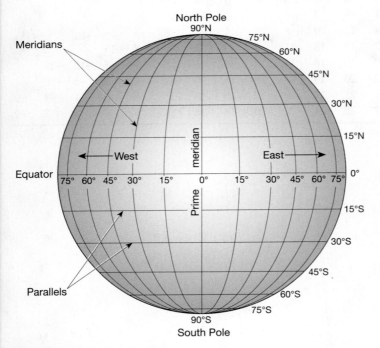

FIGURE D.1 Earth's grid system.

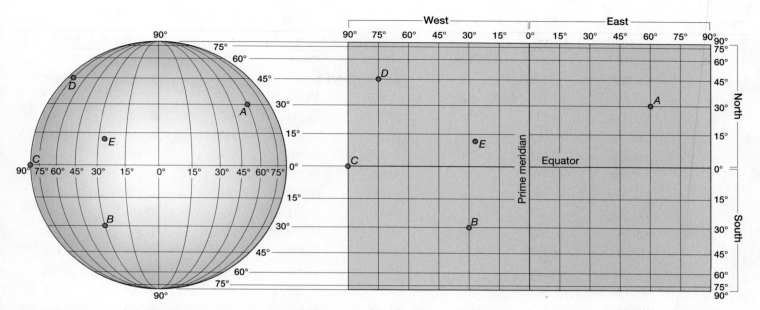

FIGURE D.2   Locating places using the grid system. For both diagrams: Point A is latitude 30 degrees N, longitude 60 degrees E; Point B is latitude 30 degrees S, longitude 30 degrees W; Point C is latitude 0 degrees, longitude 90 degrees W; Point D is latitude 45 degrees N, longitude 75 degrees W; Point E is approximately latitude 10 degrees N, longitude 25 degrees W.

Determining the shortest distance between two points on a globe can be done easily and fairly accurately using the "globe and string" method. The arc of a great circle is the shortest distance between two points on a sphere. To determine the great circle distance (as well as observe the great circle route) between two places, stretch the string between the locations in question. Then, measure the length of the string along the equator (since it is a great circle with degrees marked on it) to determine the number of degrees between the two points. To calculate the distance in kilometers or miles, simply multiply the number of degrees by 111 or 69, respectively.

Table D.1

°Lat.	Length of 1° Long. km	Length of 1° Long. miles	°Lat	Length of 1° Long. km	Length of 1° Long. miles	°Lat.	Length of 1° Long. km	Length of 1° Long. miles
0	111.367	69.172	30	96.528	59.955	60	55.825	34.674
1	111.349	69.161	31	95.545	59.345	61	54.131	33.622
2	111.298	69.129	32	94.533	58.716	62	52.422	62.560
3	111.214	69.077	33	93.493	58.070	63	50.696	31.488
4	111.096	69.004	34	92.425	57.407	64	48.954	30.406
5	110.945	68.910	35	91.327	56.725	65	47.196	29.314
6	110.760	68.795	36	90.203	56.027	66	45.426	28.215
7	110.543	68.660	37	89.051	55.311	67	43.639	27.105
8	110.290	68.503	38	87.871	54.578	68	41.841	25.988
9	110.003	68.325	39	86.665	53.829	69	40.028	24.862
10	109.686	68.128	40	85.431	53.063	70	38.204	23.729
11	109.333	67.909	41	84.171	52.280	71	36.368	22.589
12	108.949	67.670	42	82.886	51.482	72	34.520	21.441
13	108.530	67.410	43	81.575	50.668	73	32.662	20.287
14	108.079	67.130	44	80.241	49.839	74	30.793	19.126
15	107.596	66.830	45	78.880	48.994	75	28.914	17.959
16	107.079	66.509	46	77.497	48.135	76	27.029	16.788
17	106.530	66.168	47	76.089	47.260	77	25.134	15.611
18	105.949	65.807	48	74.659	46.372	78	23.229	14.428
19	105.337	65.427	49	73.203	45.468	79	21.320	13.242
20	104.692	65.026	50	71.727	44.551	80	19.402	12.051
21	104.014	64.605	51	70.228	43.620	81	17.480	10.857
22	103.306	64.165	52	68.708	42.676	82	15.551	9.659
23	102.565	63.705	53	67.168	41.719	83	13.617	8.458
24	101.795	63.227	54	65.604	40.748	84	11.681	7.255
25	100.994	62.729	55	64.022	39.765	85	9.739	6.049
26	100.160	62.211	56	62.420	38.770	86	7.796	4.842
27	99.297	61.675	57	60.798	37.763	87	5.849	3.633
28	98.405	61.121	58	59.159	36.745	88	3.899	2.422
29	97.481	60.547	59	57.501	35.715	89	1.950	1.211
30	96.528	59.955	60	55.825	34.674	90	0	0

GLOSSARY

Aa flow   A type of lava flow that has a jagged blocky surface.

Ablation   A general term for the loss of ice and snow from a glacier.

Abrasion   The grinding and scraping of a rock surface by the friction and impact of rock particles carried by water, wind, or ice.

Absolute instability   The condition of air that has an environmental lapse rate that is greater than the dry adiabatic rate (1°C per 100 meters).

Absolute magnitude   The apparent brightness of a star if it were viewed from a distance of 10 parsecs (32.6 light-years). Used to compare the true brightness of stars.

Absolute stability   The condition of air that has an environmental lapse rate that is less than the wet adiabatic rate.

Abyssal plain   Very level area of the deep-ocean floor, usually lying at the foot of the continental rise.

Accretionary wedge   A large wedge-shaped mass of sediment that accumulates in subduction zones. Here sediment is scraped from the subducting oceanic plate and accreted to the overriding crustal block.

Active continental margin   Usually narrow and consisting of highly deformed sediments. They occur where oceanic lithosphere is being subducted beneath the margin of a continent.

Adiabatic temperature change   Cooling or warming of air caused when air is allowed to expand or is compressed, not because heat is added or subtracted.

Advection fog   A fog formed when warm, moist air is blown over a cool surface.

Air   The mixture of gases and particles that make up Earth's atmosphere. Nitrogen and oxygen are most abundant.

Air mass   A large body of air that is characterized by a sameness of temperature and humidity.

Air-mass weather   The conditions experienced in an area as an air mass passes over it. Because air masses are large and fairly homogeneous, air-mass weather will be fairly constant and may last for several days.

Air pressure   Force exerted by the weight of the air above.

Albedo   The reflectivity of a substance, usually expressed as a percentage of the incident radiation reflected.

Alluvial fan   A fan-shaped deposit of sediment formed when a stream's slope is abruptly reduced.

Alluvium   Unconsolidated sediment deposited by a stream.

Alpine glacier   A glacier confined to a mountain valley, which in most instances had previously been a stream valley.

Andesetic composition   See *Intermediate composition.*

Aneroid barometer   An instrument for measuring air pressure that consists of evacuated metal chambers that are very sensitive to variations in air pressure.

Angular unconformity   An unconformity in which the strata below dip at an angle different from that of the beds above.

Anticline   A fold in sedimentary strata that resembles an arch.

Anticyclone   A high-pressure center characterized by a clockwise flow of air in the Northern Hemisphere.

Apparent magnitude   The brightness of a star when viewed from Earth.

Aquicludes   Impermeable beds that hinder or prevent groundwater movement.

Aquifer   Rock or soil through which groundwater moves easily.

Arête   A narrow knifelike ridge separating two adjacent glaciated valleys.

Artesian well   A well in which the water rises above the level where it was initially encountered.

Asteroids   Thousands of small planetlike bodies, ranging in size from a few hundred kilometers to less than a kilometer, whose orbits lie mainly between those of Mars and Jupiter.

Asthenosphere   A subdivision of the mantle situated below the lithosphere. This zone of weak material exists below a depth of about 100 kilometers and in some regions extends as deep as 700 kilometers. The rock within this zone is easily deformed.

Astronomical unit (AU)   Average distance from Earth to the Sun; 1.5×10^8 km, or 93×10^6 miles.

Astronomy   The scientific study of the universe; it includes the observation and interpretation of celestial bodies and phenomena.

Atmosphere   The gaseous portion of a planet; the planet's envelope of air. One of the traditional subdivisions of Earth's physical environment.

Atoll   A continuous or broken ring of coral reef surrounding a central lagoon.

Atom   The smallest particle that exists as an element.

Atomic number   The number of protons in the nucleus of an atom.

Backswamp   A poorly drained area on a floodplain that results when natural levees are present.

Bajada   An apron of sediment along a mountain front created by the coalescence of alluvial fans.

Barograph   A recording barometer.

Barometer   An instrument that measures atmospheric pressure.

Barometric tendency   See *Pressure tendency.*

Barred spiral   A galaxy having straight arms extending from its nucleus.

Barrier island   A low, elongated ridge of sand that parallels the coast.

Basaltic composition   A compositional group of igneous rocks in which the rock contains substantial dark silicate minerals and calcium-rich plagioclase feldspar.

Base level   The level below which a stream cannot erode.

Basin   A circular downfolded structure.

Batholith   A large mass of igneous rock that formed when magma was emplaced at depth, crystallized, and subsequently exposed by erosion.

Bathymetry   The measurement of ocean depths and the charting of the topography of the ocean floor.

Baymouth bar   A sandbar that completely crosses a bay, sealing it off from the open ocean.

Beach drift   The transport of sediment in a zigzag pattern along a beach caused by the uprush of water from obliquely breaking waves.

Beach nourishment   Large quantities of sand added to the beach system to offset losses caused by wave erosion.

Bed load   Sediment that is carried by a stream along the bottom of its channel.

Big bang theory   The theory that proposes that the universe originated as a single mass, which subsequently exploded.

Biogenous sediment   Seafloor sediments consisting of material of marine-organic origin.

Biosphere   The totality of life on Earth; the parts of the lithosphere, hydrosphere, and atmosphere in which living organisms can be found.

Black hole   A massive star that has collapsed to such a small volume that its gravity prevents the escape of all radiation.

Blowout (deflation hollow)   A depression excavated by the wind in easily eroded deposits.

Bowen's reaction series   A concept proposed by N. L. Bowen that illustrates the relationships between magma and the minerals crystallizing from it during the formation of igneous rocks.

Breakwater   A structure protecting a nearshore area from breaking waves.

Bright nebula   A cloud of glowing gas excited by ultraviolet radiation from hot stars.

Brittle failure   The loss of strength by a material usually in the form of sudden fracturing.

Caldera   A large depression typically caused by collapse or ejection of the summit area of a volcano.

Capacity   The total amount of sediment a stream is able to transport.

Catastrophism The concept that Earth was shaped by catastrophic events of a short-term nature.

Cavern A naturally formed underground chamber or series of chambers most commonly produced by solution activity in limestone.

Celestial sphere An imaginary hollow sphere upon which the ancients believed the stars were hung and carried around Earth.

Cenozoic era A time span on the geologic calendar beginning about 66 million years ago following the Mesozoic era.

Chemical bond A strong attractive force that exists between atoms in a substance. It involves the transfer or sharing of electrons that allows each atom to attain a full valence shell.

Chemical sedimentary rock Sedimentary rock consisting of material that was precipitated from water by either inorganic or organic means.

Chinook A wind blowing down the leeward side of a mountain and warming by compression.

Cinder cone A rather small volcano built primarily of pyroclastics ejected from a single vent.

Circle of illumination The great circle that separates daylight from darkness.

Cirque An amphitheater-shaped basin at the head of a glaciated valley produced by frost wedging and plucking.

Cirrus One of three basic cloud forms; also one of the three high cloud types. They are thin, delicate ice-crystal clouds often appearing as veil-like patches or thin, wispy fibers.

Cleavage The tendency of a mineral to break along planes of weak bonding.

Climate A description of aggregate weather conditions; the sum of all statistical weather information that helps describe a place or region.

Cloud A form of condensation best described as a dense concentration of suspended water droplets or tiny ice crystals.

Clouds of vertical development A cloud that has its base in the low height range but extends upward into the middle or high altitudes.

Coarse-grained texture An igneous rock texture in which the crystals are roughly equal in size and large enough so that individual minerals can be identified with the unaided eye.

Cold front A front along which a cold air mass thrusts beneath a warmer air mass.

Color An obvious mineral characteristic that is often unreliable as a diagnostic property.

Columnar joints A pattern of cracks that form during cooling of molten rock to generate columns that are generally six-sided.

Comet A small body that generally revolves around the Sun in an elongated orbit.

Competence A measure of the largest particle a stream can transport; a factor dependent on velocity.

Composite cone A volcano composed of both lava flows and pyroclastic material.

Compound A substance formed by the chemical combination of two or more elements in definite proportions and usually having properties different from those of its constituent elements.

Concordant A term used to describe intrusive igneous masses that form parallel to the bedding of the surrounding rock.

Condensation The change of state from a gas to a liquid.

Condensation nuclei Tiny bits of particulate matter that serve as surfaces on which water vapor condenses.

Conditional instability The condition of moist air with an environmental lapse rate between the dry and wet adiabatic rates.

Conduction The transfer of heat through matter by molecular activity. Energy is transferred through collisions from one molecule to another.

Conduit A pipelike opening through which magma moves toward Earth's surface. It terminates at a surface opening called a vent.

Cone of depression A cone-shaped depression in the water table immediately surrounding a well.

Confined aquifer An aquifer that has impermeable layers (aquitards) both above and below.

Conformable Layers of rock deposited without interruption.

Contact metamorphism Changes in rock caused by the heat from a nearby magma body.

Continental (c) air mass An air mass that forms over land; it is normally relatively dry.

Continental drift theory A theory that originally proposed that the continents are rafted about. It has essentially been replaced by the plate tectonics theory.

Continental margin That portion of the seafloor adjacent to the continents. It may include the continental shelf, continental slope, and continental rise.

Continental rift A linear zone along which continental lithosphere stretches and pulls apart. Its creation may mark the beginning of a new ocean basin.

Continental rise The gently sloping surface at the base of the continental slope.

Continental shelf The gently sloping submerged portion of the continental margin extending from the shoreline to the continental slope.

Continental slope The steep gradient that leads to the deep-ocean floor and marks the seaward edge of the continental shelf.

Continental volcanic arc Mountains formed in part by igneous activity associated with the subduction of oceanic lithosphere beneath a continent. Examples include the Andes and the Cascades.

Convection The transfer of heat by the movement of a mass or substance. It can take place only in fluids.

Convergence The condition that exists when the distribution of winds within a given area results in a net horizontal inflow of air into the area. Since convergence at lower levels is associated with an upward movement of air, areas of convergent winds are regions favorable to cloud formation and precipitation.

Convergent plate boundary A boundary in which two plates move together, causing one of the slabs of lithosphere to be consumed into the mantle as it descends beneath an overriding plate.

Coral reef Structure formed in a warm, shallow, sunlit ocean environment that consists primarily of the calcite-rich remains of corals as well as the limy secretions of algae and the hard parts of many other small organisms.

Core The innermost layer of Earth based on composition. It is thought to be largely an iron-nickel alloy with minor amounts of oxygen, silicon, and sulfur.

Coriolis force (effect) The deflective force of Earth's rotation on all free-moving objects, including the atmosphere and oceans. Deflection is to the right in the Northern Hemisphere and to the left in the Southern Hemisphere.

Correlation Establishing the equivalence of rocks of similar age in different areas.

Crater The depression at the summit of a volcano, or that which is produced by a meteorite impact.

Creep The slow downhill movement of soil and regolith.

Crevasse A deep crack in the brittle surface of a glacier.

Cross-bedding Structure in which relatively thin layers are inclined at an angle to the main bedding. Formed by currents of wind or water.

Cross-cutting A principle of relative dating. A rock or fault is younger than any rock (or fault) through which it cuts.

Crust The very thin outermost layer of Earth.

Crystal form The external appearance of a mineral as determined by its internal arrangement of atoms.

Crystallization The formation and growth of a crystalline solid from a liquid or gas.

Crystal settling During the crystallization of magma, the earlier-formed minerals are denser than the liquid portion and settle to the bottom of the magma chamber.

Cumulus   One of three basic cloud forms; also the name given one of the clouds of vertical development. Cumulus are billowy individual cloud masses that often have flat bases.

Cup anemometer   An instrument used to determine wind speed.

Curie point   The temperature above which a material loses its magnetization.

Cutoff   A short channel segment created when a river erodes through the narrow neck of land between meanders.

Cyclone   A low-pressure center characterized by a counterclockwise flow of air in the Northern Hemisphere.

Dark nebula   A cloud of interstellar dust that obscures the light of more distant stars and appears as an opaque curtain.

Deep-ocean basin   The portion of the seafloor that lies between the continental margin and the oceanic ridge. This region comprises almost 30 percent of Earth's surface.

Deep-ocean trench   A narrow, elongated depression on the floor of the ocean.

Deep-sea fan   A cone-shaped deposit at the base of the continental slope. The sediment is transported to the fan by turbidity currents that follow submarine canyons.

Deflation   The lifting and removal of loose material by wind.

Deformation   General term for the processes of folding, faulting, shearing, compression, or extension of rocks.

Degenerate matter   Incomprehensibly dense material formed when stars collapse and form a white dwarf.

Delta   An accumulation of sediment formed where a stream enters a lake or ocean.

Dendritic pattern   A stream system that resembles the pattern of a branching tree.

Density   The weight-per-unit volume of a particular material.

Deposition   The process by which water vapor is changed directly to a solid without passing through the liquid state.

Desalination   The removal of salts and other chemicals from seawater.

Desert   One of the two types of dry climate; the driest of the dry climates.

Desert pavement   A layer of coarse pebbles and gravel created when wind removed the finer material.

Detrital sedimentary rock   Rock formed from the accumulation of material that originated and was transported in the form of solid particles derived from both mechanical and chemical weathering.

Dew point   The temperature to which air has to be cooled in order to reach saturation.

Dike   A tabular-shaped intrusive igneous feature that cuts through the surrounding rock.

Dip-slip fault   A fault in which the movement is parallel to the dip of the fault.

Discharge   The quantity of water in a stream that passes a given point in a period of time.

Disconformity   A type of unconformity in which the beds above and below are parallel.

Discordant   A term used to describe plutons that cut across existing rock structures, such as bedding planes.

Dissolved load   That portion of a stream's load carried in solution.

Distributary   A section of a stream that leaves the main flow.

Diurnal tidal pattern   A tidal pattern exhibiting one high tide and one low tide during a tidal day; a daily tide.

Diurnal tide   Tides characterized by a single high and low water height each tidal day.

Divergence   The condition that exists when the distribution of winds within a given area results in a net horizontal outflow of air from the region. In divergence at lower levels the resulting deficit is compensated for by a downward movement of air from aloft; hence, areas of divergent winds are unfavorable to cloud formation and precipitation.

Divergent plate boundary   A region where the rigid plates are moving apart, typified by the mid-oceanic ridges.

Divide   An imaginary line that separates the drainage of two streams; often found along a ridge.

Dome   A roughly circular upfolded structure similar to an anticline.

Doppler effect   The apparent change in wavelength of radiation caused by the relative motions of the source and the observer.

Doppler radar   In addition to the tasks performed by conventional radar, this new generation of weather radar can detect motion directly and hence greatly improve tornado and severe storm warnings.

Drainage basin   The land area that contributes water to a stream.

Drawdown   The difference in height between the bottom of a cone of depression and the original height of the water table.

Drift   See *Glacial drift*.

Drumlin   A streamlined asymmetrical hill composed of glacial till. The steep side of the hill faces the direction from which the ice advanced.

Dry adiabatic rate   The rate of adiabatic cooling or warming in unsaturated air. The rate of temperature change is 1°C per 100 meters.

Ductile deformation   A type of solid-state flow that produces a change in the size and shape of a rock body without fracturing. Occurs at depths where temperatures and confining pressures are high.

Dune   A hill or ridge of wind-deposited sand.

Earthquake   The vibration of Earth produced by the rapid release of energy.

Echo sounder   An instrument used to determine the depth of water by measuring the time interval between emission of a sound signal and the return of its echo from the bottom.

Elastic rebound   The sudden release of stored strain in rocks that results in movement along a fault.

Electron   A negatively charged subatomic particle that has a negligible mass and is found outside an atom's nucleus.

Element   A substance that cannot be decomposed into simpler substances by ordinary chemical or physical means.

Elements of weather and climate   Those quantities or properties of the atmosphere that are measured regularly and that are used to express the nature of weather and climate.

Elliptical galaxy   A galaxy that is round or elliptical in outline. It contains little gas and dust, no disk or spiral arms, and few hot, bright stars.

Emergent coast   A coast where land that was formerly below sea level has been exposed either because of crustal uplift or a drop in sea level or both.

Emission nebula   A gaseous nebula that derives its visible light from the fluorescence of ultraviolet light from a star in or near the nebula.

End moraine   A ridge of till marking a former position on the front of a glacier.

Entrenched meander   A meander cut into bedrock when uplifting rejuvenated a meandering stream.

Environmental lapse rate   The rate of temperature decrease with increasing height in the troposphere.

Eon   The largest time unit on the geologic time scale, next in order of magnitude above era.

Ephemeral stream   A stream that is usually dry because it carries water only in response to specific episodes of rainfall. Most desert streams are of this type.

Epicenter   The location on Earth's surface that lies directly above the forces of an earthquake.

Epoch   A unit of the geologic calendar that is a subdivision of a period.

Equatorial low   A belt of low pressure lying near the equator and between the subtropical highs.

Equatorial system   A method of locating stellar objects much like the coordinate system used on Earth's surface.

Equinox (spring or autumnal)   The time when the vertical rays of the Sun are striking the equator. The length of daylight and darkness is equal at all latitudes at equinox.

Era A major division on the geologic calendar; eras are divided into shorter units called periods.

Erosion The incorporation and transportation of material by a mobile agent, such as water, wind, or ice.

Eruption column Buoyant plumes of hot, ash-laden gases that can extend thousands of meters into the atmosphere.

Escape velocity The initial velocity an object needs to escape from the surface of a celestial body.

Esker Sinuous ridge composed largely of sand and gravel deposited by a stream flowing in a tunnel beneath a glacier near its terminus.

Estuary A funnel-shaped inlet of the sea that formed when a rise in sea level or subsidence of land caused the mouth of a river to be flooded.

Evaporation The process of converting a liquid to a gas.

Evaporite A sedimentary rock formed of material deposited from solution by evaporation of the water.

External process Process such as weathering, mass wasting, or erosion that is powered by the Sun and transforms solid rock into sediment.

Extrusive Igneous activity that occurs outside the crust.

Eye A zone of scattered clouds and calm averaging about 20 kilometers in diameter at the center of a hurricane.

Eye wall The doughnut-shaped area of intense cumulonimbus development and very strong winds that surrounds the eye of a hurricane.

Fault A break in a rock mass along which movement has occurred.

Fault-block mountain A mountain formed by the displacement of rock along a fault.

Fault scarp A cliff created by movement along a fault. It represents the exposed surface of the fault prior to modification by weathering and erosion.

Felsic composition See *Granitic composition.*

Fetch The distance that the wind has traveled across the open water.

Fine-grained texture A texture of igneous rocks in which the crystals are too small for individual minerals to be distinguished with the unaided eye.

Fiord A steep-sided inlet of the sea formed when a glacial trough was partially submerged.

Fissure A crack in rock along which there is a distinct separation.

Fissure eruption An eruption in which lava is extruded from narrow fractures or cracks in the crust.

Flood The overflow of a stream channel that occurs when discharge exceeds the channel's capacity. The most common and destructive geologic hazard.

Flood basalts Flows of basaltic lava that issue from numerous cracks or fissures and commonly cover extensive areas to thicknesses of hundreds of meters.

Floodplain The flat, low-lying portion of a stream valley subject to periodic inundation.

Focus (earthquake) The zone within Earth where rock displacement produces an earthquake.

Fog A cloud with its base at or very near Earth's surface.

Fold A bent rock layer or series of layers that were originally horizontal and subsequently deformed.

Foliated texture A texture of metamorphic rocks that gives the rock a layered appearance.

Foliation A term for a linear arrangement of textural features often exhibited by metamorphic rocks.

Footwall block The rock surface below a fault.

Foreshocks Small earthquakes that often precede a major earthquake.

Fossil magnetism See *Paleomagnetism.*

Fossils The remains or traces of organisms preserved from the geologic past.

Fossil succession Fossil organisms succeed one another in a definite and determinable order, and any time period can be recognized by its fossil content.

Fracture Any break or rupture in rock along which no appreciable movement has taken place.

Fracture zone Linear zone of irregular topography on the deep-ocean floor that follows transform faults and their inactive extensions.

Freezing The change of state from a liquid to a solid.

Freezing nuclei Solid particles that serve as cores for the formation of ice crystals.

Front The boundary between two adjoining air masses having contrasting characteristics.

Frontal fog Fog formed when rain evaporates as it falls through a layer of cool air.

Frontal wedging Lifting of air resulting when cool air acts as a barrier over which warmer, lighter air will rise.

Frost wedging The mechanical breakup of rock caused by the expansion of freezing water in cracks and crevices.

Fumarole A vent in a volcanic area from which fumes or gases escape.

Galactic cluster A system of galaxies containing from several to thousands of member galaxies.

Geocentric The concept of an Earth-centered universe.

Geologic time scale The division of Earth history into blocks of time, such as eons, eras, periods, and epochs. The time scale was created using relative dating principles.

Geology The science that examines Earth, its form and composition, and the changes it has undergone and is undergoing.

Geostrophic wind A wind, usually above a height of 600 meters (2000 feet), that blows parallel to the isobars.

Geyser A fountain of hot water ejected periodically.

Giant (star) A luminous star of large radius.

Glacial drift An all-embracing term for sediments of glacial origin, no matter how, where, or in what shape they were deposited.

Glacial erratic An ice-transported boulder that was not derived from bedrock near its present site.

Glacial striations Scratches and grooves on bedrock caused by glacial abrasion.

Glacial trough A mountain valley that has been widened, deepened, and straightened by a glacier.

Glacier A thick mass of ice originating on land from the compaction and recrystallization of snow that shows evidence of past or present flow.

Glassy texture A term used to describe the texture of certain igneous rocks, such as obsidian, that contain no crystals.

Glaze A coating of ice on objects formed when supercooled rain freezes on contact.

Graben A valley formed by the downward displacement of a fault-bounded block.

Gradient The slope of a stream; generally measured in feet per mile.

Granitic composition A compositional group of igneous rocks in which the rock is composed almost entirely of light-colored silicates.

Greenhouse effect The transmission of short-wave solar radiation by the atmosphere coupled with the selective absorption of longer-wavelength terrestrial radiation, especially by water vapor and carbon dioxide.

Groin A short wall built at a right angle to the shore to trap moving sand.

Ground moraine An undulating layer of till deposited as the ice front retreats.

Groundwater Water in the zone of saturation.

Guyot A submerged flat-topped seamount.

Gyre The large, circular surface-current pattern found in each ocean.

Hail Nearly spherical ice pellets having concentric layers and formed by the successive freezing of layers of water.

Half-life The time required for one half of the atoms of a radioactive substance to decay.

Hanging valley A tributary valley that enters a glacial trough at a considerable height above its floor.

Hanging wall block The rock surface immediately above a fault.

Hardness The resistance a mineral offers to scratching.

Hard stabilization Any form of artificial structure built to protect a coast or to prevent the movement of sand along a beach. Examples include groins, jetties, breakwaters, and seawalls.

Heliocentric The view that the Sun is at the center of the solar system.

Hertzsprung-Russell (H-R) diagram A plot of stars according to their absolute magnitudes and spectral types.

High clouds Clouds that normally have their base above 6000 meters; the base may be lower in winter and at high-latitude locations.

Horn A pyramid-like peak formed by glacial action in three or more cirques surrounding a mountain summit.

Horst An elongated, uplifted block of crust bounded by faults.

Hot spot A concentration of heat in the mantle capable of producing magma, which in turn extrudes onto Earth's surface. The intraplate volcanism that produced the Hawaiian Islands is one example.

Hot spring A spring in which the water is 6°–9°C (10°–15°F) warmer than the mean annual air temperature of its locality.

Hubble's law Relates the distance to a galaxy and its velocity.

Humidity A general term referring to water vapor in the air but not to liquid droplets of fog, cloud, or rain.

Hurricane A tropical cyclonic storm having winds in excess of 119 kilometers (74 miles) per hour.

Hydrogen burning The conversion of hydrogen through fusion to form helium.

Hydrogenous sediment Seafloor sediments consisting of minerals that crystallize from seawater. An important example is manganese nodules.

Hydrologic cycle The unending circulation of Earth's water supply. The cycle is powered by energy from the Sun and is characterized by continuous exchanges of water among the oceans, the atmosphere, the geosphere, and the biosphere.

Hydrosphere The water portion of our planet; one of the traditional subdivisions of Earth's physical environment.

Hygrometer An instrument designed to measure relative humidity.

Hygroscopic nuclei Condensation nuclei having a high affinity for water, such as salt particles.

Hypothesis A tentative explanation that is tested to determine if it is valid.

Ice cap A mass of glacial ice covering a high upland or plateau and spreading out radially.

Ice sheet A very large, thick mass of glacial ice flowing outward in all directions from one or more accumulation centers.

Igneous rock A rock formed by the crystallization of molten magma.

Immature soil A soil lacking horizons.

Inclination of the axis The tilt of Earth's axis from the perpendicular to the plane of Earth's orbit.

Inclusion A piece of one rock unit contained within another. Inclusions are used in relative dating. The rock mass adjacent to the one containing the inclusion must have been there first in order to provide the fragment.

Index fossil A fossil that is associated with a particular span of geologic time.

Infrared Radiation with a wavelength from 0.7 to 200 micrometers.

Inner core The solid innermost layer of Earth, about 1300 kilometers (800 miles) in radius.

Interior drainage A discontinuous pattern of intermittent streams that do not flow to the ocean.

Intermediate composition A compositional group of igneous rocks, in which the rock contains at least 25 percent dark silicate minerals. The other dominant mineral is plagioclase feldspar.

Internal process Processes such as volcanic activity, earthquakes, and mountain building that derive their energy from Earth's interior.

Interstellar dust Dust and gases found between stars.

Intraplate volcanism Igneous activity that occurs within a tectonic plate away from plate boundaries.

Intrusion See *Pluton.*

Intrusive Igneous rock that formed below Earth's surface.

Iron meteorite One of the three main categories of meteorites. This group is composed largely of iron with varying amounts of nickel (5–20 percent). Most meteorite finds are irons.

Irregular galaxy A galaxy that lacks symmetry.

Island arc See *Volcanic island arc.*

Isobar A line drawn on a map connecting points of equal atmospheric pressure, usually corrected to sea level.

Isotherms Lines connecting points of equal temperature.

Isotopes Varieties of the same element that have different mass numbers; their nuclei contain the same number of protons but different numbers of neutrons.

Jet stream Swift high-altitude winds (120–240 kilometers per hour).

Jovian planet The Jupiter-like planets Jupiter, Saturn, Uranus, and Neptune. These planets have relatively low densities.

Kame A steep-sided hill composed of sand and gravel originating when sediment collected in openings in stagnant glacial ice.

Karst topography A topography consisting of numerous depressions called sinkholes.

Kettle Depressions created when blocks of ice became lodged in glacial deposits and subsequently melted.

Kuiper belt A region outside the orbit of Neptune where most short-period comets are thought to originate.

Laccolith A massive igneous body intruded between preexisting strata.

Lahar Mudflows on the slopes of volcanoes that result when unstable layers of ash and debris become saturated and flow downslope, usually following stream channels.

Land breeze A local wind blowing from land toward the water during the night in coastal areas.

Latent heat The energy absorbed or released during a change in state.

Lateral moraine A ridge of till along the sides of an alpine glacier composed primarily of debris that fell to the glacier from the valley walls.

Lava Magma that reaches Earth's surface.

Lightning A sudden flash of light generated by the flow of electrons between oppositely charged parts of a cumulonimbus cloud or between the cloud and the ground.

Light-year The distance light travels in a year; about 6 trillion miles.

Liquefaction A phenomenon, sometimes associated with earthquakes, in which soils and other unconsolidated materials containing abundant water are turned into a fluidlike mass that is not capable of supporting buildings.

Lithification The process, generally cementation and/or compaction, of converting sediments to solid rock.

Lithosphere The rigid outer layer of Earth, including the crust and upper mantle.

Lithospheric plate A coherent unit of Earth's rigid outer layer that includes the crust and uppermost mantle.

Local Group The cluster of 20 or so galaxies to which our galaxy belongs.

Localized convective lifting Unequal surface heating that causes localized pockets of air (thermals) to rise because of their buoyancy.

Loess Deposits of windblown silt, lacking visible layers, generally buff-colored, and capable of maintaining a nearly vertical cliff.

Longshore current A nearshore current that flows parallel to the shore.

Low clouds Clouds that form below a height of about 2000 meters.

Lower mantle See *Mesosphere.*

Lunar regolith A thin, gray layer on the surface of the Moon, consisting of loosely compacted, fragmented material believed to have been formed by repeated meteoric impacts.

Luster The appearance or quality of light reflected from the surface of a mineral.

Mafic composition See *Basaltic composition.*

Magma A body of molten rock found at depth, including any dissolved gases and crystals.

Magnetic reversal A change in the polarity of Earth's magnetic field that occurs over time intervals of roughly 200,000 years.

Magnetic time scale   The history of magnetic reversals through geologic time.

Magnetometer   A sensitive instrument used to measure the intensity of Earth's magnetic field.

Magnitude (earthquake)   The total amount of energy released during an earthquake.

Magnitude (stellar)   A number given to a celestial object to express its relative brightness.

Main-sequence stars   A sequence of stars on the Hertzsprung-Russell diagram, containing the majority of stars, that runs diagonally from the upper left to the lower right.

Mantle   The 2900-kilometer- (1800-mile-) thick layer of Earth located below the crust.

Mantle plume   A source of some intraplate basaltic magma, these structures originate at great depth and, upon reaching the crust, spread laterally, creating a localized volcanic zone called a hot spot.

Maria   The Latin name for the smooth areas of the Moon formerly thought to be seas.

Marine terrace   A wave-cut platform that has been exposed above sea level.

Maritime (m) air mass   An air mass that originates over the ocean. These air masses are relatively humid.

Massive   An igneous pluton that is not tabular in shape.

Mass number   The number of neutrons and protons in the nucleus of an atom.

Mass wasting   The downslope movement of rock, regolith, and soil under the direct influence of gravity.

Meander   A looplike bend in the course of a stream.

Mean solar day   The average time between two passages of the Sun across the local celestial meridian.

Medial moraine   A ridge of till formed when lateral moraines from two coalescing alpine glaciers join.

Melting   The change of state from a solid to a liquid.

Mercury barometer   A mercury-filled glass tube in which the height of the mercury column is a measure of air pressure.

Mesosphere (atmosphere)   The layer of the atmosphere immediately above the stratosphere and characterized by decreasing temperatures with height.

Mesosphere (geology)   The part of the mantle that extends from the core-mantle boundary to a depth of 660 kilometers. Also known as the lower mantle.

Mesozoic era   A time span on the geologic calendar between the Paleozoic and Cenozoic eras—from about 245 to 66.4 million years ago.

Metallic bond   A chemical bond present in all metals that may be characterized as an extreme type of electron sharing in which the electrons move freely from atom to atom.

Metamorphic rock   Rocks formed by the alteration of preexisting rock deep within Earth (but still in the solid state) by heat, pressure, and/or chemically active fluids.

Metamorphism   The changes in mineral composition and texture of a rock subjected to high temperatures and pressures within Earth.

Meteor   The luminous phenomenon observed when a meteoroid enters Earth's atmosphere and burns up; popularly called a "shooting star."

Meteorite   Any portion of a meteoroid that survives its traverse through Earth's atmosphere and strikes Earth's surface.

Meteoroid   Small, solid particles that have orbits in the solar system.

Meteorology   The scientific study of the atmosphere and atmospheric phenomena; the study of weather and climate.

Meteor shower   Many meteors appearing in the sky caused when Earth intercepts a swarm of meteoritic particles.

Middle clouds   Clouds that occupy the height range from 2000 to 6000 meters.

Middle-latitude (Midlatitude) cyclone   Large low-pressure center with a diameter often exceeding 1000 kilometers (600 miles) that moves from west to east and may last from a few days to more than a week and usually has a cold front and a warm front extending from the central area of low pressure.

Mid-ocean ridge   A continuous elevated zone on the floor of all the major ocean basins and varying in width from 500 to 5000 kilometers (300 to 3000 miles). The rifts at the crests of these ridges represent divergent plate boundaries.

Mineral   A naturally occurring, inorganic crystalline material with a unique chemical composition.

Mineral resource   All discovered and undiscovered deposits of a useful mineral that can be extracted now or at some time in the future.

Mixed tidal pattern   A tidal pattern exhibiting two high tides and two low tides per tidal day with a large inequality in high water heights, low water heights, or both. Coastal locations that experience such a tidal pattern may also show alternating periods of diurnal and semidiurnal tidal patterns. Also called mixed semidiurnal.

Model   A term often used synonymously with hypothesis but is less precise because it is sometimes used to describe a theory as well.

Modified Mercalli intensity scale   A 12-point scale developed to evaluate earthquake intensity based on the amount of damage to various structures.

Mohs hardness scale   A series of 10 minerals used as a standard in determining hardness.

Moment magnitude   A more precise measure of earthquake magnitude than the Richter scale that is derived from the amount of displacement that occurs along a fault zone.

Monsoon   Seasonal reversal of wind direction associated with large continents, especially Asia. In winter the wind blows from land to sea; in summer, from sea to land.

Mountain breeze   The nightly downslope winds commonly encountered in mountain valleys.

Natural levees   The elevated landforms that parallel some streams and act to confine their waters, except during floodstage.

Neap tide   The lowest tidal range, occurring near the times of the first and third quarters of the Moon.

Nebula   A cloud of interstellar gas and/or dust.

Nebular theory   A model for the origin of the solar system that supposes a rotating nebula of dust and gases that contracted to form the Sun and planets.

Neutron   A subatomic particle found in the nucleus of an atom. The neutron is electronically neutral and has a mass approximately that of a proton.

Neutron star   A star of extremely high density composed entirely of neutrons.

Nonconformity   An unconformity in which older metamorphic or intrusive igneous rocks are overlain by younger sedimentary strata.

Nonfoliated texture   Metamorphic rocks that do not exhibit foliation.

Nonrenewable resource   A resource that forms or accumulates over such long time spans that it must be considered as fixed in total quantity.

Normal fault   A fault in which the rock above the fault plane has moved down relative to the rock below.

Normal polarity   A magnetic field that is the same as that which exists at present.

Nucleus (atomic)   The small, heavy core of an atom that contains all of its positive charge and most of its mass.

Nucleus (comet)   The small central body of a comet, typically 1 to 10 kilometers in diameter.

Nuée ardente   Incandescent volcanic debris buoyed up by hot gases that moves downslope in an avalanche fashion.

Numerical date   Date that specifies the actual number of years that have passed since an event occurred.

Oceanic ridge   See *Mid-ocean ridge.*

Oceanography   The scientific study of the oceans and oceanic phenomena.

Octet rule   Atoms combine in order that each may have the electron arrangement of a noble gas; that is, the outer energy level contains eight neutrons.

Oort cloud   A spherical shell composed of comets that orbit the Sun at distances generally greater than 10,000 times the Earth–Sun distance.

Ore   Usually a useful metallic mineral that can be mined at a profit. The term is also applied to certain nonmetallic minerals such as fluorite and sulfur.

Original horizontality   Layers of sediments generally deposited in a horizontal or nearly horizontal position.

Orogenesis   The processes that collectively result in the formation of mountains.

Orographic lifting   Mountains acting as barriers to the flow of air force the air to ascend. The air cools adiabatically, and clouds and precipitation may result.

Outer core   A layer beneath the mantle about 2200 kilometers (1364 miles) thick that has the properties of a liquid.

Outgassing   The escape of gases that had been dissolved in magma.

Outwash plain   A relatively flat, gentle sloping plain consisting of materials deposited by meltwater streams in front of the margin of an ice sheet.

Overrunning   Warm air gliding up a retreating cold air mass.

Oxbow lake   A curved lake produced when a stream cuts off a meander.

Ozone   A molecule of oxygen containing three oxygen atoms.

Pahoehoe flow   A lava flow with a smooth-to-ropey surface.

Paleoclimatology   The study of ancient climates; the study of climate and climate change prior to the period of instrumental records using proxy data.

Paleomagnetism   The natural remnant magnetism in rock bodies. The permanent magnetization acquired by rock that can be used to determine the location of the magnetic poles and the latitude of the rock at the time it became magnetized.

Paleozoic era   A time span on the geologic calendar between the Precambrian and Mesozoic eras—from about 570 million to 245 million years ago.

Pangaea   The proposed supercontinent, which 200 million years ago began to break apart and form the present landmasses.

Parasitic cone   A volcanic cone that forms on the flank of a larger volcano.

Parcel   An imaginary volume of air enclosed in a thin elastic cover. Typically it is considered to be a few hundred cubic meters in volume and is assumed to act independently of the surrounding air.

Partial melting   The process by which most igneous rocks melt. Since individual minerals have different melting points, most igneous rocks melt over a temperature range of a few hundred degrees. If the liquid is squeezed out after some melting has occurred, a melt with a higher silica content results.

Passive continental margin   Margin that consists of a continental shelf, continental slope, and continental rise. They are not associated with plate boundaries and therefore experience little volcanism and few earthquakes.

Period   A basic unit of the geologic calendar that is a subdivision of an era. Periods may be divided into smaller units called epochs.

Permeability   A measure of a material's ability to transmit water.

Perturbation   The gravitational disturbance of the orbit of one celestial body by another.

Phanerozoic eon   That part of geologic time represented by rocks containing abundant fossil evidence. The eon extending from the end of the Proterozoic eon (570 million years ago) to the present.

Physical environment   The part of the environment that encompasses water, air, soil, and rock, as well as conditions such as temperature, humidity, and sunlight.

Piedmont glacier   A glacier that forms when one or more alpine glaciers emerge from the confining walls of mountain valleys and spread out to create a broad sheet in the lowlands at the base of the mountains.

Pipe   A vertical conduit through which magmatic materials have passed.

Planetary nebula   A shell of incandescent gas expanding from a star.

Plate   One of numerous rigid sections of the lithosphere that moves as a unit over the material of the asthenosphere.

Plate tectonics   The theory that proposes that Earth's outer shell consists of individual plates that interact in various ways and thereby produce earthquakes, volcanoes, mountains, and the crust itself.

Playa lake   A temporary lake in a playa.

Pleistocene epoch   An epoch of the Quaternary period beginning about 1.6 million years ago and ending about 10,000 years ago. Best known as a time of extensive continental glaciation.

Plucking (quarrying)   The process by which pieces of bedrock are lifted out of place by a glacier.

Pluton   A structure that results from the emplacement and crystallization of magma beneath the surface of Earth.

Pluvial lake   A lake formed during a period of increased rainfall. During the Pleistocene epoch this occurred in some nonglaciated regions during periods of ice advance elsewhere.

Polar (P) air mass   A cold air mass that forms in a high-latitude source region.

Polar easterlies   In the global pattern of prevailing winds, winds that blow from the polar high toward the subpolar low. These winds, however, should not be thought of as persistent winds, such as the trade winds.

Polar front   The stormy frontal zone separating air masses of polar origin from air masses of tropical origin.

Polar high   Anticyclones that are assumed to occupy the inner polar regions and are believed to be thermally induced, at least in part.

Polar wandering   As the result of paleomagnetic studies in the 1950s, researchers proposed that either the magnetic poles migrated greatly through time or the continents had gradually shifted their positions.

Porosity   The volume of open spaces in rock or soil.

Porphyritic texture   An igneous texture consisting of large crystals embedded in a matrix of much smaller crystals.

Positive-feedback mechanism   As used in climatic change, any effect that acts to reinforce the initial change.

Precambrian   All geologic time prior to the Paleozoic era.

Precession   A slow motion of Earth's axis that traces out a cone over a period of 26,000 years.

Precipitation fog   Fog formed when rain evaporates as it falls through a layer of cool air.

Pressure gradient   The amount of pressure change occurring over a given distance.

Pressure tendency   The nature of the change in atmospheric pressure over the past several hours. It can be a useful aid in short-range weather prediction.

Prevailing wind   A wind that consistently blows from one direction more than from any other.

Primary pollutants   Those pollutants emitted directly from identifiable sources.

Primary (P) wave   A type of seismic wave that involves alternating compression and expansion of the material through which it passes.

Proton   A positively charged subatomic particle found in the nucleus of an atom.

Proton–proton chain   A chain of thermonuclear reactions by which nuclei of hydrogen are built up into nuclei of helium.

Protostar   A collapsing cloud of gas and dust destined to become a star.

Psychrometer   A device consisting of two thermometers (wet-bulb and dry-bulb) that is rapidly whirled and, with the use of tables, yields the relative humidity and dew point.

Ptolemaic model   An Earth-centered system of the universe.

Pulsar   A variable radio source of small size that emits radio pulses in very regular periods.

Pycnocline   A layer of water in which there is a rapid change of density with depth.

Pyroclastic flow   A highly heated mixture, largely of ash and pumice fragments, traveling down the flanks of a volcano or along the surface of the ground.

Pyroclastic material   The volcanic rock ejected during an eruption, including ash, bombs, and blocks.

Pyroclastic texture   An igneous rock texture resulting from the consolidation of individual rock fragments that are ejected during a violent eruption.

Radial pattern   A system of streams running in all directions away from a central elevated structure, such as a volcano.

Radiation or electromagnetic radiation   The transfer of energy (heat) through space by electromagnetic waves.

Radiation fog   Fog resulting from radiation heat loss by Earth.

Radiation pressure   The force exerted by electromagnetic radiation from an object such as the Sun.

Radioactive decay (Radioactivity)   The spontaneous decay of certain unstable atomic nuclei.

Radiometric dating   The procedure of calculating the absolute ages of rocks and minerals that contain radioactive isotopes.

Radiosonde   A lightweight package of weather instruments fitted with a radio transmitter and carried aloft by a balloon.

Rain   Drops of water that fall from a cloud and have a diameter of at least 0.5 millimeter.

Rainshadow desert   A dry area on the lee side of a mountain range. Many middle-latitude deserts are of this type.

Rectangular pattern   A drainage pattern characterized by numerous right-angle bends that develops on jointed or fractured bedrock.

Red giant   A large, cool star of high luminosity; a star occupying the upper right portion of the Hertzsprung-Russell diagram.

Reflecting telescope   A telescope that concentrates light from distant objects by using a concave mirror.

Reflection nebula   A relatively dense dust cloud in interstellar space that is illuminated by starlight.

Refracting telescope   A telescope that employs a lens to bend and concentrate the light from distant objects.

Refraction   The process by which the portion of a wave in shallow water slows, causing the wave to bend and tend to align itself with the underwater contours.

Regional metamorphism   Metamorphism associated with the large-scale mountain-building processes.

Regolith   The layer of rock and mineral fragments that nearly everywhere covers Earth's land surface.

Rejuvenation   A change, often caused by regional uplift, that causes the force of erosion to intensify.

Relative dating   Rocks placed in their proper sequence or order. Only the chronologic order of events is determined.

Relative humidity   The ratio of the air's water-vapor content to its water-vapor capacity.

Renewable resource   A resource that is virtually inexhaustible or that can be replenished over relatively short time spans.

Reserve   Already identified deposits from which minerals can be extracted profitably.

Retrograde motion   The apparent westward motion of the planets with respect to the stars.

Reverse fault   A fault in which the material above the fault plane moves up in relation to the material below.

Reverse polarity   A magnetic field opposite to that which exists at present.

Revolution   The motion of one body about another, as Earth about the Sun.

Richter scale   A scale of earthquake magnitude based on the motion of a seismograph.

Ridge push   A mechanism that may contribute to plate motion. It involves the oceanic lithosphere sliding down the oceanic ridge under the pull of gravity.

Rift valley   A region of Earth's crust along which divergence is taking place.

Rime   A thin coating of ice on objects produced when supercooled fog droplets freeze on contact.

Rock   A consolidated mixture of minerals.

Rock cycle   A model that illustrates the origin of the three basic rock types and the interrelatedness of Earth materials and processes.

Rock flour   Ground-up rock produced by the grinding effect of a glacier.

Rock-forming minerals   The few dozen most abundant minerals that make up most common rocks. Minerals rich in oxygen and silicon (silicate minerals) dominate this group.

Rotation   The spinning of a body, such as Earth, about its axis.

Salinity   The proportion of dissolved salts to pure water, usually expressed in parts per thousand (‰).

Santa Ana   The local name given a chinook wind in southern California.

Saturation   The maximum possible quantity of water vapor that the air can hold at any given temperature and pressure.

Scoria cone   See *Cinder cone.*

Sea arch   An arch formed by wave erosion when caves on opposite sides of a headland unite.

Sea breeze   A local wind blowing from the sea during the afternoon in coastal areas.

Seafloor spreading   The process of producing new seafloor between two diverging plates.

Seamount   An isolated volcanic peak that rises at least 1000 meters (3000 feet) above the deep-ocean floor.

Sea stack   An isolated mass of rock standing just offshore, produced by wave erosion of a headland.

Seawall   A barrier constructed to prevent waves from reaching the area behind the wall. Its purpose is to defend property from the force of breaking waves.

Secondary (S) wave   A seismic wave that involves oscillation perpendicular to the direction of propagation.

Sediment   Unconsolidated particles created by the weathering and erosion of rock, by chemical precipitation from solution in water, or from the secretions of organisms and transported by water, wind, or glaciers.

Sedimentary rock   Rock formed from the weathered products of preexisting rocks that have been transported, deposited, and lithified.

Seismic sea wave   A rapidly moving ocean wave generated by earthquake activity that is capable of inflicting heavy damage in coastal regions.

Seismic waves   A form of elastic energy released during an earthquake that causes vibrations in the materials that transmit them.

Seismogram   The record made by a seismograph.

Seismograph   An instrument that records earthquake waves.

Seismology   The study of earthquakes and seismic waves.

Semidiurnal tidal pattern   A tidal pattern exhibiting two high tides and two low tides per tidal day with small inequalities between successive highs and successive lows; a semidaily tide.

Shield volcano   A broad, gently sloping volcano built from fluid basaltic lavas.

Silicate   Any one of numerous minerals that have the oxygen and silicon tetrahedron as their basic structure.

Silicon-oxygen tetrahedron   A structure composed of four oxygen atoms surrounding a silicon atom that constitutes the basic building block of silicate minerals.

Sill   A tabular igneous body that was intruded parallel to the layering of preexisting rock.

Sink hole   A depression produced in a region where soluble rock has been removed by groundwater.

Slab-pull   A mechanism that contributes to plate motion in which cool, dense oceanic crust sinks into the mantle and "pulls" the trailing lithosphere along.

Slab suction   One of the driving forces of plate motion, it arises from the drag of the subducting plate on the adjacent mantle. It is an induced mantle circulation that pulls both the subducting and overriding plates toward the trench.

Sleet   Frozen or semifrozen rain formed when raindrops freeze as they pass through a layer of cold air.

Slip face   The steep, leeward slope of a sand dune; it maintains an angle of about 34 degrees.

Small solar system bodies   Objects in the solar system that are not planets or dwarf planets. Examples include comets and asteroids.

Snow   A solid form of precipitation produced by sublimation of water vapor.

Solstice (summer or winter)   The time when the vertical rays of the Sun are striking either the Tropic of Cancer or the Tropic of Capricorn. Solstice represents the longest or shortest day (length of daylight) of the year.

Sonar   Instrument that uses acoustic signals (sound energy) to measure water depths. Sonar is an acronym for *so*und *na*vigation and *r*anging.

Sorting   The process by which solid particles of various sizes are separated by moving water or wind. Also the degree of similarity in particle size in sediment or sedimentary rock.

Source region   The area where an air mass acquires its characteristic properties of temperature and moisture.

Specific gravity   The ratio of a substance's weight to the weight of an equal volume of water.

Specific humidity   The weight of water vapor compared with the total weight of the air, including the water vapor.

Spiral galaxy   A flattened, rotating galaxy with pinwheellike arms of interstellar material and young stars winding out from its nucleus.

Spit   An elongated ridge of sand that projects from the land into the mouth of an adjacent bay.

Spreading center   See *Divergent plate boundary.*

Spring   A flow of groundwater that emerges naturally at the ground surface.

Spring tide   The highest tidal range. Occurs near the times of the new and full moons.

Stable air   Air that resists vertical displacement. If it is lifted, adiabatic cooling will cause its temperature to be lower than the surrounding environment; if it is allowed, it will sink to its original position.

Stalactite   The icicle-like structure that hangs from the ceiling of a cavern.

Stalagmite   The columnlike form that grows upward from the floor of a cavern.

Steam fog   Fog having the appearance of steam; produced by evaporation from a warm-water surface into the cool air above.

Stellar parallax   A measure of stellar distance.

Steppe   One of the two types of dry climate. A marginal and more humid variant of the desert that separates it from bordering humid climates.

Stock   A pluton similar to but smaller than a batholith.

Stony-iron meteorite   One of the three main categories of meteorites. This group, as the name implies, is a mixture of iron and silicate minerals.

Stony meteorite   One of the three main categories of meteorites. Such meteorites are composed largely of silicate minerals with inclusions of other minerals.

Storm surge   The abnormal rise of the sea along a shore as a result of strong winds.

Strata   Parallel layers of sedimentary rock.

Stratified drift   Sediments deposited by glacial meltwater.

Stratosphere   The layer of the atmosphere immediately above the troposphere, characterized by increasing temperatures with height due to the concentration of ozone.

Stratovolcano   See *Composite cone.*

Stratus   One of three basic cloud forms, also the name given one of the low clouds. They are sheets or layers that cover much or all of the sky.

Streak   The color of a mineral in powdered form.

Strike-slip fault   A fault along which the movement is horizontal.

Subduction zone   A long, narrow zone where one lithospheric plate descends beneath another.

Sublimation   The conversion of a solid directly to a gas without passing through the liquid state.

Submarine canyon   A seaward extension of a valley that was cut on the continental shelf during a time when sea level was lower, or a canyon carved into the outer continental shelf, slope, and rise by turbidity currents.

Submergent coast   A coast with a form that is largely the result of the partial drowning of a former land surface either because of a rise of sea level or subsidence of the crust or both.

Subpolar low   Low pressure located at about the latitudes of the Arctic and Antarctic circles. In the Northern Hemisphere the low takes the form of individual oceanic cells; in the Southern Hemisphere there is a deep and continuous trough of low pressure.

Subtropical high   Not a continuous belt of high pressure but rather several semipermanent, anticyclonic centers characterized by subsidence and divergence located roughly between latitudes 25 and 35 degrees.

Supergiant   A very large star of high luminosity.

Supernova   An exploding star that increases in brightness many thousands of times.

Superposition   In any underformed sequence of sedimentary rocks, each bed is older than the layers above and younger than the layers below.

Surf   A collective term for breakers; also the wave activity in the area between the shoreline and the outer limit of breakers.

Surface waves   Seismic waves that travel along the outer layer of the Earth.

Suspended load   The fine sediment carried within the body of flowing water.

Syncline   A linear downfold in sedimentary strata; the opposite of anticline.

Tablemount   See *Guyot.*

Tabular   Term used to describe a feature such as an igneous pluton having two dimensions that are much longer than the third. A pluton that is thin in one dimension.

Tectonic plate   See *Lithospheric plate.*

Terrane   A crustal block bounded by faults, whose geologic history is distinct from the histories of adjoining crustal blocks.

Terrestrial planet   Any of the Earthlike planets including Mercury, Venus, Mars, and Earth.

Terrigenous sediment   Seafloor sediment derived from weathering and erosion on land.

Texture   The size, shape, and distribution of the particles that collectively constitute a rock.

Theory   A well-tested and widely accepted view that explains certain observable facts.

Thermal metamorphism   See *Contact metamorphism.*

Thermocline   A layer of water in which there is a rapid change in temperature in the vertical dimension.

Thermohaline circulation   Movements of ocean water caused by density differences brought about by variations in temperature and salinity.

Thermosphere   The region of the atmosphere immediately above the mesosphere and characterized by increasing temperatures due to absorption of very shortwave solar energy by oxygen.

Thrust fault   A low-angle reverse fault.

Thunderstorm   A storm produced by a cumulonimbus cloud and always accompanied by lightning and thunder. It is of relatively short duration and usually accompanied by strong wind gusts, heavy rain, and sometimes hail.

Tidal current   The alternating horizontal movement of water associated with the rise and fall of the tide.

Tidal delta   A deltalike feature created when a rapidly moving tidal current emerges from a narrow inlet and slows, depositing its load of sediment.

Tidal flat   A marshy or muddy area that is covered and uncovered by the rise and fall of the tide.

Tide   Periodic change in the elevation of the ocean surface.

Till   Unsorted sediment deposited directly by a glacier.

Tombolo   A ridge of sand that connects an island to the mainland or to another island.

Tornado   A small, very intense cyclonic storm with exceedingly high winds, most often produced along cold fronts in conjunction with severe thunderstorms.

Tornado warning A warning issued when a tornado has actually been sighted in an area or is indicated by radar.

Tornado watch A forecast issued for areas of about 65,000 square kilometers (25,000 square miles), indicating that conditions are such that tornadoes may develop; it is intended to alert people to the possibility of tornadoes.

Trade winds Two belts of winds that blow almost constantly from easterly directions and are located on the equatorward sides of the subtropical highs.

Transform boundary A boundary in which two plates slide past one another without creating or destroying lithosphere.

Transform fault A major strike-slip fault that cuts through the lithosphere and accommodates motion between two plates.

Transpiration The release of water vapor to the atmosphere by plants.

Trellis pattern A system of streams in which nearly parallel tributaries occupy valleys cut in folded strata.

Trench An elongated depression in the seafloor produced by bending of oceanic crust during subduction.

Tropical (T) air mass A warm-to-hot air mass that forms in the subtropics.

Tropical depression By international agreement, a tropical cyclone with maximum winds that do not exceed 61 kilometers (38 miles) per hour.

Tropical storm By international agreement, a tropical cyclone with maximum winds between 61 and 119 kilometers (38 and 74 miles) per hour.

Tropic of Cancer The parallel of latitude, 23½ degrees north latitude, marking the northern limit of the Sun's vertical rays.

Tropic of Capricorn The parallel of latitude, 23½ degrees south latitude, marking the southern limit of the Sun's vertical rays.

Troposphere The lowermost layer of the atmosphere. It is generally characterized by a decrease in temperature with height.

Tsunami A rapidly moving ocean wave generated by earthquake activity that is capable of inflicting heavy damage in coastal regions.

Turbidity current A downslope movement of dense, sediment-laden water created when sand and mud on the continental shelf and slope are dislodged and thrown into suspension.

Ultramafic composition A compositional group of igneous rocks in which the rock contains mostly olivine and pyroxene.

Ultraviolet Radiation with a wavelength from 0.2 to 0.4 micrometer.

Unconformity A surface that represents a break in the rock record, caused by erosion or nondeposition.

Uniformitarianism The concept that the processes that have shaped Earth in the geologic past are essentially the same as those operating today.

Unsaturated zone The area above the water table where openings in soil, sediment, and rock are not saturated with water but filled mainly with air.

Unstable air Air that does not resist vertical displacement. If it is lifted, its temperature will not cool as rapidly as the surrounding environment, and so it will continue to rise on its own.

Upslope fog Fog created when air moves up a slope and cools adiabatically.

Upwelling The rising of cold water from deeper layers to replace warmer surface water that has been moved away.

Valley breeze The daily upslope winds commonly encountered in a mountain valley.

Valley glacier See *Alpine glacier*.

Valley train A relatively narrow body of stratified drift deposited on a valley floor by meltwater streams that issue from a valley glacier.

Vapor pressure That part of the total atmospheric pressure attributable to water-vapor content.

Vent A conduit that connects a magma chamber to a volcanic crater.

Vesicular texture A term applied to fine-grained igneous rocks that contain many small cavities called vesicles, which are openings on the outer portion of a lava flow that were created by escaping gases.

Viscosity A measure of a fluid's resistance to flow.

Visible light Radiation with a wavelength from 0.4 to 0.7 micrometer.

Volatiles Gaseous components of magma dissolved in the melt. Volatiles will readily vaporize (form a gas) at surface pressures.

Volcanic bomb A streamlined pyroclastic fragment ejected from a volcano while molten.

Volcanic island arc A chain of volcanic islands generally located a few hundred kilometers from a trench where there is active subduction of one oceanic plate beneath another.

Volcanic neck An isolated, steep-sided, erosional remnant consisting of lava that once occupied the vent of a volcano.

Volcano A mountain formed of lava and/or pyroclastics.

Warm front A front along which a warm air mass overrides a retreating mass of cooler air.

Water table The upper level of the saturated zone of groundwater.

Wave-cut cliff A seawater-facing cliff along a steep shoreline formed by wave erosion at its base and mass wasting.

Wave-cut platform A bench or shelf in the bedrock at sea level, cut by wave erosion.

Wave height The vertical distance between the trough and crest of a wave.

Wavelength The horizontal distance separating successive crests or troughs.

Wave period The time interval between the passage of successive crests at a stationary point.

Wave refraction See *Refraction*.

Weather The state of the atmosphere at any given time.

Weathering The disintegration and decomposition of rock at or near the surface of Earth.

Well An opening bored into the zone of saturation.

Westerlies The dominant west-to-east motion of the atmosphere that characterizes the regions on the poleward side of the subtropical highs.

Wet adiabatic rate The rate of adiabatic temperature change in saturated air. The rate of temperature change is variable, but it is always less than the dry adiabatic rate.

White dwarf A star that has exhausted most or all of its nuclear fuel and has collapsed to a very small size; believed to be near its final stage of evolution.

Wind Air flowing horizontally with respect to Earth's surface.

Wind vane An instrument used to determine wind direction.

Yazoo tributary A tributary that flows parallel to the main stream because a natural levee is present.

Zone of accumulation The part of a glacier characterized by snow accumulation and ice formation. Its outer limit is the snowline.

Zone of saturation Zone where all open spaces in sediment and rock are completely filled with water.

Zone of wastage The part of a glacier beyond the zone of accumulation, where all of the snow from the previous winter melts, as does some of the glacial ice.

INDEX

Aa flows, 212
Abrasion, 291
  glacial, 118
  wind, 133
Absorption, 325
Abyssal plains, 273
Accretion, 199
Accretionary wedge, 198–99, 272
Accumulation, zone of, 116
Adiabatic cooling, 348–49, 352
Aerosols, 313
Aftershocks, 174–75
Agate, 61
Aggregates, 23
Agricultural chemicals, 103
Air, 311. *See also* Atmosphere
  around cyclones, 399
  lifting, 349–51
  stability, 352–54
  stable, 351
Air masses, 392–94, 401–2
Air pressure, 311, 372–73
  changes in, 315–16
  measuring, 373–74
Alaska earthquake of 1964, 184–85, 188
Albedo, 324, 333–34
Alluvial channels, 84–86
Alluvial fans, 130
Alluvium, 84
Alpha particles, 250
Alpine Fault, 157–58
Alpine-Himalaya belt, 183, 196
Altocumulus clouds, 355, 357
Altostratus clouds, 355, 358
Amagest (Ptolemy), 421
Amber, 248
American Philosophical Society, 147
Amphibole, 49, 52
Andes, 196
Andesite, 51
Andromeda Galaxy, 473
Anemometers, 385–86
Angel Falls, 88
Angle of repose, 77
  of cinders, 216–17
Anhydrite, 276
Anorthosite, 435
Antarctic Ice Sheet, 126
Anthracite, 61–62
Anticlines, 192
Anticyclones, 378–82, 399
Appalachian Mountains, 145
Aquifers, 96, 99–100. *See also* Groundwater
Aquitards, 96
Arabian Desert, 128
Archaeology, 245
Arctic Ocean, 260
Arêtes, 119–20
Army Corps of Engineers, 93
Arroyos, 129
Artifacts, 245
Ash, volcanic, 47, 213, 231–32
ASOS. *See* Automated Surface Observing System
Asteroid belt, 446–47
Asteroids, 446–47
Asthenosphere, 8, 149, 189
Astronomical unit (AU), 425
Astronomy, 5
  history of, 420–22
  modern, 422–28
Athropocene epoch, 254
Atlantic Ocean, 260. *See also* North Atlantic Ocean

Atmosphere, 7
  composition of, 311–14
  general circulation of, 381–82
  global warming and, 326–28
  greenhouse effect and, 325
  of planets, 431–33
  stability of, 351–54
  thermal structure of, 316
Atmospheric pollution, 14, 24
Atomic number, 24–25, 249
Atoms, 24–25, 28, 249
AU. *See* Astronomical unit
Automated Surface Observing System (ASOS), 16

Backswamps, 91
Backwash, 289
Bacon, Francis, 385
Bacteria, 9
Bajadas, 130
Barographs, 373–74
Barometers, 373–74
Barometric tendency, 379
Barrier islands, 294, 296
Bars, 294–95
Basalt, 51
  columnar jointing in, 226
  in crust, 189
  flood, 222–23
Base level, 86–89
Basin and Range Province, 195
Basins, 192
  deep-ocean, 272–73
  drainage, 79–80
  ocean, 8, 272–73
  ocean currents and, 284
Batholiths, 198, 226
Bathymetry, 266
Bayeux Tapestry, 420
Beaches, 289–93
  drift, 292
  nourishment, 298–99
Bedding planes, 63
Bed load, 83, 131–32
Bedrock
  channels, 84
  glacial deposits and, 121
Beds, 63
Benguela Current, 284–85
Bering Sea, 261
Beta particles, 250
Big bang theory, 476–77
Big crunch, 477
Bingham Canyon, 38–39
Biological activity, 56
Biosphere, 8–9
Biotite mica, 49
Black dwarfs, 470
Black Hills, 192–93
Black holes, 468, 471
Black smokers, 276
Blowouts, 132–33
Body waves, 176
Bombs, 213
Bonneville Salt Flats, 62
Bowen, N. L., 51–52
Bowen's reaction series, 52–53
Brahe, Tycho, 423–24, 459
Braided channels, 86–87
Breakwaters, 297–98
Breccia, 57–59
Breezes, 382–84
Brightness, stellar, 459–60

Brittle failure, 191
Bronze Age, 22
Bruno, Giodano, 423
Bullard, Edward, 143
Burrows, 248

Calcareous ooze, 275
Calcite, 33, 37, 62
Calcium carbonates, 275
Calderas, 215, 221
  Crater Lake-type, 221–22
  craters v., 214
  Hawaiian-type, 222
  Yellowstone-type, 222
California Current, 360
Calories, 342
Calving, 116
Cambrian Tapeats Sandstone, 243
Capacity, stream, 84
Cape Disappointment, 360
Carbon-14, 251–52
Carbonaceous chondrite, 450
Carbonates, 33, 37
Carbon dioxide
  in atmosphere, 312
  chemical weathering and, 56
  concentration, 327
  greenhouse effect and, 325
  karst topography and, 105
  rising levels of, 326
  volcanic monitoring and, 232
Carbonic acid, 56
Carbonization, 247
Catastrophism, 239
Caverns, 95, 102–3
Celestial sphere, 420
Cementation, 57, 62
Cenozoic era, 253–54
Center of mass, 461
CFCs. *See* Chlorofluorocarbons
Chalk, 60
Chamberlain, R. T., 147
Chang Heng, 176
Channelization, 93
Chemical compounds, 25
Chemosynthesis, 276
Chert, 22, 61
Chikyu, 277
Chimborazo volcano, 210
Chinooks, 384–85
Chlorine, 27
Chlorofluorocarbons (CFCs), 314
Chlorophyll concentration, 286
Chrons, 162
Cinder cones, 214, 216–18
Cinders, 213, 216–17
Circle of illumination, 317
Circular orbital motion, 289
Cirques, 119
Cirrocumulus clouds, 355, 357
Cirrostratus clouds, 355, 357
Cirrus clouds, 355, 357, 399
Clay, 26, 33
Cleavage, 31–32, 35–36
Climate, 310–11
  arid, 127–29
  human impact on, 325–28
  ocean currents and, 284–85
  seafloor sediment and, 276–77
Climatology, tornado, 404–5
Cloudbursts, 362
Cloudiness, 311

Clouds. *See also specific cloud types*
  classification of, 356
  in cold fronts, 396
  condensation and, 355–59
  formation of, 78, 348–49
  funnel, 405
  high, 355
  low, 355–57
  middle, 355
  in middle-latitude cyclones, 398–99
  temperature control and, 333–34
  types of, 355–57
  of vertical development, 359
  in warm fronts, 396
Coal, 23
  anthracite, 61–62
  bituminous, 61
  formation, 61–62
  lignite, 61
  Paleozoic glaciation and, 146
  sedimentary rock and, 57
Coast and Geodetic Survey, 187
Coasts
  emergent, 300
  leeward, 333
  submergent, 300–301
  windward, 333
Collision-coalescence process, 362
Collisions, 200–202
Color, 29
  stellar, 460
Colorado River, 84
Columbia Plateau, 223, 227
Columnar joints, 225–26
Comas, 447–48
Comets, 446–49
Compaction, 57, 62
Competence, 83–84
Composite cones, 218–21
Condensation, 342–43
  adiabatic cooling and,
    348–49
  cloud formation and, 355–59
  latent heat of, 348
  nuclei, 355
Conduction, 322
Conduits, 214
Cone of depression, 98
Confining pressure, 65–66
Conglomerate, 57, 59
Continental-continental
    convergence, 155–56
Continental divides, 79–80
Continental drift, 142–44, 143–47. *See also*
    Plate tectonics
  rejection of, 147
Continental escape, 201
Continental margins, 267–72
  active, 197–98, 272
  passive, 197, 268–72
  volcanic island arcs and, 200
Continental rifting, 151–52
Continental rise, 271
Continental shelf, 268–70
Continental slopes, 271
Continental volcanic arcs, 153–55,
    228, 272
Continents, 8
  barometric influence of, 382
  collisions of, 200–201
Convection, 322
  localized, 349
  mantle, 164–67
  plate-mantle, 166–67
Convective circulation, 322
Convergence, 152–56, 349–51, 378, 383

Convergent boundaries, 149–50, 152–56, 197–99,
    228–30
Copernicus, Nicolaus, 422–23
Coprolites, 248
Coquina, 60
Core, 7–8, 190
Coriolis effect, 283, 285
  Northern Hemisphere v.
    Southern Hemisphere, 378
  wind and, 375–77
Correlation, 244–45
  fossils and, 248–49
  of strata, 246
Cosmology, 458, 475
Cotopaxi volcano, 210
Country rock, 224
Covalent bonds, 26–28
Crab Nebula, 470–71
Crater Lake, 220–21
Craters, 214–15
  calderas v., 214
  impact, 433
  lunar, 434–35
Crests, 287
Crevasses, 115
Critical density, 477
Critical settling velocity, 84
Cross beds, 135–36
Cross-cutting relationships. *See* Principle of
    cross-cutting relationships
Crust, 7–8, 189
  elements of, 34
  temperature of, 65
Cryovolcanism, 446
Crystalline structure, 22
Crystallization, 45–47. *See also*
    Recrystallization
  of silicate minerals, 36
  stages of, 52
Crystal settling, 52
Crystal shape, 30, 32
Cumulonimbus clouds, 358–59
  hail and, 363–64
  rain and, 362
Cumulus clouds, 355, 358
  thermals and, 403
Cup anemometers, 385–86
Curie point, 160
Currents. *See* Ocean currents
Cutoffs, 86, 93
Cyclones, 378–82. *See also*
    Hurricanes
  airflow around, 399
  extratropical, 400
  mature, 399
  meaning of, 400
  meso-, 404–5, 408
  middle-latitude, 350, 397–99
  tropical, 400
Cygnus X-1, 471

Dams
  base level and, 88
  flood-control, 93
  floods and, 92
Dark matter, 477
Dark nebulae, 465
Darwin, Charles, 252
Dating
  with radioactivity, 249–52
  radiocarbon, 251–52
  radiometric, 159, 161, 250–52, 255
  relative, 240–43, 245
Daughter products, 250
Dead Sea, 262, 264
Dead Sea Scrolls, 252

Death Valley, 130–31, 349
Debris flows, 75
Decompression melting, 159, 230
Deep Sea Drilling Project, 159
Deep-sea fans, 271
Deep zone, 265
Deferents, 422
Deflation, 132–33
Deforestation, 327
Deformation, 175, 191, 244
Degenerate matter, 469
Deltas, 89–91, 304
Denali National Park, 122
Dendritic drainage patterns,
    91–92
Density, 33, 264–65
Deposition, 84, 242, 343, 347
  glacial, 121–24
  renewed, 244
  shoreline features from, 294
  wind, 134–35
Desert pavement, 133
Deserts, 126–29
  evolution of, 130
  rainshadow, 348–49
Detrital rocks, 57–59
Detritus, 57
Dew, 348
Dew point, 346–47, 360
Dialogue of the Great World Systems (Galileo),
    427
Diatoms, 275
Diatremes, 223
Differential stress, 66
Dikes, 224–25
Dike swarms, 224
Dinosaurs, 254
Diorite, 51
Discharge, 81–82
Disconformities, 243
Dissolved load, 83
Distributaries, 89–90
Divergence, 378
Divergent boundaries, 150–52, 230
Divides, 79–80
Domes, 192
Doppler radar, 408
Doppler shifts, 475–76
Dot diagrams, 26
Double refraction, 33
Drainage
  basins, 79–80
  interior, 130
  patterns, 91–92
Drawdown, 98
Drilling, 159
Dripstone, 103
Drizzle, 362
Drumlins, 124
Dry adiabatic rate, 348
Ductile deformation, 191
Dunes, 129, 134–36
Dust, 132, 213
  as aerosols, 313
  interstellar, 464

Earth, 5–6
  age of, 240
  formation of, 189
  inclination of axis of, 318
  internal structure of, 188–90
  motion of, 317
  nonrotating, 381
  orbit of, 429
  Sun relationship, 316–17
  topography of, 268–69

Earthflows, 75
Earthquakes, 8, 172, 174, 179,
        181, 194
    belts, 183
    causes of, 172–73
    destruction from, 15, 183–88
    fire and, 185–86
    glaciers and, 124
    human-triggered, 175
    locating, 178
    mass wasting triggers and, 77
    notable, 182
    transform faults and, 156
Earth science, 4–9
    range of, 12
    studying, 17
Earth system, 9–10
East African Rift, 152–53
Eastern California Shear Zone, 176
East Pacific Rise, 150, 166, 273
East Rift Zone, 216
Echo sounders, 266
Economic value, 38
    of continental shelves, 269
    of sedimentary rock, 57
EF intensity scale. *See* Enhanced Fujita
        intensity scale
Eismitte, 147
Elastic deformation, 191
Elastic rebound, 173, 175
Electrical charge, 24
Electrical repulsion, 469–70
Electromagnetic spectrum, 322
Electrons, 24, 26, 249
Elements, 25, 311
    of crust, 34
    of rock-forming minerals, 34
Elliptical galaxies, 474
Emission nebulae, 464
Energy use, 13
Enhanced Fujita (EF) intensity scale,
        406–7
Environment, 11–12
Environmental lapse rate, 316, 352
Environmental problems, 14
    of groundwater, 100–102
Environmental Protection Agency, 314
Eons, 252
Ephemeral streams, 81, 128–29
Epicenters, 172–73
    determining, 178
    travel-time graph, 179
Epicycles, 422
Epochs, 254
Equal areas, law of, 424–25
Equatorial lows, 381
Equinoxes, 318–21
Eras, 253
Erosion, 74, 82–83, 239
    angular unconformities and, 244
    base level and, 86–87
    glacial, 117–21
    lunar, 436
    problems, 299–300
    river systems and, 80
    shoreline features from, 293–94
    wave, 290–91
    wind, 129, 131–33
Eruption columns, 210
Eruptions. *See* Volcanic eruptions
Escape velocity, 433
Eskers, 124
Estuaries, 301
Evaporation, 78, 332, 342–43
Evaporites, 61, 276
Exfoliation domes, 54–56

External processes, 74
Eye wall, 410

Facts, 15
Fathoms, 266
Faults, 172, 192
    cyclical, 183
    detachment, 194
    dip-slip, 193–96
    earthquake belts and, 183
    glaciers and, 124
    normal, 193, 195
    reverse, 194–95
    strike-slip, 194–95
    thrust, 194–95
    transform, 149–50, 156–57, 175
Fault scarps, 193–94
Feldspars, 36, 50
    plagioclase, 52
    potassium, 52
Fetch, 287
Fiords, 120–21
Fire, earthquakes and, 185–86
Fissures, 222–23
Flint, 61
Floodplains, 88
Floods, 15, 92–94
    causes of, 92
    control, 93–94
    flash, 92, 129
    from hurricanes, 413
    natural levees and, 91
Fluids, chemically active, 66
Fluorescence, 464
Focus, 172–73
Fog
    advection, 359–60
    caused by cooling, 359–60
    cloud formation v., 348
    evaporation, 360–61
    frontal, 361
    precipitation, 361
    radiation, 360
    steam, 361
    upslope, 360
Folds, 192, 244
Foliated rock, 68
Foliation, 66
Footwall block, 193
Forecast cones, 414
Foreshocks, 174–75
Fossil magnetism. *See*
        Paleomagnetism
Fossils, 63, 245–49
    assemblages, 248
    chemical, 248
    continental drift and, 143–44
    correlation and, 248–49
    etymology of, 244
    index, 248
    types of, 247–48
Fossil succession principle, 248
Fracture, 32–33
Fracture zones, 115, 157
Franciscan Formation, 199
Franklin, Benjamin, 285
Freezer burn, 343
Freshwater, 94, 126
Friction, 376–77
Frontal wedging, 349–50
Fronts, 350, 395–97
    cold, 396–97
    occluded, 397
    polar, 382
    stationary, 397
    warm, 395–96

Frost, 343, 347
Frost wedging, 54–55
Fumaroles, 215
Fusion, 464

Gabbro, 51
Gaging stations, 82
Galactic clusters, 475
Galaxies, 473–75
Galileo Galilei, 425–28
Gases, 26, 213. *See also* Volatiles
Gas giants, 430
Gastroliths, 248
Gems, 36
Geocentrism, 420
Geochemistry, 142
Geologic structures, 191–96
Geologic time scale, 11–12, 238–39, 252–55
Geology, 4–5, 239–40
Geophysics, 142
Geosphere, 6–8
Geysers, 97–98, 230
Gilbert, G. K., 226
Glacial abrasion, 118
Glacial drift, 121–22
Glacial erratics, 121–22
Glacial striation, 118
Glacial troughs, 118
Glaciation, 117–21
    Ice Age, 126
    Paleozoic, 146
    Pangaea and, 146
Glaciers, 112–14
    accumulation v. wastage, 115–17
    budget of, 115–17
    deposits by, 121–24
    erosion by, 117–21
    Ice Age, 124–29
    movement of, 114–17
    piedmont, 113–14
    in retreat, 117
Glass, volcanic, 47–49, 216
Glaze, 363
Global Positioning System (GPS), 147
Global warming, 326–28. *See also*
        Greenhouse effect
    projected impacts of, 331
    sea level and, 299
Glossopteris, 144
Gneiss, 68, 252
Gobi Desert, 128, 349
Gold, 28
GPS. *See* Global Positioning
        System
Grabens, 193, 195
Graded bedding, 271–72
Gradients, 80–81
Grand Canyon, 76, 84, 238, 243
Granite, 23, 50
    chemical weathering of, 56
    formation of, 52
Granodiorite, 189
Gravel, 58
Gravity, 74–76, 428
Great Basin Desert, 349
Great Glen Fault, 194, 196
Great Lakes, 125–26
Great Plains, 132
Great Salt Lake, 125, 262
Great Sand Dunes National
        Park, 135
Great Sandy Desert, 128
Great Slave Lake, 252
Greenhouse effect, 325, 437.
        See also Global warming
Groins, 296–98

Groundwater, 94–95. *See also* Aquifers
  contamination, 101–2
  distribution of, 95–96
  environmental problems of, 100–102
  geologic work of, 102–5
  movement, 96–97
  as nonrenewable resource, 100
  storage, 96
  subsidence and, 100–101
  travertine and, 60
  wells and, 98–99
Guayaquil, 333
Gulf Stream, 283–84
Gullies, 79, 82
Guyots, 273
Gypsum, 37–38, 60, 276
Gyres, 282–84

Habit, 30
Hail, 363–64
Half-life, 250–51
Halite, 23, 37, 276
Halley's Comet, 420, 449
Hanging wall block, 193
Hardness, 31. *See also* Mohs scale
Hard stabilization, 295–98
The Harmony of the Worlds (Kepler), 425
Hawaiian Island Emperor Seamount chain,
  159–60
Heat. *See also* Infrared radiation
  latent, 313, 342–43, 348
  mechanism of, 321–23
  metamorphism and, 65
  specific, 332
  temperature v., 321
Heliocentrism, 423
Hematite, 37
Henry Mountains, 226–27
Herschel, William, 461
Hertzsprung-Russell diagram (H-R diagram),
  462–63, 466, 469
High Plains Aquifer, 101
Highs, 378–82
Hillary, Edmund, 197
Himalayas, 142, 201–2
Historical geology, 4–5
Hoar frost, 347
Holden, John, 145
Holocene epoch, 254
Horizontality. *See* Principle of
  original horizontality
Horns, 119–20
Horsehead Nebula, 466
Horsts, 193
Host rock, 224
Hot spots, 159–60, 230
Hot-spot track, 159
Hot springs, 97
H-R diagram. *See* Hertzsprung-Rusell diagram
Hubble, Edwin, 473, 475–76
Hubble's law, 476
Hubble Space Telescope, 443–44, 451, 459
Humidity, 311, 344–48. *See also* Water vapor
Hurricane Katrina, 408, 412
Hurricane Rita, 392
Hurricanes, 408–14
  eye of, 410
  formation, 410–11
  tracking, 413–14
Hutton, James, 238–39, 242–44
Huygens, Christopher, 442
Hydrocarbons, 248
Hydrogen, 27–29, 464–67
Hydrologic cycle, 78–79, 112
Hydrosphere, 6–7, 9, 94
Hydrothermal vents, 276

Hygrometers, electric, 348
Hygroscopic nuclei, 355
Hypothesis, 15–16

Ice, 342
  caps, 113–14
  crystal process, 362
  nuclei, 362
  sea, 263
  shelves, 113
Ice Age, 121
  effect of, 124–25
  estuaries and, 301
  glaciers, 124–29
  loess deposits in, 134
Icebergs, 116
Ice sheets, 112–14, 147
  equatorial, 146
  Ice Age and, 126
ICS. *See* International Committee of
  Stratigraphy
Igneous activity, 224–30
Igneous bodies, tabular, 224–25
Igneous rock, 45–52
  chemical weathering of, 56
  classifying, 50–51
  common, 51
  compositions of, 49–51
  extrusive, 46
  formation of, 51–52
  intrusive, 46
  plutonic, 46
  textures, 47–49
  ultramafic, 51
  volcanic, 46
Impressions, 247
Inclusions, 241–42
Indian Ocean, 260
Indonesia earthquake of 2004, 187
Industrialization, 326
Inertia, 428
Infiltration, 78–79
Infrared radiation, 323. *See also* Heat
Inselbergs, 131
Integrated Ocean Drilling Program (IODP),
  159–60, 277
Intensity scales, 179–80
Interface, 287
Intergovernmental Panel on Climate Change
  (IPCC), 326–27
Internal processes, 74
International Astronomical Union, 451
International Committee of Stratigraphy (ICS),
  254
International Union of Geological
  Sciences, 254
Interstellar matter, 464–65
Intertropical convergence zone, 383
Intrusions, 224
Inverse relationships, 264
IODP. *See* Integrated Ocean Drilling Program
Ionic bonds, 26–27
Ions, 26
Iowa State University, 400–401
IPCC. *See* Intergovernmental Panel on Climate
  Change
Iron
  in core, 190
  in meteoroids, 459
  ores, 37
Irregular galaxies, 474–75
Irrigation, 101
Island archipelagos, 228
Island arcs. *See* Volcanic island arcs
Isobars, 375
Isotherm, 329, 332

Isotopes, 28, 249
  parent, 250
  in radioactive dating, 251

Jasper, 61
Jeffreys, Harold, 147
Jet streams, 377
JOIDES Resolution, 158–59
Jupiter, 440–42

Kaibab Formation, 238
Kalahari Desert, 128
Kames, 124
Kant, Immanuel, 473
Karakoram Range, 196
Karats, 28
Karst topography, 104–5
Kauai, 160
Kelvins, 460
Kepler, Johannes, 423–25
Kerguelen Plateau, 273
Kettles, 124
Kilauea, 215–16, 222, 232
Kinetic energy, 321
Knik River, 87
Krakatau, 228
Kuiper, Gerald, 448
Kuiper belt, 448–49, 451

Laboratory work, 15
Laccoliths, 226
Lahars, 220–21
Lake Agassiz, 124–25
Lake-effect snows, 394–95
Lakes
  oxbow, 86
  playa, 130
  pluvial, 125
  proglacial, 124
Laki fissure, 223
Laminar flow, 80
Land bridges, 144
Landfills, 103
Landforms
  depositional, 89–91
  by glacial erosion, 118–21
  mass wasting and, 75–76
  temperature control and, 331–33
Land hemisphere, 260
Landslides, 74. *See also* Mass wasting
  ground subsidence and, 185
  without triggers, 77
Lapilli, 213
Lapse rate, 316
Latent heat, 313, 342–43, 348
Latitude, temperature distribution and, 336
Lava, 44–47, 52
  basaltic, 47, 211
  tubes, 212–13
  types, 211
Lava Creek Tuff, 222
Lava flows, 211–12
  from composite cones, 218
  from Parícutin, 217–18
  from shield volcanoes, 215
Laws, 16
Leakey, Louis, 152
Leakey, Mary, 152
Lehars, 231
Levees, 91, 93–94
Libby, Willard F., 252
Light
  diffused, 325
  transmittance of, 29
Lightning, 401–3
Limestone, 23, 60, 67

Liquefaction, 184–85
Lithification, 45, 62
Lithosphere, 7–8, 148
  growth of, 151
  structure of, 189
Local Group, 475
Localized convective lifting, 349, 351
Loess, 134, 182
Logarithmic scales, 181
Loma Prieta earthquake, 172, 179, 185
Longshore transport, 292–93
Low-pressure systems, 397
Lows, 378–82
Luminosity, 459
Lunar highlands, 434
Lunar regolith, 436
Luster, 29

Madeira Abyssal Plain, 267
Mafic rocks. *See* Basalt
Magma, 44, 46
  basaltic, 210–11
  composition of, 49, 210
  divergent plate boundaries and, 230
  evolution of, 53
  viscosity of, 209–10
Magma chambers, 210, 221, 232
Magmatic differentiation, 52
Magnetic field, 160–62
Magnetic poles, 161–63
Magnetic reversal, 162–63
Magnetic time scale, 162
Magnetite, 37, 160
Magnetometers, 163
Magnitude (seismic)
  moment, 182
  scales, 179–82
Magnitude (stellar)
  absolute, 460
  apparent, 459–60
Mancos Shale, 255
Manganese nodules, 275–76
Mantle, 7–8, 189–90
  convection, 164–67
  lower, 190
  plumes, 159–60, 230
Marble, 67–68
Maria, 434–35
Mariana Trench, 272
Marine terraces, 293
Mars, 160, 438–40
Mass number, 28, 249
Mass wasting, 74–77
Matterhorn, 120
Matthews, D. H., 163
Mauna Loa, 215–16, 222
Meandering, 85–86, 89
Measuring
  air pressure, 373–74
  distance between stars, 458–59
  precipitation, 364–66
  temperature, 328–30
  wind, 385
Megathust, 183
Mendocino Fault, 157–58
Mercalli, Giuseppe, 180
Mercury, 436–37
Mesaverde Formation, 255
Mesocyclones, 404–5, 408
Mesopause, 316
Mesosaurus, 144
Mesosphere, 316
Mesozoic era, 143–44, 253
Metallic bonds, 27
Metallic substances, 26
Metal sulfides, 276

Metamorphic rock, 45, 63–68
  brittle, 66
  common, 67–69
  ductile, 66
  foliated, 68
  nonfoliated, 68
  texture of, 66–68
Metamorphism, 63–64
  contact, 64–65
  drivers of, 65–66
  regional, 64
  thermal, 64–65
Meteorites, 188, 450–51
Meteoroids, 446, 449–51
Meteorology, 5
Meteors, 449
Meteor showers, 449
Methane, 326
Methods, 17
Microcontinents, 199
Micrometeorites, 436, 449
Mid-Atlantic Ridge, 150, 157, 166, 273
Mid-Indian Ridge, 273
Mid-ocean ridge. *See* Oceanic ridge
Milky Way Galaxy, 465, 472–73
Millibars, 373
Minas Basin, 302
Mineralogy, 22
Mineral resources, 13, 38
Minerals, 22–24
  groups, 34–37
  nonsilicate, 34, 36–37
  optical properties of,
    28–30
  physical properties of,
    28–33
  reserves, 38
  rock-forming, 34
  silicate, 34–37
  strength of, 30–33
Mining, 38
Mississippi River, 79–80
  artificial cutoffs and, 93
  delta, 90
  discharge, 81
  Ice Age and, 124
  relocation and, 299
Mixing ration, 344
Modified Mercalli Intensity Scale, 179–80
Mohs scale, 31
Molds, 247
Molecules, 26
Monsoons, 284, 382
Montreal Protocol, 314
Moon, of Earth, 5–6, 434–36
  features of, 426
  surface of, 434–36
  tides and, 301–2
Moons
  of Jupiter, 441–42
  of Neptune, 445–46
  of Saturn, 443
Moraines, 122–23
Morrison Formation, 255
Motion, laws of, 428
Mountains
  building, 196–202
  collisional, 199–202
  compressional, 196–97
  deserts and, 129
  fault-block, 193, 195
Mount Etna, 218
Mount Kerkeslin, 315
Mount Kilimanjaro, 227
Mount Mazama, 220
Mount Pelée, 219–20

Mount Pinatubo, 232
Mount Rainier, 216, 220, 230–31
Mount Ruapehu, 211
Mount Rushmore National Memorial, 47
Mount St. Helens, 208–9, 220
Mount Vesuvius, 46
Mount Waialeale, 350
Mudflows. *See* Lahars
Muir Glacier, 117

Namib Desert, 128, 135
National Climate Data Center, 310
National Lightning Detection Network, 401
National Weather Service, 373
Nebulae, 464–65, 468
Nebular theory, 429–30
Necks, volcanic, 223–24
Neptune, 444–46
Neutrons, 24
Nevado del Ruiz, 221
Newfoundland, 145
Newton, Isaac, 428
Nimbostratus clouds, 355–57, 358, 362
Nitrogen, 312
Nitrous oxide, 326
Noble gases, 26
Nonconformities, 243
Nonfoliated rock, 68
Nonrenewable resources, 13–14
Norgay, Tenzing, 197
North American Cordillera, 196, 199
North Atlantic Drift, 284
North Atlantic Ocean, 270, 283
Northern Hemisphere, 333
  Coriolis effect and, 378
  glaciers in, 126
  ice sheets in, 112
  ocean currents of, 283–84
  oceans in, 260
  temperature distribution and, 336
Northridge earthquake, 172
Novae, 420, 461
Nucleus, 24, 249
  of comets, 447–48
Nuée Ardente, 218–20
Nullahs, 129
Numerical date, 240

Obsidian, 23, 48–49
Occultation, 444
Ocean currents, 282–85
  climate and, 284–85
  deep, 285–86
  ebb, 304
  flood, 304
  longshore, 293
  rip, 289
  tidal, 303–4
Ocean Drilling Project, 159
Oceanic-continental convergence, 153–54
Oceanic-oceanic convergence, 154–55
Oceanic plateaus, 273
Oceanic ridge, 147, 273–74
Oceanography, 5, 260
Oceans
  basins, 8, 272–73
  depth, 263
  floor, 265–67
  geography of, 260
  layering of, 264–65
  seafloor sediments and, 275–77
  temperature, 263
  volume of, 6
  zones of, 265
Octet rule, 26
Ogallala Formation, 96

Olivine, 49, 52
Olympus Mons, 160, 438–39
On the Revolution of the Heavenly Spheres
(Copernicus), 423
Ontong Java Plateau, 199, 273
Oort, Jan, 449
Oort cloud, 448–49
Orbits, 422, 429
Ores, 38
Organic compounds, 23
Organ Pipe Cactus National Monument, 127
The Origin of Continents and Oceans (Wegener),
143
Orogenesis, 196
Orographic lifting, 349–50
Outgassing, 262
Outwash plains, 122–24
Overrunning, 395
Oversteepening, 77
Overwash, 299–300
Oxbow lakes, 86
Oxygen, 312, 325
Ozone, 314–15, 325

Pacific Ocean, 260
Pahoehoe flows, 212
Paleoclimatic data, 146
Paleomagnetism, 160–61
Paleontology, 245
Paleozoic era, 146, 253
Pangaea, 143
breakup of, 163–64
glaciation and, 146
subduction zones of, 199–200
Panthalassa, 162
Parasitic cones, 215
Parcels, 348
Parícutin, 217–18
Partial melting, 153–54
Patagonia Desert, 349
Peridotite, 51, 189
Periodic table, 25
Periods, 253
Permafrost, 438
Permeability, 96
Petrification, 247
Petroleum, 13
Phanerozoic eon, 252–53
Physical environment, 11–12
Physical geology, 4–5
Piccard, Jacques, 272
Pilkey, Orrin, 298
Pipes, 214, 223–24
Planetary nebulae, 468
Planetesimals, 429–30
Planets, 430–33, 436–46. *See also* Solar system
characteristics of, 430
dwarf, 429, 446, 451
extrasolar, 433
impacts on, 433
Jovian, 430
orbit of, 429
terrestrial, 430
Plate boundaries, 50
changing, 158
convergent, 149–50, 152–56, 197–99, 228–30
divergent, 150–52, 230
earthquake belts and, 183
transform fault, 149–50, 156–58, 175
volcanism and, 228–30
Plates, 147
changing of, 157
converging, 152–56
diverging, 150–52
motion of, 164–67
subducting, 197–99
tectonic stresses on, 173

Plate tectonics, 147–49. *See also* Continental
drift
igneous activity and, 227–30
testing, 158–63
theory of, 142
Playas, 130
Pleistocene epoch, 126, 254
Plucking, 117–18
Pluto, 451
Plutons, 224, 226
Point bars, 86
Polar easterlies, 382
Polar highs, 382
Polarity, 162
Polar wandering, 161–63
Pollutants, hazardous, 101
Pollution. *See* Atmospheric pollution
Pompeii, 46
Porosity, 96
Powell, John Wesley, 238
Precambrian time, 254
Precambrian Unkar Group, 243
Precipitation, 311, 361–66
fog, 361
formation of, 361–62
measuring, 364–66
types, 362–64
Predictions, 16
Pressure. *See also* Air pressure
centers, 380
confining, 65–66
gradient, 374
metamorphism and, 65
Primary (P) waves, 176–77
Principal shells, 24
Principle of cross-cutting relationships, 241
Principle of original horizontality, 241
Protons, 24, 249
Protoplanets, 430
Protostars, 465–67
Proxima Centauri, 458
Ptolemaic model, 422
Ptolemy, 421–22
Pulido, Dionisio, 217
Pulsars, 470–71
Pulsating variables, 461
Pumice, 23, 49
P waves. *See* Primary waves
Pycnocline, 264
Pyrite, 34
Pyroclastic flows, 218–20, 231
Pyroclastic materials, 213
from cinder cones, 216
from composite cones, 218
lunar, 436
from shield volcanoes, 216
from Yellowstone-type calderas, 222
Pyroxene, 49, 52

Quartz, 22, 36, 49–50
chemical weathering and, 56
formation, 52
sandstone, 60
Quartzite, 68
Quaternary period, 254
Quito, 333

Rabaul Caldera, 232
Radar
altimeters, 267
Doppler, 408
weather, 365–66
Radial drainage patterns, 91–92
Radiation, 322–23
Radioactive decay, 28, 250–51
Radioactivity, 249–52
Radiolaria, 275

Radiosonde, 316–17
Rafting, 144
Rain, 362
freezing, 363
gauges, 364–65
hurricanes and, 413
measuring, 364–65
Rainshadows, 129, 348–49
Rapids, 82, 88
Recrystallization, 66
Rectangular drainage patterns,
91–92
Red giants, 461–63, 467
Red Sea, 132
Reflection, 324
Reflection nebulae, 464
Refraction, 33
Reid, H. F., 172–73
Relative humidity, 344–45
Relocation, 299
Renewable resources, 13–14
Replacement, 247
Reserves, 38
Resources, 12–14
Retrograde motion, 421, 437
Revolution, 317
Rhône Glacier, 115
Rhyolite, 50
Richter, Charles, 180–81
Richter scale, 180–81
Ridge push, 166
Riggs Glacier, 117
Rills, 79, 82
Rime, 364
Ring of Fire, 227
Rip currents, 289
River systems, 80
Rock cycle, 44–46
Rock flour, 118
Rocks, 23. *See also specific rock types*
conformable, 242
continental, 189
country, 224
deformation, 175, 191
detrital, 57–59
elastic limit of, 191
host, 224
intermediate, 51
nonfoliated, 68
parent, 63
ultramafic, 51
Rockslides, 75
Rocky Mountains, 196
Rotation, 317
Runoff, 79

Saffir-Simpson Hurricane Scale, 412
Sahara Desert, 128–29
St. Pierre, 219–20
Salinity, 261–63
Salt. *See also* Halite
flats, 61, 130
rock, 60
sea, 262
table, 26–27
San Andreas Fault, 157, 172, 192
Sand movement, 291–93
Sandstone, 58, 60
San Francisco earthquake of 1906, 172–74,
181, 194
fire and, 185–86
Santa Ana winds, 384–85
Sargassum, 284
Saturation, 344
Saturation, zone of, 95–96
Saturn, 442–45
Scales, 11

Scarps, fault, 193–94
Scattering, 324–25
Schist, 68
Scientific inquiry, 14–17
Scientific revolution, 142
Scoria, 49, 216
Scott, Robert, 144
Scott, W. B., 147
Sea arches, 293–94, 297
Seafloor spreading, 151, 159, 162–63
Sea level
    changing, 125
    rises in, 299
    submergent coasts and, 301
Seamounts, 158–59, 273
Seasons, 317–18
Sea stacks, 293–94
Seawalls, 297–98
Seawater, 261–63, 286
Secondary (S) waves, 176–77
Sedimentary layers, 242
Sedimentary rocks, 45, 57–63
    chemical, 57, 59–62
    classification of, 58–62
    detrital, 57–59
    features of, 63
    identification of, 59
Sediments, 45, 57
    biochemical, 60
    biogenous, 275
    hydrogenous, 275–76
    production, 80
    seafloor, 275–77
    shoreline, 290
    suspended, 84
    terrigenous, 275
    turbidity currents and, 271–72
Seismic energy, 8
Seismic reflection profiles, 266–67
Seismic waves, 172, 184, 188–90
Seismograms, 176, 178, 189
Seismographs, 176–78
Seismology, 176–78
Sequence of formation, 240
Sewage, 101–2
Shale, 58, 60, 64
Sheet flow, 82
Sheeting, 54–56
Shiprock, 223–24
Shoreline, 286–87
    evolution of, 295
    features, 293–95
    processes, 289–93
    shift, 330
    stabilization, 295–300
Siccar Point, 244
Sidescan sonar, 266
Sierra Nevadas, 226
Silica, 49
    cementation of, 62
    chemical weathering and, 56
    viscosity and, 209
Silicates, 34–37
    dark, 49
    light, 49–50
Siliceous ooze, 275
Silicon-oxide tetrahedron, 34–36
Sills, 224–26
Silt, 58
Siltstone, 58
Sinkholes, 95, 104–5
Sites, 245
Slab pull, 166
Slack water, 304
Slate, 64, 68
Sleet, 363
Sling psychrometer, 347

Slip face, 135
Slippage, 173–74
Slopes, 76–77
Slumps, 75
Small solar system bodies, 446
Smog, 315
Snow, 363
    glaciers and, 115–17
    lake-effect, 394–95
    measuring, 365
Snowbelts, 394
Soda straw, 103–4
Sodium, 27
Solar nebula, 429
Solar radiation, 323–25
    angle of, 319
    wind and, 374
Solar system, 428–33
Solar wind, 448
Solidification, 45, 46
Solstices, 318–21
Sonar, 266
Sorting, 84
Soufriere Hills volcano, 231
Source regions, 393
Southern Hemisphere, 333
    Coriolis effect and, 378
    glaciers in, 126
    ice sheets in, 112–13
    ocean currents of, 283–84
    oceans in, 260
    temperature distribution and, 336
Space, 11
SPC. See Storm Prediction Center
Specific gravity, 33
Specific heat, 332
Spiral galaxies, 474
Spits, 294–95, 297
Spreading centers, 151
Springs, 97–98
Stability, atmospheric, 351–54
Stabilization, 295–300
Stalactites, 103–4
Stalagmites, 103–4
Stars, 458–61
    binary, 461
    brightness of, 459–60
    death of, 467–69
    evolution of, 465–69
    main-sequence, 462
    neutron, 468, 470–71
    stable main-sequence, 467
    variable, 461
Stellar brightness, 459–60
Stellar masses, 461
Stellar parallax, 423, 458–59
Stellar remnants, 469–71
Steppes, 127
Still water level, 287
Stocks, 226
Storm Prediction Center (SPC), 407
Storm surges, 288, 412–13
Strata, 63, 246
Stratified drift, 121
Stratosphere, 314, 316
Stratus clouds, 355–57
Streak, 29–30
Streamflow, 80
Streams
    capacity, 84
    channels, 80–81, 84–86
    competence, 83–84
    deposition, 84
    ephemeral, 81, 128–29
    intermittent, 81
    longitudinal profile of, 82
    transportation in, 83–84

trunk, 80
valleys, 87–89
Stress, differential, 66–67
Strike, of faults, 194
Subduction zones, 152, 197–201
    active continental margins and, 272
    composite cones and, 218
Sublimation, 343
Submarine canyons, 271–72
Subpolar lows, 382
Subsidence, 100–101, 185, 244
Subsystems, 10
Subtropical highs, 128, 381
Suction vortices, 404
Sulfates, 37
Sulfur dioxide, 232
Sun. See also Solar radiation
    altitude of, 317
    angle of, 319
    earth relationship, 316–17
Supai Group, 241
Supercells, 404
Superclusters, 475
Supercontinent, 143
Supercooling, 362
Supergiants, 463
Supernovae, 420, 461, 468–69, 470
Superposition, 240–41
Surface mixed zone, 265
Surf zone, 289
Surges (volcanic), 219
Suspended load, 83
S waves. See Secondary waves
Swells, 288
Swiss Alps, 120
Synclines, 192
Systems, 10

Tablemounts, 273
Takla Makan, 349
Tambora volcanic eruption, 211
Tarns, 119
Tectonic stresses, 173
Telescopes, 425–26. See also Hubble Space
        Telescope
    radio, 472
Temperature
    adiabatic cooling and, 348–49, 352
    air, 311
    air pressure v., 315–16
    atmospheric, 312
    control, 330–34
    depth and, 262
    dew-point, 346–47
    distribution, 332
    extremes, 334
    gradient, 329
    heat v., 321
    measuring, 328–30
    in middle-latitude cyclones, 399
    salinity and, 262
    stellar, 460
    in warm fronts, 396
    water vapor and, 345–46
    world distribution of, 335–36
Tenacity, 31
Terrae, 434
Terranes, 199–201
Tertiary period, 254
Tests, 275
Theory, 16
Theory of the Earth (Hutton), 239
Thermal energy, 321. See also Heat
Thermals, 351, 403
Thermistors, 331
Thermocline, 263
Thermohaline circulation, 286

Thermometers, 347
Thermosphere, 316
Thoreau, Henry David, 124
Thunder, 402
Thunderstorms, 359, 400–403
Tibetan Plateau, 201
Tidal patterns, 302–3
Tides, 301–4
Till, 117, 121
Time, 11
Tombolos, 294, 297
Tornadoes, 400, 403–8
Tower karst, 105
Tracking forecast, 413–14
Tracks, 248
Trade Winds, 282, 381–82, 386
Transactions of the Royal Society of Edinburgh, 239
Transform fault boundaries, 149–50, 156–58, 175
Transition zone, 265
Transparency, 325
Transpiration, 78
Transportation, 83
Travel-time graph, 179
Travertine, 60, 103
Trellis drainage patterns, 92
Trenches
    deep-ocean, 153, 272–73
    distribution of, 153
    transform faults and, 156
Trend, of faults, 194
Triangulation, 178
Tri-State Tornado, 407
Tropical depressions, 411
Tropical disturbances, 410
Tropical storms, 411
Tropic of Cancer, 318
Tropic of Capricorn, 318–19
Tropopause, 316
Troposphere, 7, 315
Troughs, 118, 287
Tsunamis, 183, 186–88
Tsunami Warning Center, 187–88
Turbidites, 271–72
Turbidity currents, 271–72
Turbulent flow, 80
Turnagain Heights, 186
Typhoons. *See* Hurricanes

Ultramafic rocks, 51
Ultraviolet (UV) radiation, 314, 323, 464
Unconformities, 242–44
Uniform Building Code, 184
Uniformitarianism, 239
United Nations, 328
Universe, 475–77
Unsaturated zone, 95–96
Unzen Volcano, 219
Upwelling, 285–86
Ural Mountains, 201
Uranium, 250
Uranus, 444–46
Ussher, James, 239
UV radiation. *See* Ultraviolet radiation

Valence electrons, 24
Valles Marineris, 438–39
Valleys
    deepening, 88
    glaciers, 112
    hanging, 118–19

rift, 151, 274
shelf, 269
stream, 87–89
trains, 122–24
widening, 88
Vegetation, 77
Vents, 214–15
Venus, 426–27, 437–38
Vine, Fred, 163
Viscosity, 209–10
Visual binaries, 461
Volatiles, 209–10, 210–11
Volcanic eruptions
    causes of, 210–11
    fissure, 222–23
    lateral, 219
    materials in, 211–13
    nature of, 209–11
    style of, 214–18
Volcanic island arcs, 155, 197
    continental margins and, 200
    convergent plate boundaries and, 228
    deep-ocean trenches and, 272
Volcanism
    intraplate, 230
    on Mars, 439
    plate boundaries and, 228–30
    zones of, 229
Volcanoes, 153–55. *See also* Cinder cones;
        Composite cones
    anatomy of, 214
    Hawaiian-type, 210
    hazards of, 231–32
    living with, 230–32
    monitoring, 232
    shield, 215–16
    structures, 214–19
    on Venus, 438
Vortices, 403–4

Wadis, 129
Walden (Thoreau), 124
Walden Pond, 124
Walsh, Don, 272
Washes, 129
Wastage, zone of, 116
Water, 6. *See also* Freshwater; Groundwater;
        Hydrologic cycle; Seawater
    in arid climates, 128–29
    in atmosphere, 313
    balance, 78
    chemical weathering and, 56
    deficiency, 127
    distribution of, 7, 261
    on Mars, 439–40
    mass wasting triggers and, 77
    running, 79–80
    slack, 304
    states of, 342–43
    still level, 287
    table, 95
    temperature control and, 331–33
    usage, 83
    work of, 82–84
Waterfalls, 88
Water hemisphere, 260, 333
Water vapor, 342, 344–48
    evaporation fog and, 360–61
    greenhouse effect and, 325
    temperature and, 345–46

Wave-cut cliffs, 293
Wave-cut platforms, 293
Wavelength, 287, 322–23
Waves, 287–89
    base, 289
    erosion by, 290–91
    height, 287
    period, 287
    refraction, 291–92
    types, 176
Weather, 310–11
    air-mass, 392
    charts, 377
    daily, 354
    of middle-latitude cyclones, 397–99
    radar, 365–66
Weathering, 45, 54–57, 74
    chemical, 56–57
    lunar, 436
    mechanical, 54–56
    products of, 57
    sea salt and, 262
Wedging
    accretionary, 198–99, 272
    frontal, 349–50
    frost, 54–55
Wegener, Alfred, 143–47
Welded tuff, 213
Wells, 98–100
Westerlies, 282, 382, 386
West Wind Drift, 284
Wet adiabatic rate, 348–49
Whitecaps, 287
White dwarfs, 461, 463–64, 467–68, 469–70
White Point dunes, 135
Wilson, J. Tuzo, 156
Wind
    abrasion, 133
    anticyclonic, 378
    belts, 282
    cyclonic, 378
    damage, 413
    deposits, 134–35
    erosion, 129, 131–33
    factors affecting, 374–77
    geostrophic, 376–77
    local, 382–85
    measuring, 385
    prevailing, 385
    Santa Ana, 384–85
    shadows, 134
    solar, 448
    speed, 385
    Sun and, 317
    waves and, 287–88
    weather and, 311
World Meteorological Organization (WMO), 310,
        328, 411
World Weather Watch, 310

Yazoo tributaries, 91
Yellowstone National Park, 98, 222
Yosemite National Park, 118

Zion Canyon, 135